D1242060

The Art of American Humor:
An Anthology

The Art of American Humor: An Anthology

E 70

Edited with notes by BROM WEBER

Thomas Y. Crowell Company : New York : Established 1834

ACKNOWLEDGMENTS

Acknowledgment is gratefully made to the authors, agents, and publishers who have granted permission to use the following selections from copyrighted publications:

"The Egg," by Sherwood Anderson. Copyright © 1921 by B. W. Huebsch, Inc., renewed 1948 by Eleanor Anderson. Reprinted by permission of Harold Ober Associates Incorporated.

"Oil of Dog," from *The Collected Writings of Ambrose Bierce.* Reprinted by permission of The Citadel Press.

"A Funeral Elegy Upon . . . Mr. John Foster . . . ," by Joseph Capen, by permission of Massachusetts Historical Society.

"Chaplinesque," from *Complete Poems and Selected Letters and Prose of Hart Crane.* By permission of Liveright, Publishers, New York. Copyright © 1933, 1958, 1966 by Liveright Publishing Corporation.

"here is little Effie's head," from *Poems 1923–1954* by E. E. Cummings. Reprinted by permission of Harcourt, Brace & World, Inc. Copyright 1925 by E. E. Cummings.

To Eden and Kyle

Foreword

Brom Weber has put together a collection brim-filled with wit, satire, sly jocularity, slapstick, good sense, and tomfoolery that may help explain why so many of our most effectively serious Americans seem often to have glanced toward truth, sometimes almost covertly, from behind a comic mask. Even the sedate Mr. Emerson sometimes smiled, though his best quips were delivered with straight and sober face, for he knew as well as the rest of us that Yankee audiences delight in the subtle, small explosion of the double-take. Truth has always been an elusive quarry, often best approached quietly by indirection—this Thoreau knew, and Hawthorne also, who was a master of relaxed drollery. At other times, she can be startled from hiding by a quick guffaw or antic gesture such as Mark Twain or young Washington Irving perfected. Disguises seem often necessary, like those Emily Dickinson assumed when her eyes twinkled more than a maiden lady's should, or verbal acrobatics like those Nathaniel Ward and Ogden Nash have perfected. With some, man's fated inability ever to realize more than a portion of divine plan—his destined inability finally to succeed except in human terms—has been, despite its self-assuring undertone of tragedy, a comic spectacle. For the American view has been a man-centered view, which has celebrated splendid possibilities for human improvement at the same time that it has noticed the probabilities—inevitably absurd, self-absorbing, and extremely human —that everyone will make many mistakes on the way. How glorious are the dreams man contrives; how humbling and entertaining and man-like the spectacle he presents as he stumbles in their pursuit. The historian or philosopher or psychologist of laughter will find in this collection much that will beguile and puzzle, but much also of a view of man which most Americans admire because it is their own.

LEWIS LEARY
Columbia University

Preface

He was awakened towards daybreak by a crowing of cocks, and when he awoke, the others were either asleep, or had gone away; there remained only Socrates, Aristophanes, and Agathon, who were drinking out of a large goblet which they passed round, and Socrates was discoursing to them. Aristodemus was only half awake, and he did not hear the beginning of the discourse; the chief thing which he remembered was Socrates compelling the other two to acknowledge that the genius of comedy was the same with that of tragedy, and that the true artist in tragedy was an artist in comedy also (PLATO, *Symposium* 223).——And the argument implies that there are combinations of pleasure and pain in lamentations, and in tragedy and comedy, not only on the stage, but on the greater stage of human life; and so in endless other cases (PLATO, *Philebus* 50).

The American has long been famous, sometimes infamous, for a sense of humor that seems to have permeated every atom of his being and experience. He has valued his humor highly, nurturing it with a persistence almost as great as that devoted to action, technology, and acquisition. American literary humor, consequently, has been pored over for keys to the better understanding of American culture and character. This would be admirable were it not that so much humor has been overlooked. During the late nineteenth century, for example, it was fashionable for critics of American culture to regard the literary comedians—Charles Farrar Browne and others—as the sole creators of American humor. In more recent times, with better though still limited vision, the frontier humorists have been extolled as the only valuable stars in the humorous constellation. It is necessary to become familiar with the whole panorama of American literary humor in order to appreciate its role in American life.

To do this one must free oneself from narrow views of humor and the responses considered proper to it. In general, existing theories of humor and laughter provide little guidance, for they merely tend to confirm those views rather than to expand them. Some theories simplify and depreciate humor by regarding it either as a social corrective or as a social opiate, as a mechanism of individual aggression or as a mechanism of individual defense, even as an expression of the dourest pessimism. Other theories magnify the character of humor until its identity is blurred and it ends up a misty metaphysical idea. Whatever the theory, and there have been many from Plato's time until this day, it has been derived too often from a reading of too small a range of materials. Usually, too, the theorist has narrowly emphasized a single mode of analysis, such as the psychological, the sociological, or the philosophical.

This book aims to facilitate the appreciation of American literary humor by presenting, for the first time, its full range and variety from its beginnings in the seventeenth century to the present. These are the materials with which any meaningful thinking about American humor must begin. Their diversity is remarkable. American humor has expressed itself in ways ranging from the obviously jocular and clownish to subtler forms such as the comedy of manners or ideas. It has been childishly playful, as in nonsense rhymes, and it has been serious in effect and has dealt with the gravest problems of man and society. It has been derisive and sympathetic, brutal and genial.

As might well be expected, American humor has evoked more than one kind of response. Some of the pieces in this book have excited laughter, others have elicited smiles; many have aroused imperceptible amusement, and a few, ribald or otherwise bold, have evoked shocked pleasure. The best humor has contained a diversity of elements and called forth a complex response.

The cliché that the humor of every age is perishable is refuted by the extraordinary vitality of American humor. Those who now enjoy the wit and nonsense of Ogden Nash may find the wit and nonsense of the Puritans equally amusing. The delights offered by James Thurber can also be savored in Benjamin Franklin's writings. Some humor has perished, of course, but it has deserved its fate. Its literary standards have been low and it has catered to the superficial and fleeting whims of its audience.

The idea that humor is intrinsically trivial or low is also refuted by the selections in this volume. Many of the greatest American writers have created humorous literature that is great and durable when judged by the most exacting standards. I must confess that the discovery is not entirely my own. During the past three decades, critics and scholars have been re-evaluating Poe, Hawthorne, Melville, James, Robinson, Frost, Eliot, and others with a stimulating perception of their varied and neglected humor. Much still remains to be done in this regard. But there is no good reason why we should not now begin to enjoy reading these major figures with a fuller awareness of their intentions and achievements.

The sensitivity of American humorists to their European origins and the constant influx of immigrants have kept American humor from sinking into provinciality. In its earliest days American humor absorbed the literary traditions of Western culture, and it has gained much thereafter from familiarity with important developments in European literature. At the same time, American humor did not reject indigenous resources capable of enriching its art. Native American folklore, landscape, character types, and language have been incorporated effectively into its texture. The combination of imported and native elements has given American humor an impressively unique universality.

Probably one of the most striking characteristics of American humor has been its critical spirit. Throughout its history our humor has subjected itself and its world to an enlivening scrutiny. Undoubtedly the American penchant for self-analysis and self-criticism has been encouraged by the wisdom of its fools and satirists.

Many of the selections in this book have never been anthologized before, and some have not been reprinted since their first appearance. Quality, not novelty, has led to their inclusion here. Some familiar classics have been used for the same reason. Selections have been arranged chronologically by author to facilitate study of the development of American literary humor, with but a few exceptions from the rule for the same purpose. They may be read in any order by the general reader. Whenever the choice was possible, selections were made from poetry and prose regarded as finished literary expression by their authors in preference to such informal works as journals and letters. Selections are complete and unabridged. I have not hesitated to reprint whole chapters from the novels of major writers when such chapters best represent their authors' humor and do not suffer by presentation as separate entities. Every effort has been made to obtain authoritative texts. For clarity, I have corrected obvious printers' errors and in some pieces have normalized spelling and punctuation without alteration of the language.

Headnotes provide information about the authors of selections for the student and will be of interest to the general reader too. The relative length of headnotes is no measure of the importance of a writer. Minor figures have been discussed at greater length than their betters when they are little-known or it has been desirable to introduce essential general information. Each headnote cites the source of the selection, generally its first appearance in book form, and usually directs the reader to useful supplementary books dealing with the author. A selective bibliography of books and other aids valuable for the further study of American literary humor appears at the end of the book.

Every student of American literary humor must admit his deep indebtedness to the late Bernard DeVoto and Constance Rourke, as well as to Walter Blair, Van Wyck Brooks, and Franklin J. Meine; I do so gladly. I wish sufficient space existed for me to thank all from whose books and articles I have learned much, but whose names do not appear either in the headnotes or the bibliography. However, I cannot keep from acknowledging the pioneering scholarship of Harold S. Jantz, Perry Miller, and Samuel Eliot Morison, which led me to observe the humor in New England Puritan literature with an unjaundiced eye. My colleagues—Professors Bernard Bowron, Charles H. Foster, J. C. Levenson, William Van O'Connor, and Mary C. Turpie—generously contributed their knowledge and interest over a lengthy period. For special courtesies I am grateful to Professor Herbert R. Brown (*New England Quarterly*), Elizabeth Cunliffe (Rutgers University Press), Philip S. Foner (Citadel Press), Louise Hinds (Barnes & Noble), Thomas H. Johnson, Stephen T. Riley (Massachusetts Historical Society), Clifford K. Shipton (American Antiquarian Society), Professor Donald E. Stanford (Louisiana State University), and to the California State Library, Library of Congress, and Yale University Press. The gracious cooperation of the staff of the University of Minnesota Library was truly limitless.

B.W.

Contents

The Art of American Humor:
An Anthology

Nathaniel Ward (1578–1652)

In 1626, several years before the Puritans settled in Massachusetts, the Reverend Richard Bernard, a Puritan minister in Old England, published a sermon in which he asked his reader to be "Christianly merry." Bernard's justification for Christian merriment was that "There is a kind of smiling and joyful laughter, for anything I know, which may stand with sober gravity, and with the best man's piety." *The Isle of Man,* Bernard's sermon, appeared in at least eleven editions from 1626 to 1683, before, during, and after the Puritan reign in England. Many of Bernard's Puritan colleagues who sailed off to settle New England carried with them an identical sense of the propriety, even the necessity, of Christian joy and laughter. Sobered though they became by the responsibilities of political and ecclesiastical power, the Puritans of New England never arrived at the general view that mirth was something inimical to a godly life. Their literature and lives demonstrate that they recognized the truth in Puritan poet John Milton's statement of 1641 that laughter "hath oft-times a strong and sinewy force in teaching and confuting." A year later, explaining why it was that his prose satires undertook *"to rip up the wounds of Idolatry and Superstition with a laughing countenance,"* Milton rested his case upon two lines of the Roman satirist Horace: *"—Jesting decides great things/Stronglier, and better oft then earnest can."*

There is a logical progression from the Reverend Bernard and John Milton to the Reverend Benjamin Colman, a leading Boston Puritan minister of the late seventeenth and early eighteenth centuries. Colman was one of those in whom the great Calvinist Jonathan Edwards detected the apparent degeneration of Puritan orthodoxy in New England. But Colman, whose three sermons on humor (*The Government & Improvement of Mirth,* Boston, 1707) are typical of the currents Edwards fought against, merely articulated what had long been implicit in New England life. Though Colman's argument is in part based upon some early eighteenth-century ideas and thus does not precisely mirror all earlier Puritan attitudes, *The Government & Improvement of Mirth* reveals essentially the same favorable attitude toward laughter and joy as had found expression in seventeenth-century Puritan life and literature. Colman contended that nature, God, and Christianity had made mirth and song both beautiful in themselves as well as useful to man. Thus he wrote:

We daily need some respite & diversion, without which we dull our Powers; a little intermission sharpens 'em again. It spoils the *Bow* to keep it always bent, and the *Viol* if always strain'd up. Mirth is some loose or relaxation to the labouring Mind or Body. . . . 'Tis design'd by nature to chear and revive us thro' all the toils and troubles of life. . . .

1

Mirth and song could be corrupted, however, when they were no longer motivated by love of man and God but by selfishness. "Civil & Natural Mirth" was a "decent . . . lawful . . . Duty," whereas "Carnal & Vicious Mirth" was to be "condemned and avoided." The highest form of mirth was "Spiritual & Holy Joy." A passage in Colman's preface chiding antagonists of mirth aptly summarizes his argument, though it does not allude fully enough to the many different virtues inherent in "Civil & Natural Mirth" which he elucidated at length in his book:

That by no means must they seem to place any thing of Religion in being *Dull and heavy, sad and disconsolate, sour and morose.* Not only does Religion *Allow* but it *Obliges* unto chearfulness with Sobriety: It gives the most reason for it, and is serv'd by it: None have that *License,* and in none is it so Decent and Comely as in them that are good. Mirth was not made for the Profane and Ungodly, Especially *Spiritual Joy* is the peculiar Duty and Priviledge of Saints: They are under Bonds to exhibit the Pleasures and *Satisfactions of Religion,* if it be possible to convince the Ungodly how *Superior they are* to all those of *Sense* which this World has to boast of. If men are for *Mirth, This* is worthy to be called so and aspir'd after! A Joy that is Solid, Pure, Perfective, Purmanent! Stronger than all Afflictions, and abiding in Death! A light in those shades, and a Triumph 'ore those Terrors!

It is relevant that the Biblical text upon which Colman based his sermon —"Is any among you afflicted? let him pray. Is any merry? let him sing psalms." (*James* 5:13)—also appeared on the title page of the first book published by the Puritans in New England, *The Bay Psalm Book* (1640). Among the many other texts which Colman cited in order to establish the sanctity of mirth was one from Psalm 126: "Then was our Mouth fill'd with Laughter, and our Tongue with Singing;——The Lord hath done great things for us, Whereof we are glad."

It need not be startling, therefore, for us to learn that a Puritan minister of early seventeenth-century New England joyfully played with language like such later masters of nonsense as Laurence Sterne, Lewis Carroll, Edward Lear, and T. S. Eliot. For the Reverend Nathaniel Ward "lepidity" (levity) was "very necessary, if not unavoydable." *The Simple Cobler of Aggawam in America* (1647), Ward's best known work, dealt with serious matters of religion and politics such as the relation of Charles I to the English Parliament and the necessity of union between church and state. Ward wittily suggested, however, that such apparent "faults" of his book as its jocosity should be "commended" rather than "mended": "To speak to light heads with heavy words, were to break their necks: to cloathe Summer matter, with Winter Rugge, would make the Reader sweat. It is musick to me, to heare every Ditty speak its spirit in its apt tune: every breast, to sing its proper part, and every creature, to expresse it self in its natural note: should I heare a Mouse roare like a Beare, a

Cat low like an Oxe, or a Horse whistle like a Red-breast, it would scare me.

> The world's a well strung fidle, mans tongue the quill,
> That fills the world with fumble for want of skill,
> When things and words in tune and tone doe meet,
> The universall song goes smooth and sweet."

As for the "affected termes" with which he studded his prose, why, they were used to "helpe disedged appetites with convenient condiments, and bangled ears, with pretty quicke pluckes."

The friskiness of the Reverend Ward was in part necessary since he wished to speak in character; the simple New England cobbler in whose image Ward cavorted was after all an "uplandish Rusticke," one of the first in the long merry succession of humorous common fools in American literature who are not among "the disputers of this world" but, blessed with homely shrewdness, can wisely "guesse when men speake true or false divinity" or satirically belabor foolish wives for ostentation and foolish husbands for other faults. The Reverend Ward's fondness for verbal play also stemmed from his literary sophistication, his knowledge of what the best English poets and prosewriters of the earlier Elizabethan period and his own age were producing. He was, in fact, a worldly individual in more than a literary sense alone.

Born in England, Ward was educated as a lawyer, travelled abroad, and then became a Puritan minister in England. Driven from his pastorate for nonconformity, Ward emigrated to Massachusetts in 1634 and served as minister at Agawam (Ipswich). Ill-health forced him to resign and from 1638 to 1641 he was one of the legal figures who helped draft the "Body of Liberties," the first codification of civil law in New England. Made homesick by the growing success of Puritanism in England, the Reverend Ward left North America in 1646, taking with him the manuscript of the *Simple Cobler*. Speaking in the first person, the honest American artisan gave sage advice to his English cousins. The text is taken from the first edition, London, 1647.

WOMEN'S FASHIONS

Should I not keep promise in speaking a little to Womens fashions, they would take it unkindly: I was loath to pester better matter with such stuffe; I rather thought it meete to let them stand by themselves, like the *Quæ Genus* in the Grammar, being Deficients, or Redundants, not to bee brought under any Rule: I shall therefore make bold for this once, to borrow a little of their loose-tongue Liberty, and mispend a word or two upon their long-wasted, but short-skirted patience: a little use of my stirrup will doe no harme.

Ridentem dicere verum, quid prohibet?

Gray Gravity it selfe can well beteame,
That Language be adapted to the Theme.
He that to Parrots speaks, must parrotise;
He that instructs a foole, may act th' unwise.

It is known more then enough, that I am neither Nigard, nor Cinick, to the due bravery of the true Gentry: if any man mislikes a bully mong drassock more then I, let him take her for all mee: I honour the woman that can honour her self with her attire: a good Text alwayes deserves a fair Margent: I am not much offended, if I see a trimme, far trimmer than she wears it: in a word, whatever Christianity or Civility will allow, I can afford with *London* measure: but when I heare a nugiperous Gentledame inquire what dresse the Queen is in this week; what the nudiustertian fashion of the Court; I mean the very newest: with egge to be in it in all haste, what-ever it be; I look at her as the very gizzard of a trifle, the product of a quarter of a cypher, the epitome of nothing, fitter to be kickt, if she were of a kickable substance, than either honoured or humoured.

To speak moderately, I truely confesse, it is beyond the ken of my understanding to conceive, how those women should have any true grace, or valuable vertue, that have so little wit, as to disfigure themselves with such exotick garbes, as not only dismantles their native lovely lustre, but transclouts them into gant bar-geese, ill-shapen shotten shell-fish, Egyptian Hieroglyphicks, or at the best into French flurts of the pastery, which a proper English woman should scorn with her heeles: it is no marvell they weare drailes on the hinder part of their heads, having nothing as it seems in the fore-part, but a few Squirrills braines, to help them frisk from one ill-favor'd fashion to another.

These whimm' Crown'd shees, these fashion-fancying wits,
Are empty thin brain'd shells, and fiddling Kits,

The very troublers and impoverishers of mankind. I can hardly forbeare to commend to the world a saying of a Lady living sometime with the Queen of *Bohemiah*, I know not where she found it, but it is pitty it should be lost.

The world is full of care, much like unto a bubble;
Women and care, and care and women, and women and care and trouble.

The Verses are even enough for such odde pegma's. I can make my self sick at any time, with comparing the dazzling splender wherewith our Gentlewomen were embellished in some former habits, with the gut-foundred goosdome, wherewith they are now surcingled and debauched. We have about five or six of them in our Colony: if I see any of them accidentally, I cannot cleanse my fancy of them for a month after. I have been a solitary widdower almost twelve years, purposed lately to make a step over to my Native Country for a yoke-fellow: but when I consider how women there have tripe-wifed themselves with their cladments, I have no heart to the voyage, lest their nauseous shapes and the Sea, should work too sorely upon my stomach. I speak sadly; me thinks it should break the hearts of Englishmen, to see so many goodly Englishwomen imprisoned in French Cages, peering out of their hood-holes for some men of mercy to help them with a little wit, and no body relieves them.

It is a more common then convenient saying, that nine Taylors make a man: it were well if nineteene could make a woman to her minde: if Taylors were men indeed, well furnished but with meere morall principles, they would disdain to be led about like Apes, by such mimic Marmosets. It is a most unworthy thing, for men that have bones in them, to spend their lives in making fiddle-cases for futilous womens phansies; which are the very pettitoes of infirmity, the gyblets of perquisquilian toyes. I am so charitable to think, that most of that mystery, would work the cheerfuller while they live, if they might be well discharged of the tyring slavery of mis-tyring women: it is no little labour to be continually putting up English-women into Out-landish caskes; who if they be not shifted anew, once in a few moneths, grow too sowre for their Husbands. What this Trade will answer for themselves when God shall take measure of Taylors consciences is beyond my skill to imagine. There was a time when

> The joyning of the Red-Rose with the White
> Did set our State into a Damask plight.

But now our Roses are turned to *Flore de lices*, our Carnations to Tulips, our Gilliflowers to pansies, our City-Dames, to an indenominable Quaemalry of overturcas'd things. Hee that makes Coates for the Moone, had need take measure every noone; and he that makes for women, every Moone, to keep them from Lunacy.

I have often heard diverse Ladies vent loud feminine complaints of the wearisome varieties and chargable changes of fashion: I marvell themselves prefer not a Bill of redresse. I would *Essex* * Ladies would lead the *Chore*, for the honour of their County and persons; or rather the thrice honourable Ladies of the Court, whom it best beseemes: who may wel presume of a *Le Roy le veult* from our sober King, a *Les Seigneurs ont Assentus* from our prudent Peers, and the like Assentus from our con-

* All the Counties and shires of England have had wars in them since the Conquest, but Essex, which is onely free, and should be thankful.

siderate, I dare not say wife-worne Commons: who I beleeve had much rather passe one such Bill, than pay so many Taylors Bills as they are forced to doe.

Most deare and unparallel'd Ladies, be pleased to attempt it: as you have the precellency of the women of the world for beauty and feature; so assume the honour to give, and not take Law from any, in matter of attire: if ye can transact so faire a motion among your selves unanimously, I dare say, they that most renite, will least repent. What greater honour can your Honors desire, then to build a Promontory precedent to all foraigne Ladies, to deserve so eminently at the hands of all the English Gentry, present and to come; and to confute the opinion of all the wise men in the world; who never thought it possible for women to doe so good a work?

Though Nathaniel Ward had posed as a folksy detractor of the ways of woman in his *Simple Cobler*, it would seem that he was not really a misogynist. So we must assume from the poetic commendation which he contributed to Mrs. Anne Bradstreet's *The Tenth Muse Lately sprung up in America* (London, 1650). Ward poked light fun at himself and the lady poetess in the course of praising her. Envisioning himself as a crabbed old Apollo, Ward proceeded to humanize the Greek gods in the best humorous spirit of classical mythology. Even with the aid of spectacles the satirizer of women's fashions cannot decide whether the Puritan New England poet is either better or worse than the French poet Du Bartas. The gods, noting that he is worn out by the difficulty of the decision, laughingly inform him that they find his uncertainty no marvel, for Du Bartas is actually the model whom Mrs. Bradstreet had emulated. At last the discomfited Apollo can render a verdict. But he does so mock-grudgingly, ridiculously exaggerating her achievement.

TEXT: *The Poems of Mrs. Anne Bradstreet*, Boston, Mass., 1897.

MERCURY SHOWED APOLLO BARTAS' BOOK

Mercury showed Apollo Bartas' book,
Minerva this, and wished him well to look
And tell uprightly which did which excel.
He viewed and viewed, and vowed he could not tell.
They bid him hemisphere his moldy nose
With's cracked leering-glasses, for it would pose
The best brains he had in's old pudding-pan,

Sex weighed, which best—the woman, or the man?
He peered, and pored, and glared, and said, forwore,
"I'm e'en as wise now as I was before."
They both 'gan laugh, and said it was no mar'l,
The auth'ress was a right Du Bartas girl.
"Good sooth!" quoth the old Don, "tell ye me so?
I muse whither at length these girls will go.
It half revives my chill frost-bitten blood
To see a woman once do aught that's good;
And shod by Chaucer's boots and Homer's furs,
Let men look to't lest women wear the spurs."

Long after Nathaniel Ward had died he was complimented by the
Reverend Cotton Mather for "wit and sense." Apparently other Puritan
ministers were equally enthusiastic, for the commonplace book of the
Reverend Thomas Welde (1653–1702) of Dunstable preserved the following ribald ditty for his amusement. Puritan poets were fond of the witty
effects obtained from such poetic devices as anagrams and acrostics. Since
much Puritan verse was written for elegiac purposes, anagrams were frequently composed around the names of the dead and incorporated into
funeral elegies. Ward's lines praise the skill of elegist John Wilson (1588–
1667), a Puritan minister.

TEXT: Harold S. Jantz, "The First Century of New England Verse,"
Proceedings of the American Antiquarian Society, LIII (1944), 228.

MR. WARD OF ANAGRAMS THUS

We poor Agawams
Are so stiff in the hams
That we cannot make Anagrams.
But Mr. John Wilson,
The great Epigrammatist,
Can let out an Anagram
Even as he list.

In view of Ward's clerical background, it is possible that the last two
lines contain a Biblical allusion to *John* 3:8: "The wind bloweth where it
listeth . . ." On the other hand, it may be that the Reverend Ward was

a reader of seventeenth-century English jest books or humor anthologies. A number of these—*Oxford Jests, Witts Recreations, Book of Jests, Nuga Venales,* and *Witts Cabinett*—are known to have been owned by Puritan New Englanders and ordered from booksellers by them. These jest books ranged from short proverbs and epigrams to long poems executed in the "fantastick" styles of George Herbert and John Donne, from the vulgar bawdiness of the street and tavern to the subtlety of the most refined verbal wit. One will find the writings of Shakespeare, Milton, and Sidney alongside the epigrams of unknown hacks. One of the jest books cited, *Witts Recreations Selected from the Finest Fancies of Moderne Muses* (1640), was read by young Seaborn Cotton (1633–1686) while he was studying theology at Harvard in 1648–1654. The commonplace book of Cotton, who became a minister at Hampton, New Hampshire, contains numerous transcriptions from *Witts Recreations,* many of them marked by much bawdiness. *Witts Recreations* may have inspired Ward's little piece on the Reverend Wilson, for *Facetiae* (London, 1874; cumulative reprint of *Witts Recreations,* 1640, 1641, 1654) contains an epigram remarkably similar to Ward's lines:

To my Reader

My person is another as I list,
I now but act the Epigrammatist.

Thomas Morton (?1580-1647)

Historians taking their cue from Puritan chroniclers have tended to regard Thomas Morton as an irresponsible scalawag who would have converted sedate New England into chaos if he had had his way. Trained in law but not in diplomacy, Morton arrived from England in 1622 for the first of several unsuccessful attempts to settle in the New World on his own terms; he died there in 1647. For over a quarter of a century he plagued Puritan and Pilgrim alike, calling down upon himself their righteous wrath as well as military invasion, confiscation and destruction of his property, deportation to England, imprisonment, and repeated expulsion. It is difficult to decide whether Morton was detested and persecuted because he liked "frisking together" with Indian maidens, encouraged his followers to carouse, wrote drinking songs for their Bacchanalian revels, and erected a Maypole around which the inhabitants of the settlement he named Merry Mount were wont to dance long hours, or because he was an Anglican who successfully competed with the Puritans and Pilgrims for the Indian fur trade. The master of the revels, or "lord of misrule" as he was dubbed by Governor William Bradford, avenged himself permanently upon his enemies in the *New English Canaan or New Canaan* (Amsterdam, 1637), a skillful and vigorous satire which ridiculed the righteous with invective, slander, burlesque, anecdote, nicknames, and irony. The mock-heroic battle scenes stigmatize Governor Endicott as "Captain Littleworth" and diminutive Miles Standish as "Captain Shrimp"; the pages on which they wage war anticipate the burlesque battles in Washington Irving's *History of New York* and Henry David Thoreau's *Walden*. Morton's portrait of Doctor Samuel Fuller (Book III, Chapter XVIII), Plymouth physician, magistrate, and deacon, is a typical seventeenth-century "character" sketch. The glee with which Fuller's confusion between spiritual and physical healing is shown resulting in heavenly migrations is similar to that with which the misadventures of the doctor (or lawyer or clergyman) are subsequently related in American humorous literature.

TEXT: *New English Canaan*, Amsterdam, 1637.

OF A DOCTOR MADE AT A COMMENCEMENT IN NEW CANAAN

The Church of Plymouth, having due regard to the weal public and the Brethren that were to come over, and knowing that they would be busily employed to make provision for the cure of Souls, and therefore might

9

neglect the body for the time, did hold themselves to be in duty bound to make search for a fitting man, that might be able, (if so neede requir'd,) to take the charge upon him in that place of employment: and therefore called a Council of the whole Synagogue: amongst which company, they chose out a man that long time had been nursed up in the tender bosom of the Church: one that had special gifts: he could write and read; nay, more: he had ta'en the oath of abjuration, which is a special step, yea, and a main degree unto preferment. Him they wean, and out of Phaos box fit him with special gifts of no less worth: they style him Doctor, and forth they send him to gaine employment and opinion.

What luck is it I cannot hit on his name: but I will give you him by a periphrasis, that you may know him when you meet him next.

He was born at Wrington, in the County of Somerset, where he was bred a Butcher. He wears a long beard, and a Garment like the Greek that begged in Paul's Church. This new made Doctor comes to Salem to congratulate: where he finds some are newly come from Sea, and ill at ease.

He takes the patient, and the urinal: eyes the state there; finds the Crasis Symptoms, and the attomi natantes: and tells the patient that his disease was winde, which he had ta'en by gaping feasting overboard at Sea; but he would quickly ease him of that grief, and quite expell the wind. And this he did perform, with his gifts he had: and then he handled the patient so handsomely, that he eased him of all the wind he had in an instant.[1]

And yet I hope this man may be forgiven, if he[2] were made a fitting Plant for Heaven.

How he went to work with his gifts is a question; yet he did a great cure for Captain Littleworth . . . he cured him of a disease called a wife: and yet I hope this man may be forgiven, if she were made a fitting plant for heaven.

By this means he was allowed 4 £ a month, and the chirurgeon's chest, and made Physician General of Salem: where he exercised his gifts so well, that of full 42 that there he took to cure, there is not one that has more cause to complain or can say black's his eye. This saved Captain Littleworth's credit, that had trucked away the victuals: though it brought forth a scandal on the Country by it: and then I hope this man may be forgiven, if they were all made fitting plants for Heaven.

But in mine opinion, he deserves to be set upon a palfrey and led up and down in triumph through New Canaan, with a collar of Guerdons about his neck, as was one of like desert in Richard the Second's time through the streets of London, that men might know where to find a Quacksalver.

[1] The sea-sick patient died.
[2] The patient.

Edward Johnson (1598–1672)

Edward Johnson was one of the distinguished secular figures who combined practical affairs and letters to further the growth of Massachusetts. English-born, a man of some wealth, he debarked at Boston in 1630 and soon was active in Indian trade and land development. In 1640 Johnson was one of seven men delegated to plan the newly authorized town of Charlestown Village (Woburn), a responsibility proudly and humorously described in the poem below. The poem appears at the opening of the Woburn town records, for Johnson was the town's first clerk and kept its records for many years. Johnson later occupied many other official town posts and also assisted the colonial government in a variety of military, surveying, and legal assignments. Capable of expressing himself in prose and poetry and imbued with an epic vision of the Puritan settlement of New England, he wrote one of the most interesting of its histories (A History of New-England . . . 1628 . . . 1652, [London, 1654], known more familiarly as Wonder-Working Providence) and may also have been the author of the good-humored Good news from New-England (London, 1648).

TEXT: Johnson's Wonder-Working Providence, 1628–1651, ed. J. Franklin Jameson, New York, 1910.

IN PENNILESS AGE I WOBURN TOWN BEGAN

In penniless age I Woburn Town began;
Charlestown first moved the Court my lines to span.
To view my land place, compiled body rear,
Nowell, Sims, Sedgwick, these my patrons were.
Some fearing I'll grow great upon these grounds,
Poor I was put to nurse among the clowns,
Who being taken with such mighty things
As had been work of noble queens and kings,
'Til babe 'gan cry and great disturbance make;
Nurses repent they did her undertake.
One leaves her quite; another he doth hie
To foreign lands, free from the baby's cry;
Two more of seven, seeing nursing proved so thwart,
Thought it more ease in following of the cart.
A neighbor by, hoping the babe would be
A pretty girl, to rocking her went he.

Two nurses less daunted than the rest,
First houses finish; thus the girl gane dressed.
It's rare to see how this poor town did rise
By weakest means, too weak in great ones' eyes.
And sure it is that mettle's clear extraction
Had never share in this poor town's erection;
Without which mettle and some fresh supplies
Patrons conclude she never up would rise.
If ever she 'mongst ladies have a station,
Say 'twas from parents, not her education.
And now conclude the Lord's own hand it was
That with weak means did bring this work to pass;
Not only town but sister church to add
Which out of dust and ashes now is had.
Then all [who] inhabit Woburn Town, make
The Lord, not means, stay of all you undertake.*

* [Original text: "Then all Inhabit woburne Towne, stay make/The lord, not means, of all you undertake."]

Anonymous

This ballad, supposed to have been composed in the 1630's, may be the work of Edward Johnson, for it echoes his humorous spirit and style. Whoever the author may have been, he was familiar with the conditions of existence in the earliest New England settlements and capable of communicating the wry doggedness which enabled the settlers to maintain their pious zeal in a hostile environment, even the discomfort of having to wear patched ("clouted") garments. The seriousness underlying most Puritan humor emerges sharply in the last stanza when the author's good-natured forbearance forsakes him as he satirizes Puritans who lacked the spiritual fortitude to endure hardship.

TEXT: *Collections of the Massachusetts Historical Society*, 3d ser., VII (1838), 29–30.

OUR FOREFATHER'S SONG

> *New England's annoyances you that would know them,*
> *Pray ponder these verses which briefly doth shew them.*

I

The place where we live is a wilderness wood,
Where grass is much wanting that's fruitful and good:
Our mountains and hills and our valleys below,
Being commonly covered with ice and with snow:
And when the northwest wind with violence blows,
Then every man pulls his cap over his nose:
But if any's so hardy and will it withstand,
He forfeits a finger, a foot, or a hand.

II

But when the spring opens we then take the hoe,
And make the ground ready to plant and to sow;
Our corn being planted and seed being sown,
The worms destroy much before it is grown;
And when it is growing some spoil there is made,
By birds and by squirrels that pluck up the blade;
And when it is come to full corn in the ear,
It is often destroyed by raccoon and by deer.

III

And now our garments begin to grow thin,
And wool is much wanted to card and to spin;
If we can get a garment to cover without,
Our other in garments are clout upon clout;
Our clothes we brought with us are apt to be torn,
They need to be clouted soon after they're worn,
But clouting our garments they hinder us nothing,
Clouts double, are warmer than single whole clothing.

IV

If fresh meat be wanting, to fill up our dish,
We have carrots and turnips as much as we wish;
And is there a mind for a delicate dish
We repair to the clam banks, and *there* we catch fish.
Instead of pottage and puddings and custards and pies,
Our pumpkins and parsnips are common supplies;
We have pumpkins at morning and pumpkins at noon;
If it was not for pumpkins we should be undone.

V

If barley be wanting to make into malt,
We must be contented and think it no fault;
For we can make liquor to sweeten our lips,
Of pumpkins and parsnips and walnut tree chips.*

VI

Now while some are going let others be coming,
For while liquor's boiling it must have a scumming;
But I will not blame them, for birds of a feather,
By seeking their fellows are flocking together.
But you whom the Lord intends hither to bring,
Forsake not the honey for fear of the sting;
But bring both a quiet and contented mind,
And all needful blessings you surely will find.

* [The ballad was dictated in 1785 by an elderly lady of ninety-six, a fact explaining
the absence of the last four lines of this stanza but also making us wonder how she
managed to keep all the rhymes in mind.]

Anne Bradstreet (?1612–1672)

Born in England, Mrs. Anne Bradstreet arrived in Massachusetts in 1630. Simon Bradstreet, her husband, was to become a distinguished governor and judge and to provide his wife with leisure that enabled her to develop into the most prolific and accomplished Puritan poet before Edward Taylor (pp. 38–42). Whimsical touches of light irony and fancy as well as verbal wit enliven Mrs. Bradstreet's writings, most often in poems dealing with herself as writer, mother, and wife. She jibed gaily at arrogant men who decried lady authors and would banish them to the sewing room. With similar merriment she announced that "I had eight birds hatcht in one nest,/Four Cocks there were, and Hens the rest." "The Author to Her Book," which appeared in the second (1678) edition of her poems, rises above the conventional seventeenth-century appeal for the reader's forbearance. Mrs. Bradstreet draws humorously upon maternal experience and charmingly transcends her irritation at the printing and publishing mistakes which had marred the first appearance of her poems in 1650.

TEXT: *The Poems of Mrs. Anne Bradstreet*, Boston, Mass., 1897.

THE AUTHOR TO HER BOOK

Thou ill-formed offspring of my feeble brain,
Who after birth didst by my side remain
Till snatched from thence by friends, less wise than true,
Who thee abroad exposed to public view,
Made thee in rags, halting to th' press to trudge,
Where errors were not lessened (all may judge).
At thy return my blushing was not small,
My rambling brat (in print) should mother call;
I cast thee by as one unfit for light,
Thy visage was so irksome in my sight;
Yet being mine own, at length affection would
Thy blemishes amend, if so I could:
I washed thy face, but more defects I saw,
And rubbing off a spot, still made a flaw.
I stretched thy joints to make thee even feet,
Yet still thou run'st more hobbling than is meet;
In better dress to trim thee was my mind,
But nought save home-spun cloth in th' house I find.
In this array, 'mongst vulgars mayst thou roam;

In critics' hands, beware thou dost not come;
And take thy way where yet thou are not known.
If for thy father asked, say thou hadst none;
And for thy mother—she, alas, is poor,
Which caused her thus to send thee out of door.

Anonymous

The kind of verbal tomfoolery for which the Reverend Nathaniel Ward complimented the Reverend John Wilson in "Mr. Ward of Anagrams Thus" (p. 7) is exemplified in this work by an unknown author. For the seventeenth-century Puritan, death was not only ever-present but also a welcome phenomenon; Samuel Sewall's "A Specimen of New English Celibacy" implies this quite clearly. The grim comic aura of the medieval "Dance of Death" hung visibly over New England. Furthermore, English literature had already converted the funeral elegy into a form providing for the expression of secular comment and emotion in addition to spiritual sorrow. Many an elegy was read more for its satiric and entertaining commentary than for a listing of virtues of the departed one who was the ostensible subject. Indeed, mock-serious epitaphs, elegiac parodies, and satiric elegies became extremely common during the political and ecclesiastical conflicts between Puritans and Cavaliers. Puritan poet John Milton wrote two humorous elegies, for example, on the death in 1630 of Thomas Hobson, who had served as postman between Cambridge University and London. Though Milton knew Hobson well and apparently liked him too, the two elegies are replete with an obvious humor of allusion and observation as well as with clever puns. These poems were highly popular during Milton's lifetime, perhaps more so than his other greater works. Milton first published "On the University Carrier" and "Another on the same" in 1645, when he issued his first volume of poetry. But the two elegies on Hobson had already appeared in 1640 in a jest book, *The Banquet of Jests* (repr. 1657). They made another appearance in *Wit Restor'd*, a jest book of 1658. *Witts Recreations*, a jest book whose 1640 edition was read by the Reverend Seaborn Cotton during his Harvard years (1648–1654), also contained a number of humorous epitaphs on the death of Hobson. It is not surprising, therefore, that American Puritan poets found death to be a theme around which to release some of the psychic tension forbidden expression in such carnal diversions as Maypole dancing, card playing, and the like. In a poem such as the "Anagram on Thomas Dudley" the humor is primarily verbal. The lines were sent to the Massachusetts governor in 1645, eight years before he died, as a composition which would please rather than terrify him. As the seventeenth century drew closer to the eighteenth, Puritan elegiac verse became more humorous and less lugubrious in the hands of practitioners such as the Reverend Nicholas Noyes. One of Benjamin Franklin's earliest humorous writings, No. 7 of the "Dogood Papers" (1722), ridiculed the late Puritan funeral elegy because few traces of real concern for death were visible in the verse.

TEXT: *New England Historical and Genealogical Register*, XXXIII (1879), 64.

ANAGRAM ON THOMAS DUDLEY

Thomas Dudley
ah! old, must dye
A death's head on your hand you neede not weare,
A dying head you on your shoulders beare.
You need not one to minde you, you must dye;
You in your name may spell mortalitye.
Young men may dye, but old men these dye must;
T'will not be long before you turne to dust.
Before you turne to dust! Ah! must; old! dye!
What shall younge do, when old in dust do lye?
When old in dust lye, what N. England do?
When old in dust do lye, it's best dye too.

Edward Bulkeley (1614–1686)

The Reverend Mr. Bulkeley of Marshfield and Concord, Massachusetts, was deeply moved by the death of his fellow clergyman, Samuel Stone of Hartford, Connecticut. Both men had been born in England and both had been students at Cambridge; Bulkeley may have known Stone when the latter was minister at Cambridge, Massachusetts. In any event, as Bulkeley's fanciful threnody demonstrates, he explored the resources of his verbal ingenuity to pay fit homage to Stone. In punning upon Stone's name, Bulkeley was sure to please his audience. Cotton Mather, who is sometimes more entertaining than trustworthy as a historian, wrote in *Magnalia Christi Americana* of the arrival of the Reverends John Cotton, Thomas Hooker, and Stone in 1633, as follows:

Which glorious triumvirate coming together, made the poor people in the wilderness, at their coming, to say, that the God of heaven had supplied them with what would in some sort answer their three great necessities; *Cotton* for their *clothing*, *Hooker* for their *fishing*, and *Stone* for their *building*. . . .

The wittiness of Bulkeley's poem resides in more than the number of times that Samuel Stone's name provides occasion for a pun. Bulkeley strove to give his puns complexity of allusion and also to make them relevant to the Puritan vision of a clergyman's faith, virtue, knowledge, and strength. Nicholas Noyes' "To My Worthy Friend, Mr. James Bayley . . ." (pp. 43–46) was probably influenced by Bulkeley's elegy.

TEXT: Nathaniel Morton, *New Englands Memoriall*, Cambridge, Mass., 1669.

A THRENODIA

upon our Churches second dark Eclipse, happening *July 20, 1663,* by Deaths Interposition between us and that Great Light and Divine Plant, Mr. *Samuel Stone,* late of *Hartford* in *New-England.*

Last Spring this Summer may be Autumn *styl'd,*
Sad withering Fall *our Beauties which despoyl'd:*
Two choicest Plants, *our* Norton *and our* Stone,
Your Justs *threw down; remov'd, away are gone.*
One Year brought Stone *and* Norton *to their Mother;*
In one Year April July *them did smother.*
Dame Cambridge, *Mother to this darling Son;*

Emmanuel, Northampt' *that heard this one;*
Essex, *our* Bay; Hartford, *in Sable clad;*
Come bear your parts in this Threnodia *sad.*
In losing One, *Church* many lost: O *then,*
Many *for* One, *come be sad singing men.*
May Nature, Grace *and* Art *be found in* one
So *high, as to be found in* few *or* none?
In him these Three, *with full-fraught hand contested,*
With which by each he should be most invested.
The Largess *of the* Three *it was so great*
On *him, the* Stone *was held a* Light compleat:
A Stone *more than the* Eben-ezer *fam'd;*
Stone, *splendent Diamond, right* Orient *nam'd;*
A Cordial Stone, *that often cheerèd hearts*
With pleasant Wit, *with Gospel rich imparts;*
Whet-Stone, *that Edge files off th' obtusest Minde;*
Load-Stone, *that drew the Iron Heart unkinde;*
A Ponderous Stone, *that would the Bottom sound*
Of Scripture-depths, and bring out Arcanes *found;*
A Stone *for Kingly* David's *use so fit,*
As would not fail Goliah's *Front to hit;*
A Stone *an* Antidote, *that brake the course*
Of Gangrene Errour by Convincing force;
A Stone Acute, *fit to divide and square;*
A Squarèd Stone, *become Christs Building rare;*
A Peter's Living lively Stone, (*so Reared*)
As 'live, *was* Hartford's *life;* dead, *death is feared.*
In Hartford *old,* Stone *first drew Infant-breath;*
In New *effus'd his last:* O *there beneath*
His Corpse *are laid, near to his darling Brother,*
Of whom, dead, oft he sigh'd, "Not such another."
"Heaven is the more desireable" (*said he*)
For Hooker, Shepard, *and* Haynes' Company."

Samuel Danforth (1626–1674)

The New England almanac for 1639 was the second work printed by the Puritans on their first press; it preceded the *Bay Psalm Book*. Almanacs were produced annually thereafter, under the editorship of Harvard students such as Samuel Danforth, later minister at Roxbury. Before long the New England almanac began to resemble its English cousins. The calendar of seasons, tidal changes, court sessions, and astronomical phenomena was supplemented by prognosticating verse, historical chronologies, advertisements for books and patent medicines, and entertaining prose. The almanac gradually became a secular book, still dispensing useful facts but also providing Harvard poets with an outlet for their efforts and readers with the kind of humorous writing to be found in English jest books. Danforth's almanac verses of 1647 are gnomic proverbs whose allegorical meanings have been expounded by Kenneth B. Murdock in *Handkerchiefs for Paul*, from which the text below has been taken. But the little poems are also amusing and they encouraged later almanac editors to print greater amounts of humor. Even a casual reading of seventeenth-century almanacs such as those of John Richardson, William Brattle, and John Tulley will reveal that the Yankee tone and bawdiness of Benjamin Franklin's *Poor Richard's Almanac* had been well-established by his Puritan forbears. Franklin would not have been averse to printing, with perhaps some editorial polishing, the following lines from Richardson's 1670 almanac:

> *Conjunctions* lastly all which you will finde,
> Of *Male* and *Female Planets* (if you minde)
> Do tell of some great Changes to be wrought,
> Men to *four-footèd creatures* will be brought.

or the following prose and verse from Tulley's 1688 almanac:

On the Twenty eighth day of this month is like to be a very comfortable smell of *Pancakes* and *Fritters*. The Nights are still cold and long, which may cause great Conjunctions betwixt the Male and Female Planets of our sublunary Orb, the effects whereof may be seen about nine months after, and portend great charges of Midwife, Nurse, and Naming the Bantling.

> *The Sun is entered now into the* Crab,
> *And days are hot, therefore beware a Drab;*
> *With French diseases, they'll thy body fill,*
> *Being such as bring* Grist *to the Surgeon's Mill.*

TEXT: *Handkerchiefs for Paul*, ed. Kenneth B. Murdock, Cambridge, Mass., 1927.

VERSES FOR EVERY MONTH IN THE YEAR

[MARCH]

A Coal-white Bird appeares this spring
That neither cares to sigh or sing.
This when the merry Birds espy,
They take her for some enemy.
Why so, when as she humbly stands
Only to shake you by your hands?

[APRIL]

That which hath neither tongue nor wings
This month how merrily it sings:
To see such, out for dead who lay
To cast their winding sheets away?
Freinds! would you live? some pills then take
When head and stomack both do ake.

[MAY]

White Coates! whom choose you! whom you list:
Some Ana-tolleratorist:
Wolves, lambs, hens, foxes to agree
By setting all opinion-free:
If Blue-coates do not this prevent,
Hobgoblins will be insolent.

[JUNE]

Who dig'd this spring of Gardens here,
Whose mudded streames at last run cleare?
But why should we such water drink?
Give loosers what they list to think,
Yet know, one God, one Faith profest
To be New-England's interest.

[JULY]

The wooden Birds are now in sight,
Whose voices roare, whose wings are white,
Whose mawes are fill'd with hose and shooes,
With wine, cloth, sugar, salt and newes;

When they have eas'd their stomacks here,
They cry, farewell untill next yeare.

[AUGUST]

Many this month I do fore-see
Together by the eares will bee:
Indian and English in the field
To one another will not yield.
Some weeks continue will this fray,
Till they be carted all away.

[SEPTEMBER]

Four heads should meet and counsell have,
The chickens from the kite to save,
The idle drones away to drive,
The little Bees to keep i'th hive.
How honey may be brought to these
By making fish to dance on trees.

[OCTOBER]

If discontented Bellies shall
Wish that the highest now might fall:
Their wish fulfilled they shall see,
Whenas within the woods they bee.
Poor Tinker think'st our shrubs will sing:
The Bramble here shall be our King.

[NOVEMBER]

None of the wisest now will crave
To know what winter we shall have.
It shall be milde, let such be told,
If that it be not over cold.
Nor over cold shall they it see,
If very temperate it bee.

[DECEMBER]

It may be now some enemy—
Not seen, but felt, will make you fly.
Where is it best then to abide:
I think close by the fire side.
If you must fight it out i'th field,
Your hearts let woollen breast-plates shield.

[JANUARY]

Great bridges shall be made alone,
Without ax, timber, earth or stone,
Of crystal metall, like to glasse;
Such wondrous works soon come to passe.
If you may then have such a way,
The Ferry-man you need not pay.

[FEBRUARY]

Our Lillies which refus'd to spin
All winter past, shall now begin
To feel the lash of such a Dame,
Whom some call Idleness by name.
Excepting such who all this time
Had reason good against my rime.

Samuel Bailey

The conflict between highbrow and lowbrow in American life has often been pictured in humorous literature supporting one or the other side. It all began quite early because some Harvard almanac compilers could not resist laughing at the superstition and ignorance of their agrarian readers. When John Richardson's 1670 almanac treated the farmer as a ludicrous, unlearned bumpkin in "The Country-man's Apocrypha," retaliation followed swiftly. Nothing is known about Samuel Bailey, whose light-hearted satire was found early in the nineteenth century hidden away among the dusty records of the Providence, Rhode Island, town clerk.

TEXT: *New England Historical and Genealogical Register*, IX (1855), 356.

THE COLLEGE FERULA, BEING A REPLY TO "THE COUNTRY-MAN'S APOCRYPHA"

Most learned academies, have your gowns,
And college taught you to abuse the clowns
In empty rhymes, trussed to an Almanac,
Like Tom Thumb bound on erra Pater's back?
The Devil, when at Delphos he did dwell
And cheated men to death, did use to sell
His mind, in speeches of a double sense;
Yet there was often, wit and eloquence.
They that at Harvard, now the trade do drive,
For penny oracles would keep alive
Those Grecian cheats, but cannot imitate
The wit and language, yet equivocate
As fast as he. Like heathen jugglers, they
At hocus pocus with the stars can play.
What will they sport with next, since they will creep
Behind the glorious curtain and bo-peep
With sacred mysteries, or if they grow
More modest, they will jeer the powers below.
These are grave sophisters, that are in schools
So wise they think their agèd fathers, fools
That plough and cart; and such they are indeed
Or else they would not work so hard, to breed

Their boys to flout them; but I cannot stay
Foddering of asses thus; I must away
And give my sheep their breakfast, who, I fear,
Wait at the stack, while I write verses here.

Henricus Selijns (1636–1701)

Henricus Selijns, who served as minister of Dutch Reformed churches in New York and Brooklyn for almost a quarter of a century, found life under both Dutch Calvinist and English Anglican rule congenial for his spiritual and literary labors. He maintained contact with the New England Puritans, in the 1660's dispatching a laudatory poem to Reverends John Eliot and John Wilson for their translation of the New Testament into Algonquin, and in the late 1690's writing a Latin eulogy of Cotton Mather's *Magnalia Christi Americana* (1702) which appeared in it together with a poem by Nicholas Noyes. However, the Dutch culture of Selijns was closer to the Renaissance and to Anglicanism than it was to Puritanism. New Netherland, like New England, nurtured its literary culture on traditions of the sixteenth and early seventeenth centuries. Because middle-class Protestantism had become established earlier in the Netherlands than in England, its passion for moral education subsided sooner and Dutch writers were required not only to dispense sound morality but also to write openly about love and every-day events, to be amusingly obscene, farcical, clownish, and satirical. As Ellis L. Raesly, the foremost authority on New Netherland literature, has written: "Domine Selijns was nowise frosty or narrow. He had the breadth of mind to suggest that even Paradise might have its theaters." One of Selijns' early poems was an elegy on Coccejus, his distinguished theological professor at Leyden University, in which Selijns converted "Coccejus" to the German "koch" (cook) for the sake of a witty pun. The name of another theological teacher, Heydanus, was punned upon as "heyden" (heathen). Other forms of verbal and intellectual wit distinguish his poems, many of which are genre and character sketches of the kind written by Edwin Arlington Robinson and Robert Frost, birthday and marriage songs, and light poems on women such as the three selections below. As the three poems suggest, no adequate translation of Selijns' poems has yet been made, and no edition of his work exists. Washington Irving examined the Selijns manuscripts in the early 1800's while gathering material for *History of New York*; it is regrettable that he did not translate and edit them at the time.

TEXT: Henry C. Murphy, ed. and trans., *Anthology of New Netherland*, New York, 1865.

OF SCOLDING WIVES AND THE THIRD DAY AGUE

Among the greatest plagues, one is the third day ague;
   But cross and scolding wives the greatest evils are;
With strong and pray'rful minds the first will cease to
     plague you,
   But for the last I know not what advice to dare;
     Except with patience all to suffer,
     And ne'er the first assault to proffer.

REASONS FOR AND AGAINST MARRYING WIDOWS

PRO

Fears any one his bride lest she a virgin be not,
   Or what he would, I know not;
Let him a widow choose, and let the spinsters tarry,
   Ere in such doubts he marry.

CON

To wed a widow, is it not to marry trouble,
   And *woe with woe* to double?
But be this so or not, who can take water down him
   Another had to drown in?

ON MAIDS AND CATS

A nimble cat and lazy maid,
Breed household feuds and are no aid;
But lazy cats and nimble maids,
Beyond all doubt, are greater plagues.
Once, now and then, the cat may eat,
But snoops the maid in ev'ry plate,
And makes the purse and cellar low.
How e'er it hits, *there is no dough.*[1]

[1] It is not right. [*Murphy*]

George Alsop (1638– ?)

Moses Coit Tyler, the pioneering historian of colonial American literature, held George Alsop's *A Character of the Province of Maryland* (London, 1666) in high esteem: "There was but one other American book produced in the seventeenth century that for mirthful, grotesque, and slashing energy can compare with this." Tyler had Nathaniel Ward's *Simple Cobler* in mind. But that book, fascinating in itself, is not so single-mindedly given up to "wild fun and wild nonsense" as the little masterpiece Alsop wrote to attract immigrants to Maryland. Ward had abstained from the "coarse . . . indelicate and even obscene" content and manner which Alsop with true Restoration gusto served up to capture the attention of aristocrats and commoners alike. Alsop foreshadowed the vigorous and imaginative prose of such Southern writers of a humorous cast as William Byrd, Edgar Allan Poe, George Washington Harris, and William Faulkner without being entirely superseded by them. "If I have wrote or composed any thing that's wilde and confused, it is because I am so my self," he explained to Lord Baltimore, "and the world, as far as I can perceive, is not much out of the same trim. . . ." Jokes, puns, abuses, anecdotes, tall tales, vivid images and vain promises tumble over one another in a prose of electric tempo. Virtually a parody of the author's traditional apology for his own work, the poem below illustrates Alsop's uninhibited jocularity and his literary skill. Who this early master of American humor was is still a biographical puzzle. Hints scattered about in his book indicate that he may have been an educated, anti-Puritan Englishman who spent four years (1658–1662) in Maryland as an indentured servant.

TEXT: Newton D. Mereness, ed., *A Character of the Province of Maryland*, Cleveland, Ohio, 1902.

THE AUTHOR TO HIS BOOK

When first *Apollo* got my brain with Childe,
He made large promise never to beguile,
But like an honest Father, he would keep
Whatever Issue from my Brain did creep:
With that I gave consent, and up he threw
Me on a Bench, and strangely he did do;
Then every week he daily came to see
How his new Physick still did work with me.

And when he did perceive he'd done the feat,
Like an unworthy man he made retreat,
Left me in desolation, and where none
Compassionated when they heard me groan.
What could he judge the Parish then would think,
To see me fair, his Brat as black as Ink?
If they had eyes, they'd swear I were no Nun,
But got with Child by some black *Africk* Son,
And so condemn me for my Fornication,
To beat them Hemp to stifle half the Nation.
Well, since 'tis so, I'll alter this base Fate,
And lay his Bastard at some Noble's Gate;
Withdraw my self from Beadles, and from such,
Who would give twelve pence I were in their clutch:
Then, who can tell? this Child which I do hide,
May be in time a Small-beer Col'nel *Pride*.
But while I talk, my business it is dumb,
I must lay double-clothes unto thy Bum,
Then lap thee warm, and to the world commit
The Bastard Off-spring of a New-born wit.
Farewel, poor Brat, thou in a monstrous World,
In swaddling bands, thus up and down art hurl'd;
There to receive what Destiny doth contrive,
Either to perish, or be sav'd alive.
Good Fate protect thee from a Critick's power,
For if he comes, thou'rt gone in half an hour,
Stifl'd and blasted, 'tis their usual way,
To make that Night, which is as bright as Day.
For if they once but wring, and screw their mouth,
Cock up their Hats, and set the point Due-South,
Armes all akimbo, and with belly strut,
As if they had *Parnassus* in their gut:
These are the Symtomes of the murthering fall
Of my poor Infant, and his burial.
Say he should miss thee, and some ign'rant Asse
Should find thee out, as he along doth pass,
It were all one, he'd look into thy Tail,
To see if thou wert Feminine or Male;
When he'd half starv'd thee, for to satisfie
His peeping Ign'rance, he'd then let thee lie;
And vow by's wit he ne'er could understand,
The Heathen dresses of another Land:
Well, 'tis no matter, wherever such as he
Knows one grain, more than his simplicity.

Now, how the pulses of my Senses beat,
To think the rigid Fortune thou wilt meet;
Asses and captious Fools, not six in ten
Of thy Spectators will be real men,
To Umpire up the badness of the Cause,
And screen my weakness from the rav'nous Laws,
Of those that will undoubted sit to see
How they might blast this new-born Infancy:
If they should burn him, they'd conclude hereafter,
'Twere too good death for him to die a Martyr;
And if they let him live, they think it will
Be but a means for to encourage ill,
And bring in time some strange *Antipod'ans*,
A thousand Leagues beyond *Philippians*,
To storm our Wits; therefore he must not rest,
But shall be hang'd, for all he has been prest:
Thus they conclude.—My Genius comforts give,
In Resurrection he will surely live.

Benjamin Tompson (1642–1714)

Though he wrote humorous poetry, the career of Benjamin Tompson was apparently not a happy one. The playfulness visible in such early poems as "The Grammarians Funeral" and "On a Fortification" is rarely to be found in the solemn elegies which he composed as if to order during his later years. Educated at Harvard, Tompson became a schoolmaster who sought but never obtained preferment and security. Though Cotton Mather had been Tompson's pupil in the Boston "free school," the influential minister did not exert himself in his mentor's behalf. A further explanation of Tompson's difficulties may be found in his propensity for caustic satire which expressed itself early in *New Englands Crisis* (Boston, 1676). Written about King Philip's War and published two years before that bloodiest of all colonial Indian conflicts came to an official end, Tompson's poetic account not only heaps sarcastic abuse upon the Indian but also subjects the New England Puritan to scornful ridicule. Like most satirists, Tompson yearned for the good old days. "The Prologue" to *New Englands Crisis* finds little good in manners and customs of the 1670's; Tompson's sharp eye for pretentious and ridiculous details is revealed in the social distinctions, European fashions, fancy foods, tobacco, and imported delicacies which he cites as symbols of declining faith and strength. Nor did Tompson forbear to attack his Alma Mater's poets for failing to memorialize the tragedy of King Philip's War in epic lines: "What meanes this silence of *Harvardine* quils/While *Mars* triumphant thunders on our hills./Have pagan priests their Eloquence confin'd/To no mans use but the mysterious mind?" Had Tompson not been so indignant, it is likely that the light humor of "On a Fortification," the concluding poem of *New Englands Crisis*, might have been more prevalent in his work and brought him favorable attention. In that poem, though some rebuke is implicit, the absurd details of the "Amazonian" episode are amusing. Intellectual pleasure and emotional delight glow in the elaborately developed lines of "The Grammarians Funeral," a poem Tompson wrote to eulogize the death of the schoolmaster whose job he inherited in 1681. The poem was published in 1708 to mark the death of another schoolmaster, Ezekiel Cheever. Like the William Lily alluded to in the fourth line, Cheever was a notable Latin grammarian who had taken Tompson's place in the Boston "free school."

TEXT: "The Grammarians Funeral," Samuel Abbott Green, *Ten Facsimile Reproductions Relating to New England,* Boston, Mass., 1902; "The Prologue" and "On a Fortification," Benjamin Tompson, *New-England's [sic] Crisis,* Boston, Mass., 1894.

THE GRAMMARIANS FUNERAL

Eight Parts of *Speech* this Day wear *Mourning Gowns*
Declin'd *Verbs, Pronouns, Participles, Nouns.*
And not declined, *Adverbs* and *Conjunctions,*
In *Lilies* Porch they stand to do their functions.
With *Preposition;* but the most affection
Was still observed in the *Interjection.*
The *Substantive* seeming the limbed best,
Would set an hand to bear him to his Rest.
The *Adjective* with very grief did say,
Hold me by strength, or I shall faint away.
The Clouds of Tears did over-cast their faces,
Yea all were in most lamentable *Cases.*
The five *Declensions* did the Work decline,
And *Told* the *Pronoun Tu,* The work is thine:
But in this case those have no call to go
That want the *Vocative,* and can't say O!
The *Pronouns* said that if the *Nouns* were there,
There was no need of them, they might them spare:
But for the sake of *Emphasis* they would,
In their Discretion do what ere they could.
Great honour was confer'd on *Conjugations,*
They were to follow next to the *Relations.*
Amo did love him best, and *Doceo* might
Alledge he was his Glory and Delight.
But *Lego* said by me he got his skill,
And therefore next the *Herse* I follow will.
Audio said little, hearing them so hot,
Yet knew by him much Learning he had got.
O *Verbs* the *Active* were, Or *Passive* sure,
Sum to be *Neuter* could not well endure.
But this was common to them all to Moan
Their load of grief they could not soon *Depone.*
A doleful Day for *Verbs,* they look so *moody,*
They drove Spectators to a Mournful Study.
The *Verbs* irregular, 'twas thought by some,
Would break no rule, if they were pleas'd to come.
Gaudeo could not be found; fearing disgrace
He had with-drawn, sent *Mœreo* in his Place.
Possum did to the utmost he was able,

And bore as stout as if he'd been A *Table*.
Volo was willing, *Nolo* some-what stout,
But *Malo* rather chose, not to stand out.
Possum and *Volo* wish'd all might afford
Their help, but had not an *Imperative* W*ord*.
Edo from Service would by no means Swerve.
Rather than fail, he thought the *Cakes* to Serve.
Fio was taken in a fit, and said,
By him a Mournful *POEM* should be made.
Fero was willing for to bear a part,
Altho' he did it with an aking heart.
Feror excus'd, with grief he was so Torn,
He could not bear, he needed to be born.

Such *Nouns* and *Verbs* as we defective find,
No *Grammar* Rule did their attendance bind.
They were excepted, and exempted hence,
But *Supines*, all did blame for negligence.
Verbs Offspring, *Participles* hand-in-hand,
Follow, and by the same direction stand:
The rest Promiscuously did croud and cumber,
Such Multitudes of each, they wanted Number.
Next to the Corps to make th' attendance even,
Jove, Mercury, Apollo came from heaven.
And V*irgil, Cato*, gods, men, Rivers, Winds,
With *Elegies*, Tears, Sighs, came in their kinds.
Ovid from *Pontus* hast's Apparrell'd thus,
In Exile-weeds bringing *De Tristibus:*
And *Homer* sure had been among the Rout,
But that the Stories say his Eyes were out.
Queens, Cities, Countries, Islands, Come
All Trees, Birds, Fishes, and each word in *Um*.

What *Syntax* here can you expect to find?
Where each one bears such discomposed mind.
Figures of Diction and Construction,
Do little: Yet stand sadly looking on.
That such a Train may in their motion *chord*,
Prosodia gives the measure Word for Word.

THE PROLOGUE

The times wherein old *Pompion* was a Saint,
When men fared hardly yet without complaint
On vilest *Cates*; the dainty *Indian Maize*

Was eat with *Clam-shells* out of wooden Trays
Under thatcht *Huts* without the cry of *Rent*,
And the best *Sauce* to every Dish, *Content*.
When Flesh was food, & hairy skins made coats,
And men as well as birds had chirping Notes.
When Cimnels were accounted noble bloud
Among the tribes of common herbage food.
Of *Ceres*' bounty form'd was many a knack
Enough to fill *poor Robin's Almanack*.
These golden times (too fortunate to hold)
Were quickly sinned away for love of gold.
Twas then among the bushes, not the street,
If one in place did an inferiour meet,
"Good morrow Brother, is there ought you want?
Take freely of me, what I have you ha'nt."
Plain *Tom* and *Dick* would pass as current now,
As ever since *Your Servant Sir* and bow.
Deep-skirted doublets, *puritanick* capes,
Which now would render men like upright Apes,
Was comelier wear our wiser Fathers thought
Than the cast fashions from all *Europe* brought.
Twas in those dayes an honest *Grace* would hold
Till an hot puddin grew at heart a cold.
And men had better stomachs to religion
Than I to capon, turkey-cock or pigeon.
When honest Sisters met to pray, not prate
About their own and not their neighbours' state.
During *Plain Dealing's* Reign, that worthy Stud
Of th' ancient planters' race before the flood,
These times were good, Merchants car'd not a rush
For other fare than *Jonakin and Mush*.
Although men fared and lodged very hard,
Yet Innocence was better than a Guard.
Twas long before spiders & wormes had drawn
Their dungy webs or hid with cheating Lawn
New-England's beauties, which still seem'd to me
Illustrious in their own simplicity.
Twas ere the neighbouring *Virgin-land* had broke
The Hogsheads of her worse than hellish smoke.
Twas ere the Islands sent their Presents in,
Which but to use was counted next to sin.
Twas ere a *Barge* had made so rich a freight
As *Chocholatte*, dust-gold and bits of eight.
Ere wines from *France* and *Moscovadoe* too,

Without the which the drink will scarcely do,
From western Isles, ere fruits and delicacies,
Did rot maids' teeth & spoil their hansome faces.
Or ere these times did chance the noise of war
Was from our towns and hearts removèd far.
No Bugbear Comets in the crystal air
To drive our Christian Planters to despair.
No sooner pagan malice peepèd forth
But Valour snib'd it; then were men of worth
Who by their prayers slew thousands Angel-like,
Their weapons are unseen with which they strike.
Then had the Churches rest, as yet the coales
Were covered up in most contentious souls.
Freeness in Judgment, union in affection,
Dear love, sound truth, they were our grand protection.
These were the twins which in our Councells sate,
These gave prognosticks of our future fate;
If these be longer liv'd our hopes increase,
These wars will usher in a longer peace:
But if *New-England's* love die in its youth
The grave will open next for blessed Truth.
This *Theme* is out of date, the peacefull hours
When Castles needed not but pleasant bowers.
Not ink, but bloud and tears now serve the turn
To draw the figure of *New-England's* Urne.
New England's hour of passion is at hand,
No power except Divine can it withstand;
Scarce hath her glass of fifty years run out,
But her old prosperous Steeds turn heads about,
Tracking themselves back to their poor beginnings,
To fear and fare upon their fruits of sinnings:
So that the mirrour of the Christian world
Lies burnt to heaps in part, her Streamers furl'd;
Grief reigns, joyes flee and dismal fears surprize,
Not dastard spirits only but the wise.
Thus have the fairest hopes deceiv'd the eye
Of the big swoln Expectant standing by.
Thus the proud Ship after a little turn
Sinks into *Neptune's* arms to find its Urn.
Thus hath the heir to many thousands born
Been in an instant from the mother torn.
Ev'n thus thine infant cheeks begin to pale,
And thy supporters through great losses fail.

This is the *Prologue* to thy future woe,
The *Epilogue* no mortal yet can know.

ON A FORTIFICATION AT BOSTON BEGUN BY WOMEN

Dux Fœmina Facti

A Grand attempt some Amazonian Dames
Contrive whereby to glorify their names;
A Ruff for *Boston* Neck of mud and turfe,
Reaching from side to side, from surfe to surfe,
Their nimble hands spin up like Christmas pies,
Their pastry by degrees on high doth rise.
The wheel at home counts it an holiday,
Since while the Mistress worketh it may play.
A tribe of female hands, but many hearts,
Forsake at home their pasty-crust and tarts
To knead the dirt; the samplers down they hurle,
Their undulating silks they closely furle.
The pick-axe one as a Commandress holds,
While t'other at her awkness gently scolds.
One puffs and sweats, the other mutters "Why
Can't you promove your work so fast as I?"
Some dig, some delve, and others' hands do feel
The little waggons weight with single wheel.
And lest some fainting fits the weak surprize,
They want no sack nor cakes, they are more wise.
These brave essays draw forth Male stronger hands
More like to Daubers than to Martial bands:
These do the work, and sturdy bulwarks raise,
But the beginners well deserve the praise.

Edward Taylor (?1645-1729)

The Reverend Edward Taylor, whose poetical works were not published until the late 1930's, is undoubtedly the best of the known Puritan poets of New England. Born in England, he arrived in Massachusetts in 1668 and attended Harvard as a classmate of Samuel Sewall (see pp. 47-48). From 1671 until the end of his life, Taylor served as minister and physician of Westfield, Massachusetts. Before his death he left instructions that his literary works were not to be published even though poetry had been a major part of his daily life. Several plausible reasons for Taylor's wish suggest themselves. An orthodox Puritan of the old school, he abhorred the liberal tendencies of latter-day Puritanism and his poetry embodied the strict theological convictions which he upheld as a minister. Deeply religious and also highly emotional, Taylor wrote much poetry of intense spiritual passion whose fervor, erotic imagery, and vision of Christ would have seemed old-fashioned to newfangled eighteenth-century Puritans. Finally, Taylor was an artistic child of the early seventeenth-century metaphysical poets. John Donne and George Herbert would have appreciated Taylor's "fantastick" imagery, his syntactical compressions and inversions, his witty paradoxes, his boldly intimate approach to God and Christ. Few of Taylor's contemporaries, apart from Cotton Mather who had died in 1719, would have discerned more than reprehensible nonsense in his intricate lines. Yet Taylor is one of the few writers who, like Donne and Herbert before him, have rapturously expressed the "Spiritual & Holy Joy" for which the Reverend Benjamin Colman had pleaded in 1707 (see Nathaniel Ward, pp. 1-2). "The Preface" to *God's Determinations* illustrates the manner in which Taylor utilized English literary tradition and his own spiritual and imaginative resources to create a joyous paean•celebrating God's omnipotent wisdom and power. To turn the trick Taylor humorously diminished God to the level of a village artisan; the wonders of the universe—earth, sky, rivers, oceans, sun, stars— are diminished by being regarded as the homely products of an all-round village handyman. This craftsman of wood, mortar, stone, fire, textile, metal, this master of interior decoration, is a playful being who, like the heroes of ancient mythology, rolls the sun in the bowling alley of the universe. Then, like a clap of thunder, Taylor restores God to His sovereign majesty. Now it is the turn of man, who cannot ever hope to duplicate the heroic figure cut by God as a man, to be diminished with the appellation of "nothing Man." Taylor's homely imagery, his delight in concrete details drawn from the homes, gardens, fields, animals, and lives of the people of Westfield, Massachusetts, indicate that he was an enthusiast of experience who found much that aroused "Civil & Natural

38

Mirth." Taylor is known, for example, to have had a special fancy for natural history, the results of which served him charmingly in "Upon a Wasp Chilled with Cold." Prefiguring the blithe and fanciful poems of Emily Dickinson on bees, humming birds, leaves, and flowers, Taylor's poem is compassionate and gay without becoming sentimental. One can imagine that Taylor found the wasp beneath an apple tree and then, raised to spiritual ecstasy by the joyful recovery of the wasp, climbed the waiting ladder to meet God direct.

The Puritan, we know, believed it proper to combine laughter with scornful anger when fighting for his beliefs. Taylor's own bent for satire was strong. One of his last poems, "Verses made upon Pope Joan," is an unrestrained scatological attack upon Catholicism which might have been composed in the early seventeenth century and reveals Taylor's familiarity with the satirist John Cleveland (1613–1658) and with *Scoggan's Jests*, the most popular of early English jest books. Like Benjamin Tompson, Taylor believed that "nothing Man's" sinfulness and arrogance inevitably led to crisis. The storms and floods of 1683 are described in the matter-of-fact language of a Puritan village physician.

TEXT: *The Poems of Edward Taylor*, ed. Donald E. Stanford, New Haven, Conn., 1960.

THE PREFACE TO "GOD'S DETERMINATIONS"

Infinity, when all things it beheld
In Nothing, and of Nothing all did build;
Upon what Base was fixt the Lathe wherein
He turn'd this Globe, and riggald it so trim?
Who blew the Bellows of His Furnace Vast?
Or held the Mould wherein the world was Cast?
Who laid its Corner Stone? Or whose Command?
Where stand the Pillars upon which it stands?
Who Laced and Filleted the earth so fine,
With Rivers like green Ribbons Smaragdine?
Who made the Sea its Selvedge, and it locks
Like a Quilt Ball within a Silver Box?
Who Spread its Canopy? Or Curtains Spun?
Who in this Bowling Alley bowld the Sun?
Who made it always when it rises set:
To go at once both down, and up to get?
Who th' Curtain rods made for this Tapestry?
Who hung the twinckling Lanthorns in the Sky?
Who? who did this? or who is He? Why, know

It's Only Might Almighty this did do.
His hand hath made this noble worke which Stands
His Glorious Handiwork not made by hands.
Who spake all things from nothing; and with ease
Can speake all things to nothing, if He please.
Whose Little finger at His pleasure Can
Out mete ten thousand worlds with halfe a Span:
Whose Might Almighty can by half a looks
Root up the rocks and rock the hills by th' roots.
Can take this mighty World up in His hande,
And shake it like a Squitchen or a Wand.
Whose single Frown will make the Heavens shake
Like as an aspen leafe the Winde makes quake.
Oh! what a might is this! Whose single frown
Doth shake the world as it would shake it down?
Which All from Nothing fet, from Nothing, All:
Hath All on Nothing set, lets Nothing fall.
Gave All to nothing Man indeed, whereby
Through nothing, man all might Him Glorify.
In Nothing then embossed the brightest Gem
More precious than all preciousness in them.
But Nothing man did throw down all by sin:
And darkened that lightsome Gem in him,
   That now his Brightest Diamond is grown
   Darker by far than any Coalpit Stone.

UPON A WASP CHILLED WITH COLD

The Bear that breaths the Northern blast
Did numb, Torpedo-like, a Wasp
Whose stiffened limbs encrampt, lay bathing
In Sol's warm breath and shine as saving,
Which with her hands she chafes and stands
Rubbing her Legs, Shanks, Thighs, and hands.
Her petty toes and fingers' ends,
Nipped with this breath, she out-extends
Unto the Sun, in greate desire
To warm her digits at that fire.
Doth hold her Temples in this state
Where pulse doth beate, and head doth ache.
Doth turn and stretch her body small,

Doth Comb her velvet Capital—
As if her little brain pan were
A Volume of Choice precepts cleare;
As if her satin jacket hot
Contained Apothecary's Shop
Of Nature's receipts, that prevails
To remedy all her sad ailes;
As if her velvet helmet high
Did turret rationality.
She fans her wing up to the Winde
As if her Petticoat were lined
With reasons fleece, and hoists her sails
And humming flies in thankfull gales
Unto her dun Curled palace Hall
Her warm thanks-offering for all.

     Lord, cleare my misted sight that I
May hence view thy Divinity.
Some sparkes whereof thou up dost hasp
Within this little downy Wasp.
In whose small Corporation we
A school and a schoolmaster see
Where we may learn, and easily find
A nimble Spirit bravely mind
Her worke in e'ry limb: and lace
It up neate with a vitall grace,
Acting each part though ne'er so small
Here of this Fustian animall.
Till I enravisht Climb into
The Godhead on this Lather do.
Where all my pipes inspired upraise
An Heavenly musick furred with praise.

UPON THE SWEEPING FLOOD AUG: 13.14. 1683

Oh! that I'd had a tear to've quencht that flame
    Which did dissolve the Heavens above
      Into those liquid drops that Came
        To drown our Carnal love.
Our cheeks were dry and eyes refused to weep.
Tears bursting out ran down the sky's darke Cheek.

Were th'Heavens sick? must we their Doctors be
    And physick them with pills, our sin?
    To make them purge and Vomit, see,
        And Excrements out fling?
We've griev'd them by such Physick that they shed
Their Excrements upon our lofty heads.

Nicholas Noyes (1647–1717)

A friend who visited Nicholas Noyes in 1686 enthusiastically recorded that the Puritan minister of Salem, Massachusetts, *"is all that's delightful in Conversation,* so easy Company, and so far from all constraint, that 'tis a real Pleasure to talk with him. . . ." A poem Noyes wrote in praise of Cotton Mather's *Magnalia Christi Americana* exemplifies the deep pleasure in intelligence, art, and high spirits which Puritanism transmitted to later generations: "He's all *design,* and by his *craftier wiles*/Locks fast his reader, and the time beguiles:/Whilst *wit* and *learning* move themselves aright,/Thro' ev'ry line, and *colour* in our sight,/So interweaving *profit* with delight;/And curiously inlaying both together,/That he must needs find both, who looks for either." Noyes' own wit has come down to us in both oral tradition and in his few surviving poems. An inveterate punster, his funeral elegies are in the traditional Puritan pattern. The tribute to James Bayley, three years younger than Noyes and like him a native of Newbury, Massachusetts, was composed at least eight months before Bayley's death in 1707. Samuel Sewall, who brought the elegy to Bayley on May 27, 1706, reported that the dying man sent good wishes to Noyes "with much Thanks for his verses which had been a great Comfort to him. . . ."

TEXT: Ola Elizabeth Winslow, *American Broadside Verse*, New Haven, Conn., 1930, facsimile facing p. 21.

TO MY WORTHY FRIEND, MR. JAMES BAYLEY, LIVING (IF LIVING) IN ROXBURY

My Old Companion! and my Friend!
I cannot Come, and therefore send.
Some pity should be shown to One
That's heavy laden with the Stone;
That's wearied out with fits of pain
Returning like Clouds after Rain.
Alas! my Brother, what can I
Do for thee, more than Pray and Cry,
To Counsel, and to comfort try,
And bear a part by Sympathy?
Excuse me, though I Write in Verse,
It's usual on a Dead man's Hearse:
Thou many a Death hast under-gone,

And Elegies made of thine own.
  Our Saviour's Funeral Obsequies,
One Celebrates before His eyes;
And He the Ointment kindly takes,
That for His Burial she makes.
Two Saints array'd in glorious dress,
Appear, and talk of His Decease;
Whose Death from thine did take the Sting,
And wholesome make that Poison thing.
And I have seen thine hand, and Pen,
Play on that Cockatrice's den
In measur'd Lines, as if inspir'd,
And *Paroxisms* had only fir'd
An holy Soul with flaming zeal,
That flesh-pains it could scarcely feel.
What, in one breath, both Live and Die,
Groan, Laugh, Sigh, Smile, Cry, Versify?
Is this the Stone? Are these the pains
Of that Disease that plagues the Reins?
That slyly steals into the bladder?
Then bites, and stings like to the Adder.
Is this the Scourge of Studious men?
That leaves unwhipt scarce five of ten
And Whips them once, and over again.
In Christ's School there's smart Discipline,
To make His Scholars more divine;
Blest they who do not take offence,
Whose joy lies in the Future Tense;
Who when they are in most distress,
Love Christ the more, and not the less.
His Yoke is easy, burthen light,
To them that understand things right;
And none will afterward complain,
Who Hell escape, and Heaven obtain.
  Well! if this Stone should do its worst,
It cannot make thee be accurst:
For if thou shouldst be Ston'd to Death,
And this way Pelted out of Breath,
Thou wilt like *Stephen* fall asleep,
And free from pain for ever keep.
  Great Pains, with as great Patience, may
Fall little short of *Martyr's* Pay:
For Christ's Rewards are all of Grace,
No Merit but His, in either case.

Our Lord thee good Example offer'd,
Who learn'd Obedience while He suffer'd,
Who for the joy was set before Him,
Endur'd the Cross He bore, and bore Him,
Who though He Pray'd it might be gone,
Yet also said, Thy will be done.
That Stone which builders did refuse,
For thy Foundation choose, and use.
    Think also when thine Agonies
Are most intense, and force loud cryes,
They are not worthy to compare
With those that Christ for thee did bear:
Yea, think what Christ for thee hath done,
Who took an harder, heavier Stone
Out of thine *Heart* and it is gone.
Who did thy Wounded *Spirit* cure
Of Soul-pains, that none can endure,
And this is easier to be borne,
For in the *Flesh* abides this thorne:
And if Christ do not it remove,
Sufficient is His Grace, and Love,
To give thee comfort, and Support,
Because this pain is light, and short;
And works for thee the Glory great,
That doth exceed in length, and weight.
Besides, these Torments can't compare,
With Torments that *Eternal* are:
For they are utterly undone,
That roll the *Sisyphean* Stone;
Not they whose pains are limited,
And are releas'd, as soon as dead.
Add one thought more; that this distress
Makes thee partake of *Holiness:*
The more the flesh is hack'd, and hew'd,
The more Corruption is subdu'd.
Life is to thee the less endear'd,
And *Death* by thee is the less fear'd:
For it's but once thou hast to dye,
And then live to Eternity.
Thy weary Body shall have Rest,
Thy Soul from thence forth shall be blest;
Thy dust be Life; for Christ shall find it,
And leave this cruel Stone behind it.
One Stone God's truth doth bring to light;

Another makes Iron sharp, and bright:
A third our grain doth Pulverize,
And Separate the chaff likewise.
Thine, all these profits bring to thee,
In nobler sense than th' other three.
Thine proves thy Grace to be Sincere;
Of rust, and dulness, doth thee clear.
And makes thee Watch, and Pray, and long
To change thy groans, for *Simeon's* Song.
Though grinding pains thy nature bruise,
They fit thee for thy Master's use:
And when thy dust shall be refin'd;
Thou shalt be neither pain'd, nor pin'd;
Nor full of petrifying juice,
Hard Studies, Heats, and Colds produce.
Then shall hid Manna be thy fare,
In which no grit, nor gravel are;
Yea, Christ will give thee a *White Stone*,
With a New Name engrav'd thereon,
To the Enjoyer only known.

    Lord, once thou saidst, Arise and Walk;
    Thy Words were Works; Mine are but Talk;
    Be pleas'd to bid thy son, Good cheer!
    And say, Thy Sins forgiven are!
    Then, Sink, or Swim; or Live, or Die,
    He will thee greatly Glorify.
    Say so to me too, so will I.
    A Man of Sorrow once Thou wast,
    And still a fellow-feeling hast,
    So to Thy Pity, I commend
    My self, and my afflicted Friend.

Samuel Sewall (1652–1730)

Samuel Sewall was one of the most fascinating figures in early New England. His life, like that of his friend Nicholas Noyes, bridged the period during which the religious emphasis of Puritanism was supplanted by the secular emphasis of the rising middle class. Trained for the ministry at Harvard, Sewall's marriage brought him wealth and diverted him to public affairs, politics, business, and the law. The climax of his career was his ten-year service as Chief Justice of Massachusetts. Sewall's energy was prodigious, fulfilling itself with equal relish in the determined acquisition of a succession of wives and in the careful writing of a voluminous diary whose entries revivify Sewall and his contemporaries with unsparing honesty, pithy observation, sympathy, and a wry sense of humor. Sewall read classical literature in Hebrew, Greek, and Latin as well as the modern English writers; a quotation in his diary credited to Ben Jonson typifies the catholicity and bent of Sewall's temperament: "Wake, our Mirth begins to dye:/Quicken it with Tunes and Wine./Raise your Notes; you'r out; fie, fie,/This drowsiness is an ill sign." It was affectionately said of Sewall that he had generously made his extensive library available to college classmate Edward Taylor because the latter spent his life far removed from cultural amenities in the frontier settlement of Westfield. Sewall wrote many short poems in Latin and English, generally favoring the epigrammatic funeral epitaph as a form. He is typically himself in the laconic irony of the comment on Tom Child and the amusing bluntness of the observation on the departed Puritan ministers, one of whom was Nicholas Noyes.

TEXT: *Collections of the Massachusetts Historical Society*, 5th ser., Vol. VI (1879); *Proceedings of the Massachusetts Historical Society*, 2d ser., Vol. III (1888).

TOM CHILD, THE PAINTER

Tom Child had often painted Death,
But never to the Life, before:
Doing it now, he's out of Breath;
He paints it once, and paints no more.

A SPECIMEN OF NEW ENGLISH CELIBACY

Tho' Rome blaspheme the Marriage Bed,
And Vows of single life has bred;
Chaste Parker, Stoughton, Brinsmead, Noyes,
Show us the odds 'twixt Force and Choice;
These Undefiled, Contracted here,
Are gone to Heav'n and Married there.

Joseph Capen (1658–1725)

An ironic joke which Benjamin Franklin would have appreciated is provided by the revelation that, though he ridiculed Puritan elegiac verse, he was probably influenced by it in the form and content of the humorous epitaph he composed for himself in 1728 (see p. 104). The similarity of the language and imagery Franklin used and that contained in the elegy which Reverend Joseph Capen wrote upon the death of John Foster in 1681 suggests that Franklin not only laughed at Capen's poem but also borrowed a good deal from it. Printing and publishing images were appropriate for Franklin and Foster since both had been printers; the latter was the first to operate a printing press in Boston. The irony of the joke upon Franklin is heightened when it becomes apparent that Capen in turn apparently drew upon still an earlier elegy, one Benjamin Woodbridge (1622–1684) had composed in memory of the death in 1652 of the Reverend John Cotton, a revered theological writer:

> A living breathing Bible: Tables where
> Both Covenants at large engraven were;
> Gospel and Law in's Heart had each its Column
> His Head an Index to the Sacred Volume.
> His very Name a Title Page; and next,
> His Life a Commentary on the Text.
> O what a Monument of glorious worth,
> When in a New Edition he comes forth
> Without Errata's, may we think hee'll be,
> In Leaves and Covers of Eternity!

TEXT: Woodbridge—Nathaniel Morton, *New Englands Memoriall*, Cambridge, Mass., 1669; Capen—Samuel Abbott Green, *John Foster*, Boston, Mass., 1909.

A FUNERAL ELEGY UPON . . . MR. JOHN FOSTER . . .

Here lie the relict Fragments, which were took
Out of Consumption's teeth, by Death the Cook.
Voracious Appetite, dost thus devour;
Scarce aught hast left for worms t' live on an Hour
But Skin & Bones; no bones thou mak'st of that,
It is thy common trade t' eat all the fat.
Here lies that earthly House, where once did dwell
That Soul that Scarce hath left its Parallel

49

For Solid Judgment, Piety, & Parts,
And peerless Skill in all the practick Arts,
Which, as the glittering Spheres it passèd by,
Methinks I Saw it glance at Mercury;
Ascended now, 'bov Time & Tides 't abides,
Which Sometimes told the world of Times & Tides.
Next to th' Third Heavens the Stars were his delight,
Where's Contemplation dwelt both day & night,
Soaring uncertainly but now at Shore,
Whether Sol moves or Stands He doubts no more.
He—that despis'd the things the world admired,
As having Skill in rarer things acquired—
The heav'ns Interpreter, doth disappear;
The Star's translated to his proper Sphere.
What e'er the world may think did Cause his death,
Consumption, 'twas not Cupid, Stopt his breath.
The Heav'ns, which God's glory do discover,
Have lost their constant Friend & instant Lover.
Like Atlas, he help't bear up that rare Art,
Astronomy, & always took his part.
Most happy Soul, who didst not there Sit down,
But didst make after an eternal Crown.
Sage Archimede! Second Bezaleel!
Oh how didst thou in Curious works excell!
Thine Art & Skill deserve to See the Press,
And be Composèd in a Printer's dress.
Thy Name is worthy for to be enroll'd
In Printed Letters of the choicest Gold.

    Thy Death to five foretold Eclipses Sad,
A great one, unforetold, doth Superadd,
Successive to that Strange Æthereal Blaze
Whereon thou didst so oft astonish'd gaze,
Which daily gives the world Such fatal blows:
Still, what's to come we dread; God only knows.
Thy Body, which no activeness did lack,
Now's laid aside like an old Almanack.
But for the present only's out of date;
'Twill have at length a far more active State.

    Yea, though with dust thy body Soilèd be,
Yet at the Resurrection we Shall See
A fair Edition & of matchless worth,
Free from Errata, new in Heav'n Set forth:
Tis but a word from God the great Creatour,
It Shall be Done when he Saith IMPRIMATUR.

Sarah Kemble Knight (1666–1727)

Madam Knight of Massachusetts and Connecticut was one of those compassionate, good-humored, domineering New England women whose lives have been humorously embodied in such literary characters as Frances Whitcher's "Widow Bedott" and Henry James' "Miss Birdseye." Too soon a widow, Madam Knight combined her education, family commercial background, and innate toughness to compete successfully in a man's world as court recorder, writing-school operator, legal adviser, shopkeeper, land speculator, tavern keeper, and boardinghouse operator. When to all that is added the fact that at her death she left a large estate, it is little wonder that an apocryphal tale has it that she was industrious Benjamin Franklin's first teacher. However, Madam Knight's best story is exclusively her own. While travelling through New England and New York for five months in 1704–1705, the energetic lady kept a diary first published in 1825. Madam Knight's sense of irony was freely applied to the varied social milieus and characters encountered on her journey, thus preserving her work from genteel snobbery and enabling her to seize upon the ludicrous in all objects, situations, and individuals. Most refreshing is her demonstration of the humorist's most priceless virtue: the ability to laugh at oneself. Madam Knight had an intuitive ear for the fresh and vigorous in language. Humor that was indelicate elicited her laughter as much as humor that was sophisticated. All in all, Madam Knight's diary is an admirable prelude not only to Benjamin Franklin but also to such later writers as George Washington Harris, Herman Melville, Mark Twain, and William Faulkner.

TEXT: *Littell's Living Age,* LVII (June 26, 1858).

From THE JOURNAL OF MADAM KNIGHT

[Tuesday, October 3, 1704] From hènce wee kept on, with more ease than before: the way being smooth and even, the night warm and serene, and the Tall and thick Trees at a distance, especially when the moon glar'd light through the branches, fill'd my Imagination with the pleasent delusion of a Sumpteous citty, fill'd with famous Buildings and churches, with their spiring steeples, Balconies, Galleries and I know not what: Grandeurs which I had heard of, and which the stories of foreign countries had given me the Idea of.

> Here stood a Lofty church—there is a steeple,
> And there the Grand Parade—O see the people!

> That Famous Castle there, were I but nigh,
> To see the mote and Bridg and walls so high—
> They'r very fine! says my deluded eye.

Being thus agreably entertain'd without a thou't of any thing but thoughts themselves, I on a sudden was Rous'd from these pleasing Imaginations, by the Post's sounding his horn, which assured mee hee was arrived at the Stage, where we were to Lodg: and that musick was then most musickall and agreeable to mee.

Being come to Mr. Havens', I was very civilly Received, and courteously entertained, in a clean comfortable House; and the Good woman was very active in helping off my Riding clothes, and then ask't what I would eat. I told her I had some Chocolett, if shee would prepare it; which with the help of some Milk, and a little clean brass Kettle, she soon effected to my satisfaction. I then betook me to my Apartment, which was a little Room parted from the Kitchen by a single board partition; where, after I had noted the Occurrances of the past day, I went to bed, which, tho' pretty hard, Yet neet and handsome. But I could get no sleep, because of the Clamor of some of the Town tope-ers in next Room, Who were entred into a strong debate concerning the Signifycation of the name of their Country, (viz.) *Narraganset.* One said it was named so by the Indians, because there grew a Brier there, of a prodigious Highth and bigness, the like hardly ever known, called by the Indians Narragansett; And quotes an Indian of so Barberous a name for his Author, that I could not write it. His Antagonist Replied no—It was from a Spring it had its name, which hee well knew where it was, which was extreem cold in summer, and as Hott as could be imagined in the winter, which was much resorted too by the natives, and by them called Narragansett, (Hott and Cold,) and that was the originall of their place's name—with a thousand Impertinences not worth notice, which He utter'd with such a Roaring voice and Thundering blows with the fist of wickedness on the Table, that it pierced my very head. I heartily fretted, and wish't 'um tongue tyed; but with as little succes as a friend of mine once, who was (as shee said) kept a whole night awake, on a Journy, by a country Lieutenant and a Sergeant, Ensign and a Deacon, contriving how to bring a triangle into a Square. They kept calling for 'tother Gill, which while they were swallowing, was some Intermission; But presently, like Oil to fire, encreased the flame. I set my Candle on a Chest by the bed side, and setting up, fell to my old way of composing my Resentments, in the following manner:

> I ask thy Aid, O Potent Rum!
> To Charm these wrangling Topers Dumb.
> Thou hast their Giddy Brains possest—
> The man confounded with the Beast—

> And I, poor I, can get no rest.
> Intoxicate them with thy fumes:
> O still their Tongues till morning comes!

And I know not but my wishes took effect; for the dispute soon ended with 'tother Dram; and so Good night!

Wedensday, October 4th. About four in the morning, we set out for Kingston (for so was the Town called) with a French Doctor in our company. He and the Post put on very furiously, so that I could not keep up with them, only as now and then they'd stop till they see mee. This Road was poorly furnished with accommodations for Travellers, so that we were forced to ride 22 miles by the post's account, but nearer thirty by mine, before wee could bait so much as our Horses, which I exceedingly complained of. But the post encourag'd mee, by saying wee should be well accommodated anon at Mr. Devil's, a few miles further. But I questioned whether we ought to go to the Devil to be helpt out of affliction. However, like the rest of Deluded souls that post to the Infernal den, We made all possible speed to this Devil's Habitation; where alighting, in full assurance of good accommodation, wee were going in. But meeting his two daughters—as I supposed twins, they so neerly resembled each other, both in features and habit, and look't as old as the Devil himselfe, and quite as Ugly—we desired entertainm't, but could hardly get a word out of 'um, till with our Importunity, telling them our necessity, &c. they call'd the old Sophister, who was as sparing of his words as his daughters had bin, and no, or none, was the replies he made us to our demands. He differed only in this from the old fellow in tother Country: he let us depart. However, I thought it proper to warn poor Travailers to endeavour to Avoid falling into circumstances like ours, which at our next Stage I sat down and did as followeth:

> May all that dread the cruel fiend of night
> Keep on, and not at this curs't Mansion light.
> 'Tis Hell; 'tis Hell! and Devils here do dwell:
> Here dwells the Devil—surely this's Hell.
> Nothing but Wants: a drop to cool yo'r Tongue
> Can't be procur'd these cruel Fiends among.
> Plenty of horrid Grins and looks severe,
> Hunger and thirst, But pity's banish'd here—
> The Right hand keep, if Hell on Earth you fear!

Thus leaving this habitation of cruelty, we went forward; and arriving at an Ordinary about two mile further, found tolerable accommodation. But our Hostess, being a pretty full mouth'd old creature, entertain'd our fellow traveller, the French Docter, with Innumerable complaints of her bodily infirmities; and whispered to him so loud, that all the House had as full a hearing as hee: which was very diverting to the company, (of which there was a great many,) as one might see by their sneering. But poor weary I slipt out to enter my mind in my Journal, and left my Great Landlady with her Talkative Guests to themselves.

From hence we proceeded (about ten forenoon) through the Narragansett country, pretty Leisurely; and about one afternoon come to Paukataug River, which about two hundred paces over, and now very high, and no way over to to'ther side but this. I dared not venture to Ride thro, my courage at best in such cases but small, And now at the Lowest Ebb, by reason of my weary, very weary, hungry and uneasy Circumstances. So takeing leave of my company, tho' with no little Reluctance, that I could not proceed with them on my Journy, Stop at a little cottage just by the River, to wait the Water's falling, which the old man that lived there said would be in a little time, and he would conduct me safe over. This little Hutt was one of the wretchedest I ever saw a habitation for human creatures. It was supported with shores enclosed with Clapboards, laid on Lengthways, and so much asunder, that the Light come throu' every where; the doore tied on with a cord in the place of hinges; The floor the bare earth; no windows but such as the thin covering afforded, nor any furniture but a Bedd with a glass Bottle hanging at the head on't; an earthen cupp, a small pewter Basin, A Board with sticks to stand on, instead of a table, and a block or two in the corner instead of chairs. The family were the old man, his wife and two Children; all and every part being the picture of poverty. Notwithstanding both the Hutt and its Inhabitants were very clean and tidy: to the crossing the Old Proverb, that bare walls make giddy house-wives.

I Blest myselfe that I was not one of this miserable crew; and the Impressions their wretchedness formed in me caused mee on the very Spot to say:

> Tho' Ill at ease, A stranger and alone,
> All my fatigu's shall not extort a groan.
> These Indigents have hunger with their ease;
> Their best is worse by half then my disease.
> Their Miserable hutt which Heat and Cold
> Alternately without Repulse do hold;
> Their Lodgings thin and hard, their Indian fare,
> The mean Apparel which the wretches wear,
> And their ten thousand ills which can't be told,
> Makes nature er'e 'tis middle aged look old.
> When I reflect, my late fatigues do seem
> Only a notion or forgotten Dream.

I had scarce done thinking, when an Indian-like Animal come to the door, on a creature very much like himselfe, in mien and feature, as well as Ragged cloathing; and having 'lit, makes an Awkard Scratch with his Indian shoe, and a Nod, sitts on the block, fumbles out his black

Junk, dipps it in the Ashes, and presents it piping hot to his moustachio's, and fell to sucking like a calf, without speaking, for near a quarter of an hower. At length the old man said how do's Sarah do? who I understood was the wretches wife, and Daughter to the old man: he Replied —as well as can be expected, &c. So I remembered the old say, and supposed I knew Sarah's case. Butt hee being, as I understood, going over the River, as ugly as hee was, I was glad to ask him to show me the way to Saxtons, at Stoningtown; which he promising, I ventur'd over with the old man's assistance; who having rewarded to content, with my Tattertailed guide, I Rid on very slowly thro' Stoningtown, where the Road was very Stony and uneven. I asked the fellow, as we went, divers questions of the place and way, &c. I being arrived at my country Saxtons, at Stonington, was very well accommodated both as to victuals and Lodging, the only Good of both I had found since my setting out. Here I heard there was an old man and his Daughter to come that way, bound to N. London; and being now destitute of a Guide, gladly waited for them, being in so good a harbour, and accordingly, Thursday, October the 5th, about 3 in the afternoon, I sat forward with neighbour Polly and Jemima, a Girl about 18 Years old, who hee said he had been to fetch out of the Narragansetts, and said they had Rode thirty miles that day, on a sorry lean Jade, with only a Bag under her for a pillion, which the poor Girl often complain'd was very uneasy.

Wee made Good speed along, which made poor Jemima make many a sour face, the mare being a very hard trotter; and after many a hearty and bitter Oh, she at length Low'd out: "Lawful Heart father! this bare mare hurts mee Dingeely, I'me direfull sore I vow"; with many words to that purpose: "Poor Child," says Gaffer—"She us't to serve your mother so." "I don't care how mother us't to do," quoth Jemima, in a pasionate tone. At which the old man Laught, and kick't his Jade o' the side, which made her Jolt ten times harder.

About seven that Evening, we come to New London Ferry: here, by reason of a very high wind, we mett with great difficulty in getting over —the Boat tossed exceedingly, and our Horses caper'd at a very surprizing Rate, and set us all in a fright; especially poor Jemima, who desired her father to say "So Jack" to the Jade, to make her stand. But the careless parent, taking no notice of her repeated desires, She Roared out in a Passionate manner: "Pray suth father, Are you deaf? Say so Jack to the Jade, I tell you." The Dutiful Parent obeys; saying "So Jack, so Jack," as gravely as if hee'd bin to saying Catechise after Young Miss, who with her fright look't of all colors in the Rain Bow.

Being safely arrived at the house of Mrs. Prentices in N. London, I treated neighbour Polly and daughter for their diverting company, and bid them farewell; and between nine and ten at night waited on the Reverend Mr. Gurdon Saltonstall, minister of the town, who kindly Invited me to Stay that night at his house, where I was very handsomely and plentifully treated and Lodg'd; and made good the Great Character I had before heard concerning him: viz. that hee was the most affable, courteous, Generous and best of men.

Ebenezer Cooke (?1670–?1732)

Ebenezer Cooke's entertaining *Sotweed Factor* is a curious work. Its first appearance in a London edition of 1708 was ostensibly designed to thwart the promotional efforts of men like George Alsop who sought to encourage immigration to Maryland. The concluding lines of Cooke's poem, appended to the 1731 edition reprinted below, pronounce a "dreadful Curse" upon Maryland and its inhabitants. Yet Cooke's Hudibrastic satire is certainly more amusing than frightening; the relish with which he fulfilled his subtitle's promise to portray the "Feasts, Frolicks, Entertainments and Drunken Humours of the Inhabitants" would have enticed rather than repelled a prospective migrant to the sotweed (tobacco) plantations of Maryland. Cooke's biography is as uncertain as George Alsop's (see pp. 29–31). What has been hypothesized of it suggests that Cooke's ambivalent performance arose from the fact that this member of an established Maryland family had been born in England, first came to Maryland in 1694, and grew so disappointed that he returned to England where he published his dubious satirical revenge. He was soon back, however, and apparently prospered thereafter as a landowner, government official, attorney, and man of letters. The 1731 version of *The Sotweed Factor* appeared in Cooke's *The Maryland Muse*, Annapolis, Md., 1731. Apart from some minor changes and the rewritten conclusion, it retained the first edition's animation and realism.

TEXT: *The Maryland Muse* (fac.), intro. Lawrence C. Wroth, *Proceedings of the American Antiquarian Society*, XL (1934); *The Sot-Weed Factor*, London, 1708, in *Early Maryland Poetry*, ed. Bernard C. Steiner, Baltimore, Md., 1900.

THE SOTWEED FACTOR

Condemn'd by Fate, to wayward Curse,
Of Friends unkind, and empty Purse,
Plagues worse than fill'd *Pandora's* Box,
I took my Leave of *Albion's* Rocks,
With heavy Heart, concern'd that I
Was forc'd my native Soil to fly,
And the old World must bid Good-b'ye:
But Heav'n ordain'd it shou'd be so,
And to repine is vain, we know.

Freighted with Fools, from *Plimouth* Sound,
To MARYLAND our Ship was bound;
Where we arriv'd, in dreadful Pain,
Shock'd by the Terrors of the Main;
For full Three Months our wav'ring Boat
Did thro' the surly Ocean float,
And furious Storms and threatning Blasts,
Both split our Sails, and sprung our Masts:
Weary'd, yet pleas'd we did escape
Such Ills, we anchor'd at the *Cape*;
But weighing soon, we plow'd the *Bay*,
To cove it in *Piscataway*.

Intending there to open Store,
I put myself and Goods on Shore,
Where soon repair'd a numerous Crew,
In Shirts and Draw'rs, of *Scotch*-cloth blew,
With neither Stocking, Hat, nor Shoe:
These *Sotweed* Planters crowd the Shore,
In Hew as tawny as a *Moor*;
Figures, so strange, no GOD design'd
To be a Part of Human-kind:
But wanton Nature, void of Rest,
Moulded the brittle Clay in Jest.

At last, a Fancy very odd,
Took me, This was *The Land of Nod*,
Planted at first when Vagrant *Cain*
His Brother had unjustly slain;
Then, conscious of the Crime he'd done,
From Vengeance dire hither run,
And in a Hut supinely dwelt,
The first in *Furrs* and *Sotweed* dealt:
And ever since that Time, this Place
Has harbour'd a destested Race,
Who, when they could not thrive at Home;
For Refuse to these Worlds did roam,
In Hopes by Flight they might prevent
The Devil, and his fell Intent,
Obtain from Tripple-Tree Reprieve,
And Heav'n and Hell alike deceive:
But e're their Manners I display,
I think it fit I open lay
My Entertainment by the Way,
That Strangers well may be aware on

What homely Diet they must fare on;
To see that Shore where no good sense is found,
But Conversation's lost, and Manners drown'd.

    I cross'd unto the other Side
A River, whose impetuous Tide,
Those *Salvage* Borders do divide,
In such a swimming odd Invension,
I scarce can give it's due Dimension,
The *Indians* call this watry Waggon,
Canoe, a Vessel none can brag on,
Cut from a Poplar Tree, or Pine,
And fashion'd like a Trough for Swine:
In this most noble Fishing-boat,
I boldly put my self afloat,
Standing erect, with Legs stretch'd wide,
We paddled to the other Side;
Where being landed safe by Hap,
(As *Sol* fell into *Thetis*' Lap)
A ravenous Gang, bent on the Strowl,
Of Wolves for Prey, began to howl:
This put me in a pannick Fright,
Lest I shou'd be devour'd quite:
But as I there a Musing stood,
And quite benighted in the Wood,
A Female Voice pierc'd thro' my Ears,
Crying, You Rogue drive home the Steers:
I listen'd that attractive Sound,
And streight A Herd of Cattle found,
Drove by a Youth, and homeward bound.
Cheer'd with the Sight, I streight thought fit
To ask, Where I a Bed might get?
The surly Peasant bid me stay,
And ask'd, From whom I'd run away?
Surpris'd at such a sawcy Word,
I instantly lugg'd out my Sword,
Swearing I was no Fugitive,
But from *Great Britain* did arrive,
In hopes I here might better thrive.
To which he mildly made Reply,
I beg your Pardon, Sir, that I
Shou'd talk to you unmannerly:
But if you please to go with me,
To yonder House you'll welcome be.

Encountring soon the smoaky Seat,
The Planter old did thus me greet,
Whether You're come from Gaol, or College,
You're Welcome, to my certain Knowledge,
And if You'll please all Night to stay,
My Son shall put You in the Way:
Which Offer I most kindly took,
And for a Seat did round me look,
When presently among the rest
He plac'd his unknown *English* Guest,
Who found 'em drinking, for a Whet,
A Cask of Sider on the Fret:
'Till Supper came upon the Table,
On which I fed whilst I was able;
So after hearty Entertainment,
Of Drink and Victuals, without Payment,
For Planters Tables, you must know
Are free for all that come and go,
Whilst Pone, with Milk and Mush well stor'd,
In wooden Dishes grac'd the Board,
With Hominy and Sider-Pap,
Which scarce an *English* Dog would lap,
Well stuff'd with Fat from Bacon fry'd,
And with Melasses dulcify'd.
Than out our Landlord pulls his Pouch,
As greasy as the Leather Couch
On which he sat, and streight begun
To load with Weed his *Indian* Gun,
In Length scarce longer than one's Finger,
Or that for which the Ladies linger.
His Pipe smoak'd out, with awful Grace,
With Aspect grave and solemn Pace,
The Reverend Sir, walks to a Chest,
Of all his Furniture the best,
Closely confin'd within a Room,
Which seldom felt the Weight of Broom:
From thence he lugs a Cagg of Rum,
And nodding to me, thus begun:
I find, says he, *you don't much care*
For this our Indian *Country Fare;*
But let me tell you, Friend of mine,
You may be glad of it in Time,
Tho' now you're Stomach is so fine;
And if within this Land you stay,

You'll find it true what I do say:
This said, the Rundlet up he threw,
And bending backwards strongly drew;
I pluck'd as stoutly, for my Part,
Altho' it made me sick at Heart,
And got so soon into my Head,
I scarce could find my Way to Bed;
Where I was instantly convey'd,
By one that pass'd for Chamber-Maid,
Tho' by her loose and sluttish Dress,
She rather seem'd a *Bedlam-Bess.*
Curious to know from whence she came,
I press'd her to declare her Name?
She blushing, seem'd to hide her Eyes,
And thus in civil Terms replies:
In better Times, o'er to this Land
I was unhappily trepann'd,
Perchance as well I did appear,
As any Gentlewoman here,
Not then a Slave for Twice Two Year;
My Cloaths were fashionably new,
Nor were my Shifts of Scotch *Cloth blew:*
But Things are chang'd: Now at the Hoe
I daily work, and barefoot go,
In weeding Corn, and feeding Swine,
I spend my melancholly Time;
Kidnapp'd and fool'd, I hither fled,
To shun a hated Nuptial Bed;
And, to my Grief, already find
Worse Plagues than those I left behind.

Whate'er the Wand'rer did profess,
Good faith I cou'd not chuse but guess
The Cause which brought her to this Place,
Was Supping e're the Priest said Grace:
Quick as my Thoughts the Slave was fled,
Her Candle left to shew my Bed,
Which, made of Feathers soft and good,
Close in the Chimney-corner stood:
I laid me down, expecting Rest,
To be in Golden Slumbers blest;
But soon a Noise disturb'd my Quiet,
And plagu'd me with Nocturnal Riot:
A Puss, which in the Ashes lay,

With grunting Pig, began a Fray,
And prudent Dog, that Feuds might cease,
Most sharply bark'd, to keep the Peace:
This Quarrel scarcely was decided
By Stick, that ready lay provided,
But *Reynard*, arch and cunning Loon,
Crept into my Apartment soon,
In hot Pursuit of Ducks and Geese,
With full Intent the same to seize;
Their cackling Plaints with strange Surprise
Chac'd Sleep's thick Vapours from my Eyes;
Raging, I jump'd upon the Floor,
And like a drunken Sailor swore,
With Sword I fiercely laid about,
And soon dispers'd the feather'd Rout,
The Poultry out of Window flew,
And *Reynard* cautiously withdrew;
The Dogs who this Encounter heard,
Fiercely themselves to aid me rear'd,
And to the Place of Combat run,
Exactly as the Field was won,
Fretting and hot as roasted Capon,
And Greasy as a Flitch of Bacon.

I to the Orchard did repair,
To breathe the cool and open Air,
Impatient waiting for bright Day,
Extended on a Bank I lay;
But Fortune here, that sawcy Whore,
Disturb'd me worse, and plagu'd me more
Than she had done the Night before;
Hoarse croaking Frogs did round me ring,
Such Peals the Dead to Life wou'd bring,
A Noise might move their Wooden King:
I stuff'd my Ears with Cotton white,
And curs'd the melancholly Night,
For fear of being deaf outright:
But soon my Vows I did recant,
And *Hearing* as a Blessing grant,
When a confounded *Rattle-Snake*
With Hissing made my Heart to ach,
Not knowing how to fly the Foe,
Or whither in the dark to go,
By strange good Luck I took a Tree,

Prepar'd by Fate to set me free,
Where, riding on a Limb astride,
Night and the Branches did me hide,
And I the De'el and Snake defy'd.
Not yet from Plagues exempted quite,
The curs'd *Muschetoes* did me bite;
'Til rising Morn, and blushing Day,
Drove both my Fears and Ills away,
And from Night's Terrors set me free,
Discharg'd from hospitable Tree.

    I did to Planter's Booth repair,
And there at Breakfast nobly fare,
On Rasher broil'd, of infant Bear;
I thought the Cubb delicious Meat,
Which ne'er did ought but Chesnuts eat,
Nor was young *Orson's* Flesh the worse,
Because he suck'd a *Pagan* Nurse:
Our Breakfast done, the Planter stout,
Handed a Glass of Rum about.

    Pleas'd with the Treatment I did find,
I took my Leave of Host so kind,
Who, to oblige me, did provide
His eldest Son to be my Guide;
And let me Horses of his own,
A skittish Colt and aged Roan,
The four legg'd Prop of his Wife Joan.
Steering our Course in Trott or Pace,
We sail'd directly for a Place,
In MARYLAND of high Renown;
Known by the Name of *Battle-Town:*
To view the Crowds did there resort,
Which Justice made, and Law, their Sport,
In their Sagacious Country Court:
Scarce had we enter'd on the Way,
Which thro' the Woods and Marshes lay,
But *Indian* strange did soon appear
In hot Pursuit of wounded Deer;
No moral Creature can express
His wild fantastick Air and Dress;
His painted Skin, in Colours dy'd,
His sable Hair, in Satchel ty'd,
Show'd *Salvages* not free from Pride:
His tawny Thighs and Bosom bare,

Disdain'd an useless Coat to wear,
Scorn'd Summers Heat and Winters Air;
His manly Shoulders, such as please
Widows and Wives, were bath'd with Grease,
Of Cub and Bear, whose supple Oil,
Prepar'd his Limbs in Heat and Toil.

   Thus naked Picts in Battle fought,
Or undisguid'd his Mistress sought;
And knowing well his Ware was good,
Refus'd to skreen it with a Hood:
His Visage Dun, and Chin that ne'er
Did Razor feel, nor Scissars bear,
Or know the Ornament of Hair,
Look'd sternly grim; surpriz'd with Fear,
I spurr'd my Horse as he drew near;
But Roan, who better knew than I,
The little Cause I had to fly,
Seem'd by his solemn Step and Pace,
Resolv'd I shou'd the Spector face,
Nor faster mov'd, tho' spurr'd and prick'd,
Than *Balam's* Ass by Prophet kick'd;
Kekicnatop, the *Heathen* cry'd,
How is it *Tom*, my Friend reply'd;
Judging from thence, the Brute was civil,
I boldly fac'd the courteous Devil,
And lugging out a Dram of Rum,
I gave his tawny Worship some;
Who in his Language as I guess,
My Guide informing me no less,
Implor'd the Devil me to bless:
I thank'd him for his good Intent,
And forward on my Journey went;
Discoursing as along I rode,
Whether this Race was fram'd of GOD,
Or whether some malignant Power,
Had fram'd them in an evil Hour,
And from his own infernal Look,
Their dusky Form and Image took.

   From hence we fell to Argument
Whence peopl'd was this Continent?
My Friend suppos'd *Tartarians* wild,
Or *Chinese*, from their home exil'd,
Wandring thro' Mountains hid with Snow,

And Rills that in the Valleys flow,
Far to the *South* of *Mexico*,
Broke thro' the Bars which Nature cast,
And wide unbeaten Regions passed;
'Till near those Streams the human Deluge roll'd,
Which sparkling shin'd with glittering Sands of Gold;
And fetch'd *Pisarro* from the *Iberian* Shore
To rob the *Indians* of their native Store.

   I smil'd to hear my young Logician,
Thus reason like a Polititian;
Who ne'r by Father's Pains and Earning,
Had got, at Mother, *Cambridge* Learning;
Where lubber Youth just free from Birch,
Most stoutly drink to prop the Church;
Nor with grey Coat had taken Pains
To purge his Head, and cleanse his Reins;
And in Obedience to the College,
Had pleas'd himself with carnal Knowledge;
And tho' I lik'd the Youngster's Wit,
I judg'd the Truth he had not hit;
And could not chuse but smile to think,
What they cou'd do for Meat and Drink,
Who o'er so many Desarts ran,
With Brats and Wives in Carravan;
Unless perchance they'd got a Trick,
To eat no more than Porker sick,
Or could with well-contented Maws,
Quarter like Bears upon their Paws:
Thinking his Reason to confute,
I gravely thus commenc'd Dispute;
And urg'd, that tho' a *Chinese* Host
Might penetrate this *Indian* Coast,
Yet this was certainly most true,
They never could the Isles subdue;
For knowing not to steer a Boat,
They could not on the Ocean float,
Or plant their Sun-burnt Colonies,
In Regions parted by the Seas:
I thence inferr'd, *Phoenicians* old
Discover'd first, with Vessels bold,
These *Western* Shores, and planted here,
Returning once or twice a Year,

With Naval Stores, and Lasses kind,
To comfort those were left behind;
'Till by the Winds and Tempests tore,
From their intended golden Shore,
They suffer'd Shipwreck, or were drown'd,
And lost the World so newly found:
But after long and learn'd Contention,
We could not finish our Dissention;
And when that both had talk'd their Fill,
We had the self same Notion still.

Thus Parson Grave well read, and Sage,
Does in Dispute with Priest engage,
The one protests they are not wise,
Who judge by Sense, and trust their Eyes,
And vows he'd burn for it at Stake,
That Man may GOD his Maker make;
The other smiles at his Religion,
And vows he's but a learned Widgeon,
And when they've emptied all their Store,
From Books and Fathers, are not more
Convinc'd, or wiser than before.

Scarce had we finish'd serious Story,
But I espy'd the Town before me;
And roaring Planters on the Ground,
Drinking of Healths, in Circle round:
Dismounting Steed with friendly Guide,
Our Horses to a Tree we ty'd,
And forward pass'd amongst the Rout,
To chuse convenient Quarters out;
But being none were to be found,
We sat like others on the Ground,
Carousing Punch in open Air,
'Till Cryer did the Court declare:
The planting Rabble being met,
Their drunken Worships like wife fat,
Cryer proclaims the Noise shou'd cease,
And streight the Lawyers broke the Peace,
Wrangling for Plantiff and Defendant,
I thought they ne'r wou'd make an End on't,
With Nonsense, Stuff, and false Quotations,
With brazen Lies, and Allegations;
And in the Splitting of the Cause,
Us'd such strange Motions with their Paws,

As shew'd their Zeal was rather bent
In Blows to end the Argument.
A Reverend Judge, who to the Shame,
Of all the Bench, cou'd write his Name,
At Petty-Fogger took Offence,
And wonder'd at his Impudence:
My Neighbour *Dash*, with Scorn replies,
And in the Face of Justice flies;
And Scribles take on Judge's Side;
The Jury, Lawyers, and their Clients,
Contending, fight, like Earth-born Giants,
'Till Sh'riff that slily lay perdue,
Hoping Indictments would ensue;
And when—
A Hat or Wig fell in the Way,
He seiz'd 'em for the Queen, as Stray;
The Court adjourn'd in usual Manner,
In Battle, Blood and fractious Clamour.

I thought it proper to provide,
A Lodging for my self and Guide,
So to our Inn we march'd away,
Which at a little Distance lay;
Where all Things were in such Confusion,
I thought the World at its Conclusion;
A Heard of Planters on the Ground,
O'rewhelm'd with Punch, dead Drunk we found;
Others were fighting and contending,
Some burn'd their Cloaths, to save the mending;
A few whose Heads, by frequent Use,
Could better bear the potent Juice,
Gravely debated State Affairs,
Whilst I most nimbly tripp'd up Stairs,
Leaving my Friend discoursing oddly,
And mixing Things Prophane and Godly;
Just then beginning to be drunk,
As from the Company I slunk:
To every Room and Nook I crept,
In hopes I might have somewhere slept;
But all the Beding was possest,
By one or other drunken Guest;
But after looking long about,
I found an antient Corn-loft out;
Glad that I might in Quiet sleep,

And there my Bones unfractur'd keep:
I laid me down secur'd from Fray,
And foundly snor'd 'till break o'Day;
When waking fresh, I sat upright,
And found my Shoes were vanish'd quite,
Hat, Wig, and Stockings, all were fled,
From this extended *Indian* Bed:
Vex'd at the Loss of Goods and Chattle,
I swore I'd give the Rascal Battle,
Who had abus'd me in this Sort,
And Merchant-Stranger made his Sport:
I furiously descended Ladder,
No Hare in *March* was ever madder,
And did with Host and Servants quarrel,
But all in vain, for my Apparel;
For one whose Mind did much aspire
To Mischief, threw them in the Fire.
Equipp'd with neither Hat nor Shoe,
I did my coming hither rue,
And doubtful thoughts what I should do:
When looking round I saw my Friend,
Lye naked on a Table's End,
A Sight so dismal to behold,
One would have thought him dead and cold,
There ready laid, to be next Day
On Shoulders Four convey'd away:
'Till wringing of his bloody Nose,
By fighting got, we may suppose,
I found him not so fast asleep,
Might give his Friends some cause to weep:
Rise *Oronoko*, rise, said I,
And from this *Hell* and *Bedlam* fly:
My Guide starts up, and in a Maze,
With Bloodshot Eyes did round him gaze,
At Length with many Sigh and Groan,
He went in search of aged Roan;
But Roan who seldom us'd to falter,
Had fairly this Time slipt his Halter,
And not content all Night to stay,
Ty'd up from Fodder, run away;
After my Guide to catch him ran,
And so I lost both Horse and Man;
Which Disappointment tho' so great,
Did only Jest and Mirth create:

'Till one more civil than the rest,
In Conversation far the best,
Observing that for want of Roan,
I shou'd be left to walk alone,
Most readily did me intreat,
To take a Bottle at his Seat,
A Favour at that Time so great,
I blest my kind propitious Fate;
And finding soon a fresh Supply
Of Cloaths, from Store-House kept hard by,
I mounted streight on such a Steed,
Did rather Curb than Whipping need;
And Straining at the usual Rate,
With Spur of Punch which lies in Pate,
E'er long we lighted at the Gate;
Where in an antient Cedar-House,
Dwelt my new Friend, a *Cockerouse*,
Whose Fabrick, tho' 'twas built of Wood,
Had many Springs and Winters stood:
When sturdy Oaks and lofty Pines,
Were levell'd with Musk-Melon-Vines,
And Plants eradicated were,
By Hurricans drove in the Air:
There with good Punch and Apple Juice,
We spent our Time without Abuse,
'Till Midnight in her sable Vest,
Persuaded Gods and Men to rest;
And with a pleasing kind Surprize,
Indulg'd soft Slumber to my Eyes.

Fierce Æthon, Courser of the Sun,
Had half his Race exactly Run,
And breath'd on me a furious Ray,
Darting hot Beams the following Day,
When Rug in Blanket white, I lay;
But Heat and Chinces rais'd the Sinner,
Most opportunely to his Dinner;
Wild Fowl and Fish delicious Meats,
As good as *Neptune's* Doxy eats,
Began our hospitable Chear,
Fat Venison follow'd in the Rear,
And Turkeys-wild, luxurious Fare:
But what the Feast did most commend,
Was hearty Welcome from my Friend.

Thus having made a noble Feast,
I eat as well as pamper'd Priest;
Madera strong in flowing Bowles,
Fill'd with extreme Delight our Souls;
'Till wearied with a purple Flood,
Of gen'rous Wine, the Giants Blood,
As Poets feign, away I made
For some refreshing verdant Shade;
Where musing on my Rambles strange,
And Fortune, which so oft did change,
In midst of various Contemplations,
Of Fancies odd and Meditations,
I slumber'd long,—
'Till airy Night and noxious Dews,
Did Sleep's unwholsome Fetters loose,
With Vapours cold and misty Air,
To Fire-side I did repair;
Near which a jolly Female Crew,
Were deep engag'd at *Lanterloo*,
In Nightrails white, with dirty Mien,
Such Sights are scarce in *England* seen:
I thought them first some Witches, bent
On black Designs, in dire Convent;
'Till one who with affected Air,
Had nicely learn'd to Curse and Swear,
Cry'd, *Dealing's lost, 'tis but a Flam*,
And vow'd by G—*she'd have her Pam*:
When Dealing thro' the Board had run,
They ask'd me kindly, *to make one*:
Not staying often to be bid,
I sate me down as others did;
We scarce had play'd a Round about,
But that those *Indian* Frows fell out:
D-m you, says one, *tho' now so Brave,
I knew you late a Four Years Slave,
What, if for Planter's Wife you go,
Nature design'd you for the Hoe*:
Rot you, replies the other streight,
*The Captain kiss'd you for his Freight;
And if the Truth was known aright,
And how you walk'd the Streets by Night,
You'd blush, if one could blush for Shame,
Who from* Bridewell *and* Newgate *came*.
From Words they fairly tell to Blows,

And being loth to interpose,
Or meddle in the Wars of Punk,
Away to Bed in Haste I slunk:
Waking next Day with aking Head,
And Thirst that made me quit the Bed,
I rigg'd my self and soon got up,
To cool my Liver with a Cup
Of *Succahanah* fresh and clear,
Not half so good as *English* Beer,
Which ready stood in Kitchin Pail,
And was, in Fact, but *Adam's* Ale.

For Planters Cellars, you must know,
Seldom with good *October* flow,
But Perry, Quince, and Apple Juice,
Spout from the Tap, like any Sluice,
Until the Cask grows low and stale,
They're forc'd again to Goard and Pail,
The soothing Draught scarce down my Throat,
Enough to set a Ship on float,
With *Cockerouse* as I was sitting
I felt a Fever intermitting,
A fiery Pulse beat in my Veins,
From cold I felt resembling Pains;
This cursed Seasoning I remember,
Lasted from *March* 'till cold *December*;
Nor could it then its Quarter shift,
Until by *Carduus* turn'd adrift:
And had my Doct'ress wanted Skill,
Or Kitchin-Phisick at her Will
My Father's Son has lost his Lands,
And never seen the *Goodwin Sands:*
But Thanks to *Fortune,* and a *Nurse,*
Whose Care depended on my Purse,
I saw my self in good Condition,
Without the Help of a Phisician:
At length the shivering Ill reliev'd
My Heart and Head, which long had griev'd.

I then began to think with Care,
How I might sell my *British* Ware;
That with my Freight I might comply,
Did on my Charter-Party lye:
To this Intent, with Guide before,
I tript it to the *Eastern* Shore;

Where riding near a Sandy Bay,
I met a Planter in my Way,
A pious, consciencious Rogue,
As e're wore Bonnet, Hat, or Brogue,
Who neither swore, nor kept his Word,
But cheated in the Fear o' th'Lord;
And when his Debts he could not pay,
From trusting Fools he'd run away.

With this sly Zealot, soon I struck
A Bargain, for my *English* Truck,
Agreeing for Ten Thousand Weight
Of *Sotweed* good, and fit for Freight:
Broad *Oronoko*, bright and found,
The Growth and Product of his Ground;
In Cask, that shou'd contain compleat
Five Hundred of Tobacco neat.

The Contract thus betwist us made,
Not well acquainted with the Trade,
My Goods I trusted to the Cheat,
Whose Crop was then o'board the Fleet;
And going to receive my own,
I found the Bird was newly flown:
Cursing this execrable Slave
This damn'd pretended Godly Knave,
On due Revenge and Justice bent,
I instantly to Council went;
Unto an ambodexter Quack,
Who learnedly had got the Knack
Of giving Clysters, making Pills,
Of filling Bonds, and forging Wills;
And with a Stock of Impudence,
Supply'd his want of Wit and Sence,
With Looks demure, amazing People,
No wiser than a Daw on Steeple:
My Anger flushing in my Face,
I stated the preceeding Case,
And of my Money was so free
That he'd have poison'd you or me,
And hang'd his Father on a Tree,
For such another tempting Fee.

Smiling, said he, the Cause is clear,
I'll manage him, you need not fear,

The Case is judg'd, good Sir, but look
In *Galen*, no, in my Lord Cook,
I vow to G-d, I was mistook:
I'll take out a Provincial Writ,
And trownce him for his knavish Wit,
Upon my Life, I'll win the Cause,
With as much Ease I cure the Yaws:
Resolv'd to plague the Holy Brother,
I set one Rogue to catch another.

To try the Cause then fully bent,
Up to *Annapolis* I went,
A City situate on a Plain,
[1] Where scarce a House will keep out Rain;
The Buildings fram'd with *Cypress* rare,
Resembles much our *Southwark-Fair*;
But Strangers there will scarcely meet,
With Market Place, Exchange, or Street;
And if the Truth I may report,
It's not so large as *Tottenham-Court*.
St. Mary's once was in Repute,
Now Here the Judges try the Suit,
And Lawyers twice a Year dispute.
As oft the Bench most gravely meet,
Some to get drink, and some to eat
A swinging Share of Country Treat:
But as for Justice write or wrong,
Not one amongst the numerous Throng
Knows what it means, or has the Heart,
To vindicate a Stranger's Part.

Now, Court being call'd by beat of Drum,
The Judges left their Punch and Rum;
When Pettifogging Doctor draws
His Papers forth, and opens Cause;
And lest I should the Better get,
Brib'd Quack suppress'd his knavish Wit;
So Maid upon the downy Field,
Pretends a Rape, and fights to yield:
The byass'd Court without Delay,
Adjudg'd my Debt in Country Pay,
In Pipe Staves, Corn, or Flesh of Boar,
Rare Cargo for the *English* Shore.

[1] This Account of Annapolis was given Twenty Years ago, and does not resemble its present State.

Raging with Grief, full Speed I ran,
To join the Fleet at *Kickatan:*
And while I waited for a Wind,
This Wish proceeded from my Mind,

IF any Youngster cross the Ocean,
To sell his Wares—may he with Caution
Before he pays, receive each Hogshead,
Lest he be cheated by some Dogshead,
Both of his Goods and his Tobacco;
And then like me, he shall not lack-woe.
AND may that Land where Hospitality
Is every Planter's darling Quality,
Be by each Trader kindly us'd,
And may no Trader be abus'd;
Then each of them shall deal with Pleasure,
And each encrease the other's Treasure.

The third edition (1731) of *The Sotweed Factor*, which appears above, reflects in its concluding stanza the conciliatory spirit of its author, who at this time had settled in Maryland. The first edition (1708) was written with more animus, as can be seen in the original last stanza and last two lines of the preceding stanza, as follows:

> Embarqu'd and waiting for a Wind,
> I left this dreadful Curse behind.
>
> May Canniballs transported o'er the Sea
> Prey on these Slaves, as they have done on me;
> May never Merchant's trading Sails explore
> This Cruel, this Inhospitable Shoar;
> But left abandon'd by the World to starve,
> May they sustain the Fate they well deserve:
> May they turn Savage, or as *Indians* Wild,
> From Trade, Converse, and Happiness exil'd;
> Recreant to Heaven, may they adore the Sun,
> And into Pagan Superstitions run
> For Vengence ripe_____
> May Wrath Divine then lay those Regions wast
> Where no Man's Faithful, nor a Woman Chast.

William Byrd (1674-1744)

William Byrd of Virginia was the most prolific and able Southern writer of his age. Educated in England, where he also lived many years before returning home in 1726 to spend the rest of his life as a colonial planter, businessman, and official, Byrd was acquainted with Restoration playwrights William Wycherly and William Congreve and felt the impress of John Dryden, Jonathan Swift, and Alexander Pope. The verse and prose of his English years displays a talent for humorous satire like that in "The Female Creed," a ribald mockery of feminine credulity written about 1725. Despite Byrd's aptitude for satire, he was influenced by the shift in English taste, typified by Joseph Addison and the genteel *Spectator* papers, which extolled urbanity and tact as more desirable literary attributes than force and directness. In a self-portrait of 1723 Byrd expressed a creed in keeping with this taste, one which would dominate his later work: "*If he reflected upon any one t'was by Irony, which a wise man wou'd take for a banter, and a fool for a complement. His tongue was so far from embroiling the rest of his Person that upon some occasions it has happily protected it.*"

Aristocratic irony coupled with middle-class morality was desirable in early eighteenth-century Southern colonies, as the case of Byrd's brother-in-law, Robert Beverley, had shown. Author of *The History and Present State of Virginia* (1705), Beverley had been forced to retire from public life for his uninhibited criticism of the colony's leaders and policies. The ironic quality of Byrd's later writings was increased by his unhappiness at having been compelled to exchange the pleasures of London's intellectual and social life for the comparative barbarities of backwoods existence. The ironic comedy inherent in Byrd's entertainment of a provincial lady with a reading of John Gay's sophisticated London comedy is set forth exquisitely in the excerpt from "A Progress to the Mines," which Byrd wrote in 1732 as a record of a journey he made that year.

Byrd's reserved humor and literary artistry enabled him to write with distinction. It is regrettable, however, that the broad, gusty humor of his English period, so akin to that of George Alsop, Ebenezer Cooke, Beverley, and Alexander Hamilton, would not be expressed again by writers as industrious and gifted as Byrd until the early nineteenth century. Even more regrettable was Byrd's failure, whether because of disinterest or excessive tactfulness or other factors, to take steps to publish his works. With the exception of a smattering of verse and prose published in England in 1719 and 1721, all of Byrd's writings have been published in the nineteenth and twentieth centuries. This no doubt makes for the final irony in a career dedicated to that attribute.

TEXT: "The Female Creed," *Another Secret Diary of William Byrd of Westover, 1739–1741, with Letters & Literary Exercises, 1696–1726,* ed. Maude H. Woodfin and Marion Tinling, Richmond, Va., 1942; "A Progress to the Mines," *The Writings of "Colonel William Byrd . . . ,"* ed. John S. Bassett, New York, 1901. COMMENTARY: Richmond Croom Beatty, *William Byrd of Westover,* Boston, Mass., 1932.

From "THE FEMALE CREED"

19. I believe verily who ever blunders and throws down the Salt at Table, will pay for it by some dire misfortune. The Reason's as plain as Miss Primsy's affectation, for in former days salt us'd to make the Feasts of the Gods savory, and has always been usefull to man in seasoning his Soups and his Venison-pastys. It was also made use of heretofore in contracts and covenants, with design to keep them from breaking, just as we use it now to preserve our Beef and our Pork from corrupting. Therefore if it be unlucky to knock down an innocent Robin-red-breast or a swallow, because they do no harm, it must be much more unlucky, to throw down our Salt, that dos so much good. This was sufficiently verify'd in Voracio once at a City Feast, who, as he was reaching in too great a Hurry for a slice of Westphalia, happen'd to over-set one of the dirty Salts (it seems the Lord Mayor's utensils are all of this base metal, for fear his Fellow citizens shou'd pocket them up with the Sweet-meats.) Immediately upon this Disaster, a grave Aldermans Lady, who was indeed old and ugly enough to be a Witch, bad him beware, or Some mischief wou'd betide him. Voracio instead of being thankfull for this sage admonition, only answer'd her Ladyship with a very ingenious Horse-laugh not having time to wast upon idle Repartees. But the omen Soon overtook him, for being incautiously engag'd with a Plate full of Marrow Pudding, one of the Splinters of the Bone stuck so fast in his Throat, that it needed all the skill of the handy Forcipio to pluck it out. Just so Mrs. Hiccup one Sunday in her zeal to help Mr. Cant to a Tit-bit, after preaching his Congregation into a Lethargy, and himself into Convulsions, had the mishap to Spil the Salt. Tongue cant express the agonys she was in upon this accident. She burst into Such a flood of Tears, that all the other fountains of her body were dry'd up for Six & thirty hours. She beat her breast wrang her hands, and cry'd in mournfull accents, alas Mr. Cant I'm undone. The good man was full of astonishment at this Sudden outcry & stood aghast with his mouth wide open, & his Eyes fixt in his head. But learning at length the cause of this sore affliction, he did all he cou'd to pacify her, but he might sooner have pacify'd the shakeing fit of an ague. There was but one thing in nature cou'd comfort

her, and that stood in a corner cup-board of her closet, and had often assuaged her afflictions, when nothing else wou'd. Thither She retir'd for Relief, but swallowing the consolation too greedily, a few Drops went the wrong way, and had infallibly choakt her, had not good Mr. Cant, with great presence of mind set her that moment on her head, and with the end of a Tobacco-pipe, which he always carry'd about him, powerfully blow'd wind into her Tail.

20. In short I believe in the Philosophers-stone, the perpetual motion, the squareing of the circle, the tameing of a Shrew, and what is more incredible than all the rest, I believe in the constancy and Fidelity of Man. Just as my mother and Grandmother did before me, I believe all the dear creature urges about his Passion is punctually true, that his Sighs flow directly from his heart, that his Flames are unfeigned, and his addresses have never the least squint upon my Fortune, but are all fairly meant to my Person. That all the Sweet things that fall from his enchanting lips concerning the Lightening of my Eyes, the Bloom of my complexion, the easiness of my shape, the smartness of my Wit, and the engageing Turn of my Conversation, are Truths as evident as that our sex is vain, and loves to be neatly flatter'd. I believe that dear delightful man will prove as constant to my Charms, as the Tydes are to the Moon, and like them his love will flow at least twice every Four and Twenty hours. I believe that his oaths, and his vows, and his protestations will be all performed to a tittle, without the least grains of allowance. I believe these Eyes of mine will fix his Wandering heart, tho' til the moment it felt their power, it was more wavering than the Wind, and rather than not change at all, wou'd change for the Worse, like the rovering Fly, which after being cloy'd with hony, wants something Savory, and longs to finish its Repast upon a T . . . d. Nay I believe in my conscience, that tho' my Adorer loves Wine, and wenches, and gameing, more fondly than Pamperoni loves his Gut, yet my superior Prudence and attractions are sufficient to reclaim him, and to reform his wayward Inclinations into a loyal, confin'd, serious, harmless conjugal Love.

O Woman, great is thy Faith!

From "A PROGRESS TO THE MINES"

[Sept.] 20 [1732]. I continued the Bark, and then tost down my Poacht Eggs, with as much ease as some good Breeders Slip Children into the World. About Nine I left the Prudentest Orders I could think of with my Visier, then crost the River to Shaccoe's. I made a running Visit to 3 of my Quarters, where, besides finding all the People well, I had the Pleasure to see better Crops than usual both of Corn and Tobacco. I parted there with my Intendant, and pursued my Journey to Mr. Randolph's, at Tuckahoe, without meeting with any Adventure by the way. Here I found Mrs. Fleming, who was packing up her Baggage with design to follow her Husband the next day, who was gone to a new Settlement in Goochland. Both he and She have been about Seaven Years persuading themselves to remove to that retired part of the Country, tho' they had the two strong Arguments of Health and Interest for so doing. The Widow smiled graciously upon me, and entertain'd me very handsomely. Here I learnt all the tragical Story of her Daughter's humble Marriage with her Uncle's Overseer. Besides the meanness of this mortal's Aspect, the Man has not one visible Qualification, except Impudence, to recommend him to a Female's Inclinations. But there is sometimes such a Charm in that Hibernian Endowment, that frail Woman cannot withstand it, tho' it stand alone without any other Recommendation. Had she run away with a Gentleman or a pretty Fellow, there might have been some Excuse for her, tho' he were of inferior Fortune: but to stoop to a dirty Plebian, without any kind of merit, is the lowest Prostitution. I found the Family justly enraged at it; and tho' I had more good Nature than to join in her Condemnation, yet I cou'd devise no Excuse for so senceless a Prank as this young Gentlewoman had play'd. Here good Drink was more Scarce than good Victuals, the Family being reduc'd to the last Bottle of Wine, which was therefore husbanded very carefully. But the Water was excellent. The Heir of the Family did not come home till late in the Evening. He is a pretty Young Man, but had the misfortune to become his own master too soon. This puts young Fellows upon wrong pursuits, before they have Sence to Judge rightly for themselves. Tho' at the same time they have a strange conceit of their own Sufficiency, when they grow near 20 Years old, especially if they happen to have a small Smattering of Learning. Tis then they fancy themselves wiser than all their Tutors and Governors, which makes them headstrong to all advice, and above all Reproof and Admonition.

[Sept.] 21. I was sorry in the morning to find myself stopt in my Career by bad Weather brought upon us by a North-East Wind. This drives a World of Raw unkindly Vapours upon us from Newfoundland, laden with Blite, Coughs, and Pleurisys. However, I complain'd not, lest I might be suspected to be tir'd of the good Company. Tho' Mrs. Fleming was not so much upon her Guard, but mutiny'd strongly at the Rain, that hinder'd her from pursuing her dear Husband. I said what I cou'd to comfort a Gentlewoman under so sad a Disappointment. I told her a husband, that staid so much at Home as her's did, cou'd be no such violent Rarity, as for a Woman to venture her precious Health, to go daggling thro' the Rain after him, or to be miserable if she happen'd to be prevented. That it was prudent for marry'd people to fast Sometimes from one another, that they might come together again with the better Stomach. That the best things in this World, if constantly us'd, are apt to be cloying, which a little absence and Abstinence wou'd prevent. This was Strange Doctrine to a fond Female, who fancys People shou'd love with as little Reason after Marriage as before. In the afternoon Monsieur Marij, the Minister of the Parish, came to make me a Visit. He had been a Romish Priest, but found Reasons, either Spiritual or temporal, to quit that gay Religion. The fault of this new Convert is, that he looks for as much Respect from his Protestant Flock, as is paid to the Popish Clergy, which our ill-bred Hugonots dont understand. Madam Marij, had so much Curiosity as to want to come too; but another Horse was wanting, and she believ'd it would have too Vulgar an Air to ride behind her Husband. This Woman was of the true Exchange Breed, full of Discourse, but void of Discretion, and marry'd a Parson, with the Idle hopes he might some time or other come to be his Grace of Canterbury. The Gray Mare is the better Horse in that Family, and the poor man Submits to her wild Vagarys for Peace' Sake. She has just enough of the fine Lady, to run in debt, and be of no signification in her Household. And the only thing that can prevent her from undoing her loving Husband will be, that nobody will trust them beyond the 16000, which is soon run out in a Goochland store. The way of Dealing there is, for some small Merchant or Pedler to buy a Scots Pennyworth of Goods, and clap 150 p[er] cent upon that. At this Rate the Parson cant be paid much for his preaching than tis worth. No sooner was our Visitor retired, but the facetious Widow was so kind as to let me into all this Secret History, but was at the same time exceedingly Sorry that the Woman should be so indiscreet, and the man so tame as to be govern'd by an unprofitable and fantastical Wife.

[Sept.] 22. We had another wet day, to try both Mrs. Fleming's Patience and my good Breeding. The NE Wind commonly sticks by us 3 or 4 days, filling the Atmosphere with damps, injurious both to man and Beast. The worst of it was, we had no good Liquor to warm our Blood, and fortify our Spirits against so strong a Malignity. However, I was cheerful under all these Misfortunes, and expresst no Concern but a decent Fear lest my long visit might be troublesome. Since I was like to have thus much Leizure, I endeavour'd to find out what Subject a dull marry'd man cou'd introduce that might best bring the Widow to the Use of her Tongue. At length I discover'd she was a notable Quack, and therefore paid that regard to her Knowledge, as to put some Questions to her about the bad distemper that raged then in the Country. I mean the Bloody Flux, that was brought us in the Negro-ship consigned to Colo. Braxton. She told me she made use of very Simple remedys in that Case, with very good Success. She did the Business either with Hartshorn

Drink, that had Plantain Leaves boil'd in it, or else with a Strong decoction of St. Andrew's Cross, in New milk instead of Water. I agreed with her that those remedys might be very good, but would be more effectual after a dose or two of Indian Physick. But for fear this Conversation might be too grave for a Widow, I turn'd the discourse, and began to talk of Plays, & finding her Taste lay most towards Comedy, I offer'd my Service to read one to Her, which she kindly accepted. She produced the 2d part of the Beggar's Opera, which had diverted the Town for 40 nights successively, and gain'd four thousand pounds to the Author. This was not owing altogether to the Wit or Humour that Sparkled in it, but to some Political Reflections, that seem'd to hit the Ministry. But the great Advantage of the Author was, that his Interest was solicited by the Dutchess of Queensbury, which no man could refuse who had but half an Eye in his head, or half a Guinea in his Pocket. Her Grace, like Death, spared nobody, but even took my Lord Selkirk in for 2 Guineas, to repair which Extravagance he liv'd upon Scots Herrings 2 Months afterwards. But the best Story was, she made a very Smart Officer in his Majesty's Guards give her a Guinea, who Swearing at the same time twas all he had in the world, she sent him 50 for it the next day, to reward his Obedience. After having acquainted my Company with the History of the Play, I read 3 Acts of it, and left Mrs. Fleming and Mr. Randolph to finish it, who read as well as most Actors do at a Rehearsal. Thus we kill'd the time, and triumpht over the bad Weather.

Patrick Tailfer, Hugh Anderson, and David Douglas

The authors of this mid-eighteenth century attack upon General Oglethorpe, founder of Georgia, would have been delighted at the news that their literary skills would be rousing controversy more than two hundred years later. Tailfer was a Scottish physician, Anderson a merchant, and Douglas a gentleman farmer. Among the leaders of Georgia planters who believed that Oglethorpe's policies were economically ruinous and politically tyrannous, they had fled to the safety of neighboring South Carolina. There they set forth their grievances in a work primarily designed to overthrow Oglethorpe and his administration. Their literary talent was considerable, however, as the disciplined satiric irony of their "Dedication" reveals. The same savage artistry marks the rest of their book. As might be expected, those who were criticized responded with rage instead of reform. Greater urbanity characterizes the more recent responses to Tailfer, Anderson, and Douglas. The scholar Louis B. Wright wrote in 1949 that "Jonathan Swift himself need not have been ashamed of the satirical skill demonstrated in the dedication." Almost as if in direct rebuttal, the scholar Jay B. Hubbell declared in 1954 that "If not quite worthy of Jonathan Swift, it is certainly not unworthy of Benjamin Franklin or William Byrd."

TEXT: *A True and Historical Narrative of the Colony of Georgia*, Charleston, S.C., 1741.

From *A TRUE AND HISTORICAL NARRATIVE OF THE COLONY OF GEORGIA*

Dedication

To His *Excellency James Oglethorpe*, Esq; General and Commander in Chief of His Majesty's Forces in *South Carolina* and *Georgia*; and one of the Honourable Trustees for Establishing the Colony of *Georgia* in *America*, &c.

May it please Your Excellency,

AS the few surviving Remains of the Colony of *Georgia* find it necessary to present the World (and in particular *Great-Britain*) with a true State of that Province, from its first Rise, to its present Period; Your Excellency (of all Mankind) is best entitled to the Dedication, as the principal Author of its present Strength and Affluence, Freedom and Prosperity: And tho' incontestable Truths will recommend the following *Narrative* to the patient and attentive Reader; yet your Name, *Sir,* will be no little Ornament to the Frontispiece, and may possibly engage some courteous Perusers a little beyond it.

THAT Dedication and Flattery are synonimous, is the Complaint of every Dedicator, who concludes himself ingenuous and fortunate, if he can discover a less trite and direct Method of flattering than is usually practised; but we are happily prevented from the least Intention of this kind, by the repeated Offerings of the *Muses* and *News-Writers* to Your Excellency, in the publick Papers: 'Twere presumptuous even to dream of equalling or encreasing them: We therefore flatter ourselves, that Nothing we can advance will in the least shock Your Excellency's Modesty; not doubting but your Goodness will pardon any Deficiency of Elegance and Politeness, on account of our Sincerity, and the serious Truths we have the Honour to approach you with.

WE have seen the ancient Custom of sending forth Colonies, for the Improvement of any distant Territory, or new Acquisition, continued down to ourselves: but to Your Excellency alone it is owing, that the World is made acquainted with a Plan, highly refined from those of all former Projectors. They fondly imagin'd it necessary to communicate to such young Settlements the fullest Rights and Properties, all the Immunities of their Mother Countries, and Privileges rather more extensive: By such Means, indeed, these Colonies flourish'd with early Trade and Affluence; but Your Excellency's Concern for our perpetual Welfare could never permit you to propose such transitory Advantages for us: You consider'd Riches like a Divine and Philosopher, as the *Irritamenta Malorum,* and knew that they were disposed to inflate weak Minds with Pride; to pamper the Body with Luxury, and introduce a long Variety of Evils. Thus have you *Protected us from ourselves,* as Mr. *Waller* says, by keeping all Earthly Comforts from us: You have afforded us the Opportunity of arriving at the Integrity of the *Primitive Times,* by intailing a more than *Primitive Poverty* on us: The Toil, that is necessary to our bare Subsistence, must effectually defend us from the Anxieties of any further Ambition: As we have no Properties, to feed Vain-Glory and beget Contention; so we are not puzzled with any System of Laws, to ascertain and establish them: The valuable Virtue of Humility is secured to us, by your Care to prevent our procuring, or so much as seeing any *Negroes* (the only human Creatures proper to improve our Soil) lest our Simplicity might mistake the poor *Africans* for greater Slaves than ourselves: And that we might fully receive the Spiritual Benefit of those wholesome Austerities; you have wisely denied us the Use of such Spiritous Liquors, as might in the least divert our Minds from the Contemplation of our Happy Circumstances.

OUR Subject swells upon us; and did we allow ourselves to indulge our Inclination, without considering our weak Abilities, we should be tempted to launch out into many of Your Excellency's extraordinary Endowments, which do not so much regard the Affair in Hand: But as this would lead us beyond the Bounds of a Dedication; so would it engross a Subject too extensive for us, to the Prejudice of other Authors and Panegyrists; We shall therefore confine ourselves to that remarkable Scene of Your Conduct, whereby *Great-Britain* in general, and the Settlers of *Georgia* in particular, are laid under such inexpressible Obligations.

BE pleased then, *Great Sir*, to accompany our heated Imaginations, in taking a View of this Colony of *Georgia!* this Child of your auspicious Politicks! arrived at the utmost Vigor of its Constitution, at a Term when most former States have been struggling through the Convulsions of their Infancy. This early Maturity, however, lessens our Admiration, that Your Excellency lives to see (what few Founders ever aspired after) the great Decline and almost final Termination of it. So many have finish'd their Course during the Progress of the Experiment, and such Numbers have retreated from the Fantoms of Poverty and Slavery which their cowardly Imaginations pictur'd to them; that you may justly vaunt with the boldest Hero of them all,

> ——— *Like Death you reign*
> *O'er silent Subjects and a desart Plain.*
>
> BUSIRIS

YET must your Enemies (if you have any) be reduced to confess, that no ordinary Statesman could have digested, in the like Manner, so capacious a Scheme, such a copious Jumble of Power and Politicks. We shall content ourselves with observing, that all those beauteous Models of Government which the little States of *Germany* exercise, and those extensive Liberties which the Boors of *Poland* enjoy, were design'd to concenter in your System; and were we to regard the Modes of Government, we must have been strangely unlucky to have miss'd of the best where there was an Appearance of so great a Variety; for, under the Influence of our *Perpetual Dictator*, we have seen something like *Aristocracy*, *Oligarchy*, as well as the *Triumvirate*, *Decemvirate*, and *Consular Authority* of famous Republicks, which have expired many Ages before us: What Wonder then we share the same Fate? Do their Towns and Villages exist but in Story and Rubbish? We are all over Ruins; our Publick-Works, Forts, Wells, High-Ways, Light-House, Store and Water-Mills, &c. are dignified like theirs, with the same venerable Desolation. The Logg-House, indeed, is like to be the last forsaken Spot of Your Empire; yet even this, through the Death, or Desertion of those who should continue to inhabit it, must suddenly decay; the Bankrupt Jailor himself shall be soon denied the Privilege of human Conversation; and when this last Moment of the Spell expires, the whole shall vanish like the illusion of some *Eastern Magician*.

BUT let not this solitary Prospect impress Your Excellency with any Fears of having your Services to Mankind, and to the Settlers of *Georgia* in particular, buried in Oblivion; for if we diminutive Authors are allow'd to prophesy (as you know Poets in those Cases formerly did) we may confidently presage, That while the Memoirs of *America* continue to be read in *English*, *Spanish*, or the Language of the *Scots* High-Landers, Your Excellency's Exploits and Epocha will be transmitted to Posterity.

SHOULD Your Excellency apprehend the least Tincture of Flattery in any Thing already hinted, we may sincerely assure you, we intended nothing that our Sentiments did not very strictly attribute to your Merit; and, in such Sentiments, we have the Satisfaction of being fortified by all Persons of Impartiality and Discernment.

BUT to trespass no longer on those Minutes, which Your Excellency may suppose more significantly employ'd on the Sequel; let it suffice at present, to assure you, that we are deeply affected with your Favours; and tho' unable of ourselves properly to acknowledge them, we shall embrace every Opportunity of Recommending you to higher Powers, who (we are hopeful) will reward Your Excellency according to your *Merit*.

May it please Your Excellency,

Your Excellency's

Most devoted Servants,

The Land-Holders of *Georgia*,

Authors of the following *Narrative*

Joseph Green (1706–1780)

One of the most distinguished humorists of eighteenth-century Boston was Joseph Green, a Harvard-educated merchant whose uncollected poems were popular throughout the century, being reprinted even after he had embraced the loyalist cause during the Revolution and fled the country for London in 1775. Like Alexander Hamilton of Maryland (pp. 115–122), Green was an active amateur man-of-letters and an irrepressible mocker. A humorous epitaph written in his honor in the 1740's represents his character admirably: "Siste Viator, here lies one,/Whose life was whim, whose soul was pun,/And if you go too near his hearse,/He'll joke you, both in prose and verse." Green was reputed to have the largest private library in New England. He associated with prominent men of letters and learning in the Massachusetts metropolis. One of these was the Reverend Mather Byles, with whom Green engaged in a literary joust. After an occasion when the rather vain Byles extemporaneously composed a hymn on shipboard for the Massachusetts governor and was justifiably proud of the accomplishment, Green mercilessly lampooned Byles in a poem which added insult to injury by concluding with a parody of the minister's hymn. Byles replied with a savage parody of Green's lampoon and parody (see pp. 96–98). Green's satire on Byles' poetic muse rounds off the interchange and makes it one of the classic humorous battles in American literary history. In addition to denigrating the clergy, Green also took satirical note of secular affairs, as when he burlesqued a Masonic ceremonial affair in the bawdy mock-epic, *Entertainment for a Winter's Evening* (1750). Green advanced the secularization of New England humor and of literature in general, a development initiated by Benjamin Tompson (pp. 32–37) and Samuel Sewall (pp. 47–48).

TEXT: "Reverend Mather Byles . . ." and "The Poet's Lamentation . . . ," *Cyclopaedia of American Literature*, ed. Evert A. and George L. Duyckinck, New York, 1855, I; *Entertainment for a Winter's Evening*, Boston, Mass., 1750.

REVEREND MATHER BYLES WRITES A PSALM

In David's Psalms an oversight
  Byles found one morning at his tea,
Alas! that he should never write
  A proper psalm to sing at sea.

Thus ruminating on his seat,
  Ambitious thoughts at length prevail'd.
The bard determined to complete
  The part wherein the prophet fail'd.

He sat awhile and stroked his muse,*
  Then taking up his tuneful pen,
Wrote a few stanzas for the use
  Of his seafaring brethren.

The task perform'd, the bard content,
  Well chosen was each flowing word;
On a short voyage himself he went,
  To hear it read and sung on board.

Most serious Christians do aver,
  (Their credit sure we may rely on,)
In former times that after prayer,
  They used to sing a song of Zion.

Our modern parson having pray'd,
  Unless loud fame our faith beguiles,
Sat down, took out his book and said,
  "Let's sing a psalm of Mather Byles."

At first, when he began to read,
  Their heads the assembly downward hung.
But he with boldness did proceed,
  And thus he read, and thus they sung.

THE PSALM

With vast amazement we survey
  The wonders of the deep,
Where mackerel swim, and porpoise play,
  And crabs and lobsters creep.

Fish of all kinds inhabit here,
  And throng the dark abode.
Here haddock, hake, and flounders are,
  And eels, and perch, and cod.

From raging winds and tempests free,
  So smoothly as we pass,
The shining surface seems to be
  A piece of Bristol glass.

* [The Reverend Byles' cat, subject of Green's "The Poet's Lamentation. . . ."]

But when the winds and tempests rise,
   And foaming billows swell,
The vessel mounts above the skies,
   And lower sinks than hell.

Our heads the tottering motion feel,
   And quickly we become
Giddy as new-dropp'd calves, and reel
   Like Indians drunk with rum.

What praises then are due that we
   Thus far have safely got,
Amarescoggin tribe to see,
   And tribe of Penobscot.

THE POET'S LAMENTATION FOR THE LOSS OF HIS CAT, WHICH HE USED TO CALL HIS MUSE

Felis quædam delicium erat cujnsdam Adolescentis. ÆSOP

Oppress'd with grief in heavy strains I mourn
The partner of my studies from me torn.
How shall I sing? what numbers shall I chuse?
For in my fav'rite cat I've lost my muse.
No more I feel my mind with raptures fir'd,
I want those airs that Puss so oft inspir'd;
No crowding thoughts my ready fancy fill,
Nor words run fluent from my easy quill;
Yet shall my verse deplore her cruel fate,
And celebrate the virtues of my cat.

   In acts obscene she never took delight;
No caterwauls disturb'd our sleep by night;
Chaste as a virgin, free from every stain,
And neighb'ring cats mew'd for her love in vain.

   She never thirsted for the chickens' blood;
Her teeth she only used to chew her food;
Harmless as satires which her master writes,
A foe to scratching, and unused to bites,
She in the study was my constant mate;
There we together many evenings sat.
Whene'er I felt my tow'ring fancy fail,
I stroked her head, her ears, her back, and tail;

And as I stroked improv'd my dying song
From the sweet notes of her melodious tongue:
Her purrs and mews so evenly kept time,
She purr'd in metre, and she mew'd in rhyme.
But when my dulness has too stubborn prov'd,
Nor could by Puss's music be remov'd,
Oft to the well-known volumes have I gone,
And stole a line from Pope or Addison.

Ofttimes when lost amidst poetic heat,
She leaping on my knee has took her seat;
There saw the throes that rock'd my lab'ring brain,
And lick'd and claw'd me to myself again.

Then, friends, indulge my grief, and let me mourn,
My cat is gone, ah! never to return.
Now in my study, all the tedious night,
Alone I sit, and unassisted write;
Look often round (O greatest cause of pain),
And view the num'rous labors of my brain;
Those quires of words array'd in pompous rhyme,
Which braved the jaws of all-devouring time,
Now undefended and unwatch'd by cats,
Are doom'd a victim to the teeth of rats.

ENTERTAINMENT FOR A WINTER'S EVENING

O Muse renown'd for story-telling,
Fair Clio, leave thy airy dwelling.
Now while the streams like marble stand,
Held fast by Winter's icy hand;
Now while the hills are cloth'd in snow;
Now while the keen north-west winds blow;
From the bleak fields and chilling air
Unto the warmer hearth repair:
Where friends in chearful circle met
In social conversation sit.
Come, *Goddess*, and our ears regale
With a diverting Christmas tale.
O come, and in thy verse declare
Who were the men, and what they were,
And what their names, and what their fame,
And what the cause for which they came

To house of God from house of ale,
And how the parson told his tale:
How they return'd, in manner odd,
To house of ale from house of God.

Free Masons, as the story goes,
Have two saints for their patrons chose:
And both SAINT JOHNS, one the *Baptist*,
The other the *Evangelist*.
The Baptist had a *Lodge* which stood,
Of old, by JORDAN's ancient flood.
But for what secret cause the other
Has been adopted for a *brother*,
They cannot, and I will not say,
Nec scire fas est omnia.

The Masons by procession
Having already honour'd one,
(Thou, to perpetuate their glory,
CLIO, dist then relate the story.)
To show the world they mean fair play,
And that each saint should have his day,
Now order store of belly-timber
'Gainst twenty-seventh of *December*.
For that's the day of *Saint John's* feast,
Fix'd by the holy *Roman* priest.
They then in mood religious chose
Their *brother of the roll and rose*
The ceremony to commence:
He from the sacred eminence
Must first explain, and then apply
The duties of FREE MASONRY.

At length, in scarlet apron drest,
Forth rush'd the morning of the feast;
And now the bells in steeple play,
Hark, ding, dong, bells they chime away;
Until, with solemn toll and steady,
The great bell tells—the parson's ready.

MASONS at church!! strange auditory!!
And yet we have as strange in story.
For saints, as history attests,
Have preach'd to fishes, birds and beasts;
Yea stones so hard, tho' strange, 'tis true,
Have sometimes been their hearers too.

So good Saint FRANCIS, man of grace,
Himself preach'd to the *braying race*;
And further, as the story passes,
Address'd them thus—*my brother asses*.
Just so old BRITISH WEREBURGA,
As ecclesiastic writers say,
Harangued the *geese* both far and wide,
Just so the *geese* were edify'd.

The crowds attending gaze around,
And awful silence reigns profound.
Till from the seat which he'd sat arse on
Uprose and thus began the parson.

RIGHT WORSHIPFUL, at whose command
Obedient I in *Rostra* stand;
It proper is and fit to show
Unto the crowds that gape below,
Who wonder much, and well they may,
What on th' occasion I can say;
Why in the church are met together,
Especially in such cold weather,
Such folk as never did appear
So overfond of coming there.
Know then, my friends, without more pother,
That these are MASONS, I'm a BROTHER.
Masons, said I?—yes MASONS FREE;
Their *deeds* and *title* both agree.
While other sects fall out and fight
About a trifling mode or rite,
We firm by *Love* cemented stand,
'Tis *Love* unites us heart and hand,
Love to a party not confin'd,
A *Love* embracing all mankind,
Both catholic and protestant,
The *Scots* and eke *New England* saint;
ANTONIO's followers, and those
Who've CRISPIN for their patron chose,
And them, who to their idol goose
Oft sacrifice the blood of louse.
Those who with razor bright and keen,
And careful hand, each morn are seen
Devoting to SAINT NICHOLAS
The manly honours of the face.
Him too who works, ah! cruel deed!

The fatal, tough MUSCOVIAN weed!
And twists the suffocating string
In which devoted wretches swing.
(And O may gracious Heaven defend
The *brethren* from dishonest end.)
Whose cauldrons smoke with juice of Pine,
An offering to Saint CATHARINE.

O Pine salubrious! from thy veins
Distills the cure of human pains.
Hail SACRED TREE! to thee I owe
This freedom from a world of woe.
My heart tho' grateful, weak my strain,
To show thy worth I strive in vain,
Could THRACIAN ORPHEUS but impart
His tuneful lyre and matchless art;
And would propitious fates decree
Old NESTOR's length of days to me,
That lyre, that art, that length of days,
I'd spend in singing forth thy praise.
Still thou shall never want my blessing;—
—But to return from thus digressing.

RHODE-ISLAND's differing, motley tribes,
Far more than ALEC. ROSS describes,
And light that's *new*, and light that's *old*,
We in our friendly arms enfold,
Free, generous and unconfin'd,
To outward shape or inward mind.
The high and low, the great and small,
James Perkins short, and *Aston* tall,
Johnson as bulky as a house,
And W*etbred* smaller than a louse.
The grave and merry, dull and witty,
The fair and brown, deform'd and pretty,
We all agree, both wet and dry,
From drunken *Luke* to sober I.
And *Hugh*——But hark, methinks I hear
One shrewdly whisp'ring in my ear;
"Pray, Parson, don't affirm but prove;
Do they all meet and part in love?
Quarrels oft times don't they delight in,
And now and then a little fighting?
Did there not (for the SECRET's out)
In the last LODGE arise a rout?

Mackenzey with a fist of brass
Laid *Trail's* nose level with his face,
And scarcely had he let his hand go,
When he receiv'd from *Trail* a d——d blow.
Now, parson, when a nose is broken,
Pray, is it friendly *sign* or *token?*"

   'Tis true, but trifling is th' objection,
All general rules have an exception.
Oft from themselves the best men vary,
Humanum enim est errare.
But what I said I'll say again,
And what I say I will maintain:
'Tis *Love*, pure *Love*, cements the whole,
Love—of the BOTTLE and the BOWL.

   But 'tis high time to let you go
Where you had rather be, I know:
And by proceeding I delay
The weightier business of the day;
For eating *solid sense* affords,
Whilst nonsense lurks in many words.
Doubting does oft arise from thinking,
But truth is only found in drinking.
This having said, the reverend vicar
Dismiss'd them to their food and liquor.

   From church to STONE's they go to eat,
In order walking through the street;
But no *Right Worshipful* was there,
PALLAS forbade him to appear;
For, well foreseeing that the job
Would from all parts collect the mob,
He wisely catch'd a cold and staid
At home, at least, if not in bed.
So when the GREEKS 'gainst TROJANS went,
ACHILLES tarry'd in his tent;
Asham'd he hides himself, nor draws
His conquering sword in harlot's cause.

   See *Buck* before the apron'd throng
Marches with sword and book along;
The stately ram, with courage bold,
So stalks before the fleecy fold,
And so the gander, on the brink
Of River, leads his geese to drink,

And so the geese descend from gab'ling
On the dry land, in stream to dab'ling.

Three with their white sticks next are seen,
One on each side and one between;
Plump *Lewis* marches on the right,
Round as a hoop, as bottle tight,
With face full orb'd and rosy too;
So ruddy CYNTHIA oft we view,
When she, from tippling castern streams,
First throws about her evening beams,
'Tis he the *brethren* all admire,
Him for their steward they require.
'Tis he they view with wondering eyes,
'Tis he their utmost art defies;
For though with nicest skill they work all,
None of them e'er could square his circle.

Next *Belcher* with *MacDaniel* passes;
Though *brothers*, how unlike their faces!
So limners better represent
By artful contrast what they paint.

Whose he comes next?—'Tis *Pue* by name,
Pue by his nose well known to fame;
This, when the generous juice recruits,
Around a brighter radiance shoots.
So, on some promontory's height,
For NEPTUNE's sons the signal light
Shines fair, and fed by unctuous stream,
Sends off to sea a livelier beam.

But see the crowds, with what amaze
They on the 'pothecary gaze!
'Tis he, when belly suffers twitch,
Caus'd by the too retentive breech,
Adjusts with finger nice and thumb
The ivory tube to patient's bum,
Aston, high rising o'er the rest,
With his tall head and ample chest;
So towering stands the tree of JOVE,
And proud o'erlooks the neighbouring grove.

Where's honest *Luke*, that cook from London,
For without *Luke* the LODGE is undone,
'Twas he who oft dispell'd their sadness,

And fill'd the *Brethren's* hearts with gladness.
For them his ample bowls o'erflow'd,
His table groan'd beneath its load;
For them he stretch'd his utmost art;
Their honours grateful they impart,
Luke in return is made a *brother*,
And still, though broke with age and wine,
Preserves the *token* and the *sign*.

But still I see a numerous train:
Shall they, alas! unsung remain?
Sage *Hollowel* of public soul,
And laughing *Frank*, friend to the bowl,
Meek *Rea*, half smother'd in the crowd,
And *Rowe* who sings at church so loud,
Tall *De La Rue*, of GALLIC city,
Short *Box*, who trips along so pretty,
Bayard so truss, with gut well fed,
Who to the hungry deals his bread,
And twenty more crowd on my fancy,
All *brothers*—and that's all you can say.

Whene'er for aiding nature frail,
Poor bawd must follow the cart's-tail,
As through fair LONDON's streets she goes,
The mob, like fame, by moving grows;
They should'ring close, press, stink and shove,
Scarcely can the *procession* move.
Just such a street-collected throng
Guarded the *Brotherhood* along;
Just such the noise, just such the roar,
Heard from behind and from before.
'Till *lodg'd* at STONE's, nor more pursu'd,
The mob with three huzzas conclude.

And now, withdrawn from public view,
What did the *brethren* say and do?
Had I the force of STENTOR's lungs,
A voice of brass, a hundred tongues;
My tongues and voice and lungs would fail,
E'er I had finish'd half my tale;
E'er I had told their names and nation,
Their virtues, arts and occupation.
Or in fit strains had half made known
What words were spoke, what deeds were done.

CLIO, 'tis thou alone canst show 'em,
For thou'rt a goddess and must know 'em.

    But now suppress thy further rhyme,
And tell the rest another time.
Once more, perhaps, the *apron'd train*
Hereafter may invite thy strain,
Then CLIO, with descendent wing,
Shall downward fly again and sing.

Mather Byles (1707–1788)

A nephew of Cotton Mather, the Reverend Mather Byles perpetuated the Puritan tradition of learning and letters in the eighteenth-century Boston of Joseph Green and Benjamin Franklin. In his early twenties Byles frequently contributed prose and verse to the *New England Weekly Journal*, one of the best of the periodicals in which most eighteenth-century American literature appeared; Byles' humorous essay on style is typical of the Addisonian prose which he wrote at first. For a time his literary ambitions were high, and he corresponded with Alexander Pope and Dr. Isaac Watts, the famous hymnist. A volume of poems published in Boston in 1744 was filled with eulogies of Byles, a typical couplet asserting that "Harvard's honor, and New England's hope,/Bids fair to rise and sing and rival Pope." Byles' own collection, *Poems on Several Occasions* (1744), reveals a talent in the neoclassical style which might have developed in time. However, as his preface declared, he had come to regard his poetry as "Amusements of looser Hours" while "unbending his Mind from severer Studies" and thus bade "adieu to the airy Muse." The influence of punning Cotton Mather and the Puritan literary tradition was too strong in Byles, however, for him to successfully eradicate his innate propensity for humor. It continued to find oral expression in extemporaneous repartee, most vividly in fantastic punning, which endeared him to New Englanders even though in an age of growing religious liberalism he held rigidly to Puritan orthodoxy and during the Revolution supported the British. Oliver Wendell Holmes later proudly asserted that he regarded himself as being in the humorous lineage of Byles. In Nathaniel Hawthorne's story, "Howe's Masquerade," where Byles is one of the characters, the clergyman's spirit is summed up in a line of dialogue addressed to him: "'If mirth were a crime, you had never gained your doctorate in divinity.'"

TEXT: "Parody . . . ," *Cyclopaedia of American Literature*, ed. Evert A. and George L. Duyckinck, New York, 1855, I; "An Essay on Style," *The American Magazine and Historical Chronicle*, Boston, Mass., January, 1745.

PARODY OF JOSEPH GREEN'S "REVEREND MATHER BYLES WRITES A PSALM"

In Byles's works an oversight
    Green spy'd, as once he smok'd his chunk;
Alas! that Byles should never write
    A song to sing, when folks are drunk.

Thus in the chimney on his block,
    Ambition fir'd the 'stiller's pate;
He summon'd all his little stock,
    The poet's volume to complete.

Long paus'd the lout, and scratch'd his skull,
    Then took his chalk [he own'd no pen,]
And scrawl'd some doggrel, for the whole
    Of his flip-drinking brethren.

The task perform'd—not to content—
    Ill chosen was each Grub-street word;
Strait to the tavern club he went,
    To hear it bellow'd round the board.

Unknown delights his ears explore,
    Inur'd to midnight caterwauls,
To hear his hoarse companions roar,
    The horrid thing his dulness scrawls.

The club, if fame we may rely on,
    Conven'd, to hear the drunken catch,
At the three-horse-shoes, or red lion—
    Tipling began the night's debauch.

The little 'stiller took the pint
    Full fraught with flip and songs obscene,
And, after a long stutt'ring, meant
    To sing a song of Josy Green.

Soon as with stam'ring tongue, to read
    The drunken ballad, he began,
The club from clam'ring strait recede,
    To hear him roar the thing alone.

SONG

With vast amazement we survey
    The can so broad, so deep,
Where punch succeeds to strong sangree,
    Both to delightful flip.

Drink of all smacks, inhabit here,
    And throng the dark abode;
Here's rum, and sugar, and small beer,
    In a continual flood.

From cruel thoughts and conscience free,
    From dram to dram we pass;

Our cheeks, like apples, ruddy be;
  Our eyeballs look like glass.

At once, like furies up we rise,
  Our raging passions swell;
We hurl the bottle to the skies,
  But why, we cannot tell.

Our brains a tott'ring motion feel,
  And quickly we become
Sick, as with negro steaks, and reel
  Like Indians drunk with rum.

Thus lost in deep tranquility,
  We sit, supine and sot,
Till we two moons distinctly see—
  Come give us t'other pot.

AN ESSAY ON STYLE

As one great Design of many of the Entertainments in our *Magazine*, is
to cultivate *polite* Writing, and form and embellish the Style of our ingenious Countrymen: So, Instead of a Preface to this Volume, we ask
Leave to give the following Piece of *Criticism*.

> *Clamorem immensum tollit, quo pontus et omnes*
> *Intremuere undae, penitusque exterrita tellus*
> *Italiae, curvixque immugiit Aetna cavernis.*
>
> VIRG. AENEID *

There have been innumerable Authors, from *Aristotle's Rhetorick* to
Longinus's Treatise of the Sublime, and from thence down to the Com-
piler of our modern *Horn-book*, who have written Introductions to the
Art of Polite Writing. Every one that can just distinguish his Twenty Four
Letters sets up for a Judge of it; as all who are able to flourish a Goose's
Quill, pretend to be Masters of that Secret. The noblest Productions have
given Birth to many a supercillious Caveller; Criticks of all Sizes and
Dimensions have nibled round the divinest Pages; and Ignorance and
Conceit have endeavoured to shake down the most beautiful Structures,
in order to build themselves a Reputation out of the Ruins. A superious
Genius, though he seems to kindle a wide Horizon of Light all about

* [With that he roared aloud: the dreadful cry
  Shakes earth, and air, and seas; the billows fly
  Before the bellowing noise, to distant Italy.
  The neighbouring Aetna trembling all around,
  The winding caverns echo to the sound.
     Aeneid, III, 672–74, trans. John Dryden]

him, and is admired by the understanding Part of Mankind, yet he must expect to be the Occasion of a great many Absurdities, with which the unknowing and envious will strive to satyrize him: As the Sun scatters Day through a whole Frame of Worlds, but yet may, in some particular Spots, raise a Fog, or hatch a Nest of Vermin. To conclude, the Science of correct Writing having been a Subject exhausted by so many able Hands, and seeing all the Rabble of Scriblers are such indisputable Proficients in it; not to mention my own Incapacity for such an Under-taking; I shall not be so vain as to offer my Thoughts upon it: But I shall apply my Labours at this Time, to an Ornament of a contrary Nature, which is a Theme intirely New, Namely, *The Art of writing Incorrectly*.

This, I take it, is a Work that I am excellently well qualified for, and I doubt not but to convince the World that I am a perfect Master of my Subject. In the Prosecution of this useful Design, I shall show the Excel-lency of Incorrect Writing in general; I shall lay open the several Artifices, by which a Man of competent Abilities, may, with proper Application, attain to a tolerable Degree of Perfection in it; I shall produce pertinent Examples from Writers of undoubted Eminence in that improving Sci-ence: And in the last place, I may possibly address the World with a very pathetick Exhortation, to follow the Instructions which I shall give them, in order to accomplish themselves in the Art of Incorrect Writing. In short, I intend to entertain the Publick, with a regular Criticism upon Nonsense.

Authors of this Kind may be divided into two Classes, generally known under the Denomination of the *Bombastick* and the *Grubstreet*. The latter of these Characters is easily attained, provided a Man can but keep him-self from thinking, and yet so contrive Matters, as to let his Pen run along unmolested over a Sheet of White Paper, and drop a convenient Quantity of Words, at proper Intervals on it. A Person who is acquainted with this Secret, may, with great Facility and Composure of Mind, furnish himself with a comfortable Stock of Reputation, as often as he finds it requisite. This he might do, as without any Ruffle to his own Tranquility, so neither would it prove the least Disturbance to his Readers: For while he flow'd along with that unmeaning Softness, every one within the Warble of his Accents would undoubtedly dissolve away in a supine Indolence, and, (as a late Musical Author of this Species has very tenderly expressed it) be *hush'd into lulling Dreams*.

I shall, perhaps, dedicate some future Essay to the Incouragement of these worthy Gentlemen, but at this Time I intend to consider those my ingenious Fellow-Labourers, who deviate into the contrary Extream; I mean the Admirers of Bombast and Fustian.

These Writers, to avoid the Imputation of low and flat, blow up every Subject they take in Hand beyond its natural Dimensions; and nothing will please them that is not big and boisterous, wild and irregular. They wonderfully delight in Noise and Clamour; a Rattle of Words, and an

Extravagance of Imagination, they look upon as the Perfection of Rhetorick; and are Transported beyond themselves, at the Tumult and Confusion that bellows through a Hurricane of Nonsense. In short, that which Men of this Turn Applaud as the Masterpiece of good Writing, differs from the *true Sublime*, as a Boy's artificial Kite, wadling among the Clouds at the End of a Skein of Pack-thread, does from the natural Flight of an Eagle, towering with steddy Pinions up the Sky, and bearing full upon the Sun.

If this false Taste prevails amongst us, we shall quickly prove such a Generation of Blusterers, that our Country will resemble the Cave of *Aeolus*, where the Winds make their general Rendezvous, and battel and clash together in an eternal Din and Uproar. For my own Part, I look upon it to be the Duty of every one, as far as in him lies, to lend his Assistance in banking out this Inundation of Sound, which, if it finds a clear Passage, will not fail to overwhelm us in a Deluge of Folly and Absurdity.

A Friend of mine who writes in this exorbitant Style, Mr. *Richard Stentor* by Name, shall be the Hero of the present Essay. Mr. *Stentor* as to his exterior Figure, is one of the portliest Mortals that have flourished in our World, since *Goliah* over-top'd the *Philistian* Army. He is moderately speaking, Nine Foot high, and Four in Diameter. His Voice is not unlike the Roar and Rapidity of a Torrent foaming down a Mountain, and reverberated amongst the neighboring Rocks. The Hurry of Vociferation with which he drives along in the Heat of an Argument, imitates the Thunder of a Cartload of Stones poured out upon a Pavement. He was educated in a Ship of War, and one would imagine he learnt the Notes of his Gamut, from the various Whistlings of a Tempest thro' the Rigging of his Vessel. I was once so unadvised as to offer my Dissent from one of his Opinions; but I had better have held my Tongue: He turned upon me and rung me such a Peal of Eloquence, that had I not made off with the greatest Precipitation, would have gone near to have stun'd, and made me deaf all my Days. Nay, I have cause to think my Hearing has been never the better for it to this Moment.

This is a short Description of his external Accomplishments; as to the Qualifications of his Mind, they will be best perceived, by a Transcript I shall here make, from an Oration he formerly composed in *Praise of Beacon Hill*. I must inform me Readers, that it was conceived as he stood upon the Summit of that little Mount, one Training-Day, when, as he has since owned to me, the Drums and Musquets assisted his Inspiration, and augmented and deepend the Rumbling of his Periods. It begins in the following Manner—

The gloriously-transcendent, and highly-exalted Precipice, from which the sonorous Accents of my Lungs resound with repeated Echoes; is so pompous, magnificent, illustrious, and loftily-towering, that, as I twirle around my Arm *with the artful Flourish of an Orator, I seem to feel my Knucles rebound from the blew Vault of Heaven, which just arches over my Head. I stand upon an amazing Eminence that heaves itself up, on both sides steep and stupendous! high and horrendous! The spiry Teneriffe, the unshaken Atlas, or Olympus divine and celestial, when compared to this prodigious Mountain, sink to Sands, and dwindle to Atoms. It is deep-rooted in its ever-during Foundations, firm as the Earth, lasting as the Sun, immoveable as the Pillars of Nature! I behold from this awful and astonishing Scituation, the concave Expanse of un-created Space, stretch itself above: and the Land and Ocean below, spreading an Infinitude of Extension all about me. But what daring Tropes and flaming Metaphores shall I select, O aspiring Beacon! to celebrate Thee with a suitable Grandeur, or exalt thee to a becoming Dignity? How does it shoot up its in-conceivable Pinnacle into the superior Regions, and blend itself with the ceru-lian circum-ambient Aether! It mocks the fiercest Efforts of the most piercing Sight, to reach to its impenetrable Sublimities. It looks down upon the di-minish'd Spheres; the fixt Stars twinkle at an immeasurable Distance be-neath it; while the Planets roll away, unperceived, in a vast, a fathomless Pro-found *****

By this little Quotation from Mr. *Stentor's* Panegyrick on Beacon Hill, my Reader will in some Measure be able to judge of his Manner of think-ing, and expressing himself. It appears plainly that he heaps his Subject with improper and foreign Thoughts; that he strains those Thoughts into the most unnatural and ridiculous Distortions; and, last of all, that he clouds them with so many needless supernumerary Epithets, as to fling the whole Piece into this unaccountable Huddle of Impertinence and In-consistency. *Richard* is mighty fond of great sounding Words, and, let his Topick be what it will, he has perpetual Recourse to them upon all Emer-gencies. He once took it in his Head to be in Love, and wrote a Poem to his Mistress on that delicate Passion: But instead of the gentle Flow of Harmony which any one would reasonably have expected, and which is indeed essential to Compositions of that Kind, his Numbers stalked along as sturdy and outragious as in any other of his Performances. I my self counted in Fifty Six Lines of it, three *Celestials*, eight *Immortals*, eleven *Unboundeds*, six *Everlastings*, four *Eternities*, and thirteen *Infinites*; Be-sides *Bellowings, Ravings, Yellings, Horrors, Terribles, Rackets, Hubbubs,* and *Clutterings*, without Number. But what pleased me the most of any of my Friend's Compositions, was, A *Poetical Description of a Game at Push-pin*. Sure, thought I, when I read the Title, there can be nothing very loud and impetuous upon so trivial a Matter as This. How I was sur-prized out of my mistake, my Reader will in some Measure conceive, when he understands that the first Distich of the Poem runs thus,

> Rage, fire, and fury in my bosom roll,
> And all the gods rush headlong on my soul.

He then proceeded to compare the Pins to two Comets, whose Heads, as he expressed it, enlightned the boundless Desarts of the Skies with a bloody Glare, and threw behind them the ruddy Volumes of their tremendous Trains, into the tractless Wastes of Immensity. When the Pins met in the Progress of the Game, for a Similitude, he supposed the two Continents to be tossed from their Foundations, and encounter, with a direful Concussion, in the midst of the briny *Atlantick*: or rather, *says he*, as if two Systems of Worlds, Suns, Planets and all, should be hurled resistless one against another, and dash a horrible *Chaos*, from the general Ruins of Matter, and Wrecks of a whole Universe. He concluded the Poem with the following Lines, which I look upon to be the most finished Pattern of this Sort of Productions, that I have any where met with; whether I consider, the Uncouthness of the Language, the Ruggedness of the Style, or the Disproportion and Extravagance of the Images. Speaking of the Pins he says,

> The Bars of Brass, harsh-crashing, loud resound,
> And jarring discords rend th' astonish'd ground.
> So when aloft dire hurricanes arise,
> And with horrendous shatterings burst the skies,
> Dread ghastly terrors drive along in crowds,
> And hideous thunder howls amongst the clouds;
> Eternal whirlwinds on the ocean roar,
> Infinite earth-quakes rock the bounding shore.

I shall conclude these Remarks upon Bombast, with an Observation which I ought in Justice to make, in favour of those who fall into it; *viz. That no Person can be a considerable Proficient this way, who has not a good Share of natural Powers and Abilities.* Hence, when we see a Young Man delivering himself in this warm Manner, he is to be regarded as a good *Genius* run wild, for want of Cultivation from Study, and the Rules of Art: And it follows, that should such a juvenile Writer, take proper Methods to improve his Mind, in inuring himself to a close Way of Reasoning, and by conversing with the best Authors, however defective he might be in this Particular at first, he would in the End make a chaste and excellent Writer. Thus it happened to the immortal *Virgil*, whose divine *Aeneid* once shot itself into so great a Luxuriance, as to be near twenty Times as Large as it appears at this Day. As his Imagination cooled by Years, and his Judgment ripened, and hasted on to Maturity, his Style dropped the false Glare of Ornaments, and shone with an equal Purity and Elegance; His Thoughts learned to proportion themselves to his Subject, and cast themselves into that exact Symmetry of Arrangement and Disposition, in which they now charm us; And, in a word, a new Beauty began to dawn in every Line of that exquisite Work which consecrates his deathless Fame to the Admiration of all Posterity.

Benjamin Franklin (1706–1790)

The honor of having been America's first man of letters is Cotton Mather's, but Benjamin Franklin was undoubtedly America's first great literary humorist. Born in Boston, a member of Mather's congregation and reader of Mather and other Puritans, Franklin inherited the humorous tradition of New England Puritanism even though he sloughed off its theology. He was qualified to ridicule the Puritan funeral elegy in the seventh of his Dogood papers (1722) because he knew the form so well; however, his literary attitude toward the elegy was essentially no more radical than that of Noyes, Sewall, and other Puritans who regarded the elegy as a means of exercising their humorous sensibilities. Even the Poor Richard almanacs which Franklin began to write and publish in 1733 had been preceded by the Puritan almanacs of the seventeenth century. Finally, Franklin's interest in classic and contemporary European literature, English as well as continental, also was not an unusual tendency, for Cotton Mather had read Rabelais before Franklin, and Mather Byles and other Puritan contemporaries of Franklin also were writing like him in the style of Addison's *Spectator* papers. These facts hardly disparage Franklin; they do indicate that Puritan literary culture provided Franklin with the sound base upon which he proceeded to develop his undeniably superior literary talents. Franklin should not be considered a folk humorist, therefore, but a sophisticated writer conversant with the best humor of his own and earlier ages. Some of the comic bits scattered about in his folk almanacs, for example, were borrowed or adapted by him from *Witts Recreations* (1640), the same English jest book which the Reverend Seaborn Cotton had read at Harvard in the mid-seventeenth century (see pp. 8, 17). An apparently indigenous tall tale Franklin used in a 1765 satire ("The very Tails of the American Sheep are so laden with Wooll, that each has a little Car or Waggon on four little Wheels, to support & keep it from trailing on the Ground.") had appeared earlier in Book I, Chapter XVI of Rabelais' *Gargantua and Pantagruel*, though Franklin also may have come across the exaggeration in one of Oliver Goldsmith's eighteenth-century essays. Franklin's sophisticated humor is as varied and urbane as his famous prose style. The selections below provide a sampling of the wit, irony, satire, and jocularity he composed during a fifty-year period.

TEXT: "Epitaph written 1728" (MS fac.), Paul Leicester Ford, *The Many-Sided Franklin*, New York, 1899; "Alice Addertongue," *The Pennsylvania Gazette*, Sept. 7–12, 1732; "Old Mistresses Apologue" (MS), Library of Congress, Washington, D.C.; "On Humbling Our Rebellious Vassals" (1774), *Benjamin Franklin's Letters to the Press, 1758–1775*, ed.

Verner W. Crane, Chapel Hill, N.C., 1950; "The Flies" and "To the Royal Academy of *****" (1777-1781), *Franklin's Wit & Folly: The Bagatelles*, ed. Richard E. Amacher, New Brunswick, N.J., 1953. COMMENTARY: I. Bernard Cohen, *Benjamin Franklin: His Contribution to the American Tradition*, Indianapolis, Ind., 1953; Carl Van Doren, *Benjamin Franklin*, New York, 1939.

EPITAPH WRITTEN 1728

The Body of

B Franklin Printer,

(Like the Cover of an old Book

Its Contents torn out

And stript of its Lettering & Gilding)

Lies here, Food for Worms.

But the Work shall not be lost;

For it will, (as he believ'd) appear once more,

In a new and more elegant Edition

Revised and corrected,

By the Author.

ALICE ADDERTONGUE

Mr. Gazetteer,

I was highly pleased with your last Week's Paper upon SCANDAL, as the uncommon Doctrine therein preach'd is agreeable both to my Principles and Practice, and as it was published very seasonably to reprove the Impertinence of a Writer in the foregoing Thursdays *Mercury*, who at the Conclusion of one of his silly Paragraphs, laments, forsooth, that the *Fair Sex* are so peculiarly guilty of this enormous Crime: Every Blockhead ancient and modern, that could handle a Pen, has I think taken upon him to cant in the same senseless Strain. If to *scandalize* be really a *Crime*, what do these Puppies mean? They describe it, they dress it up in the most odious frightful and destestable Colours, they represent it as the worst of Crimes, and then roundly and charitably charge the whole Race of Womankind with it. Are they not then guilty of what they condemn, at the same time that they condemn it? If they accuse us of any other Crime, they must necessarily *scandalize* while they do it: But to *scandalize* us with being guilty of *Scandal*, is in itself an egregious Absurdity, and can proceed from nothing but the most consummate Impudence in Conjunction with the most profound Stupidity.

This, supposing, as they do, that to scandalize is a Crime; which you have convinc'd all reasonable People, is an Opinion absolutely erroneous. Let us leave then these Ideot Mock-Moralists, while I entertain you with some Account of my Life [and] Manners.

I am a young Girl of about thirty-five, and live at present with my Mother. I have no Care upon my Head of getting a Living, and therefore find it my Duty as well as Inclination, to exercise my Talent at CENSURE, for the Good of my Country folks. There was, I am told, a certain generous Emperor, who if a Day had passed over his Head, in which he had conferred no Benefit on any Man, used to say to his Friends, in Latin, *Diem perdidi*, that is, it seems, *I have lost a Day*. I believe I should make use of the same Expression, if it were possible for a Day to pass in which I had not, or miss'd, an Opportunity to scandalize somebody: But, Thanks be praised, no such Misfortune has befel me these dozen Years.

Yet, whatever Good I may do, I cannot pretend that I first entred into the Practice of this Virtue from a Principle of Publick Spirit; for I remember that when a Child, I had a violent Inclination to be ever talking in my own Praise, and being continually told that it was ill Manners, and once severely whipt for it, the confin'd Stream form'd itself a new Channel, and I began to speak for the future in the Dispraise of others. This I found more agreable to Company, and almost as much so to my self: For what great Difference can there be, between putting your self up, or putting your Neighbour down? *Scandal*, like other Virtues, is in part its own Reward, as it gives us the Satisfaction of making our selves appear better than others, or others no better than ourselves.

My Mother, good Woman, and I, have heretofore differ'd upon this Account. She argu'd that Scandal spoilt all good Conversation, and I insisted that without it there could be no such Thing. Our Disputes once rose so high, that we parted Tea-Table, and I concluded to entertain my Acquaintance in the Kitchin. The first Day of this Separation we both drank Tea at the same Time, but she with her Visitors in the Parlor. She would not hear of the least Objection to any one's Character, but began a new sort of Discourse in some such queer philosophical Manner as this; *I am mightily pleas'd sometimes, says she, when I observe and consider that the World is not so bad as People out of humour imagine it to be. There is something amiable, some good Quality or other in every body. If we were only to speak of People that are least respected, there is such a one is very dutiful to her Father, and methinks has a fine Set of Teeth;*

such a one *is very respectful to her Husband;* such a one *is very kind to her poor Neighbours, and besides has a very handsome Shape;* such a one *is always ready to serve a Friend, and in my Opinion there is not a Woman in Town that has a more agreeable Air and Gait.* This fine kind of Talk, which lasted near half an Hour, she concluded by saying, *I do not doubt but every one of you have made the like Observations, and I should be glad to have the Conversation continu'd upon this Subject.* Just at that Juncture I peep'd in at the Door, and never in my Life before saw such a Set of simple vacant Countenances; they looked somehow neither glad, nor sorry, nor angry, nor pleas'd, nor indifferent, nor attentive; but, (excuse the Simile) like so many blue wooden Images of Rie Doe [wry (rye) Dough]. I in the Kitchin had already begun a ridiculous Story of Mr.——'s Intrigue with his Maid, and his Wife's Behaviour upon the Discovery; at some Passages we laugh'd heartily, and one of the gravest of Mama's Company, without making any Answer to her Discourse, got up *to go and see what the Girls were so merry about:* She was follow'd by a Second, and shortly after by a Third, till at last the old Gentlewoman found herself quite alone, and being convinc'd that her Project was impracticable, came her self and finish'd her Tea with us; ever since which *Saul also has been among the Prophets,* and our Disputes lie dormant.

By Industry and Application, I have made my self the Center of all the *Scandal* in the Province, there is little stirring but I hear of it. I began the World with this Maxim, *That no Trade can subsist without Returns;* and accordingly, whenever I receiv'd a good story, I endeavour'd to give two or a better in the Room of it. My Punctuality in this Way of Dealing gave such Encouragement, that it has procur'd me an incredible deal of Business, which without Diligence and good Method it would be impossible for me to go through. For besides the Stock of Defamation thus naturally flowing in upon me, I practice an Art by which I can pump Scandal out of People that are the least enclin'd that way. Shall I discover my Secret? Yes; to let it die with me would be inhuman. If I have never heard Ill of some Person, I always impute it to defective Intelligence; *for there are none without their Faults, no not one.* If she is a Woman, I take the first Opportunity to let all her Acquaintance know I have heard that one of the handsomest or best Men in Town has said something in Praise either of her Beauty, her Wit, her Virtue, or her good Management. If you know any thing of Humane Nature, you perceive that this naturally introduces a Conversation turning upon all her Failings, past, present, and to come. To the same purpose, and with the same Success, I cause every Man of Reputation to be praised before his Competitors in Love, Business, or Esteem on Account of any particular Qualification. Near the Times of *Election,* if I find it necessary, I commend every Candidate before some of the opposite Party, listning attentively to what is said of him in answer: (But Commendations in this latter Case are not always neces-

sary, and should be used judiciously;) of late Years I needed only observe what they said of one another freely; and having for the Help of
Memory taken Account of all Informations and Accusations received,
whoever peruses my Writings after my Death, may happen to think, that
during a certain Term, the People of *Pennsylvania* chose into all their
Offices of Honour and Trust, the veriest Knaves, Fools and Rascals in
the whole Province. The Time of Election used to be a busy Time with
me, but this Year, with Concern I speak it, People are grown so good
natur'd, so intent upon mutual Feasting and friendly Entertainment, that
I see no Prospect of much Employment from that Quarter.

I mention'd above, that without good Method I could not go thro'
my Business: In my Father's Life-time I had some Instruction in Ac-
compts, which I now apply with Advantage to my own Affairs. I keep
a regular Set of Books, and can tell at an Hour's Warning how it stands
between me and the World. In my *Daybook* I enter every Article of
Defamation as it is transacted; for Scandals *receiv'd in*, I give Credit; and
when I pay them out again, I make the Persons to whom they respectively
relate *Debtor*. In my *Journal*, I add to each Story by Way of Improvement,
such probable Circumstances as I think it will bear, and in my *Ledger*
the whole is regularly posted.

I suppose the Reader already condemns me in his Heart, for this particular of *adding Circumstances*; but I justify that part of my Practice
thus. 'Tis a Principle with me, that none ought to have a greater Share
of Reputation than they really deserve; if they have, 'tis an Imposition
upon the Publick: I know it is every one's Interest, and therefore believe
they endeavour, to conceal *all* their Vices and Follies; and I hold, that
those People are *extraordinary* foolish or careless who suffer a *Fourth* of
their Failings to come to publick Knowledge: Taking then the common
Prudence and Imprudence of Mankind in a Lump, I suppose none suffer
above *one Fifth* to be discovered: Therefore when I hear of any Person's
Misdoing, I think I keep within Bounds if in relating it I only make it
three times worse than it is; and I reserve to my self the Privilege of charg-
ing them with one Fault in four, which, for aught I know, they may be
entirely innocent of. You see there are but few so careful of doing Justice
as my self; what Reason then have Mankind to complain of *Scandal?* In
a general way, the worst that is said of us is only half what *might* be said,
if all our Faults were seen.

But alas, two great Evils have lately befaln me at the same time; an
extream Cold that I can scarce speak, and a most terrible Toothach that
I dare hardly open my Mouth: For some Days past I have receiv'd ten
Stories for one I have paid; and I am not able to ballance my Accounts
without your Assistance. I have long thought that if you would make your
Paper a Vehicle of Scandal, you would double the Number of your Subscribers. I send you herewith Account of *4 Knavish Tricks, 2 crackt*

M—n—ds, 5 Cu—ld—ms, 3 drub'd Wives, and 4 Henpeck'd Husbands, all within this Fortnight; which you may, as Articles of News, deliver to the Publick; and if my Toothach continues, shall send you more; being, in the mean time, *Your constant Reader,*

ALICE ADDERTONGUE

I thank my Correspondent Mrs. Addertongue for her Good-Will; but desire to be excus'd inserting the Articles of News she has sent me; such Things being in Reality no News at all.

OLD MISTRESSES APOLOGUE

My dear Friend,   June 25. 1745.

I know of no Medicine fit to diminish the violent natural Inclinations you mention; and if I did, I think I should not communicate it to you. Marriage is the proper Remedy. It is the most natural State of Man, and therefore the State in which you are most likely to find solid Happiness. Your Reasons against entering into it at present, appear to me not well-founded. The circumstantial Advantages you have in View by postponing it, are not only uncertain, but they are small in comparison with that of the Thing itself, the being *married and settled.* It is the Man and Woman united that make the compleat human Being. Separate, she wants his Force of Body and Strength of Reason; he, her Softness, Sensibility and acute Discernment. Together they are more likely to succeed in the World. A single Man has not nearly the Value he would have in that State of Union. He is an incompleat Animal. He resembles the odd Half of a Pair of Scissars.—If you get a prudent healthy Wife, your Industry in your Profession, with her good Oeconomy, will be a Fortune sufficient.

But if you will not take this Counsel, and persist in thinking a Commerce with the Sex inevitable, then I repeat my former Advice, that in all your Amours you should *prefer old Women to young ones.* You call this a Paradox, and demand my Reasons. They are these:

1. Because as they have more Knowledge of the World, and their Minds are better stor'd with Observations, their Conversation is more improving and more lastingly agreable.

2. Because when Women cease to be handsome, they study to be good. —To maintain their Influence over Men, they supply the Diminution of Beauty by an Augmentation of Utility. They learn to do a thousand Services small and great, and are the most tender and useful of all Friends when you are sick. Thus they continue amiable. And hence there is

hardly such a thing to be found as an old Woman who is not a good Woman.—

3. Because there is no hazard of Children, which irregularly produc'd may be attended with much Inconvenience.

4. Because thro' more Experience, they are more prudent and discreet in conducting an Intrigue to prevent Suspicion. The Commerce with them is therefore safer with regard to your Reputation. And with Regard to theirs, if the Affair should happen to be known, considerate People might be rather inclin'd to excuse an old Woman, who would kindly take care of a young Man, form his Manners by her good Counsels, and prevent his ruining his Health and Fortune among mercenary Prostitutes.

5. Because in every Animal that walks upright, the Deficiency of the Fluids that fill the Muscles appears first in the highest Part: The Face first grows Lank and wrinkled; then the Neck; then the Breast and Arms; the lower Parts continuing to the Last as plump as ever: So that covering all above with a Basket, and regarding only what is below the Girdle, it is impossible of two Women to know an old from a young one. And as in the dark all Cats are grey, the Pleasure of corporal Enjoyment with an old Woman is at least equal and frequently superior; every Knack being by Practice capable of Improvement.

6. Because the Sin is less. The debauching a Virgin may be her Ruin, and make her for Life unhappy.

7. Because the Compunction is less. The having made a young Girl *miserable* may give you frequent bitter Reflections; none of which can attend the making an old Woman *happy*.

8thly & Lastly,—They are *so grateful!!*

Thus much for my Paradox.—But still I advise you to marry directly; being sincerely

Your Affectionate Friend

ON HUMBLING OUR REBELLIOUS VASSALS

To the Printer of the Public Advertiser.

SIR,

Permit me, thro' the Channel of your paper, to convey to the Premier, by him to be laid before his Mercenaries, our Constituents, my own Opinion, and that of many of my Brethren, Freeholders of this imperial Kingdom of the most feasible Method of humbling our rebellious Vassals of North America. As we have declared by our Representatives that we are the supreme Lords of their Persons and Property, and their occupying our Territory at such a remote Distance without a proper Controul from us, except at a very great Expence, encourages a mutinous Disposition, and may, if not timely prevented, dispose them in perhaps less than a Century to deny our Authority, slip their necks out of the Collar, and from being Slaves set up for Masters, more especially when it is considered that they are a robust, hardy People, encourage early Marriages, and their Women being amazingly prolific, they must of consequence in 100 years be very numerous, and of course be able to set us at Defiance. Effectually to prevent which, as we have an undoubted Right to do, it is humbly proposed, and we do hereby give it as Part of our Instructions to our Representatives, that a Bill be brought in and passed, and Orders immediately transmitted to G——l G——e, our Commander in Chief in North America, in consequence of it, that all the Males there be c—st—ed. He may make a Progress thro' the several Towns of North America at the Head of five Battalions, which we hear our experienced Generals, who have been consulted, think sufficient to subdue America if they were in open Rebellion; for who can resist the intrepid Sons of Britain, the Terror of France and Spain, and the Conquerors of America in Germany. Let a Company of Sow-gelders, consisting of 100 Men, accompany the Army, On their Arrival at any Town or Village, let Orders be given that on the blowing of the Horn all the Males be assembled in the Market Place. If the Corps are Men of Skill and Ability in their Profession, they will make great Dispatch, and retard but very little the Progress of the Army. There may be a Clause in the Bill to be left at the Discretion of the General, whose Powers ought to be very extensive, that the most notorious Offenders, such as Hancock, Adams, &c. who have been the Ringleaders in the Rebellion of our Servants, should be shaved quite close. But that none of the Offenders may escape in the Town of Boston, let all the Males there suffer the latter Operation, as it will be conformable to the modern Maxim that is now generally adopted by our worthy Constituents, that it is better that ten innocent Persons should suffer than that one guilty should escape. It is true, Blood will be shed, but probably not many Lives lost. Bleeding to a certain Degree is salutary. The English, whose Humanity is celebrated by all the World, but particularly by themselves, do not desire the Death of the Delinquent, but his Reformation. The Advantages arising from this Scheme being carried into Execution are obvious. In the Course of fifty years it is probable we shall not have one rebellious Subject in North America. This will be laying the Axe to the Root of the Tree. In the mean time a considerable Expence may be saved to the Managers of the Opera, and our Nobility and Gentry be entertained at a cheaper Rate by the fine Voices of our own C—st—i, and the Specie remain in the Kingdom, which now, to an enormous Amount, is carried every Year to Italy. It might likewise be of

Service to our Levant Trade, as we could supply the Grand Signor's Seraglio, and the Harams of the Grandees of the Turkish Dominions with Cargos of Eunuchs, as also with handsome Women, for which America is as famous as Circassia. I could enumerate many other Advantages. I shall mention but one: It would effectually put a Stop to the Emigrations from this Country now grown so very fashionable.

No Doubt you will esteem it expedient that this useful Project shall have an early Insertion, that no Time may be lost in carrying it into Execution.

I am, Mr. Printer,
(For myself and in Behalf of a Number of
independent Freeholders of Great Britain)
Your humble Servant,
A FREEHOLDER OF OLD SARUM

THE FLIES

To Madame He——s

The flies of the apartments of M. F——n request permission to present their respects to Mme. H——s, and to express in their best language their gratitude for the protection that she has kindly wished to give them, Bizz izzzz *ouizz a ouizzzz izzzzzzzz*, etc.

We have lived a long time under the hospitable roof of the said good man F——n. He has given us lodging gratis; we have also eaten and drunk the whole year at his expense without its having cost us anything. Often when his friends have used up a bowl of his punch, he has left a sufficient quantity to intoxicate a hundred of us other flies. We have drunk freely there, and after that we have made our sallies, our circles and our cotillions very prettily in the air of his chamber, and we have gaily consummated our little amours under his [very] nose. Finally, we should have been the most happy people in the world if he had not permitted to remain over the top of his wainscoting a number of our declared enemies, who stretched their tiny web threads in order to capture us, and who would destroy us without pity. People of temperament and subtle and fierce, abominable crowd! You, very excellent lady—had the goodness to order that all these assassins with their habitations and their snares be swept; and your orders (as they always must be) have been immediately executed. Since this time we live happily, and we enjoy the beneficence of the said good man F——n without fear.

There only remains one thing for us to wish in order to assure the permanence of our good fortune; permit us to say it

Bizz izzzz ouizz a ouizzzz izzzzzzz, etc.

Henceforth it is your responsibility to see that [yours and his] be made into a single household.

TO THE ROYAL ACADEMY OF *****

Gentlemen, *I have perused your late mathematical Prize Question, proposed in lieu of one in Natural Philosophy, for the ensuing year, viz.* "Une figure quelconque donnée, on demande d'y inscrire le plus grand nombre de fois possible une autre figure plus-petite quelconque, qui est aussi donnée." [1] *I was glad to find by these following Words,* "l'Académie a jugé que cette découverte, en étendant les bornes de nos connoissances, ne seroit pas sans UTILITÉ," [2] *that you esteem* Utility *an essential Point in your Enquiries, which has not always been the case with all Academies; and I conclude therefore that you have given this Question instead of a philosophical, or as the Learned express it, a physical one, because you could not at the time think of a physical one that promis'd greater* Utility.

Permit me then humbly to propose one of that sort for your consideration, and through you, if you approve it, for the serious Enquiry of learned Physicians, Chemists, &c. of this enlightened Age.

It is universally well known, That in digesting our common Food, there is created or produced in the Bowels of human Creatures, a great Quantity of Wind.

That the permitting this Air to escape and mix with the Atmosphere, is usually offensive to the Company, from the fetid Smell that accompanies it.

That all well-bred People therefore, to avoid giving such Offence, forcibly restrain the Efforts of Nature to discharge that Wind.

That so retain'd contrary to Nature, it not only gives frequently great present Pain, but occasions future Diseases, such as habitual Cholics, Ruptures, Tympanies, &c. often destructive of the Constitution, & sometimes of Life itself.

Were it not for the odiously offensive Smell accompanying such Escapes, polite People would probably be under no more Restraint in discharging such Wind in Company, than they are in spitting, or in blowing their Noses.

My Prize Question therefore should be, To discover some Drug wholesome & not disagreable, to be mix'd with our common Food, or Sauces,

---

[1] [Given any single figure, one is asked to inscribe there the greatest number of times another smaller figure, which is also given. *Trans. R. E. Amacher*]

[2] [The academy has judged that this discovery, by widening the boundaries of our knowledge, will not be without utility. *Trans. R. E. Amacher*]

that shall render the Natural Discharges, of Wind from our Bodies, not only inoffensive, but agreable as Perfumes.

That this is not a chimerical Project, and altogether impossible, may appear from these Considerations. That we already have some Knowledge of Means capable of Varying that Smell. He that dines on stale Flesh, especially with much Addition of Onions, shall be able to afford a Stink that no Company can tolerate; while he that has lived for some Time on Vegetables only, shall have that Breath so pure as to be insensible to the most delicate Noses; and if he can manage so as to avoid the Report, he may any where give Vent to his Griefs, unnoticed. But as there are many to whom an entire Vegetable Diet would be inconvenient, and as a little Quick-Lime thrown into a Jakes will correct the amazing Quantity of fetid Air arising from the vast Mass of putrid Matter contain'd in such Places, and render it rather pleasing to the Smell, who knows but that a little Powder of Lime (or some other thing equivalent) taken in our Food, or perhaps a Glass of Limewater drank at Dinner, may have the same Effect on the Air produc'd in and issuing from our Bowels? This is worth the Experiment. Certain it is also that we have the Power of changing by slight Means the Smell of another Discharge, that of our Water. A few Stems of Asparagus eaten, shall give our Urine a disagreable Odour; and a Pill of Turpentine no bigger than a Pea, shall bestow on it the pleasing Smell of Violets. And why should it be thought more impossible in Nature, to find Means of making a Perfume of our Wind than of our Water?

For the Encouragement of this Enquiry, (from the immortal Honour to be reasonably expected by the Inventor) let it be reasonably considered of how small Importance to Mankind, or to how small a Part of Mankind have been useful those Discoveries in Science that have heretofore made Philosophers famous. Are there twenty Men in Europe at this Day, the happier, or even the easier, for any Knowledge they have pick'd out of Aristotle? What Comfort can the Vortices of Descartes give to a Man who has Whirlwinds in his Bowels! The Knowledge of Newton's mutual Attraction of the Particles of Matter, can it afford Ease to him who is rack'd by their mutual Repulsion, and the cruel Distensions it occasions? The Pleasure arising to a few Philosophers, from seeing, a few Times in their Life, the Threads of Light untwisted, and separated by the New-tonian Prism into seven Colours, can it be compared with the Ease and Comfort every Man living might feel seven times a Day, by discharging freely the Wind from his Bowels? Especially if it be converted into a Perfume: For the Pleasures of one Sense being little inferior to those of another, instead of pleasing the Sight he might delight the Smell of those about him, & make Numbers happy, which to a benevolent Mind must afford infinite Satisfaction. The generous Soul, who now endeavours to find out whether the Friends he entertains like best Claret or Burgundy, Cham-

pagne or Madeira, would then enquire also whether they chose Musk or Lilly, Rose or Bergamot, and provide accordingly. And surely such a Liberty of Ex-pressing *one's* Scent-iments, *and* pleasing one another, *is of infinitely more Importance to human Happiness than that Liberty of the* Press, *or of* abusing one another, *which the English are so ready to fight & die for.—In short, this Invention, if compleated, would be, as* Bacon *expresses it,* bringing Philosophy home to Mens Business and Bosoms. *And I cannot but conclude, that in Comparison therewith, for universal and* continual UTILITY, *the Science of the Philosophers above-mentioned, even with the Addition, Gentlemen, of your* "Figure quelconque" *and the Figures inscrib'd in it, are, all together, scarcely worth a*

FART-HING

Alexander Hamilton (1712–1756)

The *Itinerarium* of Alexander Hamilton is one of the most fascinating works in early eighteenth-century Southern literature. For four months during 1744, the Scottish-born Maryland physician travelled in search of health. His trip took him from his home town of Annapolis, Maryland, along the eastern seaboard as far north as Maine. The journal of his trip is as vivid and racy as the earlier journal of Sarah Kemble Knight (see pp. 51–56) and as humorous too. In many ways, particularly in its character descriptions, ironic tone, and eye for incongruity, Hamilton's *Itinerarium* is as absorbing as the journals of Thoreau and contains many passages which are remarkably similar, even though Hamilton was not published until 1907. The man revealed in the *Itinerarium* was well educated and highly cultured, an amateur in music and drawing, familiar with painting, a student of manners, a reader of Rabelais, Montaigne, Cervantes, Shakespeare, Pope, and Fielding. Like Ebenezer Cooke and William Byrd, Hamilton had a range of interest and knowledge which carried him outside the pale of his own upper class; he also possessed the faculty of being able to pinpoint the good and the bad without prior reference to class status. As a result, Hamilton found cause for amusement and ridicule in a heterogeneous set of situations and individuals. After returning from his trip, Hamilton continued his search for amusement in cosmopolitan Annapolis. Together with a handful of other convivial men, one of whom was the printer of the *Maryland Gazette*—a publication as much a literary periodical as it was a newspaper—Hamilton founded the Tuesday Club "designed for humor, and . . . a sort of farcical Drama of Mock Majesty." Hamilton served as secretary and historian; he wrote a three-volume "serio-comic history" of the club which ran to 1900 pages and covered a ten-year period. A fellow-club member wrote in 1809 that Hamilton had been "a most cheerful facetious companion amongst his friends, whom he never failed to delight with the effusions of his wit, humor, and drollery, in which acquirements he had no equal. . . . Altho' his jokes are occasionally somewhat indelicate, and he frequently chants the pleasure of the bowl [in the Club history], no man exceeded him in temperance and purity of morals."

TEXT: *Gentleman's Progress: The Itinerarium of Dr. Alexander Hamilton, 1744*, ed. Carl Bridenbaugh, Chapel Hill, N.C., 1948.

From *ITINERARIUM*

NUTTING ISLAND

Friday, June 22d. [1744] . . . Early this morning two passengers came on board of the sloop, a man and a woman, both Dutch. The man was named Marcus Van Bummill. He came on board drunk and gave us a surfet of bad English. If any body laughed when he spoke, he was angry, being jealous that they thought him a fool. He had a good deal of the bully and braggadocio in him, but when thwarted or threatened, he seemed faint hearted and cowardly. Understanding that I was a valitudinarian, he began to advise me how to manage my constitution. "You drink and whore too much," said he, "and that makes you thin and sickly. Could you abstain as I have done and drink nothing but water for 6 weeks, and have to do with no women but your own lawfull wife, your belly and cheeks would be like mine, look ye, plump and smooth and round." With that he clapt his hands upon his belly and blowd up his cheeks like a trumpeter. He brought on board with him a runlett of rum, and, taking it into his head that somebody had robed him of a part of it, he went down into the hold and fell a swearing bitterly by *Dunder Sacramentum,* and *Jesu Christus.* I, being upon deck and hearing a strange noise below, looked down and saw him expanding his hands and turning up his eyes as if he had been att prayers. He was for having us all before a magistrate about it, but att last Knockson, the master of the sloop, swore him into good humour again and perswaded him that his rum was all safe. He quoted a deal of scripture, but his favorite topics when upon that subject was about King David, and King Solomon, and the shape and size of the Tower of Babel. He pretended to have been mighty familiar with great folks when they came in his way, and this familiarity of his was so great as even to scorn and contemn them to their faces. After a deal of talk and rattle, he went down and slept for four hours and, when he waked, imagined he had slept a whole day and a night, swearing it was Saturday night when it was only Friday afternoon. There was a Dutch woman on board, remarkably ugly, upon whom this Van Bummill cast a loving eye and wanted much to be att close conference with her.

NEW YORK

Friday, July 6th. . . . I went to the inn to see my horses, and finding them in good plight, Mr. Waghorn desired me to walk into a room where were some Boston gentlemen that would be company for me in my journey there. I agreed to set out with them for Boston upon Monday morning. Their names were Messrs. Laughton and Parker, by employment traders. There was in company an old grave don who, they told me, was both a parson and physitian. Being a graduate, he appeared to be in a mean attire. His wig was remarkably weather beaten, the hairs being all as streight as a rush and of an orange yellow at the extremitys, but that it had been once a fair wig you might know by the appearance of that part which is covered by the hat, for that head wear, I suppose, seldom went off unless att propper times to yield place to his night cap. The uncovered part of his wig had changed its hue by the sun beams and rain alternatly beating upon it. This old philosopher had besides, as part of his wearing aparrell, a pair of old greasy gloves not a whit less ancient than the wig, which lay carefully folded up upon the table before him. And upon his legs were a pair of old leather spatter-dashes, clouted in twenty different places and buttoned up all along the outside of his leg with brass buttons. He was consumedly grave and sparing of his talk, but every now and then a dry joke escaped him.

Att the opposite side of the table sat another piece of antiquity, one Major Spratt, a thin, tall man, very phtisicall and addicted much to a dry cough. His face was adorned and set out with very large carbuncles, and he was more than half seas over in liquor. I understood he professed poetry and often applied himself to rhiming, in which he imagined himself a very good artist. He gave us a specimen of his poetry in an epitaph which he said he had composed upon one Purcell, a neighbour of his, lately dead; asked us if we did not think it excellent and the best of that kind ever we heard. He repeated it ten times over with a ludicrous air and action. "Gentlemen," said he, "pray take notise now, give good attention. It is perhaps the concisest, wittiest, prittiest epigram or epitaph, call it what you will, that you ever heard. Shall I get you pen and ink to write it down? Perhaps you mayn't remember it else. It is highly worth your noting. Pray observe how it runs,—

> Here lyes John Purcell;
> And whether he be in heaven or in hell,
> Never a one of us all can tell."

This poet asked me very kindly how I did and took me by the hand, tho I never had seen him in my life before. He said he liked me for the sake of my name, told me he was himself nearly related to Coll. Hamilton in the Jerseys, son of the late Govr. Hamilton there. Then from one digression to another he told me that the coat he had upon his back was 30 years old. I believed him, for every button was as large as an ordinary turnip, the button holes att least a quarter of a yard long, and the pocket holes just down att the skirts.

After some confused topsy turvy conversation, the landlord sung a bawdy song att which the grave parson-doctor got up, told us that was a language he did not understand, and therefor took his horse and rid away; but in little more than half an hour or three quarters returned again and told us he had forgot his gloves and had rid two miles of his way before he missed them. I was surprized at the old man's care of such a greasy bargain as these gloves. They were fit for nothing but to be wore by itchified persons under a course of sulphur, and I don't know but the doctor had lent them to some of his patients for that purpose, by which means they had imbibed such a quantity of grease. The landlord told me he was a man worth 5000 pounds sterl. and had got it by frugality. I replied that this instance of the gloves was such a demonstration of carefullness that I wondered he was not worth twice as much.

At four a'clock I came to my lodging and drank tea with Mrs. Hog, and Mr. John Watts, a Scots gentleman, came to pay me a visit. Att 5 I went to the coffee house, and there meeting with Mr. Dupeyster, he carried me to the tavern where in a large room was conveen'd a certain club of merry fellows. Among the rest was H——d, the same whom I extolled before for his art in touching the violin, but that indeed seemed to be his principall excellency. Other things he pretended to but fell short. He affected being a witt and dealt much in pointed satyre, but it was such base metall that the edge or point was soon turned when put to the proof. When any body spoke to him, he seemed to give ear in such a careless manner as if he thought all discourse but his own triffling and insignificant. In short he was fit to shine no where but among your good natured men and ignorant blockheads. There was a necessity for the first to bear with the stupidity of his satire and for the others to admire his pseudosophia and quaintness of his speeches and, att the same time, with their blocks, to turn the edge and acuteness of his wit. He dealt much in proverbs and made use of one which I thought pritty significant when well applied. It was *the devil to pay and no pitch hot?* An interrogatory adage metaphorically derived from the manner of sailors who pay their ship's bottoms with pitch. I back'd it with *great cry and little wool, said the devil when he shore his hogs,* applicable enough to the ostentation and clutter he made with his learning.

There was in this company one Dr. McGraa, a pretended Scots-man, but by brogue a Teague. He had an affected way of curtsieing instead of bowing when he entered a room. He put on a modest look uncommon to his nation, spoke little, and when he went to speak, leaned over the table and streeched out his neck and face, goose-like, as if he had been going to whisper you in the ear. When he drank to any in the company, he would not speak but kept bowing and bowing, sometimes for the space of a minute or two, till the person complimented either observed him of his own accord or was hunched into attention by his next neighbour; but it was hard to know who he bowed to upon account of his squinting. However, when the liquor began to heat him a little, he talked at the rate of three words in a minute, and sitting next me (he was very complaisant in his cups), he told me he had heard my name mentioned by some Marylanders and asked me if I knew his unkle Grierson in Maryland. I returned his compliments in as civil a manner as possible, and for half an hour we talked of nothing but waiting upon one another at our lodgings, but after all this complimentary farce and promises of serving and waiting was over, I could not but observe that none of us took the trouble to enquire where the one or the other lodged. I never met with a man so wrapt up in himself as this fellow seemed to be, nor did I ever see a face where there was so much effronterie under a pretended mask of modesty.

There was, besides, another doctor in company named Man, a doctor of a man of war. The best thing I saw about him was that he would drink nothing but water, but he eat lustily at supper, and nothing remarkable appeared in his discourse (which indeed was copious and insipid) but only an affected way he had of swearing by Ged att every two words; and by the motion of his hands at each time of swearing that polite and elegant oath, he would seem to let the company understand that he was no mean orator, and that the little oath was a very fine ornament to his oration.

But the most remarkable person in the whole company was one Wendal, a young gentleman from Boston. He entertained us mightily by playing on the violin the quickest tunes upon the highest keys, which he accompanied with his voice so as even to drown the violin with such nice shakings and gracings that I thought his voice outdid the instrument. I sat for some time imoveable with surprize. The like I never heard, and the thing seemed to me next a miracle. The extent of his voice is impossible to describe or even to imagine unless by hearing him. The whole company were amazed that any person but a woman or eunuch could have such a pipe and began to question his virility; but he swore that if the company pleased he would show a couple of as good witnesses as any man might wear. He then imitated severall beasts, as cats, dogs, horses, and cows, with the cackling of poultry, and all to such perfection that nothing but nature could match it. When the landlord (a clumsy, tallow faced fellow in a white jacket) came to receive his reckoning, our mimick's art struck and surprized him in such a manner that it fixed him quite, like one that had seen the Gorgon's head, and he might have passed for a statue done in white marble. He was so struck that the company might have gone away without paying and carried off all his silver tankards and spoons, and he never would have observed.

After being thus entertained I returned to my lodging att 11 o'clock.

SALEM FERRY—IPSWITCH

Tuesday, July 31. At eleven o'clock this morning Mr. Malcolm accompanied me to Salem Ferry where I crossed and rid a pleasant levell road all the way to Ipswitch, where the houses are so thick planted that it looks like one continued village. I put up at one Howel's in Ipswitch att the Sign of the Armed Knight. I waited upon Mr. John Rogers, the minister there, and delivered him a paquet of letters from his son att Annapolis. I returned again to the tavern and there met a talkative old fellow who was very inquisitive about my place of abode and occupation, as he called it. He frequently accosted me with *please your honour*, with which grand title, like some fools whom I know, I seemed highly pleased tho I was conscious it did not belong to me. When I told him I came from Maryland, he said he had frequently read of that place but never had seen it. This old fellow, by his own account, had read of every thing but had seen nothing. He affected being a schollar, or a man much given to reading or study, and used a great many hard words in discourse, which he generally missapplied.

There was likewise a young man in company who rid with me some miles on my way to Newberry. He valued himself much upon the good-ness of his horse and said that he was a prime beast as ever went upon 4 legs or wore hoofs. He told me he had a curiosity to ride to Maryland but was afraid of the terrible woods in the way and asked me if there were not a great many dangerous wild beasts in these woods. I told him that the most dangerous wild beasts in these woods were shaped exactly like men, and they went by the name of buckskins, or bucks, tho they were not bucks neither but something, as it were, betwixt a man and a beast. "Bless us! You don't say so," says he; "then surely you had needs ride with guns" (meaning my pistols). I parted with this wiseacre when I had got about half way to Newburry.

A little farther I met a fat sheep driving in a chaise, a negroe sitting upon the box. I asked the negroe if that was his master. He told me no, but that it was a weather belonging to Mr. Jones, who had strayed and would not come home without being carried. Passing by this prodigy I met another, which was two great fat women riding upon one horse.

NEWBURRY

I arrived att Newburry att seven o'clock and put up att one Choat's att the Sign of the Crown, which is a good house. Newburry is a pritty large village lying close upon the water. The houses are chiefly wood. In this town there is one handsom meeting built in a square form with a spire or steeple upon which is a little neat publick clock.

NEWBURRY FERRY—HAMPTON

Wednesday, August 1. This morning proved very rainy, and therefor I did not set out till eleven o'clock. I crossed Newburry Ferry, and rid a pleasant even road, only somewhat stonny, and in a perpetual drizzle so that I could not have an advantageous view of the country round me. Att half an hour after one I passed thro Hampton, a very long, scattered town.

Having proceeded some miles farther I was overtaken by a man who bore me company all the way to Portsmouth. He was very inquisitive about where I was going, whence I came, and who I was. His questions were all stated in the rustick civil stile. "Pray sir, if I may be so bold, where are you going?" "Prithee, friend," says I, "where are you going?" "Why, I go along the road here a little way." "So do I, friend," replied I. "But may I presume, sir, whence do you come?" "And from whence do you come, friend?" says I. "Pardon me, from John Singleton's farm," replied he, "with a bag of oats." "And I come from Maryland," said I, "with a portmanteau and baggage." "Maryland!" said my companion, "where the devil is that there place? I have never heard of it. But pray, sir, may I be so free as to ask your name?" "And may I be so bold as to ask yours, friend?" said I. "Mine is Jerry Jacobs, att your service," replied he. I told him that mine was Bombast Huynhym van Helmont, att his service. "A strange name indeed; belike your a Dutchman, sir,—a captain of a ship, belike." "No, friend," says I, "I am a High German alchymist." "Bless us! You don't say so; that's a trade I never heard of; what may you deal in sir?" "I sell air," said I. "Air," said he, "damn it, a strange commodity. I'd thank you for some wholesom air to cure my fevers which have held me these two months." I have noted down this dialogue as a specimen of many of the same tenour I had in my journey when I met with these inquisitive rusticks.

BOSTON

[August 4.] I left my horses att Barker's stables and drank tea with my landlady, Mrs. Guneau. There was in the company a pritty young lady. The character of a certain Church of England clergiman in Boston was canvassed, he having lost his living for being too sweet upon his landlady's daughter, a great belly being the consequence. I pitied him only for his imprudence and want of policy. As for the crime, considdered in a certain light it is but a peccadillo, and he might have escaped unobserved had he had the same cunning as some others of his bretheren who doubtless are as deep in the dirt as he in the mire. I shall not mention the unfortunate man's name (absit foeda calumnia), but I much commiserated his calamity and regretted the loss, for he was an excellent preacher; but the wisest men have been led into silly scrapes by the attractions of that vain sex, which, I think, explains a certain enigmatic verse.

Diceti grammatici, cur mascula nomina cunnus
Et cur Famineum mentula nomen habet *

The first is masculine, because it attracts the male, the latter feminine, because it is an effeminate follower of the other.

* ["Grammarians, tell us why 'cunnus' has masculine names/And why 'mentula' has a feminine name?" The point of these Latin lines is that "cunnus" (female genitals) is grammatically in the masculine gender whereas "mentula" (male genitals) is in the feminine. I am grateful to my colleagues, Professors Robert F. Spencer and Roy A. Swanson, for advice on the translation.]

I had the opportunity this night of seeing Mons. la Moinnerie, my fellow lodger. He was obliged to keep the house close for fear of being made a prisoner of war. He was the strangest mortal for eating ever I knew. He would not eat with the family but always in his own chamber, and he made a table of his trunk. He was always a chawing except some little intervalls of time in which he applied to the study of the English language.

Sunday, August 5. I went this morning into Monsieur's chamber and asked him how he did. He made answer in French but asked me in maimd English if I had made un bon voyage, what news, and many other little questions culled out of his grammar. I was shy of letting him know I understood French, being loath to speak that language as knowing my faultiness in the pronounciation. He told me that hier a soir he had de mos' excellen' soupé and wished I had been to eat along with him. His chamber was strangely set out: here a bason with the relicts of some soup, there a fragment of bread, here a paper of salt, there a bundle of garlick, here a spoon with some pepper in it, and upon a chair a saucer of butter. The same individual bason served him to eat his soup out of and to shave in, and in the water, where a little before he had washed his hands and face, he washed likewise his cabbages. This, too, served him for a punchbowl. He was fond of giving directions how to dress his vittles and told Nanny, the cook maid, "Ma foy, I be de good cock, Madame Nannie," said he. The maid put on an air of modest anger and said she did not understand him. "Why, here you see," says he, "my cock be good, can dress de fine viandes."

This morning I went and heard Mr. Hooper and dined with Mr. Grey. I went to meeting again in the afternoon. He (Mr. Hooper) is one of the best preachers I have heard in America, his discourse being sollid sense, strong connected reasoning, and good language. I drank tea with Mrs. Guneau in the afternoon and staid at home this night reading a little of Homer's first Iliad.

Samuel A. Peters (1735–1826)

The Reverend Samuel A. Peters, a loyalist sympathizer, has had an anomalous reputation in New England ever since American revolutionary patriots drove him out of Connecticut in 1774 and he soon retaliated by publishing his *General History of Connecticut* (London, 1781). A descendant of Puritans and educated for the Puritan ministry at Yale, he had been converted to Anglicanism and had served as rector at Hebron, Connecticut, from 1760 until his flight to London. Peters avenged himself upon his unfriendly Connecticut neighbors by ridiculing them mercilessly in his book, mixing legendry and humor with historical fact. He impatiently dismissed earlier New England historians for having "suppressed what are called in New England *unnecessary truths*" and sought to unveil the "sinister views and purposes" of "Connectitensians" by exposing "their deficiency in point of right to the soil they occupied, their wanton and barbarous persecutions, illegal practices, daring usurpations, etc." His imaginative historical method and its humorous effects have been the subject of many books and articles which have angrily or amusedly commented upon such passages as the one dealing with the event of the Windham frogs, which actually occurred in 1754 rather than in 1758. Peters made a special point of ridiculing the inconsistencies of Puritan morality, attacking the so-called Blue Laws, and dealing ironically with the phenomenon of bundling. He returned to the United States in 1805 and during his last years was involved in controversies over land titles and speculation in the territory which later became Minnesota.

TEXT: *A General History of Connecticut*, New Haven, Conn., 1829.

THE HEROIC PEOPLE OF WINDHAM

Windham, the second county in the ancient kingdom of Sassacus, or colony of Saybrook, is hilly; but, the soil being rich, has excellent butter, cheese, hemp, wheat, Indian corn, and horses. Its towns are twelve.

Windham resembles Rumford, and stands on Winnomantic river. Its meeting-house is elegant, and has a steeple, bell, and clock. Its court-house is scarcely to be looked upon as an ornament. The township forms four parishes, and is ten miles square.

Strangers are very much terrified at the hideous noise made on summer evenings by the vast number of frogs in the brooks and ponds. There are about thirty different voices among them; some of which resemble the bellowing of a bull. The owls and whippoorwills complete the rough concert, which may be heard several miles. Persons accustomed to such serenades are not disturbed by them at their proper stations; but one night, in July, 1758, the frogs of an artificial pond, three miles square, and about five from Windham, finding the water dried up, left the place in a body, and marched, or rather hopped, towards Winnomantic river. They were under the necessity of taking the road and going through the town, which they entered about midnight. The bull frogs were the leaders, and the pipers followed without number. They filled a road 40 yards wide for four miles in length, and were for several hours in passing through the town, unusually clamorous. The inhabitants were equally perplexed and frightened: some expected to find an army of French and Indians; others feared an earthquake, and dissolution of nature. The consternation was universal. Old and young, male and female, fled naked from their beds with worse shriekings than those of the frogs. The event was fatal to several women. The men, after a flight of half a mile, in which they met with many broken shins, finding no enemies in pursuit of them, made a halt, and summoned resolution enough to venture back to their wives and children; when they distinctly heard from the enemy's camp these words, *Wight, Hilderken, Dier, Tete*. This last they thought meant *treaty*; and plucking up courage, they sent a triumvirate to capitulate with the supposed French and Indians. These three men approached in their shirts, and begged to speak with the General; but it being dark, and no answer given, they were sorely agitated for some time betwixt hope and fear; at length, however, they discovered that the dreaded inimical army was an army of thirsty frogs, going to the river for a little water.

Such an incursion was never known before nor since; and yet the people of Windham have been ridiculed for their timidity on this occasion. I verily believe an army under the Duke of Marlborough, would, under like circumstances, have acted no better than they did.

THE VIRTUE OF BUNDLING

The women of Connecticut are strictly virtuous, and to be compared to the prude rather than the European polite lady. They are not permitted to read plays; cannot converse about whist, quadrille, or operas; but will freely talk upon the subjects of history, geography, and the mathematics. They are great casuists, and polemical divines; and I have known not a few of them so well skilled in Greek and Latin, as often to put to the blush learned gentlemen.

Notwithstanding the modesty of the females is such, that it would be accounted the greatest rudeness for a gentleman to speak before a lady of a garter, knee, or leg, yet it is thought but a piece of civility to ask her to *bundle;* a custom as old as the first settlement in 1634. It is certainly innocent, virtuous, and prudent; or the puritans would not have permitted it to prevail among their offspring, for whom in general they would suffer crucifixion. Children brought up with the chastest ideas, with so much religion, as to believe that the omniscient God sees them in the dark, and that angels guard them when absent from their parents, will not, nay, cannot, act a wicked thing. People who are influenced more by lust, than a serious faith in God, who is too pure to behold iniquity with approbation, ought never to *bundle.* If any man, thus a stranger to the love of virtue, of God, and the christian religion, should *bundle* with a young lady in New-England, and behave himself unseemly towards her, he must first melt her into passion, and expel heaven, death, and hell, from her mind, or he will undergo the chastisement of negroes turned mad—if he escape with life, it will be owing to the parents flying from their bed to protect him. The Indians, who had this method of courtship, when the English arrived among them in 1634, are the most chaste set of people in the world. Concubinage and fornication are vices, none of them are addicted to, except such as forsake the laws of Hobbamockow and turn christians. The savages have taken many female prisoners, carried them back three hundred miles into their country, and kept them several years, and yet not a single instance of their violating the laws of chastity has ever been known. This cannot be said of the French, or of the English, whenever Indian or other women have fallen into their hands. I am no advocate for temptation; yet must say, that *bundling* has prevailed 160 years in New-England, and, I verily believe, with ten times more chastity than the sitting on a sofa. I had daughters, and speak from near forty years' experience. *Bundling* takes place only in cold seasons of the year—the sofa in summer is more dangerous than the bed in winter. About the year 1756, Boston, Salem, Newport, and New-York, resolving to be more polite than their ancestors, forbade their daughters *bundling* on the bed with any young men whatever, and introduced a sofa to render courtship more palatable and Turkish. Whatever it was owing to, whether to the sofa, or any uncommon excess of the *feu d'esprit,* there went abroad a report, that this *raffinage* produced more *natural consequences* than all the *bundling* among the boors with their *rurales pedantes,* through every village in New-England besides.

In 1776, a clergyman from one of the polite towns, went into the country, and preached against the unchristian custom of young men and maidens lying together on a bed. He was no sooner out of the church, than attacked by a shoal of good old women, with "Sir, do you think we and our daughters are naughty, because we allow of *bundling?*" "You lead yourselves into temptation by it." They all replied at once, "Sir, have you been told thus, or has experience taught it you?" The Levite began to lift up his eyes, and to consider of his situation, and bowing, said "I have been told so." The ladies *una voce*, bawled out, "Your informants, Sir, we conclude, are those city ladies who prefer a sofa to a bed: we advise you to alter your sermon, by substituting the word *sofa* for *bundling*, and on your return home, preach it to them: for experience has told us that city folks send more children into the country without fathers or mothers to own them, than are born among us; therefore, you see, a sofa is more dangerous than a bed." The poor priest, seemingly convinced of his blunder, exclaimed, "*Nec vitia nostra, nec remedia pati possumus,*" hoping hereby to get rid of his guests: but an old matron pulled off her spectacles, and, looking the priest in the face like a Roman heroine, said, "*Noli putare me hæc auribus tuis dare.*" Others cried out to the priest to explain his Latin. "The English," said he, "is this: Wo is me that I sojourn in Meseck, and dwell in the tents of Kedar!" One pertly retorted, *Gladii decussati sun gemina presbyteri clavis.* The priest confessed his error, begged pardon, and promised never more to preach against bundling, or to think amiss of the custom; the ladies generously forgave him, and went away.

It may seem very strange to find this custom of bundling in bed attended with so much innocence in New-England, while in Europe it is thought not safe or scarcely decent to permit a young man and maid to be together in private any where. But in this quarter of the old world the viciousness of the one, and the simplicity of the other, are the result merely of education and habit. It seems to be a part of heroism, among the polished nations of it, to sacrifice the virtuous fair-one, whenever an opportunity offers, and thence it is concluded that the same principles actuate those of the new world. It is egregiously absurd to judge of all countries by one. In Spain, Portugal, and Italy, jealousy reigns; in France, England, and Holland, suspicion; in the West and East Indies, lust; in New-England, superstition. These four blind deities govern Jews, Turks, Christians, Infidels, and Heathen. Superstition is the most amiable. She sees no vice with approbation but persecution, and self-preservation is the cause of her seeing that. My insular readers will, I hope, believe me, when I tell them, that I have seen, in the West Indies, naked boys and girls, some fifteen or sixteen years of age, waiting at table and at tea, even when twenty or thirty virtuous English ladies were in the room; who were under no more embarrassment at such an awful sight in the eyes of English people that have not travelled abroad, than they would have been at the sight of so many servants in livery. Shall we censure the ladies of the West Indies as vicious above all their sex, on account of this local custom? By no means; for long experience has taught the world that the West Indian white ladies are virtuous prudes. Where superstition reigns, fanaticism will be minister of state; and the people, under the taxation of zeal, will shun what is commonly called vice with ten times more care than the polite and civilized christians, who know what is right and what is wrong from reason and revelation. Happy would it be for the world, if reason and revelation were suffered to control the mind and passions of the great and wise men of the earth, as superstition does that of the simple and less polished! When America shall erect societies for the promotion of chastity in Europe, in return for the establishment of European arts in the American capitals, then Europe will discover that there is more christian philosophy in American bundling than can be found in the customs of nations more polite.

I should not have said so much about bundling, had not a learned Divine * of the English church published his Travels through some parts of America, wherein this remarkable custom is represented in an unfavorable light, and as prevailing among the *lower class* of people. The truth is, the custom prevails among all classes, to the great honor of the country, its religion, and ladies. The virtuous may be tempted; but the tempter is despised. Why it should be thought incredible for a young man and a young woman innocently and virtuously to lie down together in a bed with a great part of their clothes on, I cannot conceive. Human passions may be alike in every region; but religion, diversified as it is, operates differently in different countries. Upon the whole, had I daughters now, I would venture to let them *bundle* on the bed, or even on the sofa, after a proper education, sooner than adopt the Spanish mode of forcing young people to prattle only before the lady's mother the chitchat of artless lovers. Could the four quarters of the world produce a more chaste, exemplary, and beautiful company of wives and daughters than are in Connecticut, I should not have remaining one favorable sentiment for the province. But the soil, the rivers, the ponds, the ten thousand landscapes, together with the virtuous and lovely women which now adorn the ancient kingdoms of Connecticote, Sassacus, and Quinnipiog, would tempt me into the highest wonder and admiration of them, could they once be freed of the skunk, the moping-owl, rattle-snake, and fanatic christian.

* Dr. Burnaby.

Hugh Henry Brackenridge (1748–1816)

Hugh Henry Brackenridge was a jurist on the western Pennsylvania frontier whose taste for satire had been developed at Princeton University and sharpened by political disappointment. Imbued with the neoclassical principles of the eighteenth-century Enlightenment, he vainly sought for balance between Federalists and Jeffersonians, between the Pennsylvania frontiersmen who militantly revolted against whiskey taxes and the national government which sent troops to arrest the rebels for treason. Temperamentally, too, Brackenridge admitted, he was "inclined to an ironical, ludicrous way of thinking and writing" which encouraged him to "make a business of laughing at the follies of others." This, he recognized, "is injurious to one's self; for there is a great deal more to be gained by soothing and praising what men do, than by finding fault with them. It may be said of satire, what was said of anger by some philosopher, It never pays the service it requires. It is your scratching, rump-tickling people, that get into place and power. I never knew any good come of wit and humour yet. They are talents which keep the owner poor."

Brackenridge's political career was a short one. Thereafter he served on the bench and worked on *Modern Chivalry*, a sprawling picaresque novel which appeared in installments from 1792 to 1815. *Modern Chivalry*, despite its loose structure and Brackenridge's authorial intrusions, is unified by its two central characters and consistent ironic humor. Captain Farrago's chief occupation is the extrication of his lower-class servant, the Irish rogue Teague, from a variety of ludicrous situations which provide the Captain with an opportunity to deliver wise, satiric observations on the condition of American life. An admirer of such humorists as Cervantes, Rabelais, Swift, Fielding, Smollett, and Sterne, Brackenridge deliberately sought to lighten his satire, frequently making fun of himself but sometimes unable to resist being doubly ironic: "I have been affecting to speak sense, whereas my business is to speak nonsense; this being the only way to keep out of the reach of criticism; because critics can say no more than you yourself allow; so that a charge of nonsense cannot hurt. It is thus that persons who have a long nose, or disproportion of some other feature, take the laugh upon themselves first, and so escape ridicule. The truth is, I will not give myself the trouble to write sense long. For I would as soon please fools as wise men; because the fools are the most numerous, and every prudent man will go with the majority."

TEXT: *Modern Chivalry . . . Part II*, Carlisle, Pa., 1804; *Modern Chivalry*, Philadelphia, Pa., 1815, I. COMMENTARY: Claude M. Newlin, *The Life and Writings of Hugh Henry Brackenridge*, Princeton, N.J., 1932.

THE BLACKGUARD PRESS

CHAPTER I

Hiatus valde deflendus, multa desiderantur

Here is a great gap. Not a word said about the travels of the Captain, from the packing up of Teague, and sending him off to France, until after the termination of the French revolution, and the armistice or convention of Amiens. Though the fact is, that he had been, all this time, travelling, and Teague had rejoined him, in the capacity of pediseque, or foot-boy, as before. As to Duncan the Scotch waiter, he had, long since, left the service, and taken a job of weaving in the neighbourhood, and was doing well. The Captain had endeavoured to persuade him to take to preaching, as many do in this country who are less qualified, but he refused, alledging, that though it was good work that pleased the customer, yet he had some scruples of conscience in undertaking the charge, not having been regularly called by ordination to the office.

Teague had been landed at Nantz, and being a real sans culotte, was liberated, as we have said, and caressed by the multitude. With considerable eclat, he made his way to Paris. We hear of him at a very early period as made use of, by Anacharsis Cloots, the orator of the human race; This was in a procession of that uncommon man, in which representatives of all nations, were introduced in their respective garbs, addressing the Convention to bring liberty and equality amongst them. Teague was in the character of an Esquimaux Indian, and passed his aboriginal Irish, for the native dialect of that people. An Irish officer or two that were present discovered the imposition, but the gillotine forbad them to speak, and they were silent.

This ultramarine person, as he was called, for they had ultramontain men enough among themselves, was a good deal distinguished during the reign of Robespierre, and was employed on many occasions, and discharged a variety of functions, so that though his morals were not much mended, nor his address much improved, sans culotism still continuing the order of the day, yet he had contracted French phrases, and could interlard his Hibernian dialect with a que voulez vous; and je demand pardon. At length however, he found himself in the conciergerie, a destination from which no talents, virtues, or even vices could exempt any man; and it was only on the fall of that monster of whom we have just made mention, that he was vomited with others from the caverns in which he had been included. How he ever got to America again it is difficult to say. We shall leave that to those who may take from his own mouth the memoirs of his travels. It is sufficient for our purpose, that he did get back, and that he is once more in the train of the Captain. The fact is, that he had joined him in a most unexpected manner, in a short time after Duncan the Scotch servant had begged to be dismissed, and applyed himself to a profession more congenial with his education.

We shall go no farther back upon the steps of the Captain, with the bog-trotter at his heels, than where we find them within a mile, or less of the village where his home was, and where he had resided some years, before he had set out on his peregrinations. Passing through a wood just as he approached the town, he saw at some distance before him the semblance of men suspended on the limbs of trees, or at least the exuviae of men, coats, waist-coats, breeches, and hats. What can this be, said the Captain? It is probable that hearing of your return, Teague, the wags of the village have been making what are called Padies, and have set them up on these trees, knowing that this way we should come along. By St. Patrick, said Teague, but I will Pady dem wid dis shalelah. I will tache dem to make Padies, and hang dem up for sign posts in de wood here. Dis is not St. Patrick's day in de morning neider: Bad luck to dem, it may be some poor fellows dat dey have hanged up in reality, for shape-stealing as dey do in Ireland.

I see nothing, said the Captain, drawing nearer, but the emptyings of ward-robes, jibbeted on these trees, through the grove: stretched on limbs, or suspended from them, a phenomenon, which I am unable to comprehend, or explain; For I see no corn growing underneath, or near about, from which, a priapus, or scare-crow might affright the birds; nor can they be the vestments of people at work, near hand, or stripped to bathe, as I see no water pond, or river, but a dry grove.

The fact is, these habiliments were of the people of the town, who had hung them up to take the dew, in order to take off the musk of a pole-cat which had affected them from the perfusions of one of these animals. The story is as follows.

Not long before this, a typographist had set up a paper in the village and having reference to the sharpness of his writing, the editor had chosen to assume the symbol, or hieroglyphic of the Porcupine, and in allusion to his quills called himself Peter Porcupine; whimsically Peter, because Peter, and Porcupine, begin with the same letter, and produces what is called an alliteration. Such respondence has been thought a beauty, in some languages, and at some periods. In the English language, it was a constitutent of poetry a few centuries ago; and though now disused, yet is retained in appellations, where fiction is at liberty, and quaintness and humour is intended. Nor was the device or synonime of Porcupine, ill chosen. For the editor could dart his quills to some purpose. To drop the figure, a happy nature had fited him for a satyrist, and felicity of education was not wanting to qualify him for the office. He had not the pleas-antry of Horace, nor the pungency of Juvenal, but an original stricture of his own that supplied the place of them. The truth is he had been bred in the barracks, and had at his finger ends, the familiar phrases of the common soldiery, with that peculiar species of wit, which is common with that occupation of men, and in that grade. Doubtless we see some-thing like it among the plebeians of all classes and denominations; The women that sell fish at a certain stand in London, have a species of it, known by the name of Billingsgate, either because there is a gate of that name near the place, or formerly was one. The miners and coal heavers have a good deal of it. The scavengers and chimney sweepers are adepts, though without the least scholastic education, or knowledge of letters whatsoever. I have known even in our own country, where we are remote from the seats of the muses, a good deal of it possessed, by way travellers, or boat men on our rivers. It is a kind of unshackled dialect; fettered by no rule of delicacy, or feeling of humanity. I have been turning in my mind what word in our English language, best expresses it, and I have found it to be that which has been given it by Thomas Paine, *black-guardism*. The editor of the Porcupine had scored the village not a little. I do not say rubbed. For that is a translation of the phrase of Horace: *urbem defricuit*; and conveys the idea of tickling, and causing a sensation in part pleasant, yet hurting a little. That was not the case here. For what man without indignation and bitter resentment, can bear the touch of the slanderer, more especially if that slander is of a private, and domestic nature and alludes to what cannot be explained or defended. Not that it is true, but a man in the just pride of standing in society, would scorn to appeal to the public or bring it before a court!

There was in the village a man of understanding, and sensibility who had been the subject of caricature by Peter, and not chusing for reasons that weighed with himself, to take it in good part, thought of retaliation. But what could he do? The same language was unbecoming a gentleman. The like strictures of foibles or of faults on the part of an adversary, could only become the character of a subordinate. Nor was it so much his ob-ject to repress the licentiousness of this buffoon as to correct the taste and judgment of the public who did not all at once distinguish the im-propriety of countenancing such ribaldry. This they continued to do by receiving his papers.

With a view to this having taken a pole-cat on the mountains, he had put it in a cage and hiring an office contiguous to that of Porcupine, he kept it, suffering the boys of the village to provoke it, and the dogs to bark at it through the bars. The consequence was, that Peter himself, and not unfrequently the female part of his family passing and repassing, were besprinkled with the effluvia and offended with the odour of the animal. The effusions were excited by the irritations of others; but friend and foe were indiscriminately the object of the vapour when they came in the way of its ascension. It was in vain to complain; the owner called himself Paul Pole-cat, and when Peter expostulated and justified his gall on the *freedom of the Press*, Paul fortified himself on the liberty of the *Express*.

But it was not Peter alone, nor his unoffending wife and family that had reason to complain of this nuisance. The children running home to their parents, and the dogs with them brought the perfume to the houses of the village. The wearing apparel of almost every one was affected with the musk; the women buried their dresses; the men in some instances did so, and in others, hung them up to the action of the air, and the dews of the adjoining wood.

The vestiges of these were the phenomena, which the Captain saw, in his approach to the town.

He had now got within sight of the main square, when a tumultuous assembly struck his eye; some with fists raised; others with sticks, and all in a menacing attitude. He could also hear tongues of people altercating with one another and using opprobrious epithets.

The fact was that the village had become divided. Those who had been the subjects of the obloquy of Porcupine, justified the emission of the cats, and were of opinion that the one had as good a right to be borne as the other. Counsel had been taken and learned opinions given. But this making the matter no better, the dissention had increased, and the people had come together in a rage.

Teague at a distance seeing this, stop'd short; said he, what means all this paple in de street? It is as bad as dat of St. Anthony in Paris, or de place de greve where dey have de gillotine. The devil burn me if I go farther, 'till your honour goes on and see what is de matter.

The Captain advancing to the populace was recognized by them, and his appearance contributed not a little to a longer suspension of hostilities.

Countrymen and fellow-citizens, said he, is this the satisfaction that I have, in returning amongst you after an absence of several years, to see man armed against man, and war waged not only in the very bosom of the republic, but in the village which I have instructed by many precepts? What can be the madness that possesses you? are not the evils of life sufficient? but you must increase them by the positive acts of your own violence. You cannot wholly preserve yourselves at all times free from the maladies of the body, or the distresses of the mind. But it is in your power greatly to assuage these, by the virtues of temperance and moderation. What fury can prompt you, to this degree of apparent resentment, and approaching tumult? Is it local or general politics? Is it any disagreement with regard to your corporate interests, or is religion the cause? Has any flagrant instance of moral turpitude, or exceeding knavery in an individual, roused you to this excess of violence, and exclamation?

Captain, said a middle aged man stepping forward, companion of his years, and who had long lived with him in the village; it is not only pleasing to see you return in apparent, good health, but more especially, at this particular moment when your interference cannot but be of the greatest use, to the citizens; not only on account of that confidence which they have in your judgment and discretion, of which they have a lively recollection; but as they must naturally think that your opportunities from travelling must have given you knowledge, and brought you home full fraught with learning and information. Your humanity is also, well remembered by them, that man, woman or child was never injured by you, in life, estate, or reputation; that on the contrary, it was always your study to do good, and compose differences. Now a misfortune has happened to the village; if I can call it a misfortune, which was at first thought a good; a printer came to this place and set up a paper, or gazette, by taking subscriptions from those that were willing to give them. His device was the Porcupine; and his motto, I forget what. Scarcely a month had gone over his head before he began to lampoon; searching into the secrets of families, and publishing matters of individuals, with which, whether true or false, the public had nothing to do; ridiculing virtue as if it was vice; and this in so low and disorderly a manner, that the more intelligent have disapproved of it; but the bulk read, and it seems to increase rather than curtail his subscribers. A young man on the other hand has come to us since you went away, and has had an academic education, had given his opinion pretty freely in companies, that this Porcupine was not a gentleman, which drew upon himself the paragraphs of Porcupine, which he has resented in a manner, that has wrought much disturbance. Meaning to burlesque his manner of writing, having gone to the mountain with a dog, or a trap, or both, and having taken a pole-cat, he puts the beast in a cage; hires that frame building that you see, one story high, and but a room on a floor, and calls it his office. Here he places the pole-cat with a man to attend it. What a running of boys; what a barking of dogs we have had! and when the children run home, and the dogs after them; what a putting of the hand upon the nose, by the servant girls and the mistresses, at the smell that accompanies. The young man justifies himself under the pretence that it is but retaliation to the worse than animal odor that proceeds from the press of Porcupine; for, as this affects the organ of smelling, that disgusts the judgment of the mind. The people are divided, as will always be the case, if for no other cause, yet for the sake of division; because the pride of one man forbids him to think just as another does. But in this case, the cause is serious and solid, for the olfactory organ is offended by Paul, but the heart itself is wounded by Peter. The adversaries of the oppossum, or what else it is, insist that it shall be put down as a nuisance, and have met with clubs, staves and knives, to carry the threat into execution. The advocates of the animal on the other hand have convened to oppose them.

But said the Captain, did I not leave you a regular corporation? Have you not power to make bye laws? and is not this done upon notice given by the chief or Assistant Burgesses? Why such hurry scurry as this? Moreover it is a weighty question that agitates the public mind; a question of right; and where the rights of the citizen come in question, I hold it a most delicate thing to decide; in a free government, more especially, where the essence of liberty is the preservation of right; and there are three rights, the right of conscience, the right of property and the right of reputation. This is a right of property; for if this animal which is ferae naturae, has been reclaimed by the owner, he has a right to put it to such use as suits his trade, or accords with his whim, provided that it does not affect the rights of others. The limit, boundary, or demarcation of this use, is a question of wise discussion and examination; and not in a tumultuous assembly, heated not with wine, but with the ardency of their own spirits. I advise therefore, and so far as my weak judgment deserves to be regarded would recommend, that each man lay down his shalelah, baton, or walking-stick, and retire for the evening; and convene to-morrow in a regular town meeting, where the adversaries and advocates on both sides may have an opportunity of being heard. You have lawyers also amongst you, who on such an occasion owe their services to the public without fee or reward; for as when the matter respects the digging a trench, or building a bridge, the mechanics speak, and ask no peculiar douceur, or perquisite; so on this occasion, the gentlemen of the long robe will not be wanting to develope a case that involves in it a nice question of law and municipal regulation. To-morrow when ye meet with the chief Burgess regularly in the chair, to keep order, and preserve decorum assign the proper times of speaking, and call to order on a deviation from the subject, as is usual in deliberative assemblies, the business can be taken up and conducted as is proper in town meetings. Besides I am just from my journey; somewhat fatigued; but more moved by the consideration that I am on horse-back, and it is not becoming that I take part in your debates as if my horse were to speak also; for though it is true that some of you may speak with perhaps as little sense as he could, were he to open his mouth and attempt utterance; yet the decency of the thing forbids, and even the exercise of the right might be questioned; for the faculty might exist, yet he could not be considered as legitimately franchised to this privilege, at least not having a right to vote in town meetings. For though in the Congress of the United States, the representatives of the territories, not yet organized into independent states, and made regular and complete members of the Union, have a right to speak, but not to vote, this is not to be drawn into precedent in subordinate corporations; for that is a special provision of the constitution within which as a groove, the states move. And it is even indecorous for myself to sit here and speak, mounted, as occupying a more elevated station; and should I descend from my cavalry, my servant whom you see yonder, is kept at bay, by an apprehension of your swords, and refuses to come up, so that I am without an attendant to hold the beast; all things considered therefore, I move, if you will excuse the expression, a chairman not yet being appointed, who might put the question, that you adjourn, or dissolve until to-morrow about this time, when the matter may be taken up as we now have it, and the affair canvassed as becomes members of the same community, and inhabitants of the same village.

It cannot be difficult to conceive that these words had a favourable effect upon the audience; as oils compose a storm. For as the waves of the ocean rise and fall suddenly, so the passions of men; and in no instance more than where they are just coming to blows; for approaching anger disposes to peace, every one having felt half a blow already on his head; and the difficulty only is to get an excuse, for returning, or sheathing the weapon. They are much obliged to a man that councils concord; and advises the putting down the brick-bat, or putting on the coat. Even in dueling it holds the same, and the principal is a friend to the second ever after, that manages the matter so wisely that no blood is shed.

It was moved and seconded before the people should retire; for the mob had insensibly begun to assume the form of a regular assembly, it was moved that in the mean time, the keeper, or as he called himself the editor of the pole-cat, should keep his charge within the claustrum, or bars of his cage, and covered with a matting, so that access might not be had to him, by man or beast, or egress on his part, of that offensive odour, which had been the cause of the disturbance. This, the partizans of the skunk, were willing to admit and sanction with their acquiescence, on condition, nevertheless, that the Porcupine in the mean time, should also restrain his quills; in other words, suspend the effusions of his press, and cease to distribute papers for a day or two while the matter was depending. This was thought reasonable, and carried by the multitude holding up their hands.

CHAPTER II

Containing Proceedings of the Town Meeting

The day following, a meeting being held, and the Chief Burgess in the chair, an advocate of Porcupine took the ground and spoke.

Gentlemen, said he, the press is the palladium of liberty. "The image that fell down from Jupiter." The freedom of the press is essential to liberty. Shackle the press, and you restrain freedom. The constitutions of the states have provided that the press shall be free. If you muzzle this, you may as well muzzle the mouth of man.

It is not the freedom of the press, said one interrupting him, it is the abuse of it that is in question.

The chief burgess called to order, and the speaker went on.

That is the point, said he, to which I meant to come. What shall be said to be the abuse of the press? In order to determine this, we must consider its use. This is,

1. The amusement of the editor. For as some men amuse themselves, shooting, fishing, or chacing with the hound, wild beasts, so men of literary taste, find their recreation in penning paragraphs for a paper, sometimes containing information, or observations on the state of empires, and the characters of great men; at other times by descending, or not rising at all, but confining themselves to the subordinate, affairs of individuals, and private persons.

2. The profit of the editor: and this depends on the number of subscribers. It is not every one that has a taste for refined writing. An editor must be "all things to all men, that he may gain some." Guts and garbage delight bears; and swine swill the trough in preference to the running stream. Black-guardism is the gout of many. Nay it is the more prevailing taste;

> "The world is naturally averse
> To all the truth it sees or hears;
> But swallows nonsense and a lie,
> With greediness and gluttony."

In Britain, or some other countries, delicacy may succeed. But the coarse stomachs of the Americans crave rather indelicacy and indecency, at least a portion of it. Rough like their own woods, and wild beasts, they digest scurrility.

Well done Porcupine, said the pole-cat man, taking the ground in his turn: well said. But this furnishes a ground to justify the introduction of the pole-cat. You talk of the freedom of the press. Here is the freedom of the express. Nay the word *expression* which is common to both institutions, the artificial one of the types, and the natural one of the cat, shews the original to be similar, and the comparison *to run on all-fours.* If the ink cast into black letter, and carrying with it pain and pungency from the ideas communicated, is tolerated; much more the volatile alkali of the animal that is now set up, is to be born, as not more offensive to body or mind. Shall the bark of trees made into powder, and this powder into a liquid, impregnated with thought, and put upon paper, and carried to the press, be accounted harmless, notwithstanding the violence of the decoction, yet the wild cats that inhabit those trees, and are denizens of the forest, be prohibited the haunts of men, because of a bag under their tails which contains an unsavoury distillation, and may be occasionally spurted upon men?

A lawyer took him up on the part of Porcupine. The principles of the common law embrace this case. It is unlawful to exercise trades in towns that occasion noisome smells; they are abateable as nuisances.

Grant it, said another on the pole-cat side; but when it is in retaliation, or in self-defence against an editor whose defamation is more offensive to the feelings of the mind, than the hogo of a civet to the sense
of smelling; or when it is used in burlesque, and by way of analogy and
symbol to explain the impropriety of encouraging personal abuse, by taking papers, it may correct by leading to reflection. The mind may be insensible to abstract lessons, but a paradigm, or object set before it may
affect. As to this man exercising his trade by the smell of a cat, it is an
occupation which can be carried on to advantage only in a town; for it is
in towns chiefly that editors assemble; and it is by seting up under our
noses, and affecting the readers, that the impression is made. For if the
public will receive into their houses for the use of themselves and families
gossip slander, let them take a little of this hartshorn with it and if they
will have the one bear the other. A ground of the common law is general
reason adapted to particular cases. I grant that it even goes so far as to
make the keeping hogs in a pen so near my window, in towns, as to offend
by the smell, a nuisance; but this is a borough incorporated, and can by a
bye law regulate a new trade. I hold it to be a matter of vote whether
this quadruped shall be tolerated or excluded.

The advocate for the press rejoined. The common law, said he, pro-
tects the press. It is the right of the tongue transfered to the hand: it
ought to be as free as the air that we breathe: The privilege as unfettered
as the organs of articulation. But what is there in the common law to
protect from the aspersion of this animal?

The pole-cat man replied. It is on principle and by analogy, said he,
that it is protected. Does not the law of water courses apply to this. If a
man divert a stream from my meadow, or obstruct one running through it,
so as to dam it up, and drown the grass, have not I a remedy; shall this
man at much expence and charge bring a beast from the mountains,
tame it, or reduce it under his dominion, and apply it to a purpose in
civilized and domestic life, and shall we say that the common law does
not protect him in the enjoyment of its musk?

The lawyer on the side of the Porcupine rejoined. So use your own said
he, that you trespass not upon another mans. If you keep your smell, and
hogs at home to your own nose, there is no objection. But in the nature
of the thing it cannot be; for the air is the natural conductor; and therefore it cannot but exist a nuisance.

Surrejoinder by the other. But after all, is it more a nuisance than the
press, which it has in view to correct?

At this instant a commotion was perceivable amongst the multitude;
not on account of what was said, or meaning any disturbance like debate;
but the rumour was that a fresh cat had been brought from the hills
above the town, and was on its way to the college-man who had offered
a reward for an additional puss to increase his stock; and as it was con-

jectured, meant to play it off under the pretext that the prohibition contained in the armistice extended only to the individual beast that he had before in his possession.

The Captain, at this, rising, said: young man, this is not fair. It is within the reason, if not the express words of the convention, that all annoyances by steam, vapour or effluviæ proceeding from a pole-cat shall be suspended during the pendency of this question; and it is an evasion to substitute another badger, and by that means attempt to elude the stipulation.

The young man got up to explain. It is far from me, said he, to elude or evade the performance of the stipulation. The fact is, that hearing, a day or two ago, that Porcupine, was about to enlarge his sheet, and for that purpose had employed a journeyman, or two more, I thought it not amiss to extend the scale of my vapour and employ two conduits instead of one. For that purpose had sent to the woods, for another cat, which is now on the way, but in a leathern bag by my directions, and not to have regress, or egress, until this assembly shall dissolve, nor for a reasonable time after, that eundo, and redeundo, or going as well as coming you may be safe let what will be the issue of the controversy; whether I am to break up stock, or be suffered to go on.

This explanation gave satisfaction, and composed the assembly.

Another speaker had now occupied the ground. I cannot say the floor, for there was no floor. I am, said he, for supporting the press. The objection is, that it is a blackguard press. But while there are blackguards to write, must they not have a press? Is it only men of polished education that have a right to express their sentiments? Let them write in magazines, or make books, or have gazettes of their own, but not restrict the right that people of a more uncultivated understanding have to amuse themselves and others with their lucubrations. You call us the Swinish Multitude, and yet refuse us the food that is natural to us. Are there not amongst us those that have no relish for disquisitions on the balance of power or form of governments, agricultural essays, or questions of finance; but can comprehend and relish a laugh raised at the expense of the master of a family; or a public character in high station; if for no other reason, but because it gratifies the self-love of those who cannot attain the same eminence? Take away from us this, and what have we more? What is the press to us, but as it amuses?

I think, said another rising, that the gentleman means irony. But let us take the matter seriously. I am on the same side with him, but not for the same reasons. I take it, that scurrility may be useful to those that bear it, and are the subjects of it. It may bring to a man's knowledge and serve to correct foibles that he would not otherwise have been conscious of, or amended. Men will hear from the buffoon or the jester, things they would not take from a friend, and scarcely from a confessor. It was on this principle that in the middle ages of Europe, a profession of men was indulged, and rewarded, in the houses of the great, called the Joculators, or Jesters. So late as the time of James I. we had one of these of the name of Archy. The Duke of Buckingham having taken offence at something that he said, had him whipped. It was thought beneath a man of honour to have taken notice of it; and inflicted punishment. I consider the bulk of our editors as succeeding to the joculators or fool-caps of the early periods; and as the knights or men of character and dignity of those times were not bound to notice the follies, however gross of jokers, so now a gentleman is not bound to notice the defamation of gazettes; nay, as in the former instance, it was deemed uncourteous, and unbecoming to resent what the fool said, so more what a printer chooses to publish. Selden in his table talk remarks, "That a gallant man, is above ill words. We have an example of this in the old Lord of Salisbury, who was a great wise man. Stone had called some Lord about the Court fool. The Lord complains and has Stone whipped. Stone cries, I might have called my Lord of Salisbury often enough, fool, before he would have had me whipped." As in the case of the Merry Andrew, even when there was no wit, it was taken for wit; so now, when an editor means to divert, however dull his abuse, it ought to be the mode to laugh, to keep those who know no better in countenance.

The Captain rising and putting himself in the attitude of speaking, seemed to claim the attention of the audience. I see here, said he, the Principal of the Academy, a man of letters and learning. I would wish to hear from him how the ancients managed these matters: in the republics of Greece and Rome especially. For since I have been abroad, and read and heard public speeches, I find that it is no unusual thing to draw similies, and illustrations from the sayings and doings of antiquity. In deliberative assemblies talking of governments, they tell you of the Amphytrionic Council; the Achean league, the Ionian confederacy. What was the freedom of the press at Athens, or at Rome?

The principal rising—The fact is, said he, there was no press at these places, or in these times. The invention of printing is of a later date. But they had in lieu of pen and ink, what they called the style, hence our phrase style, vertere stylum, and they impressed their thoughts upon wax. They made use of ink in copying upon vellum and parchment. But notwithstanding the want of a press, they were not without satyric salt in their writings. Nor are we to suppose that they were altogether free from what we denominate scurrility. They could call a spade a spade. Aristophanes was a great blackguard. His Comedy of the Clouds is a sufficient specimen. Lucilius, amongst the Romans was a rough man. Cum lutulentus flueret, &c. Do we suppose that nature was not then the same as it is now? On board the Roman gallies was there no low humour? In the Roman camps none? In the Forum no occasional ribaldry? Would not this naturally get up into higher walks? Would not this creep into corporations? Sometimes in verse; sometimes in prose: versis famosis. The poet speaks of the fesscenine verses. Amongst the Romans the Saturnalia, or days of Saturn became a festival, in which it was allowable to exercise their faculties in all intemperance of language.

This is all wide of the question, said an individual, holding his hand upon his nose; it is, shall we tolerate the pole-cat in this village?—For, maugre all the pains that may have been taken to restrain the pett, and confine it by a matting, I feel a portion of the fetor this very moment, come across my nose, by a puff of wind from that quarter, where it is. I move that the question be taken, whether, whatever becomes of the press, the nuisance of this beast, be suffered in the vicinity. For what can a news-paper do, compared with this? It is sent us and we read the publication. But this is involuntary, on our part, and there is no saving ourselves from the exhalation.

I move the previous question said a friend to the baboon; or rather an enemy to the Porcupine. I move that the press be put down, or that both go together.

There is hardship both ways, said an elderly inhabitant. In a community different interests will exist. Family interests; family attachments; party conceptions; and party interests. The passions of the heart will create differences. To have a printer all on one side, even though he be a dunce, is an inequality. What if we prevail upon the owner, or as he would call himself the publisher of the pole-cat, to give up or sell out his establishment, dismiss the wild beast, or return it to the mountains, and institute in its place, a counter press of types and black-ball that may be a match for Porcupine. O Jehu! Said a man laughing, where will you get a match for Porcupine? A man neither of conscience or shame, taught and educated as he is, with typography that is adequate? Who will be willing to be the ostensible vehicle of language becoming a scavenger? Can any one be found who will have front from insensibility of heart, or the forehead of brass, to bear the imputation? If we could get some Teague O'Regan now, that did not know what we were doing with him: that would think it an honour to be employed; that would not take amiss the proposition of making him the conduit of reproach, and dishonourable innuendo; in short, from whom it could be concealed on what account he was chosen; the project might be plausible.

The Captain, at this rising hastily; a thing unusual with him; for he was naturally grave and sedate; but suddenly feeling the impulse of the congruity, he started from his seat, and seconded the proposition of another press; for said he, the very Teague O'Regan that you want is at hand; a waiter of mine. A bog-trotter, taken, not on the Balagate, but, on the Irish mountains: an aboriginal of the island; not your Scotch-Irish, so called, a colony planted in Ulster, by king James the first of England, when he subdued the natives; but a real Paddy, with the brogue on his tongue, and none on his feet; brought up to sheep-stealing from his youth; for his ancestors inhabiting the hills, were a kind of freebooters, time immemorial, coming down to the low grounds, and plundering the more industrious inhabitants. Captured by traps set upon the hills, or surrounded in the bogs, attempting his escape, he had been tamed and employed, many years, digging Turf, before he came to my hands. I bought him from an Irish vessel, just as a curiosity, not that I expected much service from him; but to see what could be made of a rude man by care and patience. The rogue has a low humour, and a sharp tongue; unbounded impudence. And what may be a restraint upon the licentiousness of his press, should he set up one, he is a most abominable coward; the idea of cudgeling will keep him in bounds; should he over-match Porcupine, and turn upon his employers. He has all the low phrases, cant expressions, illiberal reflections, that could be collected from the company he has kept since he has had the care of my horse, and run after my heels in town and country for several years past. What is more, he has been in France, and has a spice of the language, and a tang of Jacobinism in his principles, and conversation, that will match the contrary learning carried to an exorbitant excess in Peter Porcupine. I do not know that you can do better than contribute to a paper of his setting up. He may call it the Mully-Grub, or give it some such title as will bespeak the nature, of the matter it will usually contain.

The college-man at this came forward. I am far, said he, from a disposition to spoil sport; but when the useful is mixed with the jest, I count every point gained.

Yes, said the principal of the academy, Omne tulit punctum, qui miscuit utile dulci.

I never had intended, continued the other, more than to reach the sensations of the multitude, and bring them to their senses. It is only by an appeal to feeling that the mind sometimes can be awakened. The public have now some idea of what I mean, that the licentiousness of the press, is not more a nuisance in the moral, than offensive smells are in the physical world. I agree that the cat be removed, and as a substitute, that we may taper off gradually, shall subscribe to the Mully-Grub.

The speech was applauded, and the vote taken.

John Trumbull (1750–1831)

Many eighteenth-century Americans imitated the style and form of English satirists Samuel Butler and Alexander Pope. None came as close as John Trumbull of Connecticut to providing the new nation with an original wit and sense worthy of his masters. *The Progress of Dulness* (1772–1773) and *M'Fingal* (1782) were promising ventures into social and political satire and revealed a sprightly comic talent as well. But Trumbull discovered that his gift for ridicule was jeopardizing his career and he virtually forsook literature for success as lawyer and judge. The intellectually energetic conservatism of his youth was superseded by a die-hard Federalism which brought him together with other Connecticut Federalist poets, among them Lemuel Hopkins, Timothy Dwight, and David Humphreys. The "Connecticut Wits" collectively and singly produced partisan satire of an uncompromising and abusive nature.

After the triumph of Jeffersonianism in the early nineteenth century, Federalist satirists fell into disrepute. Some of that disrepute was attached to satire itself, which seemed in its critical and controversial aspects to be contrary to the optimistic national spirit and to be divisive rather than unifying in its effect. The tendency of popular American humor in later years to be genial rather than derisive when venturing criticism owes as much to the ill feeling generated by the "Connecticut Wits" as it does to changes in philosophical and literary ideas devaluating a critical temper. Trumbull's "The Owl and the Sparrow" (1772) is an early work more characteristic of his true bent than his later Federalist writings.

TEXT: *The Poetical Works of John Trumbull*, Hartford, Conn., 1820, II. COMMENTARY: Alexander Cowie, *John Trumbull: Connecticut Wit*, Chapel Hill, N.C., 1936.

THE OWL AND THE SPARROW

A Fable [1]

In elder days, in Saturn's prime,
Ere baldness seized the head of Time,
While truant Jove, in infant pride,
Play'd barefoot on Olympus' side,

---

[1] In the course of a poetical correspondence with a friend, having received a very humorous letter in ridicule of Love, &c. I sent him this fable in return. [Footnotes have been renumbered for this printing.]

Each thing on earth had power to chatter,
And spoke the mother tongue of nature.
Each stock or stone could prate and gabble,
Worse than ten labourers of Babel.
Along the street, perhaps you'd see
A Post disputing with a Tree,
And mid their arguments of weight,
A Goose sit umpire of debate.
Each Dog you met, though speechless now,
Would make his compliments and bow,
And every Swine with congees come,
To know how did all friends at home.
Each Block sublime could make a speech,
In style and eloquence as rich,
And could pronounce it and could pen it,
As well as Chatham in the senate.

Nor prose alone.—In these young times,
Each field was fruitful too in rhymes;
Each feather'd minstrel felt the passion,
And every wind breathed inspiration.
Each Bullfrog croak'd in loud bombastic,
Each Monkey chatter'd Hudibrastic;
Each Cur, endued with yelping nature,
Could outbark Churchill's [2] self in satire;
Each Crow in prophecy delighted,
Each Owl, you saw, was second-sighted,
Each Goose a skilful politician,
Each Ass a gifted met'physician,
Could preach in wrath 'gainst laughing rogues,
Write *Halfway-covenant Dialogues*,[3]
And wisely judge of all disputes
In commonwealths of men or brutes.

'Twas then, in spring a youthful Sparrow
Felt the keen force of Cupid's arrow:
For Birds, as Æsop's tales avow,
Made love then, just as men do now,
And talk'd of deaths and flames and darts,
And breaking necks and losing hearts;
And chose from all th' aerial kind,

[2] Churchill, the English satirist.
[3] Alluding to the titles of several violent controversial productions of that day, concerning the terms of admission to church-fellowship.

Not then to tribes, like Jews, confined.
The story tells, a lovely Thrush
Had smit him from a neigh'bring bush,
Where oft the young coquette would play,
And carol sweet her siren lay:
She thrill'd each feather'd heart with love,
And reign'd the Toast of all the grove.

He felt the pain, but did not dare
Disclose his passion to the fair;
For much he fear'd her conscious pride
Of race, to noble blood allied.
Her grandsire's nest conspicuous stood,
Mid loftiest branches of the wood,
In airy height, that scorn'd to know
Each flitting wing that waved below.
So doubting, on a point so nice
He deem'd it best to take advice.

Hard by there dwelt an aged Owl,
Of all his friends the gravest fowl;
Who from the cares of business free,
Lived, hermit, in a hollow tree;
To solid learning bent his mind,
In trope and syllogism he shined,
'Gainst reigning follies spent his railing;
Too much a Stoic—'twas his failing.

Hither for aid our Sparrow came,
And told his errand and his name,
With panting breath explain'd his case,
Much trembling at the sage's face;
And begg'd his Owlship would declare
If love were worth a wise one's care.

The grave Owl heard the weighty cause,
And humm'd and hah'd at every pause;
Then fix'd his looks in sapient plan,
Stretch'd forth one foot, and thus began.

"My son, my son, of love beware,
And shun the cheat of beauty's snare;
That snare more dreadful to be in,
Than huntsman's net, or horse-hair gin.

"By others' harms learn to be wise,"
As ancient proverbs well advise.
Each villany, that nature breeds,
From females and from love proceeds.
'Tis love disturbs with fell debate
Of man and beast the peaceful state:
Men fill the world with war's alarms,
When female trumpets sound to arms;
The commonwealth of dogs delight
For beauties, as for bones, to fight.
Love hath his tens of thousands slain,
And heap'd with copious death the plain:
Samson, with ass's jaw to aid,
Ne'er peopled thus th' infernal shade.

    "Nor this the worst; for he that's dead,
With love no more will vex his head.
'Tis in the rolls of fate above,
That death's a certain cure for love;
A noose can end the cruel smart;
The lover's leap is from a cart.
But oft a living death they bear,
Scorn'd by the proud, capricious fair.
The fair to sense pay no regard,
And beauty is the fop's reward;
They slight the generous hearts' esteem,
And sigh for those, who fly from them.

    "Just when your wishes would prevail,
Some rival bird with gayer tail,
Who sings his strain with sprightlier note,
And chatters praise with livelier throat,
Shall charm your flutt'ring fair one down,
And leave your choice, to hang or drown.

    "Ev'n I, my son, have felt the smart;
A Pheasant won my youthful heart.
For her I tuned the doleful lay,[4]
For her I watch'd the night away;
In vain I told my piteous case,
And smooth'd my dignity of face;
In vain I cull'd the studied phrase,

[4] My correspondent, about that time, had also been himself a little dipped in *Amatory Verse*, as *Little* (T. Moore) calls it.

And sought hard words in beauty's praise.
Her, not my charms nor sense could move,
For folly is the food of love.
Each female scorns our serious make,
"Each woman is at heart a rake." [5]
Thus Owls in every age have said,
Since our first parent-owl was made;
Thus Pope and Swift, to prove their sense,
Shall sing, some twenty ages hence;
Then shall a man of little fame,
One —— —— sing the same."

[5] Men, some to business, some to pleasure take,
But every woman is at heart a rake.
            Pope's Essay on the characters of Women

Lemuel Hopkins (1750–1801)

The caustic force of the "Connecticut Wits" in particular and of late eighteenth-century American satire in general is exemplified by the poetry of Lemuel Hopkins. A Connecticut farmer's son who became a prominent physician and received an honorary Master of Arts degree from Yale in 1784, Hopkins was as crusty in his personal life as he was in his poetry. His philosophy was one of staunch conservatism: Calvinism in religion and Federalism in politics. The poetry of Hopkins has never been collected because so much of it was written in collaboration with other poets, and his contributions have not been identified with certainty.

TEXT: "Epitaph on a Patient Killed by a Cancer Quack" and "The Hypocrite's Hope," *The Columbian Muse*, Philadelphia, Pa., 1794; "Verses on General Ethan Allen," *American Poems, Selected and Original*, ed. Elihu Hubbard Smith, Litchfield, Conn., 1793.

EPITAPH

On a Patient Killed by a Cancer Quack

Here lies a fool flat on his back,
The victim of a Cancer Quack;
Who lost his money and his life,
By plaster, caustic, and by knife.
The case was this—a pimple rose,
South-east a little of his nose;
Which daily redden'd and grew bigger,
As too much drinking gave it vigour:
A score of gossips soon ensure
Full three score diff'rent modes of cure;
But yet the full-fed pimple still
Defied all petticoated skill;
When fortune led him to peruse
A hand-bill in the weekly news;
Sign'd by six fools of diff'rent sorts,
All cur'd of cancers made of warts;
Who recommend, with due submission,
This cancer-monger as magician;
Fear wing'd his flight to find the quack,
And prove his cancer-curing knack;

But on his way he found another,—
A second advertising brother:
But as much like him as an owl
Is unlike every handsome fowl;
Whose fame had rais'd as broad a fog,
And of the two the greater hog:
Who us'd a still more magic plaster,
That sweat forsooth, and cur'd the faster.
This doctor view'd, with moony eyes
And scowl'd up face, the pimple's size;
Then christen'd it in solemn answer,
And cried, "This pimple's name is CANCER."
"But courage, friend, I see you're pale,
"My sweating plasters never fail;
"I've sweated hundreds out with ease,
"With roots as long as maple trees;
"And never fail'd in all my trials—
"Behold these samples here in vials!
"Preserv'd to shew my wond'rous merits,
"Just as my liver is—in spirits.
"For twenty joes the cure is done—"
The bargain struck, the plaster on,
Which gnaw'd the cancer at its leisure,
And pained his face above all measure.
But still the pimple spread the faster,
And swell'd, like toad that meets disaster.
Thus foil'd, the doctor gravely swore,
It was a right rose-cancer sore;
Then stuck his probe beneath the beard,
And shew'd them where the leaves appear'd;
And rais'd the patient's drooping spirits,
By praising up the plaster's merits.—
Quoth he, "The roots now scarcely stick—
"I'll fetch her out like crab or tick;
"And make it rendezvous, next trial,
"With six more plagues, in my old vial."
Then purg'd him pale with jalap drastic,
And next applies th' infernal caustic.
But yet, this semblance bright of hell
Serv'd but to make the patient yell;
And, gnawing on with fiery pace,
Devour'd one broadside of his face—
"Courage, 'tis done," the doctor cried,
And quick th' incision knife applied:

That with three cuts made such a hole,
Out flew the patient's tortur'd soul!

   Go, readers, gentle, eke and simple,
If you have wart, or corn, or pimple;
To quack infallible apply;
Here's room enough for you to lie.
His skill triumphant still prevails,
For DEATH's a cure that never fails.

VERSES ON GENERAL ETHAN ALLEN

Lo, Allen 'scaped from British jails,
His tushes broke by biting nails,
Appears in Hyperborean skies,
To tell the world the Bible lies.
See him on green hills north afar
Glow like a self-enkindled star,
Prepar'd (with mob-collecting club
Black from the forge of Belzebub,
And grim with metaphysic scowl,
With quill just plucked from wing of owl)
As rage or reason rise or sink,
To shed his blood, or shed his ink.
Behold inspired from Vermont dens,
The seer of Antichrist descends,
To feed new mobs with Hell-born manna
On gentile lands of Susquehanna;
And teach the Pennsylvania quaker,
High blasphemies against his maker.
Behold him move, ye staunch divines!
His tall head bustling against the pines;
All front he seems like wall of brass,
And brays tremendous as an ass;
One hand is clench'd to batter noses,
While t'other scrawls 'gainst Paul and Moses.

THE HYPOCRITE'S HOPE

Blest is the man, who from the womb,
  To saintship him betakes,
And when too soon his child shall come,
  A long confession makes.

When next in Broad Church-alley, he
  Shall take his former place,
Relates his past iniquity,
  And consequential grace.

Declares how long by Satan vex'd,
  From truth he did depart,
And tells the time, and tells the text,
  That smote his flinty heart.

He stands in half-way-cov'nant sure;
  Full five long years or more,
One foot in church's pale secure,
  The other out of door.

Then riper grown in gifts and grace,
  With ev'ry rite complies,
And deeper lengthens down his face,
  And higher rolls his eyes.

He tones like Pharisee sublime,
  Two lengthy prayers a day,
The same that he from early prime,
  Had heard his father say.

Each Sunday perch'd on bench of pew,
  To passing priest he bows,
Then loudly 'mid the quav'ring crew,
  Attunes his vocal nose.

With awful look then rises slow,
  And pray'rful visage sour,
More fit to fright the apostate foe,
  Than seek a pard'ning power.

Then nodding hears the sermon next,
  From priest haranguing loud;

And doubles down each quoted text,
    From Genesis to Jude.

And when the priest holds forth address,
    To old ones born anew,
With holy pride and wrinkled face,
    He rises in his pew.

Good works he careth nought about,
    But *faith* alone will seek,
While Sunday's pieties blot out
    The knaveries of the week.

He makes the poor his daily pray'r,
    Yet drives them from his board:
And though to his own good he swear,
    Thro' habit breaks his word.

This man advancing fresh and fair,
    Shall all his race complete;
And wave at last his hoary hair,
    Arrived in Deacon's seat.

There shall he all church honours have,
    By joyous brethren given—
Till priest in fun'ral sermon grave,
    Shall send him straight to heaven.

Thomas Green Fessenden (1771–1837)

During 1836, while Nathaniel Hawthorne was editing *The American Magazine of Useful and Entertaining Knowledge* in Boston, he lived in the boarding-house kept by the family of the aged Thomas Green Fessenden. Fessenden was a dormant poet who had once been well-known in both England and America for his humorous sketches of rural New England life and for his opprobrious conservative satire. His Yankee dialect poem "The Country Lovers, or Jonathan's Courtship" (1795) has been thought to be the prototype of James Russell Lowell's "The Courtin'." By the time Hawthorne met Fessenden the latter's reputation had vanished. Much of his energy had been dissipated in journalism and crack-brained business ventures; his defense of medical quackery in *Terrible Tractoration* (1803), his unbridled political satire in favor of a defeated Federalism, and his propensity for an eighteenth-century poetic style and temper were among the factors making him unpalatable to the early nineteenth century. Even Hawthorne deplored Fessenden's decision to abandon his rustic Yankee subjects and turn to satire. Hawthorne had taken advantage of the term "Entertaining" in his magazine's title to de-emphasize its former "Useful" character and make it as amusing as possible; as editor and contributor he titillated his readers with a tall story, a comic poem, a paean for April Fool's Day, folk humor, macabre jokes, a derisive account of an academician's accident, and the like. The appearance of Fessenden's *Terrible Tractoration* in its third edition (1836) gave Hawthorne occasion in a review to call for a revival of interest in the "queer originality of thought, and aptness of ludicrous expression" of Fessenden's "laughing muse." Hawthorne printed two selections from Fessenden's poetry; confidence in his editorial judgment has led to their reappearance below. "The Patent Author's Mill" is an extract from *Terrible Tractoration;* "The Independent Farmer" is a portion of "The Cultivator's Art," a new poem appearing in the 1836 collection. Hawthorne observed that the second selection "is full of ideas so infinitely grotesque, that they actually become sublime."

TEXT: *Terrible Tractoration and Other Poems*, Boston, Mass., 1836. COMMENTARY: Porter G. Perrin, *The Life and Works of Thomas Green Fessenden*, 1771–1837, Orono, Me., 1925.

PATENT AUTHOR'S MILL

We next crave liberty to mention
Another wonderful invention;
A sort of stenographic still,
Alias a Patent Author's mill.

We fill its hopper with a set
Of letters of the alphabet,
And turn out eulogies, orations,
Or themes for July celebrations,—

News, both domestic and extraneous,
Essays, and extracts miscellaneous,
We manufacture by the means
Of said superlative machines.

This last invention also reaches
To making Congress members' speeches;
Would they adopt it, though we've said it,
T'would cent per cent enhance their credit.

We hammer'd out a lawyer's jaw mill
Which went by water like a saw-mill
With so much clamour, fire and fury,
It thunderstruck the judge and jury.

THE INDEPENDENT FARMER

We farmers are a sort of stuff
Tyrants will always find too tough
For them to work up into slaves,
The servile tools of lordly knaves.
Those men who till the stubborn soil,
Enlighten'd, and inur'd to toil,
Cannot be made to quail or cower
By traitor's art or tyrant's power.
They might as well attempt to chain
The west wind in a hurricane;—
Make rivers run up hill by frightening,
Or steal a march on kindled lightning—

The great sea-serpent, which we've read of,
Take by the tail and snap his head off—
The firmament on cloudy nights,
Illume with artificial lights,
By such an apparatus as
Is used for lighting streets with gas—
Or, having split the north pole till it's
Divided into baker's billets,
Make such a blaze as never shone,
And torrefy the frozen zone—
With clubs assail the polar bear,
And drive the monster from his lair—
Attack the comets as they run
With loads of fuel for the sun,
And overset by oppugnation
Those shining colliers of creation—
The Milky Way McAdamize,
A railway raise to span the skies,
Then make, to save Apollo's team,
The Solar Chariot go by steam.
These things shall tyrants do, and more
Than we have specified, before
Our cultivators they subdue,
While grass is green, or sky is blue.

Washington Irving (1783–1859)

Washington Irving was the first successful American professional man of letters; he was also a humorist. His great popularity did much to stimulate the growth of literary humor in the United States. Because Irving, like the other "Knickerbocker" writers who made New York City the literary capital of the United States from about 1807 to 1837, was fascinated by American lore of both formal and folk origin, humorists who emulated him incorporated native themes, locales, and characters into their writings. "The Legend of Sleepy Hollow" (1820) might well have been the model upon which the "frontier" humorists patterned their work; the atmosphere of fantasy, the characters of the rustic commoner and the effete intellectual, the conflict between their opposing values, and the macabre, practical joking which gave the victory to Brom Bones are standard ingredients found in Longstreet, George Washington Harris, and Mark Twain. Like Hawthorne, whom he resembles in many ways, Irving was also deeply indebted to European literature, that of the past as well as that of his contemporaries in England and Germany. While writing the burlesque satire of A History of New York (1809), for example, Irving drew not only upon his knowledge of Henricus Selijns and Cotton Mather but also upon Homer, Rabelais, Dryden, Swift, Fielding, and Sterne. In later works Irving revealed the influence of Scott, Tieck, and Hoffman. Irving's fusion of European and American traditions of literary and folk humor has had a lasting and salutary effect.

TEXT: A History of New York, The Works of Washington Irving (Spuyten Duyvil Edition), New York, 1881, VII; "The Legend of Sleepy Hollow," Spuyten Duyvil Edition, IX. COMMENTARY: Stanley T. Williams, The Life of Washington Irving, New York, 1935.

From A HISTORY OF NEW YORK

BOOK VI, CHAPTER VIII

Containing the Most Horrible Battle Ever Recorded in Poetry or Prose; With the Admirable Exploits of Peter the Headstrong

"Now had the Dutchmen snatched a huge repast," and finding themselves wonderfully encouraged and animated thereby, prepared to take the field. Expectation, says the writer of the Stuyvesant manuscript—Expectation now stood on stilts. The world forgot to turn round, or rather stood still, that it might witness the affray; like a round-bellied alderman, watching the combat of two chivalrous flies upon his jerkin. The eyes of all mankind, as usual in such cases, were turned upon Fort Christina. The sun, like a little man in a crowd at a puppet-show, scampered about the heavens, popping his head here and there, and endeavoring to get a peep between the unmannerly clouds that obtruded themselves in his way. The historians filled their ink-horns—the poets went without their dinners, either that they might buy paper and goose-quills, or because they could not get anything to eat. Antiquity scowled sulkily out of its grave, to see itself outdone—while even Posterity stood mute, gazing in gaping ecstasy of retrospection on the eventful field.

The immortal deities, who whilom had seen service at the "affair" of Troy—now mounted their feather-bed clouds, and sailed over the plain, or mingled among the combatants in different disguises, all itching to have a finger in the pie. Jupiter sent off his thunderbolt to a noted coppersmith, to have it furbished up for the direful occasion. Venus vowed by her chastity to patronize the Swedes, and in semblance of a blear-eyed trull paraded the battlements of Fort Christina, accompanied by Diana, as a sergeant's widow, of cracked reputation. The noted bully, Mars, stuck two horse-pistols into his belt, shouldered a rusty firelock, and gallantly swaggered at their elbow, as a drunken corporal—while Apollo trudged in their rear, as a bandy-legged fifer, playing most villainously out of tune.

On the other side, the ox-eyed Juno, who had gained a pair of black eyes over night, in one of her curtain lectures with old Jupiter, displayed her haughty beauties on a baggage-wagon—Minerva, as a brawny gin-suttler, tucked up her skirts, brandished her fists, and swore most hero-ically, in exceeding bad Dutch (having but lately studied the language), by way of keeping up the spirits of the soldiers; while Vulcan halted as a club-footed blacksmith, lately promoted to be a captain of militia. All was silent awe, or bustling preparation: war reared his horrid front, gnashed loud his iron fangs, and shook his direful crest of bristling bayonets.

And now the mighty chieftains marshalled out their hosts. Here stood stout Risingh, firm as a thousand rocks—incrusted with stockades, and intrenched to the chin in mud batteries. His valiant soldiery lined the breastwork in grim array, each having his mustachios fiercely greased, and his hair pomatumed back, and queued so stiffly, that he grinned above the ramparts like a grisly death's head.

There came on the intrepid Peter—his brows knit, his teeth set, his fists clenched, almost breathing forth volumes of smoke, so fierce was the fire that raged within his bosom. His faithful squire Van Corlear trudged valiantly at his heels, with his trumpet gorgeously bedecked with red and yellow ribbons, the remembrances of his fair mistresses at the Manhattoes. Then came waddling on the sturdy chivalry of the Hudson. There were the Van Wycks, and the Van Dycks, and the Ten Eycks—the

Van Nesses, the Van Tassels, the Van Grolls; the Van Hoesens, the Van Giesons, and the Van Blarcoms—the Van Warts, the Van Winkles, the Van Dams; the Van Pelts, the Van Rippers, and the Van Brunts. There were the Van Hornes, the Van Hooks, the Van Bunschotens; the Van Gelders, the Van Arsdales, and the Van Bummels; the Vander Belts, the Vander Hoofs, the Vander Voorts, the Vander Lyns, the Vander Pools, and the Vander Spiegles—then came the Hoffmans, the Hooghlands, the Hoppers, the Cloppers, the Ryckmans, the Dyckmans, the Hogebooms, the Rosebooms, the Oothouts, the Quackenbosses, the Roerbacks, the Garrebrantzes, the Bensons, the Brouwers, the Waldrons, the Onderdonks, the Varra Vangers, the Schermerhorns, the Stoutenburghs, the Brinkerhoffs, the Bontecous, the Knickerbockers, the Hockstrassers, the Ten Breecheses, and the Tough Breecheses, with a host more of worthies, whose names are too crabbed to be written, or if they could be written, it would be impossible for man to utter—all fortified with a mighty dinner, and, to use the words of a great Dutch poet,

"Brimful of wrath and cabbage."

For an instant the mighty Peter paused in the midst of his career, and mounting on a stump, addressed his troops in eloquent Low Dutch, exhorting them to fight like *duyvels*, and assuring them that if they conquered, they should get plenty of booty—if they fell, they should be allowed the satisfaction, while dying, of reflecting that it was in the service of their country—and after they were dead, of seeing their names inscribed in the temple of renown, and handed down, in company with all the other great men of the year, for the admiration of posterity.— Finally, he swore to them, on the word of a governor (and they knew him too well to doubt it for a moment), that if he caught any mother's son of them looking pale, or playing craven, he would curry his hide till he made him run out of it like a snake in spring time. Then lugging out his trusty sabre, he brandished it three times over his head, ordered Van Corlear to sound a charge, and shouting the words "St. Nicholas and the Manhattoes!" courageously dashed forwards. His warlike followers, who had employed the interval in lighting their pipes, instantly stuck them into their mouths, gave a furious puff, and charged gallantly under cover of the smoke.

The Swedish garrison, ordered by the cunning Risingh not to fire until they could distinguish the whites of their assailants' eyes, stood in horrid silence on the covert-way, until the eager Dutchmen had ascended the glacis. Then did they pour into them such a tremendous volley, that the very hills quaked around, and were terrified even unto an incontinence of water, insomuch that certain springs burst forth from their sides, which continue to run unto the present day. Not a Dutchman but would have bitten the dust beneath that dreadful fire, had not the protecting Minerva kindly taken care that the Swedes should, one and all, observe their usual custom of shutting their eyes and turning away their heads at the moment of discharge.

The Swedes followed up their fire by leaping the counterscarp, and falling tooth and nail upon the foe with furious outcries. And now might be seen prodigies of valor, unmatched in history or song. Here was the sturdy Stoffel Brinkerhoff brandishing his quarter-staff, like the giant Blanderon his oak tree (for he scorned to carry any other weapon), and drumming a horrific tune upon the hard heads of the Swedish soldiery. There were the Van Kortlandts, posted at a distance, like the Locrian archers of yore, and plying it most potently with the longbow, for which they were so justly renowned. On a rising knoll were gathered the valiant men of Sing-Sing, assisting marvellously in the fight, by chanting the great song of St. Nicholas; but as to the Gardeniers of Hudson, they were absent on a marauding party, laying waste the neighboring watermelon patches.

In a different part of the field were the Van Grolls of Antony's Nose, struggling to get to the thickest of the fight, but horribly perplexed in a defile between two hills, by reason of the length of their noses. So also the Van Bunschotens of Nyack and Kakiat, so renowned for kicking with the left foot, were brought to a stand for want of wind, in consequence of the hearty dinner they had eaten, and would have been put to utter rout but for the arrival of a gallant corps of voltigeurs, composed of the Hoppers, who advanced nimbly to their assistance on one foot. Nor must I omit to mention the valiant achievements of Antony Van Corlear, who, for a good quarter of an hour, waged stubborn fight with a little pursy Swedish drummer; whose hide he drummed most magnificently, and whom he would infallibly have annihilated on the spot, but that he had come into the battle with no other weapon but his trumpet.

But now the combat thickened.—On came the mighty Jacobus Varra Vanger and the fighting men of the Wallabout; after them thundered the Van Pelts of Esopus, together with the Van Rippers and the Van Brunts, bearing down all before them—then the Suy Dams, and the Van Dams, pressing forward with many a blustering oath, at the head of the warriors of Hell-gate, clad in their thunder and lightning gaberdines; and lastly, the standard-bearers and body-guard of Peter Stuyvesant, bearing the great beaver of the Manhattoes.

And now commenced the horrid din, the desperate struggle, the maddening ferocity, the frantic desperation, the confusion and self-abandonment of war. Dutchman and Swede commingled, tugged, panted, and blowed. The heavens were darkened with a tempest of missives. Bang! went the guns—whack! went the broadswords—thump! went the cudgels—crash! went the musket-stocks—blows—kicks—cuffs—scratches —black eyes and bloody noses swelling the horrors of the scene! Thick thwack, cut and hack, helter-skelter, higgledy-piggledy, hurly-burly, head over heels, rough and tumble!—Dunder and blixum! swore the Dutchmen—splitter and splutter! cried the Swedes—Storm the works! shouted Hardkoppig Peter—Fire the mine! roared stout Risingh—Tanta-rarra-ra! twanged the trumpet of Antony Van Corlear—until all voice and sound became unintelligible—grunts of pain, yells of fury, and shouts of triumph mingling in one hideous clamor. The earth shook as if struck with a paralytic stroke—trees shrunk aghast, and withered at the sight—rocks burrowed in the ground like rabbits—and even Christina creek turned from its course, and ran up a hill in breathless terror!

Long hung the contest doubtful, for though a heavy shower of rain, sent by the "cloud-compelling Jove," in some measure cooled their ardor, as doth a bucket of water thrown on a group of fighting mastiffs, yet did they but pause for a moment, to return with tenfold fury to the charge. Just at this juncture a vast and dense column of smoke was seen slowly rolling toward the scene of battle. The combatants paused for a moment, gazing in mute astonishment, until the wind, dispelling the murky cloud, revealed the flaunting banner of Michael Paw, the Patroon of Communipaw. That valiant chieftain came fearlessly on at the head of a phalanx of oyster-fed Pavonians and a corps de reserve of the Van Arsdales and Van Bummels, who had remained behind to digest the enormous dinner they had eaten. These now trudged manfully forward, smoking their pipes with outrageous vigor, so as to raise the awful cloud that has been mentioned; but marching exceedingly slow, being short of leg, and of great rotundity in the belt.

And now the deities who watched over the fortunes of the Nederlanders having unthinkingly left the field, and stepped into a neighboring tavern to refresh themselves with a pot of beer, a direful catastrophe had well-nigh ensued. Scarce had the myrmidons of Michael Paw attained the front of battle, when the Swedes, instructed by the cunning Risingh, levelled a shower of blows full at their tobacco-pipes. Astounded at this assault, and dismayed at the havoc of their pipes, these ponderous warriors gave way, and like a drove of frightened elephants broke through the ranks of their own army. The little Hoppers were borne down in the surge: the sacred banner emblazoned with the gigantic oyster of Communipaw was trampled in the dirt: on blundered and thundered the heavy-sterned fugitives, the Swedes pressing on their rear and applying their feet *a parte poste* of the Van Arsdales and the Van Bummels with a vigor that prodigiously accelerated their movements—nor did the renowned Michael Paw himself fail to receive divers grievous and dishonorable visitations of shoe-leather.

But what, oh Muse! was the rage of Peter Stuyvesant, when from afar he saw his army giving way! In the transports of his wrath he sent forth a roar, enough to shake the very hills. The men of the Manhattoes plucked up new courage at the sound; or rather, they rallied at the voice of their leader, of whom they stood more in awe than of all of the Swedes in Christendom. Without waiting for their aid, the daring Peter dashed sword in hand into the thickest of the foe. Then might be seen achievements worthy of the days of the giants. Wherever he went, the enemy shrank before him; the Swedes fled to right and left, or were driven, like dogs, into their own ditch; but as he pushed forward singly with headlong courage, the foe closed behind and hung upon his rear. One aimed a blow full at his heart; but the protecting power which watches over the great and good turned aside the hostile blade and directed it to a sidepocket, where reposed an enormous iron tobacco-box, endowed, like the shield of Achilles, with supernatural powers, doubtless from bearing the portrait of the blessed St. Nicholas. Peter Stuyvesant turned like an angry bear upon the foe, and seizing him as he fled, by an immeasurable queue, "Ah, whoreson caterpillar," roared he, "here's what shall make worms' meat of thee!" So saying, he whirled his sword, and dealt a blow that would have decapitated the varlet, but that the pitying steel struck short and shaved the queue forever from his crown. At this moment an arquebusier levelled his piece from a neighboring mound, with deadly aim; but the watchful Minerva, who had just stopped to tie up her garter, seeing the peril of her favorite hero, sent old Boreas with his bellows, who, as the match descended to the pan, gave a blast that blew the priming from the touch-hole.

Thus waged the fight, when the stout Risingh, surveying the field from the top of a little ravelin, perceived his troops banged, beaten, and kicked by the invincible Peter. Drawing his falchion and uttering a thousand anathemas, he strode down to the scene of combat with some such thundering strides as Jupiter is said by Hesiod to have taken, when he strode down the spheres to hurl his thunderbolts at the Titans.

When the rival heroes came face to face, each made a prodigious start in the style of a veteran stage-champion. Then did they regard each other for a moment with the bitter aspect of two furious ram-cats on the point of a clapper-clawing. Then did they throw themselves into one attitude, then into another, striking their swords on the ground, first on the right side, then on the left—at last at it they went, with incredible ferocity. Words cannot tell the prodigies of strength and valor displayed in this direful encounter—an encounter compared to which the far-famed battles of Ajax with Hector, of Æneas with Turnus, Orlando with Rodomont, Guy of Warwick with Colbrand the Dane, or of that renowned Welsh knight, Sir Owen of the Mountains with the giant Guylon, were all gentle sports and holiday recreations. At length the valiant Peter, watching his opportunity, aimed a blow, enough to cleave his adversary to the very chine; but Risingh, nimbly raising his sword, warded it off so narrowly, that glancing on one side, it shaved away a huge canteen in which he carried his liquor; thence pursuing its trenchant course, it severed off a deep coat pocket, stored with bread and cheese—which provant rolling among the armies, occasioned a fearful scrambling between the Swedes and Dutchmen, and made the general battle to wax more furious than ever.

Enraged to see his military stores laid waste, the stout Risingh, collecting all his forces, aimed a mighty blow full at the hero's crest. In vain did his fierce little cocked hat oppose its course. The biting steel clove through the stubborn ram beaver, and would have cracked the crown of any one not endowed with supernatural hardness of head; but the brittle weapon shivered in pieces on the skull of Hardkoppig Piet, shedding a thousand sparks, like beams of glory, round his grizzly visage.

The good Peter reeled with the blow, and turning up his eyes beheld a thousand suns, besides moons and stars, dancing about the firmament —at length, missing his footing, by reason of his wooden leg, down he came on his seat of honor with a crash which shook the surrounding hills, and might have wrecked his frame, had he not been received into a cushion softer than velvet, which Providence, or Minerva, or St. Nicholas, or some cow, had benevolently prepared for his reception.

The furious Risingh, in spite of the maxim, cherished by all true knights, that "fair play is a jewel," hastened to take advantage of the hero's fall; but, as he stooped to give a fatal blow, Peter Stuyvesant dealt him a thwack over the sconce with his wooden leg, which set a chime of bells ringing triple bob majors in his cerebellum. The bewildered Swede staggered with the blow, and the wary Peter seizing a pocket pistol, which lay hard by, discharged it full at the head of the reeling Risingh. Let not my reader mistake; it was not a murderous weapon loaded with powder and ball; but a little sturdy stone pottle charged to the muzzle with a double dram of true Dutch courage, which the knowing Antony Van Corlear carried about him by way of replenishing his valor; and which had dropped from his wallet during his furious encounter with the drummer. The hideous weapon sang through the air, and true to its course as was the fragment of rock discharged at Hector by bully Ajax, encountered the head of the gigantic Swede with matchless violence.

This heaven-directed blow decided the battle. The ponderous pericranium of General Jan Risingh sank upon his breast; his knees tottered under him; a deathlike torpor seized upon his frame, and he tumbled to the earth with such violence, that old Pluto started with affright, lest he should have broken through the roof of his infernal palace.

His fall was the signal of defeat and victory—the Swedes gave way— the Dutch pressed forward; the former took to their heels, the latter hotly pursued.—Some entered with them, pell-mell, through the sally-port— others stormed the bastion, and others scrambled over the curtain. Thus in a little while the fortress of Fort Christina, which, like another Troy, had stood a siege of full ten hours, was carried by assault, without the loss of a single man on either side. Victory, in the likeness of a gigantic ox-fly, sat perched upon the cocked hat of the gallant Stuyvesant; and it was declared, by all the writers whom he hired to write the history of his expedition, that on this memorable day he gained a sufficient quantity of glory to immortalize a dozen of the greatest heroes in Christendom.

THE LEGEND OF SLEEPY HOLLOW

Found among the Papers of the Late Diedrich Knickerbocker

> A pleasing land of drowsy head it was,
>   Of dreams that wave before the half-shut eye;
> And of gay castles in the clouds that pass,
>   For ever flushing round a summer sky.
> > *Castle of Indolence*

In the bosom of one of those spacious coves which indent the eastern shore of the Hudson, at that broad expansion of the river denominated by the ancient Dutch navigators the Tappan Zee, and where they always prudently shortened sail, and implored the protection of St. Nicholas when they crossed, there lies a small market-town or rural port, which by some is called Greensburgh, but which is more generally and properly known by the name of Tarry Town. This name was given, we are told, in former days, by the good housewives of the adjacent country, from the inveterate propensity of their husbands to linger about the village tavern on market-days. Be that as it may, I do not vouch for the fact, but merely advert to it for the sake of being precise and authentic. Not far from this village, perhaps about two miles, there is a little valley, or rather lap of land, among high hills, which is one of the quietest places in the whole world. A small brook glides through it, with just murmur enough to lull one to repose; and the occasional whistle of a quail, or tapping of a wood-pecker, is almost the only sound that ever breaks in upon the uniform tranquillity.

I recollect that, when a stripling, my first exploit in squirrel-shooting was in a grove of tall walnut-trees that shades one side of the valley. I had wandered into it at noon-time, when all nature is peculiarly quiet, and was startled by the roar of my own gun, as it broke the Sabbath stillness around, and was prolonged and reverberated by the angry echoes. If ever I should wish for a retreat, whither I might steal from the world and its distractions, and dream quietly away the remnant of a troubled life, I know of none more promising than this little valley.

From the listless repose of the place, and the peculiar character of its inhabitants, who are descendants from the original Dutch settlers, this sequestered glen has long been known by the name of SLEEPY HOLLOW, and its rustic lads are called the Sleepy Hollow Boys throughout all the neighboring country. A drowsy, dreamy influence seems to hang over the land, and to pervade the very atmosphere. Some say that the place was bewitched by a high German doctor, during the early days of the settlement; others, that an old Indian chief, the prophet or wizard of his tribe, held his pow-wows there before the country was discovered by Master Hendrick Hudson. Certain it is, the place still continues under the sway of some witching power, that holds a spell over the minds of the good people, causing them to walk in a continual reverie. They are given to all kinds of marvellous beliefs; are subject to trances and visions; and frequently see strange sights, and hear music and voices in the air. The whole neighborhood abounds with local tales, haunted spots, and twilight superstitions; stars shoot and meteors glare oftener across the valley than in any other part of the country, and the nightmare, with her whole ninefold, seems to make it the favorite scene of her gambols.

The dominant spirit, however, that haunts this enchanted region, and seems to be commander-in-chief of all the powers of the air, is the apparition of a figure on horseback without a head. It is said by some to be the ghost of a Hessian trooper, whose head had been carried away by a cannonball, in some nameless battle during the Revolutionary War, and who is ever and anon seen by the country folk, hurrying along in the gloom of night, as if on the wings of the wind. His haunts are not confined to the valley, but extend at times to the adjacent roads, and especially to the vicinity of a church at no great distance. Indeed certain of the most authentic historians of those parts, who have been careful in collecting and collating the floating facts concerning this spectre, allege that the body of the trooper, having been buried in the churchyard, the ghost rides forth to the scene of battle in nightly quest of his head; and that the rushing speed with which he sometimes passes along the Hollow, like a midnight blast, is owing to his being belated, and in a hurry to get back to the churchyard before daybreak.

Such is the general purport of this legendary superstition, which has furnished materials for many a wild story in that region of shadows; and the spectre is known, at all the country firesides, by the name of the Headless Horseman of Sleepy Hollow.

It is remarkable that the visionary propensity I have mentioned is not confined to the native inhabitants of the valley, but is unconsciously imbibed by every one who resides there for a time. However wide awake they may have been before they entered that sleepy region, they are sure, in a little time, to inhale the witching influence of the air, and begin to grow imaginative, to dream dreams, and see apparitions.

I mention this peaceful spot with all possible laud; for it is in such little retired Dutch valleys, found here and there embosomed in the great State of New York, that population, manners, and customs remain fixed; while the great torrent of migration and improvement, which is making such incessant changes in other parts of this restless country, sweeps by them unobserved. They are like those little nooks of still water which border a rapid stream; where we may see the straw and bubble riding quietly at anchor, or slowly revolving in their mimic harbor, undisturbed by the rush of the passing current. Though many years have elapsed since I trod the drowsy shades of Sleepy Hollow, yet I question whether I should not still find the same trees and the same families vegetating in its sheltered bosom.

In this by-place of nature, there abode, in a remote period of American history, that is to say, some thirty years since, a worthy wight of the name of Ichabod Crane; who sojourned, or, as he expressed it, "tarried," in Sleepy Hollow, for the purpose of instructing the children of the vicinity. He was a native of Connecticut, a State which supplies the Union with pioneers for the mind as well as for the forest, and sends forth yearly its legions of frontier woodsmen and country schoolmasters. The cognomen of Crane was not inapplicable to his person. He was tall, but exceedingly lank, with narrow shoulders, long arms and legs, hands that dangled a mile out of his sleeves, feet that might have served for shovels, and his whole frame most loosely hung together. His head was small, and flat at top, with huge ears, large green glassy eyes, and a long snipe nose, so that it looked like a weathercock perched upon his spindle neck, to tell which way the wind blew. To see him striding along the profile of a hill on a windy day, with his clothes bagging and fluttering about him, one might have mistaken him for the genius of famine descending upon the earth, or some scarecrow eloped from a cornfield.

His school-house was a low building of one large room, rudely constructed of logs; the windows partly glazed, and partly patched with leaves of old copy-books. It was most ingeniously secured at vacant hours by a withe twisted in the handle of the door, and stakes set against the window-shutters; so that, though a thief might get in with perfect ease, he would find some embarrassment in getting out: an idea most probably borrowed by the architect, Yost Van Houten, from the mystery of an eel-pot. The school-house stood in a rather lonely but pleasant situation, just at the foot of a woody hill, with a brook running close by, and a formidable birch-tree growing at one end of it. From hence the low murmur of his pupils' voices, conning over their lessons, might be heard in a drowsy summer's day, like the hum of a bee-hive; interrupted now and then by the authoritative voice of the master, in the tone of menace or command; or, peradventure, by the appalling sound of the birch, as he urged some tardy loiterer along the flowery path of knowledge. Truth to say, he was a conscientious man, and ever bore in mind the golden maxim, "Spare

the rod and spoil the child."—Ichabod Crane's scholars certainly were
not spoiled.

I would not have it imagined, however, that he was one of those
cruel potentates of the school, who joy in the smart of their subjects;
on the contrary, he administered justice with discrimination rather than
severity, taking the burden off the backs of the weak, and laying it on
those of the strong. Your mere puny stripling, that winced at the least
flourish of the rod, was passed by with indulgence; but the claims of
justice were satisfied by inflicting a double portion on some little, tough,
wrong-headed, broad-skirted Dutch urchin, who sulked and swelled and
grew dogged and sullen beneath the birch. All this he called "doing his
duty by their parents"; and he never inflicted a chastisement without
following it by the assurance, so consolatory to the smarting urchin, that
"he would remember it, and thank him for it the longest day he had to
live."

When school-hours were over, he was even the companion and play-
mate of the larger boys; and on holiday afternoons would convoy some
of the smaller ones home, who happened to have pretty sisters, or good
housewives for mothers, noted for the comforts of the cupboard. Indeed
it behooved him to keep on good terms with his pupils. The revenue arising from his school was small, and would have been scarcely sufficient to
furnish him with daily bread, for he was a huge feeder, and, though lank,
had the dilating powers of an anaconda; but to help out his maintenance,
he was, according to country custom in those parts, boarded and lodged
at the houses of the farmers, whose children he instructed. With these
he lived successively a week at a time; thus going the rounds of the neighborhood, with all his worldly effects tied up in a cotton handkerchief.

That all this might not be too onerous on the purses of his rustic
patrons, who are apt to consider the costs of schooling a grievous burden,
and schoolmasters as mere drones, he had various ways of rendering himself both useful and agreeable. He assisted the farmers occasionally in
the lighter labors of their farms; helped to make hay; mended the fences;
took the horses to water; drove the cows from pasture; and cut wood for
the winter fire. He laid aside, too, all the dominant dignity and absolute
sway with which he lorded it in his little empire, the school, and became wonderfully gentle and ingratiating. He found favor in the eyes of
the mothers, by petting the children, particularly the youngest; and like
the lion bold, which whilom so magnanimously the lamb did hold, he
would sit with a child on one knee, and rock a cradle with his foot for
whole hours together.

In addition to his other vocations, he was the singing-master of the
neighborhood, and picked up many bright shillings by instructing the
young folks in psalmody. It was a matter of no little vanity to him, on
Sundays, to take his station in front of the church-gallery, with a band

of chosen singers; where, in his own mind, he completely carried away the palm from the parson. Certain it is, his voice resounded far above all the rest of the congregation; and there are peculiar quavers still to be heard in that church, and which may even be heard half a mile off, quite to the opposite side of the mill-pond, on a still Sunday morning, which are said to be legitimately descended from the nose of Ichabod Crane. Thus, by divers little makeshifts in that ingenious way which is commonly denominated "by hook and by crook," the worthy pedagogue got on tolerably enough, and was thought, by all who understood nothing of the labor of headwork, to have a wonderfully easy life of it.

The schoolmaster is generally a man of some importance in the female circle of a rural neighborhood; being considered a kind of idle, gentleman-like personage, of vastly superior taste and accomplishments to the rough country swains, and, indeed, inferior in learning only to the parson. His appearance, therefore, is apt to occasion some little stir at the tea-table of a farm-house, and the addition of a supernumerary dish of cakes or sweetmeats, or, peradventure, the parade of a silver teapot. Our man of letters, therefore, was peculiarly happy in the smiles of all the country damsels. How he would figure among them in the churchyard, between services on Sundays! gathering grapes for them from the wild vines that overrun the surrounding trees; reciting for their amusement all the epitaphs on the tombstones; or sauntering, with a whole bevy of them, along the banks of the adjacent mill-pond; while the more bashful country bumpkins hung sheepishly back, envying his superior elegance and address.

From his half itinerant life, also, he was a kind of travelling gazette, carrying the whole budget of local gossip from house to house: so that his appearance was always greeted with satisfaction. He was, moreover, esteemed by the women as a man of great erudition, for he had read several books quite through, and was a perfect master of Cotton Mather's History of New England Witchcraft, in which, by the way, he most firmly and potently believed.

He was, in fact, an odd mixture of small shrewdness and simple credulity. His appetite for the marvellous, and his powers of digesting it, were equally extraordinary; and both had been increased by his residence in this spellbound region. No tale was too gross or monstrous for his capacious swallow. It was often his delight, after his school was dismissed in the afternoon, to stretch himself on the rich bed of clover bordering the little brook that whimpered by his school-house, and there con over old Mather's direful tales, until the gathering dusk of the evening made the printed page a mere mist before his eyes. Then, as he wended his way, by swamp and stream, and awful woodland, to the farmhouse where he happened to be quartered, every sound of nature, at that witching hour, fluttered his excited imagination; the moan of the whip-

poor-will * from the hill-side; the boding cry of the tree-toad, that har-
binger of storm; the dreary hooting of the screech-owl, or the sudden
rustling in the thicket of birds frightened from their roost. The fire-flies,
too, which sparkled most vividly in the darkest places, now and then
startled him, as one of uncommon brightness would stream across his
path; and if, by chance, a huge blockhead of a beetle came winging his
blundering flight against him, the poor varlet was ready to give up the
ghost, with the idea that he was struck with a witch's token. His only
resource on such occasions, either to drown thought or drive away evil
spirits, was to sing psalm-tunes; and the good people of Sleepy Hollow,
as they sat by their doors of an evening, were often filled with awe, at
hearing his nasal melody, "in linked sweetness long drawn out," floating
from the distant hill, or along the dusky road.

Another of his sources of fearful pleasure was, to pass long winter evenings with the old Dutch wives, as they sat spinning by the fire, with
a row of apples roasting and spluttering along the hearth, and listen to
their marvellous tales of ghosts and goblins, and haunted fields, and
haunted brooks, and haunted bridges, and haunted houses, and particularly of the headless horseman, or Galloping Hessian of the Hollow, as
they sometimes called him. He would delight them equally by his anecdotes of witchcraft, and of the direful omens and portentous sights and
sounds in the air, which prevailed in the earlier times of Connecticut;
and would frighten them wofully with speculations upon comets and
shooting stars, and with the alarming fact that the world did absolutely
turn round, and that they were half the time topsy-turvy!

But if there was a pleasure in all this, while snugly cuddling in the
chimney-corner of a chamber that was all of a ruddy glow from the
crackling wood-fire, and where, of course, no spectre dared to show his
face, it was dearly purchased by the terrors of his subsequent walk homewards. What fearful shapes and shadows beset his path amidst the dim
and ghastly glare of a snowy night!—With what wistful look did he eye
every trembling ray of light streaming across the waste fields from some
distant window!—How often was he appalled by some shrub covered with
snow, which, like a sheeted spectre, beset his very path!—How often did
he shrink with curdling awe at the sound of his own steps on the frosty
crust beneath his feet; and dread to look over his shoulder, lest he should
behold some uncouth being tramping close behind him!—and how often
was he thrown into complete dismay by some rushing blast, howling
among the trees, in the idea that it was the Galloping Hessian on one of
his nightly scourings!

All these, however, were mere terrors of the night, phantoms of the
mind that walk in darkness; and though he had seen many spectres in

* The whip-poor-will is a bird which is only heard at night. It receives its name from
its note, which is thought to resemble those words.

his time, and been more than once beset by Satan in divers shapes, in his lonely perambulations, yet daylight put an end to all these evils; and he would have passed a pleasant life of it, in despite of the devil and all his works, if his path had not been crossed by a being that causes more perplexity to mortal man than ghosts, goblins, and the whole race of witches put together, and that was—a woman.

Among the musical disciples who assembled, one evening in each week, to receive his instruction in psalmody, was Katrina Van Tassel, the daughter and only child of a substantial Dutch farmer. She was a blooming lass of fresh eighteen; plump as a partridge; ripe and melting and rosy-cheeked as one of her father's peaches, and universally famed, not merely for her beauty, but her vast expectations. She was withal a little of a coquette, as might be perceived even in her dress, which was a mixture of ancient and modern fashions, as most suited to set off her charms. She wore the ornaments of pure yellow gold, which her great-great-grandmother had brought over from Saardam; the tempting stomacher of the olden time; and withal a provokingly short petticoat, to display the prettiest foot and ankle in the country round.

Ichabod Crane had a soft and foolish heart towards the sex; and it is not to be wondered at that so tempting a morsel soon found favor in his eyes; more especially after he had visited her in her paternal mansion. Old Baltus Van Tassel was a perfect picture of a thriving, contented, liberal-hearted farmer. He seldom, it is true, sent either his eyes or his thoughts beyond the boundaries of his own farm; but within those everything was snug, happy, and well-conditioned. He was satisfied with his wealth, but not proud of it; and piqued himself upon the hearty abundance rather than the style in which he lived. His stronghold was situated on the banks of the Hudson, in one of those green, sheltered, fertile nooks in which the Dutch farmers are so fond of nestling. A great elm-tree spread its broad branches over it; at the foot of which bubbled up a spring of the softest and sweetest water, in a little well, formed of a barrel; and then stole sparkling away through the grass, to a neighboring brook, that bubbled along among alders and dwarf willows. Hard by the farm-house was a vast barn, that might have served for a church; every window and crevice of which seemed bursting forth with the treasures of the farm; the flail was busily resounding within it from morning till night; swallows and martins skimmed twittering about the eaves; and rows of pigeons, some with one eye turned up, as if watching the weather, some with their heads under their wings, or buried in their bosoms, and others swelling, and cooing, and bowing about their dames, were enjoying the sunshine on the roof. Sleek unwieldly porkers were grunting in the repose and abundance of their pens; whence sallied forth, now and then, troops of sucking pigs, as if to snuff the air. A stately squadron of snowy geese were riding in an adjoining pond, convoying whole fleets of ducks; regiments of turkeys were gobbling through the farm-yard, and guinea fowls fretting about it, like ill-tempered housewives, with their peevish discontented cry. Before the barn-door strutted the gallant cock, that pattern of a husband, a warrior, and a fine gentleman, clapping his burnished wings, and crowing in the pride and gladness of his heart— sometimes tearing up the earth with his feet, and then generously calling his ever-hungry family of wives and children to enjoy the rich morsel which he had discovered.

The pedagogue's mouth watered, as he looked upon this sumptuous promise of luxurious winter fare. In his devouring mind's eye he pictured to himself every roasting-pig running about with a pudding in his belly, and an apple in his mouth; the pigeons were snugly put to bed in a comfortable pie, and tucked in with a coverlet of crust; the geese were swimming in their own gravy; and the ducks pairing cosily in dishes, like snug married couples, with a decent competency of onion-sauce. In the porkers he saw carved out the future sleek side of bacon, and juicy relishing ham; not a turkey but he beheld daintily trussed up, with its gizzard under its wing, and, peradventure, a necklace of savory sausages; and even bright chanticleer himself lay sprawling on his back, in a side-dish, with uplifted claws, as if craving that quarter which his chivalrous spirit disdained to ask while living.

As the enraptured Ichabod fancied all this, and as he rolled his great green eyes over the fat meadow-lands, the rich fields of wheat, of rye, of buckwheat, and Indian corn, and the orchards burdened with ruddy fruit, which surrounded the warm tenement of Van Tassel, his heart yearned after the damsel who was to inherit these domains, and his imagination expanded with the idea how they might be readily turned into cash, and the money invested in immense tracts of wild land, and shingle palaces in the wilderness. Nay, his busy fancy already realized his hopes, and presented to him the blooming Katrina, with a whole family of children, mounted on the top of a wagon loaded with household trumpery, with pots and kettles dangling beneath; and he beheld himself bestriding a pacing mare, with a colt at her heels, setting out for Kentucky, Tennessee, or the Lord knows where.

When he entered the house, the conquest of his heart was complete. It was one of those spacious farm-houses, with high-ridged, but lowly-sloping roofs, built in the style handed down from the first Dutch settlers; the low projecting eaves forming a piazza along the front, capable of being closed up in bad weather. Under this were hung flails, harness, various utensils of husbandry, and nets for fishing in the neighboring river. Benches were built along the sides for summer use; and a great spinning-wheel at one end, and a churn at the other, showed the various uses to which this important porch might be devoted. From this piazza the wondering Ichabod entered the hall, which formed the centre of the mansion and the place of usual residence. Here, rows of resplendent pewter, ranged on a long dresser, dazzled his eyes. In one corner stood a huge bag of wool ready to be spun; in another a quantity of linsey-woolsey just from the loom; ears of Indian corn, and strings of dried apples and peaches, hung in gay festoons along the walls, mingled with the gaud of red peppers; and a door left ajar gave him a peep into the best parlor, where the claw-footed chairs and dark mahogany tables shone like mirrors; and irons, with their accompanying shovel and tongs, glistened from their covert of asparagus tops; mock-oranges and conch-shells decorated the mantel-piece; strings of various colored birds' eggs were suspended above it; a great ostrich egg was hung from the centre of the room, and a corner-cupboard, knowingly left open, displayed immense treasures of old silver and well-mended china.

From the moment Ichabod laid his eyes upon these regions of delight, the peace of his mind was at an end, and his only study was how to gain the affections of the peerless daughter of Van Tassel. In this enterprise, however, he had more real difficulties than generally fell to the lot of a knight-errant of yore, who seldom had anything but giants, enchanters, fiery dragons, and such like easily conquered adversaries, to contend with; and had to make his way merely through gates of iron and brass, and walls of adamant, to the castle-keep, where the lady of his heart was confined; all which he achieved as easily as a man would carve his way to the centre of a Christmas pie; and then the lady gave him her hand as a matter of course. Ichabod, on the contrary, had to win his way to the heart of a country coquette, beset with a labyrinth of whims and caprices, which were forever presenting new difficulties and impediments; and he had to encounter a host of fearful adversaries of real flesh and blood, the numerous rustic admirers, who beset every portal to her heart; keeping a watchful and angry eye upon each other, but ready to fly out in the common cause against any new competitor.

Among these the most formidable was a burly, roaring, roistering blade, of the name of Abraham, or, according to the Dutch abbreviation, Brom Van Brunt, the hero of the country round, which rang with his feats of strength and hardihood. He was broad-shouldered, and double-jointed, with short curly black hair, and a bluff but not unpleasant countenance, having a mingled air of fun and arrogance. From his Herculean frame and great powers of limb, he had received the nickname of BROM BONES, by which he was universally known. He was famed for great knowledge and skill in horsemanship, being as dexterous on horseback as a Tartar. He was foremost at all races and cockfights; and, with the ascendency which bodily strength acquires in rustic life, was the umpire in all disputes, setting his hat on one side, and giving his decisions with an air and tone admitting of no gainsay or appeal. He was always ready for either a fight or a frolic; but had more mischief than ill-will in his composition; and, with all his overbearing roughness, there was a strong dash of waggish good-humor at bottom. He had three or four boon companions, who regarded him as their model, and at the head of whom he scoured the country, attending every scene of feud or merriment for miles round. In cold weather he was distinguished by a fur cap, surmounted with a flaunting fox's tail; and when the folks at a country gathering descried this well-known crest at a distance, whisking about among a squad of hard riders, they always stood by for a squall. Sometimes his crew would be heard dashing along past the farmhouses at midnight, with whoop and halloo, like a troop of Don Cossacks; and the old dames, startled out of their sleep, would listen for a moment till the hurry-scurry had clattered by, and then exclaim, "Ay, there goes Brom Bones and his gang!" The neighbors looked upon him with a mixture of awe, admiration, and good-will; and when any madcap prank, or rustic brawl, occurred in the vicinity, always shook their heads, and warranted Brom Bones was at the bottom of it.

This rantipole hero had for some time singled out the blooming Katrina for the object of his uncouth gallantries; and though his amorous toyings were something like the gentle caresses and endearments of a bear, yet it was whispered that she did not altogether discourage his hopes. Certain it is, his advances were signals for rival candidates to retire, who felt no inclination to cross a lion in his amours; insomuch, that, when his horse was seen tied to Van Tassel's paling, on a Sunday night, a sure sign that his master was courting, or, as it is termed, "sparking," within, all other suitors passed by in despair, and carried the war into other quarters.

Such was the formidable rival with whom Ichabod Crane had to contend, and, considering all things, a stouter man than he would have shrunk from the competition, and a wiser man would have despaired. He had, however, a happy mixture of pliability and perseverance in his nature; he was in form and spirit like a supplejack—yielding, but tough; though he bent, he never broke; and though he bowed beneath the slightest pressure, yet, the moment it was away—jerk! he was as erect, and carried his head as high as ever.

To have taken the field openly against his rival would have been madness; for he was not a man to be thwarted in his amours, any more than that stormy lover, Achilles. Ichabod, therefore, made his advances in a quiet and gently insinuating manner. Under cover of his character of singing-master, he had made frequent visits at the farm-house; not that he had anything to apprehend from the meddlesome interference of parents, which is so often a stumbling-block in the path of lovers. Balt Van Tassel was an easy, indulgent soul; he loved his daughter better even than his pipe, and, like a reasonable man and an excellent father, let her have her way in everything. His notable little wife, too, had enough to do to attend to her housekeeping and manage her poultry; for, as she sagely observed, ducks and geese are foolish things, and must be looked after, but girls can take care of themselves. Thus while the busy dame bustled about the house, or plied her spinning-wheel at one end of the piazza, honest Balt would sit smoking his evening pipe at the other, watching the achievements of a little wooden warrior, who, armed with a sword in each hand, was most valiantly fighting the wind on the pinnacle of the barn. In the mean time, Ichabod would carry on his suit with the daughter by the side of the spring under the great elm, or sauntering along in the twilight,—that hour so favorable to the lover's eloquence.

I profess not to know how women's hearts are wooed and won. To me they have always been matters of riddle and admiration. Some seem to have but one vulnerable point, or door of access; while others have a thousand avenues, and may be captured in a thousand different ways. It is a great triumph of skill to gain the former, but a still greater proof of generalship to maintain possession of the latter, for the man must battle for his fortress at every door and window. He who wins a thousand common hearts is therefore entitled to some renown; but he who keeps undisputed sway over the heart of a coquette, is indeed a hero. Certain it is, this was not the case with the redoubtable Brom Bones; and from the moment Ichabod Crane made his advances, the interests of the former evidently declined; his horse was no longer seen tied at the palings on Sunday nights, and a deadly feud gradually arose between him and the preceptor of Sleepy Hollow.

Brom, who had a degree of rough chivalry in his nature, would fain have carried matters to open warfare, and have settled their pretensions to the lady according to the mode of those most concise and simple reasoners, the knights-errant of yore—by single combat; but Ichabod was too conscious of the superior might of his adversary to enter the lists against him: he had overheard a boast of Bones, that he would "double the schoolmaster up, and lay him on a shelf of his own school-house;" and he was too wary to give him an opportunity. There was something extremely provoking in this obstinately pacific system; it left Brom no alternative but to draw upon the funds of rustic waggery in his disposition, and to play off boorish practical jokes upon his rival. Ichabod became the object of whimsical persecution to Bones and his gang of rough riders. They harried his hitherto peaceful domains; smoked out his singing-school, by stopping up the chimney; broke into the school-house at night, in spite of its formidable fastenings of withe and window-stakes, and turned everything topsy-turvy: so that the poor schoolmaster began to think all the witches in the country held their meetings there. But what was still more annoying, Brom took opportunities of turning him into ridicule in presence of his mistress, and had a scoundrel dog whom he taught to whine in the most ludicrous manner, and introduced as a rival of Ichabod's to instruct her in psalmody.

In this way matters went on for some time, without producing any material effect on the relative situation of the contending powers. On a fine autumnal afternoon, Ichabod, in pensive mood, sat enthroned on the lofty stool whence he usually watched all the concerns of his little literary realm. In his hand he swayed a ferule, that sceptre of despotic power; the birch of justice reposed on three nails, behind the throne, a constant terror to evil-doers; while on the desk before him might be seen sundry contraband articles and prohibited weapons, detected upon the persons of idle urchins; such as half-munched apples, popguns, whirligigs, fly-cages, and whole legions of rampant little paper game-cocks. Apparently there had been some appalling act of justice recently inflicted, for his scholars were all busily intent upon their books, or slyly whispering behind them with one eye kept upon the master; and a kind of buzzing stillness reigned throughout the school-room. It was suddenly interrupted by the appearance of a negro, in tow-cloth jacket and trousers, a round-crowned fragment of a hat, like the cap of Mercury, and mounted on the back of a ragged, wild, half-broken colt, which he managed with a rope by way of halter. He came clattering up to the school-door with an invitation to Ichabod to attend a merry-making or "quilting frolic," to be held that evening at Mynheer Van Tassel's; and having delivered his message with that air of importance, and effort at fine language, which a negro is apt to display on petty embassies of the kind, he dashed over the brook, and was seen scampering away up the Hollow, full of the importance and hurry of his mission.

All was now bustle and hubbub in the late quiet school-room. The scholars were hurried through their lessons, without stopping at trifles; those who were nimble skipped over half with impunity, and those who were tardy had a smart application now and then in the rear, to quicken their speed, or help them over a tall word. Books were flung aside without being put away on the shelves, inkstands were overturned, benches thrown down, and the whole school was turned loose an hour before the usual time, bursting forth like a legion of young imps, yelping and racketing about the green, in joy at their early emancipation.

The gallant Ichabod now spent at least an extra half-hour at his toilet, brushing and furbishing up his best and indeed only suit of rusty black, and arranging his looks by a bit of broken looking-glass, that hung up in the school-house. That he might make his appearance before his mistress in the true style of a cavalier, he borrowed a horse from the farmer with whom he was domiciliated, a choleric old Dutchman, of the name of Hans Van Ripper, and, thus gallantly mounted, issued forth, like a knight-errant in quest of adventures. But it is meet I should, in the true spirit of romantic story, give some account of the looks and equipments of my hero and his steed. The animal he bestrode was a broken-down plough-horse, that had outlived almost everything but his viciousness. He was gaunt and shagged, with a ewe neck and a head like a hammer; his rusty mane and tail were tangled and knotted with burrs; one eye had lost its pupil, and was glaring and spectral; but the other had the gleam of a genuine devil in it. Still he must have had fire and mettle in his day, if we may judge from the name he bore of Gunpowder. He had, in fact, been a favorite steed of his master's, the choleric Van Ripper, who was a furious rider, and had infused, very probably, some of his own spirit into the animal; for, old and broken-down as he looked, there was more of the lurking devil in him than in any young filly in the country.

Ichabod was a suitable figure for such a steed. He rode with short stirrups, which brought his knees nearly up to the pommel of the saddle; his sharp elbows stuck out like grasshoppers'; he carried his whip perpendicularly in his hand, like a sceptre, and, as his horse jogged on, the motion of his arms was not unlike the flapping of a pair of wings. A small wool hat rested on the top of his nose, for so his scanty strip of forehead might be called; and the skirts of his black coat fluttered out almost to the horse's tail. Such was the appearance of Ichabod and his steed, as they shambled out of the gate of Hans Van Ripper, and it was altogether such an apparition as is seldom to be met with in broad daylight.

It was, as I have said, a fine autumnal day, the sky was clear and serene, and nature wore that rich and golden livery which we always associate with the idea of abundance. The forests had put on their sober brown and yellow, while some trees of the tenderer kind had been nipped by the frosts into brilliant dyes of orange, purple, and scarlet. Streaming files of wild ducks began to make their appearance high in the air; the bark of the squirrel might be heard from the groves of beech and hickory nuts, and the pensive whistle of the quail at intervals from the neighboring stubble-field.

The small birds were taking their farewell banquets. In the fulness of their revelry, they fluttered, chirping and frolicking, from bush to bush, and tree to tree, capricious from the very profusion and variety around them. There was the honest cock-robin, the favorite game of stripling sportsmen, with its loud querulous notes; and the twittering blackbirds flying in sable clouds; and the golden-winged woodpecker, with his crimson crest, his broad black gorget, and splendid plumage; and the cedar-bird, with its red-tipt wings and yellow-tipt tail, and its little monteiro cap of feathers; and the blue jay, that noisy coxcomb, in his gay light-blue coat and white under-clothes, screaming and chattering, nodding and bobbing and bowing, and pretending to be on good terms with every songster of the grove.

As Ichabod jogged slowly on his way, his eye, ever open to every symptom of culinary abundance, ranged with delight over the treasures of jolly autumn. On all sides he beheld vast store of apples; some hanging in oppressive opulence on the trees; some gathered into baskets and barrels for the market; others heaped up in rich piles for the cider-press. Farther on he beheld great fields of Indian corn, with its golden ears peeping from their leafy coverts, and holding out the promise of cakes and hasty-pudding; and the yellow pumpkins lying beneath them, turning up their fair round bellies to the sun, and giving ample prospects of the most luxurious of pies; and anon he passed the fragrant buckwheat fields, breathing the odor of the bee-hive, and as he beheld them, soft antici-pations stole over his mind of dainty slapjacks, well buttered, and gar-nished with honey or treacle, by the delicate little dimpled hand of Katrina Van Tassel.

Thus feeding his mind with many sweet thoughts and "sugared sup-positions," he journeyed along the sides of a range of hills which look out upon some of the goodliest scenes of the mighty Hudson. The sun gradu-ally wheeled his broad disk down into the west. The wide bosom of the Tappan Zee lay motionless and glossy, excepting that here and there a gentle undulation waved and prolonged the blue shadow of the distant mountain. A few amber clouds floated in the sky, without a breath of air to move them. The horizon was of a fine golden tint, changing gradually into a pure apple-green, and from that into the deep blue of the mid-heaven. A slanting ray lingered on the woody crests of the precipices that overhung some parts of the river, giving greater depth to the dark-gray and purple of their rocky sides. A sloop was loitering in the distance, dropping slowly down with the tide, her sail hanging uselessly against the mast; and as the reflection of the sky gleamed along the still water, it seemed as if the vessel was suspended in the air.

It was toward evening that Ichabod arrived at the castle of the Heer Van Tassel, which he found thronged with the pride and flower of the adjacent country. Old farmers, a spare leathern-faced race, in homespun coats and breeches, blue stockings, huge shoes, and magnificent pewter buckles. Their brisk withered little dames, in close crimped caps, long-waisted shortgowns, homespun petticoats, with scissors and pincushions, and gay calico pockets hanging on the outside. Buxom lasses, almost as antiquated as their mothers, excepting where a straw hat, a fine ribbon, or perhaps a white frock, gave symptoms of city innovation. The sons, in short square-skirted coats with rows of stupendous brass buttons, and their hair generally queued in the fashion of the times, especially if they could procure an eel-skin for the purpose, it being esteemed, throughout the country, as a potent nourisher and strengthener of the hair.

Brom Bones, however, was the hero of the scene, having come to the gathering on his favorite steed, Daredevil, a creature, like himself, full of mettle and mischief, and which no one but himself could manage. He was, in fact, noted for preferring vicious animals, given to all kinds of tricks, which kept the rider in constant risk of his neck, for he held a tractable well-broken horse as unworthy of a lad of spirit.

Fain would I pause to dwell upon the world of charms that burst upon the enraptured gaze of my hero, as he entered the state parlor of Van Tassel's mansion. Not those of the bevy of buxom lasses, with their luxurious display of red and white; but the ample charms of a genuine Dutch country tea-table, in the sumptuous time of autumn. Such heaped-up platters of cakes of various and almost indescribable kinds, known only to experienced Dutch housewives! There was the doughty doughnut, the tenderer oly koek, and the crisp and crumbling cruller; sweet cakes and short cakes, ginger-cakes and honey-cakes, and the whole family of cakes. And then there were apple-pies and peach-pies and pumpkin-pies; besides slices of ham and smoked beef; and moreover delectable dishes of preserved plums, and peaches, and pears, and quinces; not to mention broiled shad and roasted chickens; together with bowls of milk and cream, all mingled higgledy-piggledy, pretty much as I have enumerated them, with the motherly tea-pot sending up its clouds of vapor from the midst—Heaven bless the mark! I want breath and time to discuss this banquet as it deserves, and am too eager to get on with my story. Happily, Ichabod Crane was not in so great a hurry as his historian, but did ample justice to every dainty.

He was a kind and thankful creature, whose heart dilated in proportion as his skin was filled with good cheer; and whose spirits rose with eating as some men's do with drink. He could not help, too, rolling his large eyes round him as he ate, and chuckling with the possibility that he might one day be lord of all this scene of almost unimaginable luxury and splendor. Then, he thought, how soon he'd turn his back upon the old school-house; snap his fingers in the face of Hans Van Ripper, and every other niggardly patron, and kick any itinerant pedagogue out-of-doors that should dare to call him comrade!

Old Baltus Van Tassel moved about among his guests with a face dilated with content and good-humor, round and jolly as the harvest-moon. His hospitable attentions were brief, but expressive, being confined to a shake of the hand, a slap on the shoulder, a loud laugh, and a pressing invitation to "fall to, and help themselves."

And now the sound of the music from the common room, or hall, summoned to the dance. The musician was an old gray-headed negro, who had been the itinerant orchestra of the neighborhood for more than half a century. His instrument was as old and battered as himself. The greater part of the time he scraped on two or three strings, accompanying every movement of the bow with a motion of the head; bowing almost to the ground and stamping with his foot whenever a fresh couple were to start.

Ichabod prided himself upon his dancing as much as upon his vocal powers. Not a limb, not a fibre about him was idle; and to have seen his loosely hung frame in full motion, and clattering about the room, you would have thought Saint Vitus himself, that blessed patron of the dance, was figuring before you in person. He was the admiration of all the negroes; who, having gathered, of all ages and sizes, from the farm and the neighborhood, stood forming a pyramid of shining black faces at every door and window, gazing with delight at the scene, rolling their white eyeballs, and showing grinning rows of ivory from ear to ear. How could the flogger of urchins be otherwise than animated and joyous? the lady of his heart was his partner in the dance, and smiling graciously in reply to all his amorous oglings; while Brom Bones, sorely smitten with love and jealousy, sat brooding by himself in one corner.

When the dance was at an end, Ichabod was attracted to a knot of the sager folks, who, with old Van Tassel, sat smoking at one end of the piazza, gossiping over former times, and drawing out long stories about the war.

This neighborhood, at the time of which I am speaking, was one of those highly favored places which abound with chronicle and great men. The British and American line had run near it during the war; it had, therefore, been the scene of marauding, and infested with refugees, cowboys, and all kinds of border chivalry. Just sufficient time had elapsed to enable each story-teller to dress up his tale with a little becoming fiction, and, in the indistinctness of his recollection, to make himself the hero of every exploit.

There was the story of Doffue Martling, a large blue-bearded Dutchman, who had nearly taken a British frigate with an old iron nine-pounder from a mud breastwork, only that his gun burst at the sixth discharge. And there was an old gentleman who shall be nameless, being too rich a mynheer to be lightly mentioned, who, in the battle of Whiteplains, being an excellent master of defence, parried a musket-ball with a small sword, insomuch that he absolutely felt it whiz round the blade, and glance off at the hilt; in proof of which he was ready at any time to show the sword, with the hilt a little bent. There were several more that had been equally great in the field, not one of whom but was persuaded that he had a considerable hand in bringing the war to a happy termination.

But all these were nothing to the tales of ghosts and apparitions that succeeded. The neighborhood is rich in legendary treasures of the kind. Local tales and superstitions thrive best in these sheltered long-settled retreats; but are trampled underfoot by the shifting throng that forms the population of most of our country places. Besides, there is no encouragement for ghosts in most of our villages, for they have scarcely had time to finish their first nap, and turn themselves in their graves, before their surviving friends have travelled away from the neighborhood; so that when they turn out at night to walk their rounds, they have no acquaintance left to call upon. This is perhaps the reason why we so seldom hear of ghosts, except in our long-established Dutch communities.

The immediate cause, however, of the prevalence of supernatural stories in these parts was doubtless owing to the vicinity of Sleepy Hollow. There was a contagion in the very air that blew from that haunted region; it breathed forth an atmosphere of dreams and fancies infecting all the land. Several of the Sleepy Hollow people were present at Van Tassel's, and, as usual, were doling out their wild and wonderful legends. Many dismal tales were told about funeral trains, and mourning cries and wailings heard and seen about the great tree where the unfortunate Major André was taken, and which stood in the neighborhood. Some mention was made also of the woman in white, that haunted the dark glen at Raven Rock, and was often heard to shriek on winter nights before a storm, having perished there in the snow. The chief part of the stories, however, turned upon the favorite spectre of Sleepy Hollow, the headless horseman, who had been heard several times of late, patrolling the country; and, it was said, tethered his horse nightly among the graves in the churchyard.

The sequestered situation of this church seems always to have made it a favorite haunt of troubled spirits. It stands on a knoll, surrounded by locust-trees and lofty elms, from among which its decent whitewashed walls shine modestly forth, like Christian purity beaming through the shades of retirement. A gentle slope descends from it to a silver sheet of water, bordered by high trees, between which, peeps may be caught at the blue hills of the Hudson. To look upon its grass-grown yard, where the sunbeams seem to sleep so quietly, one would think that there at least the dead might rest in peace. On one side of the church extends a wide woody dell, along which raves a large brook among broken rocks and trunks of fallen trees. Over a deep black part of the stream, not far from the church, was formerly thrown a wooden bridge; the road that led to it, and the bridge itself, were thickly shaded by overhanging trees, which cast a gloom about it, even in the daytime, but occasioned a fearful darkness at night. This was one of the favorite haunts of the headless horseman; and the place where he was most frequently encountered. The tale was told of old Brouwer, a most heretical disbeliever in ghosts, how he met the horseman returning from his foray into Sleepy Hollow, and was obliged to get up behind him; how they galloped over bush and brake, over hill and swamp, until they reached the bridge; when the horseman suddenly turned into a skeleton, threw old Brouwer into the brook, and sprang away over the tree-tops with a clap of thunder.

This story was immediately matched by a thrice marvellous adventure of Brom Bones, who made light of the galloping Hessian as an arrant jockey. He affirmed that, on returning one night from the neighboring village of Sing Sing, he had been overtaken by this midnight trooper; that he had offered to race with him for a bowl of bunch, and should have won it too, for Dareddevil beat the goblin horse all hollow, but, just as they came to the church-bridge, the Hessian bolted, and vanished in a flash of fire.

All these tales, told in that drowsy undertone with which men talk in the dark, the countenances of the listeners only now and then receiving a casual gleam from the glare of a pipe, sank deep in the mind of Ichabod. He repaid them in kind with large extracts from his invaluable author, Cotton Mather, and added many marvellous events that had taken place in his native State of Connecticut, and fearful sights which he had seen in his nightly walks about the sleepy Hollow.

The revel now gradually broke up. The old farmers gathered together their families in their wagons, and were heard for some time rattling along the hollow roads, and over the distant hills. Some of the damsels mounted on pillions behind their favorite swains, and their light-hearted laughter, mingling with the clatter of hoofs, echoed along the silent woodlands, sounding fainter and fainter until they gradually died away—and the late scene of noise and frolic was all silent and deserted. Ichabod only lingered behind, according to the custom of country lovers, to have a *tête-à-tête* with the heiress, fully convinced that he was now on the high road to success. What passed at this interview I will not pretend to say, for in fact I do not know. Something, however, I fear me, must have gone wrong, for he certainly sallied forth, after no very great interval, with an air quite desolate and chopfallen.—Oh, these women! these women! Could that girl have been playing off any of her coquettish tricks?—Was her encouragement of the poor pedagogue all a mere sham to secure her conquest of his rival?—Heaven only knows, not I!—Let it suffice to say, Ichabod stole forth with the air of one who had been sacking a hen-roost, rather than a fair lady's heart. Without looking to the right or left to notice the scene of rural wealth on which he had so often gloated, he went straight to the stable, and with several hearty cuffs and kicks, roused his steed most uncourteously from the comfortable quarters in which he was soundly sleeping, dreaming of mountains of corn and oats, and whole valleys of timothy and clover.

It was the very witching time of night that Ichabod, heavy-hearted and crestfallen, pursued his travel homewards, along the sides of the lofty hills which rise above Tarry Town, and which he had traversed so cheerily in the afternoon. The hour was as dismal as himself. Far below him, the Tappan Zee spread its dusky and indistinct waste of waters, with here and there the tall mast of a sloop riding quietly at anchor under the land. In the dead hush of midnight he could even hear the barking of the watch-dog from the opposite shore of the Hudson; but it was so vague and faint as only to give an idea of his distance from this faithful companion of man. Now and then, too, the long-drawn crowing of a cock, accidently awakened, would sound far, far off, from some farm-house away among the hills—but it was like a dreaming sound in his ear. No signs of life occurred near him, but occasionally the melancholy chirp of a cricket, or perhaps the guttural twang of a bull-frog, from a neighboring marsh, as if sleeping uncomfortably, and turning suddenly in his bed.

All the stories of ghosts and goblins that he had heard in the afternoon, now came crowding upon his recollection. The night grew darker and darker; the stars seemed to sink deeper in the sky, and driving clouds occasionally hid them from his sight. He had never felt so lonely and dismal. He was, moreover, approaching the very place where many of the scenes of the ghost-stories had been laid. In the centre of the road stood an enormous tulip-tree, which towered like a giant above all the other trees of the neighborhood, and formed a kind of landmark. Its limbs were gnarled, and fantastic, large enough to form trunks for ordinary trees, twisting down almost to the earth, and rising again into the air. It was connected with the tragical story of the unfortunate André, who had been taken prisoner hard by; and was universally known by the name of Major André's tree. The common people regarded it with a mixture of respect and superstition, partly out of sympathy for the fate of its ill-starred namesake, and partly from the tales of strange sights and doleful lamentations told concerning it.

As Ichabod approached this fearful tree, he began to whistle: he thought his whistle was answered,—it was but a blast sweeping sharply through the dry branches. As he approached a little nearer, he thought he saw something white, hanging in the midst of the tree,—he paused and ceased whistling; but on looking more narrowly, pereceived that it was a place where the tree had been scathed by lightning, and the white wood laid bare. Suddenly he heard a groan,—his teeth chattered and his knees smote against the saddle: it was but the rubbing of one huge bough upon another, as they were swayed about by the breeze. He passed the tree in safety; but new perils lay before him.

About two hundred yards from the tree a small brook crossed the road, and ran into a marshy and thickly wooded glen, known by the name of Wiley's swamp. A few rough logs, laid side by side, served for a bridge over this stream. On that side of the road where the brook entered the wood, a group of oaks and chestnuts, matted thick with wild grape-vines, threw a cavernous gloom over it. To pass this bridge was the severest trial. It was at this identical spot that the unfortunate André was captured, and under the covert of those chestnuts and vines were the sturdy yeomen concealed who surprised him. This has ever since been considered a haunted stream, and fearful are the feelings of the school boy who has to pass it alone after dark.

As he approached the stream, his heart began to thump; he summoned up, however, all his resolution, gave his horse half a score of kicks in the ribs, and attempted to dash briskly across the bridge; but instead of start-ing forward, the perverse old animal made a lateral movement, and ran broadside against the fence. Ichabod, whose fears increased with the de-lay, jerked the reins on the other side, and kicked lustily with the contrary foot: it was all in vain; his steed started, it is true, but it was only to plunge to the opposite side of the road into a thicket of brambles and alder bushes. The schoolmaster now bestowed both whip and heel upon the starveling ribs of old Gunpowder, who dashed forward, snuffling and snorting, but came to a stand just by the bridge, with a suddenness that had nearly sent his rider sprawling over his head. Just at this moment a plashy tramp by the side of the bridge caught the sensitive ear of Ichabod. In the dark shadow of the grove, on the margin of the brook, he beheld something huge, misshapen, black, and towering. It stirred not, but seemed gathered up in the gloom, like some gigantic monster ready to spring upon the traveller.

The hair of the affrighted pedagogue rose upon his head with terror. What was to be done? To turn and fly was not too late; and besides, what chance was there of escaping ghost or goblin, if such it was, which could ride upon the wings of the wind? Summoning up, therefore, a show of courage, he demanded in stammering accents—"Who are you?" He re-ceived no reply. He repeated his demand in a still more agitated voice. Still there was no answer. Once more he cudgelled the sides of the in-flexible Gunpowder, and, shutting his eyes, broke forth with involuntary fervor into a psalm-tune. Just then the shadowy object of alarm put itself in motion, and, with a scramble and a bound, stood at once in the middle of the road. Though the night was dark and dismal, yet the form of the unknown might now in some degree be ascertained. He appeared to be a horseman of large dimensions, and mounted on a black horse of powerful frame. He made no offer of molestation or sociability, but kept aloof on one side of the road, jogging along on the blind side of old Gunpowder, who had now got over his fright and waywardness.

Ichabod, who had no relish for this strange midnight companion, and bethought himself on the adventure of Brom Bones with the Galloping Hessian, now quickened his steed, in hopes of leaving him behind. The stranger, however, quickened his horse to an equal pace. Ichabod pulled up, and fell into a walk, thinking to lag behind,—the other did the same. His heart began to sink within him; he endeavored to resume his psalm-tune, but his parched tongue clove to the roof of his mouth, and he could not utter a stave. There was something in the moody and dogged silence of this pertinacious companion, that was mysterious and appalling. It was soon fearfully accounted for. On mounting a rising ground, which brought the figure of his fellow-traveller in relief against the sky, gigantic in height, and muffled in a cloak, Ichabod was horror-struck, on perceiving that he was headless!—but his horror was still more increased, on observing that the head, which should have rested on his shoulders, was carried before him on the pommel of the saddle: his terror rose to desperation; he rained a shower of kicks and blows upon Gunpowder, hoping, by a sudden movement, to give his companion the slip, —but the spectre started full jump with him. Away then they dashed, through thick and thin; stones flying, and sparks flashing at every bound. Ichabod's flimsy garments fluttered in the air, as he stretched his long lank body away over his horse's head, in the eagerness of his flight.

They had now reached the road which turns off to Sleepy Hollow; but Gunpowder, who seemed possessed with a demon, instead of keeping up it, made an opposite turn, and plunged headlong downhill to the left. This road leads through a sandy hollow, shaded by trees for about a quarter of a mile, where it crosses the bridge famous in goblin story, and just beyond swells the green knoll on which stands the whitewashed church.

As yet the panic of the steed had given his unskilful rider an apparent advantage in the chase; but just as he had got half-way through the hollow, the girths of the saddle gave way, and he felt it slipping from under him. He seized it by the pommel, and endeavored to hold it firm, but in vain; and had just time to save himself by clasping old Gunpowder round the neck, when the saddle fell to earth, and he heard it trampled underfoot by his pursuer. For a moment the terror of Hans Van Ripper's wrath passed across his mind—for it was his Sunday saddle; but this was no time for petty fears; the goblin was hard on his haunches; and (unskilful rider that he was!) he had much ado to maintain his seat; sometimes slipping on one side, sometimes on another, and sometimes jolted on the high ridge of his horse's backbone, with a violence that he verily feared would cleave him asunder.

An opening in the trees now cheered him with the hopes that the church-bridge was at hand. The wavering reflection of a silver star in the bosom of the brook told him that he was not mistaken. He saw the walls of the church dimly glaring under the trees beyond. He recollected the place where Brom Bones's ghostly competitor had disappeared. "If I can but reach that bridge," thought Ichabod, "I am safe." Just then he heard the black steed panting and blowing close behind him; he even fancied that he felt his hot breath. Another convulsive kick in the ribs, and old Gunpowder sprang upon the bridge; he thundered over the resounding planks; he gained the opposite side; and now Ichabod cast a look behind to see if his pursuer should vanish, according to rule, in a flash of fire and brimstone. Just then he saw the goblin rising in his stirrups, and in the very act of hurling his head at him. Ichabod endeavored to dodge the horrible missile, but too late. It encountered his cranium with a tremendous crash,—he was tumbled headlong into the dust, and Gunpowder, the black steed, and the goblin rider, passed by like a whirlwind.

The next morning the old horse was found without his saddle, and with the bridle under his feet, soberly cropping the grass at his master's gate. Ichabod did not make his appearance at breakfast;—dinner-hour came, but no Ichabod. The boys assembled at the school-house, and strolled idly about the banks of the brook; but no schoolmaster. Hans Van Ripper now began to feel some uneasiness about the fate of poor Ichabod, and his saddle. An inquiry was set on foot, and after diligent investigation they came upon his traces. In one part of the road leading to the church was found the saddle trampled in the dirt; the tracks of horses' hoofs deeply dented in the road, and evidently at furious speed, were traced to the bridge, beyond which, on the bank of a broad part of the brook, where the water ran deep and black, was found the hat of the unfortunate Ichabod, and close beside it a shattered pumpkin.

The brook was searched, but the body of the schoolmaster was not to be discovered. Hans Van Ripper, as executor of his estate, examined the bundle which contained all his worldly effects. They consisted of two shirts and a half; two stocks for the neck; a pair or two of worsted stockings; an old pair of corduroy small-clothes; a rusty razor; a book of psalm-tunes, full of dogs' ears, and a broken pitchpipe. As to the books and furniture of the school-house, they belonged to the community, excepting Cotton Mather's History of Witchcraft, a New England Almanac, and a book of dreams and fortune-telling; in which last was a sheet of foolscap much scribbled and blotted in several fruitless attempts to make a copy of verses in honor of the heiress of Van Tassel. These magic books and the poetic scrawl were forthwith consigned to the flames by Hans Van Ripper; who from that time forward determined to send his children no more to school; observing, that he never knew any good come of this same reading and writing. Whatever money the schoolmaster possessed, and he had received his quarter's pay but a day or two before, he must have had about his person at the time of his disappearance.

The mysterious event caused much speculation at the church on the following Sunday. Knots of gazers and gossips were collected in the churchyard, at the bridge, and at the spot where the hat and pumpkin had been found. The stories of Brouwer, of Bones, and a whole budget of others, were called to mind; and when they had diligently considered them all, and compared them with the symptoms of the present case, they shook their heads, and came to the conclusion that Ichabod had been carried off by the Galloping Hessian. As he was a bachelor, and in nobody's debt, nobody troubled his head any more about him. The school was removed to a different quarter of the Hollow, and another pedagogue reigned in his stead.

It is true, an old farmer, who had been down to New York on a visit several years after, and from whom this account of the ghostly adventure was received, brought home the intelligence that Ichabod Crane was still alive; that he had left the neighborhood, partly through fear of the goblin and Hans Van Ripper, and partly in mortification at having been suddenly dismissed by the heiress; that he had changed his quarters to a distant part of the country; had kept school and studied law at the same time, had been admitted to the bar, turned politician, electioneered, written for the newspapers, and finally had been made a justice of the Ten Pound Court. Brom Bones too, who shortly after his rival's disappearance conducted the blooming Katrina in triumph to the altar, was observed to look exceedingly knowing whenever the story of Ichabod was related, and always burst into a hearty laugh at the mention of the pumpkin; which led some to suspect that he knew more about the matter than he chose to tell.

The old country wives, however, who are the best judges of these matters, maintain to this day that Ichabod was spirited away by supernatural means; and it is a favorite story often told about the neighborhood round the winter evening fire. The bridge became more than ever an object of superstitious awe, and that may be the reason why the road has been altered of late years, so as to approach the church by the border of the mill-pond. The school-house, being deserted, soon fell to decay, and was reported to be haunted by the ghost of the unfortunate pedagogue; and the ploughboy, loitering homeward of a still summer evening, has often fancied his voice at a distance, chanting a melancholy psalm-tune among the tranquil solitudes of Sleepy Hollow.

POSTSCRIPT,

Found in the Handwriting of Mr. Knickerbocker

The preceding Tale is given, almost in the precise words in which I heard it related at a Corporation meeting of the ancient city of Manhattoes, at which were present many of its sagest and most illustrious burghers. The narrator was a pleasant, shabby, gentlemanly old fellow, in pepper-and-salt clothes, with a sadly humorous face; and one whom I strongly suspected of being poor,—he made such efforts to be entertaining. When his story was concluded, there was much laughter and approbation, particularly from two or three deputy aldermen, who had been asleep the greater part of the time. There was, however, one tall, dry-looking old gentleman, with beetling eyebrows, who maintained a grave and rather severe face throughout: now and then folding his arms, inclining his head, and looking down upon the floor, as if turning a doubt over in his mind. He was one of your wary men, who never laugh, but upon good grounds—when they have reason and the law on their side. When the mirth of the rest of the company had subsided and silence was restored, he leaned one arm on the elbow of his chair, and, sticking the other akimbo, demanded, with a slight but exceedingly sage motion of the head, and contraction of the brow, what was the moral of the story, and what it went to prove?

The story-teller, who was just putting a glass of wine to his lips, as a refreshment after his toils, paused for a moment, looked at his inquirer with an air of infinite deference, and, lowering the glass slowly to the table, observed, that the story was intended most logically to prove:—

"That there is no situation in life but has its advantages and pleasures—provided we will but take a joke as we find it:

"That, therefore, he that runs races with goblin troopers is likely to have rough riding of it.

"Ergo, for a country schoolmaster to be refused the hand of a Dutch heiress, is a certain step to high preferment in the state."

The cautious old gentleman knit his brows tenfold closer after this explanation, being sorely puzzled by the ratiocination of the syllogism; while, methought, the one in pepper-and-salt eyed him with something of a triumphant leer. At length he observed, that all this was very well, but still he thought the story a little on the extravagant—there were one or two points on which he had his doubts.

"Faith, sir," replied the story-teller, "as to that matter, I don't believe one half of it myself."

D. K.

Augustus B. Longstreet (1790–1870)

Georgia Scenes (1835) by Augustus B. Longstreet is the first major work of the "frontier" or "Southwestern" humorists who also include T. B. Thorpe, Johnson J. Hooper, and George Washington Harris. These writers had their heyday before the Civil War, significantly influencing such contemporaries as Edgar Allan Poe and Herman Melville and leaving an imprint upon later authors such as Mark Twain, Ernest Hemingway, and William Faulkner. In general, "frontier" humor stimulated a literature which was mirthful, realistic, free of sentimentality, uninhibited in references to sex and other physical matters, accurate in rendering vernacular speech, colloquial in style, and sufficiently curious about character to portray the ordinary man as more than an animal and sometimes even worthy of admiration. None of the elements of "frontier" humor were new in American literature; many of the most capable "frontier" humorists were familiar with American and English literary traditions where such elements were to be found and also knew the work of contemporary humorists such as Washington Irving and Charles Dickens. The "frontier" humorists were usually educated, upper-class professionals who had been either born or educated in the old, established Northern and Southern states or whose families had migrated from them not too long before the 1800's. A variety of social and personal circumstances led these men to combine old literary elements into a new and unique humorous literature. Living in the expanding, unsettled, and turbulent states of the old Southwest (Georgia, Alabama, Mississippi, and Louisiana), Longstreet and his fellows pursued their careers as lawyers, doctors, teachers, politicians, and newspapermen in a world which was chaotic and disturbingly free of established cultural values. Their work required them to travel frequently under crude and trying conditions, bringing them into intimate contact with new types of men, with new occupations, virtues, and adventures. Accustomed to writing in connection with their professional duties, the men who became "frontier" humorists began to set forth their mingled delight and fear at the incongruous contrasts arising from the collision of new and old cultures. Outlets for their ambivalent writings were at hand in scores of newly founded newspapers, some of them edited by the "frontier" humorists and generally without staff or free-lance contributors to fill the papers' empty columns.

Longstreet's sketches, which he began printing in his Milledgeville (Georgia) *Southern Recorder* in 1833, at first reading seem to contain more fear than delight. A native Georgian, Longstreet had studied law in Federalist Connecticut and was successively a lawyer, judge, newspaper editor, politician, Methodist minister, and college president. The violence, crudity, and amorality of the "new country" evoked his explicit condemnation. His fictional sketches purported to be documentary records of tumultuous social history; he often emphasized his own moral and social distance from distressing events and persons by framing his accounts with opening and closing sections composed in a genteel, eighteenth-century essay style. But "The Horse-Swap" (1833) and other pieces reveal that, in addition to composing righteous, respectable satire, Longstreet also expressed a deeply affectionate and amused interest in his varied characters, in their dialect, and in their way of life. Furthermore, Longstreet laughed as derisively and pleasantly at members of his own class as he did at poor whites. *Georgia Scenes* drew an enthusiastic review from Poe: "Seldom— perhaps never in our lives—have we laughed as immoderately over any book as over the one now before us." "The Horse-Swap" received Poe's special praise for "its delineation of Southern bravado, and the keen sense of the ludicrous evinced in the portraiture of the steeds."

TEXT: *Georgia Scenes*, Augusta, Ga., 1835. COMMENTARY: John Donald Wade, *Augustus Baldwin Longstreet*, New York, 1924.

THE HORSE-SWAP

During the session of the Supreme Court in the village of ——, about three weeks ago, when a number of people were collected in the principal street of the village, I observed a young man riding up and down the street, as I supposed, in a violent passion. He galloped this way, then that, and then the other; spurred his horse to one group of citizens, then to another; then dashed off at half-speed, as if fleeing from danger; and, suddenly checking his horse, returned first in a pace, then in a trot, and then in a canter. While he was performing these various evolutions he cursed, swore, whooped, screamed, and tossed himself in every attitude which man could assume on horseback. In short, he *cavorted* most magnanimously (a term which, in our tongue, expresses all that I have described, and a little more), and seemed to be setting all creation at defiance. As I like to see all that is passing, I determined to take a position a little nearer to him, and to ascertain, if possible, what it was that affected him so sensibly. Accordingly I approached a crowd before which he had stopped for a moment, and examined it with the strictest scrutiny. But I could see nothing in it that seemed to have anything to do with the cavorter. Every man appeared to be in good humor, and all minding their own business. Not one so much as noticed the principal figure. Still he went on. After a semicolon pause, which my appearance seemed to produce (for he eyed me closely as I approached), he fetched a whoop, and swore that "he could out-swap any live man, woman, or child that ever walked these hills, or that ever straddled horseflesh since the days of old daddy Adam." "Stranger," said he to me, "did you ever see the *Yallow* Blossom from Jasper?"

"No," said I, "but I have often heard of him."

"I'm the boy," continued he; "perhaps a *leetle*, jist a *leetle* of the best man at a horse-swap that ever trod shoe-leather."

I began to feel my situation a little awkward, when I was relieved by a man somewhat advanced in years, who stepped up and began to survey the *"Yallow Blossom's"* horse with much apparent interest. This drew the rider's attention, and he turned the conversation from me to the stranger.

"Well, my old coon," said he, "do you want to swap *hosses?*"

"Why, I don't know," replied the stranger; "I believe I've got a beast I'd trade with you for that one, if you like him."

"Well, fetch up your nag, my old cock; you're jist the lark I wanted to get hold of. I am perhaps a *leetle*, jist a *leetle*, of the best man at a horse-swap that ever stole *cracklins* out of his mammy's fat gourd. Where's your *hoss?*"

"I'll bring him presently; but I want to examine your horse a little."

"Oh, look at him," said the Blossom, alighting and hitting him a cut— "look at him! He's the best piece of *hoss*flesh in the thirteen united univarsal worlds. There's no sort o' mistake in little Bullet. He can pick up miles on his feet, and fling 'em behind him as fast as the next man's *hoss*, I don't care where he comes from. And he can keep at it as long as the sun can shine without resting."

During this harangue little Bullet looked as if he understood it all, believed it, and was ready at any moment to verify it. He was a horse of goodly countenance, rather expressive of vigilance than fire; though an unnatural appearance of fierceness was thrown into it by the loss of his ears, which had been cropped pretty close to his head. Nature had done but little for Bullet's head and neck; but he managed, in a great measure, to hide their defects by bowing perpetually. He had obviously suffered severely for corn; but if his ribs and hip-bones had not disclosed the fact, *he* never would have done it; for he was in all respects as cheerful and happy as if he commanded all the corn-cribs and fodder-stacks in Georgia. His height was about twelve hands; but as his shape partook somewhat of that of the giraffe, his haunches stood much lower. They were short, strait, peaked, and concave. Bullet's tail, however, made amends for all his defects. All that the artist could do to beautify it had been done; and all that horse could do to compliment the artist, Bullet did. His tail was nicked in superior style, and exhibited the line of beauty in so many directions that it could not fail to hit the most fastidious taste in some of them. From the root it dropped into a graceful festoon, then rose in a handsome curve, then resumed its first direction, and then mounted suddenly upward like a cypress knee to a perpendicular of about two and a half inches. The whole had a careless and bewitching inclination to the right. Bullet obviously knew where his beauty lay, and took all occasions to display it to the best advantage. If a stick cracked, or if any one moved suddenly about him, or coughed, or hawked, or spoke a little louder than common, up went Bullet's tail like lightning; and if the *going up* did not please, the *coming down* must of necessity, for it was as different from the other movement as was its direction. The first was a bold and rapid flight upward, usually to an angle of forty-five degrees. In this position he kept his interesting appendage until he satisfied himself that nothing in particular was to be done; when he commenced dropping it by half inches, in second beats, then in triple time, then faster and shorter, and faster and shorter still, until it finally died away imperceptibly into its natural position. If I might compare sights to sounds, I should say its *settling* was more like the note of a locust than anything else in nature.

Either from native sprightliness of disposition, from uncontrollable activity, or from an unconquerable habit of removing flies by the stamping of the feet, Bullet never stood still, but always kept up a gentle fly-scaring movement of his limbs, which was peculiarly interesting.

"I tell you, man," proceeded the Yellow Blossom, "he's the best live hoss that ever trod the grit of Georgia. Bob Smart knows the hoss. Come here, Bob, and mount this hoss, and show Bullet's motions." Here Bullet bristled up, and looked as if he had been hunting for Bob all day long, and had just found him. Bob sprang on his back. "Boo-oo-oo!" said Bob, with a fluttering noise of the lips, and away went Bullet as if in a quarter race, with all his beauties spread in handsome style.

"Now fetch him back," said Blossom. Bullet turned and came in pretty much as he went out.

"Now trot him by." Bullet reduced his tail to *customary*, sidled to the right and left airily, and exhibited at least three varieties of trot in the short space of fifty yards.

"Make him pace!" Bob commenced twitching the bridle and kicking at the same time. These inconsistent movements obviously (and most naturally) disconcerted Bullet; for it was impossible for him to learn from them whether he was to proceed or stand still. He started to trot, and was told that wouldn't do. He attempted a canter, and was checked again. He stopped, and was urged to go on. Bullet now rushed into the wide field of experiment, and struck out a gait of his own that completely turned the tables upon his rider, and certainly deserved a patent. It seemed to have derived its elements from the jig, the minuet, and the cotillion. If it was not a pace, it certainly had *pace* in it, and no man would venture to call it anything else; so it passed off to the satisfaction of the owner.

"Walk him!" Bullet was now at home again, and he walked as if money were staked on him.

The stranger, whose name I afterwards learned was Peter Ketch, having examined Bullet to his heart's content, ordered his son Neddy to go and bring up Kit. Neddy soon appeared upon Kit, a well-formed sorrel of the middle size, and in good order. His *tout-ensemble* threw Bullet entirely in the shade, though a glance was sufficient to satisfy any one that Bullet had the decided advantage of him in point of intellect.

"Why, man," said Blossom, "do you bring such a hoss as that to trade for Bullet? Oh, I see, you've no notion of trading!"

"Ride him off, Neddy!" said Peter. Kit put off at a handsome lope.

"Trot him back!" Kit came in at a long, sweeping trot, and stopped suddenly at the crowd.

"Well," said Blossom, "let me look at him; maybe he'll do to plough."

"Examine him," said Peter, taking hold the bridle close to the mouth; "he's nothing but a tacky. He ain't as *pretty* a horse as Bullet, I know, but he'll do. Start 'em together for a hundred and fifty *mile*, and if Kit ain't twenty mile ahead of him at the coming out, any man may take Kit for nothing. But he's a monstrous mean horse, gentlemen; any man may see that. He's the scariest horse, too, you ever saw. He won't do to hunt on, nohow. Stranger, will you let Neddy have your rifle to shoot off him? Lay the rifle between his ears, Neddy, and shoot at the blaze in that stump. Tell me when his head is high enough."

Ned fired and hit the blaze, and Kit did not move a hair's-breadth.

"Neddy, take a couple of sticks, and beat on that hogshead at Kit's tail."

Ned made a tremendous rattling, at which Bullet took fright, broke his bridle, and dashed off in grand style, and would have stopped all further negotiations by going home in disgust, had not a traveller arrested him and brought him back; but Kit did not move.

"I tell you, gentlemen," continued Peter, "he's the scariest horse you ever saw. He ain't as gentle as Bullet, but he won't do any harm if you watch him. Shall I put him in a cart, gig, or wagon for you, stranger? He'll cut the same capers there he does here. He's a monstrous mean horse."

During all this time Blossom was examining him with the nicest scrutiny. Having examined his frame and limbs, he now looked at his eyes.

"He's got a curious look out of his eyes," said Blossom.

"Oh yes, sir," said Peter, "just as blind as a bat. Blind horses always have clear eyes. Make a motion at his eyes, if you please, sir."

Blossom did so, and Kit threw up his head rather as if something pricked him under the chin than as if fearing a blow. Blossom repeated the experiment, and Kit jerked back in considerable astonishment.

"Stone-blind, you see, gentlemen," proceeded Peter; "but he's just as good to travel of a dark night as if he had eyes."

"Blame my buttons," said Blossom, "if I like them eyes!"

"No," said Peter, "nor I neither. I'd rather have 'em made of diamonds; but they'll do—if they don't show as much white as Bullet's."

"Well," said Blossom, "make a pass at me."

"No," said Peter, "you made the banter, now make your pass."

"Well, I'm never afraid to price my hosses. You must give me twenty-five dollars boot."

"Oh, certainly; say fifty, and my saddle and bridle in. Here, Neddy, my son, take away daddy's horse."

"Well," said Blossom, "I've made my pass, now you make yours."

"I'm for short talk in a horse-swap, and therefore always tell a gentleman at once what I mean to do. You must give me ten dollars."

Blossom swore absolutely, roundly, and profanely that he never would give boot.

"Well," said Peter, "I didn't care about trading; but you cut such high shines that I thought I'd like to back you out, and I've done it. Gentlemen, you see I've brought him to a back."

"Come, old man," said Blossom, "I've been joking with you. I begin to think you do want to trade; therefore, give me five dollars and take Bullet. I'd rather lose ten dollars any time than not make a trade, though I hate to fling away a good hoss."

"Well," said Peter, "I'll be as clever as you are. Just put the five dollars on Bullet's back, and hand him over; it's a trade."

Blossom swore again, as roundly as before, that he would not give boot; and, said he, "Bullet wouldn't hold five dollars on his back, nohow. But, as I bantered you, if you say an even swap, here's at you."

"I told you," said Peter, "I'd be as clever as you; therefore, here goes two dollars more, just for trade sake. Give me three dollars, and it's a bargain."

Blossom repeated his former assertion; and here the parties stood for a long time, and the bystanders (for many were now collected) began to taunt both parties. After some time, however, it was pretty unanimously decided that the old man had backed Blossom out.

At length Blossom swore he "never should be backed out for three dollars after bantering a man"; and, accordingly, they closed the trade.

"Now," said Blossom, as he handed Peter the three dollars, "I'm a man that, when he makes a bad trade, makes the most of it until he can make a better. I'm for no rues and after-claps."

"That's just my way," said Peter; "I never goes to law to mend my bargains."

"Ah, you're the kind of boy I love to trade with. Here's your hoss, old man. Take the saddle and bridle off him, and I'll strip yours; but lift up the blanket easy from Bullet's back, for he's a mighty tender-backed hoss."

The old man removed the saddle, but the blanket stuck fast. He attempted to raise it, and Bullet bowed himself, switched his tail, danced a little, and gave signs of biting.

"Don't hurt him, old man," said Blossom, archly; "take it off easy. I am, perhaps, a leetle of the best man at a horse-swap that ever catched a coon."

Peter continued to pull at the blanket more and more roughly, and Bullet became more and more *cavortish*, insomuch that, when the blanket came off, he had reached the *kicking* point in good earnest.

The removal of the blanket disclosed a sore on Bullet's back that seemed to have defied all medical skill. It measured six full inches in length and four in breadth, and had as many features as Bullet had motions. My heart sickened at the sight; and I felt that the brute who had been riding him in that situation deserved the halter.

The prevailing feeling, however, was that of mirth. The laugh became loud and general at the old man's expense, and rustic witticisms were liberally bestowed upon him and his late purchase. These Blossom continued to provoke by various remarks. He asked the old man "if he thought Bullet would let five dollars lie on his back." He declared most seriously that he had owned that horse three months, and had never discovered before that he had a sore back, "or he never should have thought of trading him," etc., etc.

The old man bore it all with the most philosophic composure. He evinced no astonishment at his late discovery, and made no replies. But his son Neddy had not disciplined his feelings quite so well. His eyes opened wider and wider from the first to the last pull of the blanket, and when the whole sore burst upon his view, astonishment and fright seemed to contend for the mastery of his countenance. As the blanket disappeared, he stuck his hands in his breeches pockets, heaved a deep sigh, and lapsed into a profound reverie, from which he was only roused by the cuts at his father. He bore them as long as he could; and, when he could contain himself no longer, he began, with a certain wildness of expression which gave a peculiar interest to what he uttered: "His back's mighty bad off; but dod drot my soul if he's put it to daddy as bad as he thinks he has, for old Kit's both blind and *deef*, I'll be dod drot if he ein't!"

"The devil he is!" said Blossom.

"Yes, dod drot my soul if he *ein't!* You walk him, and see if he *ein't.* His eyes don't look like it; but he'd *jist as leve go agin the* house with you, or in a ditch, as anyhow. Now you go try him." The laugh was now turned on Blossom, and many rushed to test the fidelity of the little boy's report. A few experiments established its truth beyond controversy.

"Neddy," said the old man, "you oughtn't to try and make people discontented with their things. Stranger, don't mind what the little boy says.

If you can only get Kit rid of them little failings you'll find him all sorts of a horse. You are a *leetle* the best man at a horse-swap that ever I got hold of but don't fool away Kit. Come, Neddy, my son, let's be moving; the stranger seems to be getting snappish."

Ralph Waldo Emerson (1803–1882)

Thomas Carlyle, an effective humorist in his own right, held that no other American author but Benjamin Franklin could have written Ralph Waldo Emerson's *English Traits* (1856). The unique combination of "nobleness, wisdom, humor" highly regarded by Carlyle permeates the character sketches, anecdotes, and observations which Emerson wrote after visiting England for a second time in the late 1840's. The title of the chapter appearing below succinctly illustrates Emerson's intellectual wit and tongue-in-cheek mirthfulness. "Cockayne" alludes most obviously to the tiny land of arrogant self-indulgence satirized in the fourteenth-century English poem, *The Land of Cockaygne*; "Cockayne" is often used to designate the "Land of Cockneys"; finally, "cock" (male bird) symbolizes a braggart or boaster in popular nineteenth-century American humorous literature and in more esoteric humorous writings such as Melville's "Cock-A-Doodle-Doo!" and James' "The Point of View." Emerson's writings other than *English Traits* do not fuse the grave and the amusing as successfully. In them the racy images of the essays, the playfulness of "Fable" (1846), and the satiric tone of "Ode" (1847) seem to stand isolated from each other, a condition which often has led to their being overlooked as elements present in all of his works even though widely dispersed rather than integrated. The humor and earthiness of Emerson's youthful private journals, now being published for the first time in unexpurgated form, are so pronounced that Emerson must have found it excruciating to tone down those qualities of his temperament and all but conceal them in his published writings. The New England Brahmin paid a crippling price for his solemn pomposity. Only when he forgot about himself as a sober American institution was he again able to unleash the high humor of *English Traits*.

TEXT: "Fable" and "Ode," *The Complete Works of Ralph Waldo Emerson* (Centenary Edition), Boston, Mass., 1904, IX; *English Traits, Emerson's Complete Works* (Riverside Edition), Boston, Mass., 1883, V.

FABLE

The mountain and the squirrel
Had a quarrel,
And the former called the latter 'Little Prig;'
Bun replied,
'You are doubtless very big;

But all sorts of things and weather
Must be taken in together,
To make up a year
And a sphere.
And I think it no disgrace
To occupy my place.
If I'm not so large as you,
You are not so small as I,
And not half so spry.
I'll not deny you make
A very pretty squirrel track;
Talents differ; all is well and wisely put;
If I cannot carry forests on my back,
Neither can you crack a nut.'

COCKAYNE

The English are a nation of humorists. Individual right is pushed to the uttermost bound compatible with public order. Property is so perfect that it seems the craft of that race, and not to exist elsewhere. The king cannot step on an acre which the peasant refuses to sell. A testator endows a dog or a rookery, and Europe cannot interfere with his absurdity. Every individual has his particular way of living, which he pushes to folly, and the decided sympathy of his compatriots is engaged to back up Mr. Crump's whim by statutes and chancellors and horse-guards. There is no freak so ridiculous but some Englishman has attempted to immortalize by money and law. British citizenship is as omnipotent as Roman was. Mr. Cockayne is very sensible of this. The pursy man means by freedom the right to do as he pleases, and does wrong in order to feel his freedom, and makes a conscience of persisting in it.

He is intensely patriotic, for his country is so small. His confidence in the power and performance of his nation makes him provokingly incurious about other nations. He dislikes foreigners. Swedenborg, who lived much in England, notes "the similitude of minds among the English, in consequence of which they contract familiarity with friends who are of that nation, and seldom with others; and they regard foreigners as one looking through a telescope from the top of a palace regards those who dwell or wander about out of the city." A much older traveller, the Venetian who wrote the "Relation of England," [1] in 1500, says:—"The English are great lovers of themselves and of every thing belonging to them. They think that there are no other men than themselves and no other world

[1] Printed by the Camden Society.

but England; and whenever they see a handsome foreigner, they say that he looks like an Englishman and it is a great pity he should not be an Englishman; and whenever they partake of any delicacy with a foreigner, they ask him whether such a thing is made in his country." When he adds epithets of praise, his climax is, "So English"; and when he wishes to pay you the highest compliment, he says, I should not know you from an Englishman. France is, by its natural contrast, a kind of blackboard on which English character draws its own traits in chalk. This arrogance habitually exhibits itself in allusions to the French. I suppose that all men of English blood in America, Europe or Asia, have a secret feeling of joy that they are not French natives. Mr. Coleridge is said to have given public thanks to God, at the close of a lecture, that he had defended him from being able to utter a single sentence in the French language. I have found that Englishmen have such a good opinion of England, that the ordinary phrases in all good society, of postponing or disparaging one's own things in talking with a stranger, are seriously mistaken by them for an insuppressible homage to the merits of their nation; and the New Yorker or Pennsylvanian who modestly laments the disadvantage of a new country, log-huts and savages, is surprised by the instant and unfeigned commiseration of the whole company, who plainly account all the world out of England a heap of rubbish.

The same insular limitation pinches his foreign politics. He sticks to his traditions and usages, and, so help him God! he will force his island by-laws down the throat of great countries, like India, China, Canada, Australia, and not only so, but impose Wapping on the Congress of Vienna and trample down all nationalities with his taxed boots. Lord Chatham goes for liberty and no taxation without representation;—for that is British law; but not a hobnail shall they dare make in America, but buy their nails in England;—for that also is British law; and the fact that British commerce was to be re-created by the independence of America, took them all by surprise.

In short, I am afraid that English nature is so rank and aggressive as to be a little incompatible with every other. The world is not wide enough for two.

But beyond this nationality, it must be admitted, the island offers a daily worship to the old Norse god Brage, celebrated among our Scandinavian forefathers for his eloquence and majestic air. The English have a steady courage that fits them for great attempts and endurance: they have also a petty courage, through which every man delights in showing himself for what he is and in doing what he can; so that in all companies, each of them has too good an opinion of himself to imitate anybody. He hides no defect of his form, features, dress, connection, or birthplace, for he thinks every circumstance belonging to him comes recommended to you. If one of them have a bald, or a red, or a green head, or bow legs, or a scar, or mark, or a paunch, or a squeaking or a raven voice, he has persuaded himself that there is something modish and becoming in it, and that it sits well on him.

But nature makes nothing in vain, and this little superfluity of self-regard in the English brain is one of the secrets of their power and history. It sets every man on being and doing what he really is and can. It takes away a dodging, skulking, secondary air, and encourages a frank and manly bearing, so that each man makes the most of himself and loses no opportunity for want of pushing. A man's personal defects will commonly have, with the rest of the world, precisely that importance which they have to himself. If he makes light of them, so will other men. We all find in these a convenient meter of character, since a little man would be ruined by the vexation. I remember a shrewd politician, in one of our western cities, told me that "he had known several successful statesmen made by their foible." And another, an ex-governor of Illinois, said to me, "If the man knew anything, he would sit in a corner and be modest; but he is such an ignorant peacock that he goes bustling up and down and hits on extraordinary discoveries."

There is also this benefit in brag, that the speaker is unconsciously expressing his own ideal. Humor him by all means, draw it all out and hold him to it. Their culture generally enables the travelled English to avoid any ridiculous extremes of this self-pleasing, and to give it an agreeable air. Then the natural disposition is fostered by the respect which they find entertained in the world for English ability. It was said of Louis XIV., that his gait and air were becoming enough in so great a monarch, yet would have been ridiculous in another man; so the prestige of the English name warrants a certain confident bearing, which a Frenchman or Belgian could not carry. At all events, they feel themselves at liberty to assume the most extraordinary tone on the subject of English merits.

An English lady on the Rhine hearing a German speaking of her party as foreigners, exclaimed, "No, we are not foreigners; we are English; it is you that are foreigners." They tell you daily in London the story of the Frenchman and Englishman who quarrelled. Both were unwilling to fight, but their companions put them up to it; at last it was agreed that they should fight alone, in the dark, and with pistols: the candles were put out, and the Englishman, to make sure not to hit any body, fired up the chimney,—and brought down the Frenchman. They have no curiosity about foreigners, and answer any information you may volunteer with "Oh, Oh!" until the informant makes up his mind that they shall die in their ignorance, for any help he will offer. There are really no limits to this conceit, though brighter men among them make painful efforts to be candid.

The habit of brag runs through all classes, from the "Times" newspaper through politicians and poets, through Wordsworth, Carlyle, Mill and

Sydney Smith, down to the boys of Eton. In the gravest treatise on political economy, in a philosophical essay, in books of science, one is surprised
by the most innocent exhibition of unflinching nationality. In a tract on
Corn, a most amiable and accomplished gentleman writes thus:—"Though
Britain, according to Bishop Berkeley's idea, were surrounded by a wall
of brass ten thousand cubits in height, still she would as far excel the
rest of the globe in riches, as she now does both in this secondary quality
and in the more important ones of freedom, virtue and science." [2]

The English dislike the American structure of society, whilst yet trade,
mills, public education and Chartism are doing what they can to create
in England the same social condition. America is the paradise of the
economists; is the favorable exception invariably quoted to the rules of
ruin; but when he speaks directly of the Americans the islander forgets
his philosophy and remembers his disparaging anecdotes.

But this childish patriotism costs something, like all narrowness. The
English sway of their colonies has no root of kindness. They govern by
their arts and ability; they are more just than kind; and whenever an
abatement of their power is felt, they have not conciliated the affection
on which to rely.

Coarse local distinctions, as those of nation, province or town, are
useful in the absence of real ones; but we must not insist on these accidental lines. Individual traits are always triumphing over national ones.
There is no fence in metaphysics discriminating Greek, or English, or
Spanish science. Aesop and Montaigne, Cervantes and Saadi are men of
the world; and to wave our own flag at the dinner table or in the University is to carry the boisterous dulness of a fire-club into a polite circle.
Nature and destiny are always on the watch for our follies. Nature trips
us up when we strut; and there are curious examples in history on this
very point of national pride.

George of Cappadocia, born at Epiphania in Cilicia, was a low parasite
who got a lucrative contract to supply the army with bacon. A rogue and
informer, he got rich and was forced to run from justice. He saved his
money, embraced Arianism, collected a library, and got promoted by a
faction to the episcopal throne of Alexandria. When Julian came, A.D. 361,
George was dragged to prison; the prison was burst open by the mob and
George was lynched, as he deserved. And this precious knave became, in
good time, Saint George of England, patron of chivalry, emblem of victory and civility and the pride of the best blood of the modern world.

Strange, that the solid truth-speaking Briton should derive from an
impostor. Strange, that the New World should have no better luck,—
that broad America must wear the name of a thief. Amerigo Vespucci, the
pickledealer at Seville, who went out, in 1499, a subaltern with Hojeda,
and whose highest naval rank was boatswain's mate in an expedition that

[2] William Spence.

never sailed, managed in this lying world to supplant Columbus and baptize half the earth with his own dishonest name. Thus nobody can throw stones. We are equally badly off in our founders; and the false pickle-dealer is an offset to the false bacon-seller.

ODE

Inscribed to W. H. Channing

Though loath to grieve
The evil time's sole patriot,
I cannot leave
My honied thought
For the priest's cant,
Or statesman's rant.

If I refuse
My study for their politique,
Which at the best is trick,
The angry Muse
Puts confusion in my brain.

But who is he that prates
Of the culture of mankind,
Of better arts and life?
Go, blindworm, go,
Behold the famous States
Harrying Mexico
With rifle and with knife!

Or who, with accent bolder,
Dare praise the freedom-loving mountaineer?
I found by thee, O rushing Contoocook!
And in thy valleys, Agiochook!
The jackals of the negro-holder.

The God who made New Hampshire
Taunted the lofty land
With little men;—
Small bat and wren
House in the oak:—
If earth-fire cleave
The upheaved land, and bury the folk,
The southern crocodile would grieve.

Virtue palters; Right is hence;
Freedom praised, but hid;
Funeral eloquence
Rattles the coffin-lid.

What boots thy zeal,
O glowing friend,
That would indignant rend
The northland from the south?
Wherefore? to what good end?
Boston Bay and Bunker Hill
Would serve things still;—
Things are of the snake.

The horseman serves the horse,
The neatherd serves the neat,
The merchant serves the purse,
The eater serves his meat;
'T is the day of the chattel,
Web to weave, and corn to grind;
Things are in the saddle,
And ride mankind.

There are two laws discrete,
Not reconciled,—
Law for man, and law for thing;
The last builds town and fleet,
But it runs wild,
And doth the man unking.

'T is fit the forest fall,
The steep be graded,
The mountain tunnelled,
The sand shaded,
The orchard planted,
The glebe tilled,
The prairie granted,
The steamer built.

Let man serve law for man;
Live for friendship, live for love,
For truth's and harmony's behoof;
The state may follow how it can,
As Olympus follows Jove.

    Yet do not I implore
The wrinkled shopman to my sounding woods,

Nor bid the unwilling senator
Ask votes of thrushes in the solitudes.
Every one to his chosen work;—
Foolish hands may mix and mar;
Wise and sure the issues are.
Round they roll till dark is light,
Sex to sex, and even to odd;—
The over-god
Who marries Right to Might,
Who peoples, unpeoples,—
He who exterminates
Races by stronger races,
Black by white faces,—
Knows to bring honey
Out of the lion;
Grafts gentlest scion
On pirate and Turk.

The Cossack eats Poland,
Like stolen fruit;
Her last noble is ruined,
Her last poet mute:
Straight, into double band
The victors divide;
Half for freedom strike and stand;—
The astonished Muse finds thousands at her side.

Nathaniel Hawthorne (1804–1864)

The moral and intellectual concerns of Nathaniel Hawthorne did not prevent him from expressing what his friend Herman Melville described as "a wild moonlight of contemplative humor . . . a humor so spiritually gentle, so high, so deep, and yet so richly relishable, that it were hardly inappropriate in an angel. It is the very religion of mirth. . . ." Henry James later chided those who mistakenly judged Hawthorne to be gloomy and misanthropic: "The old Puritan moral sense, the consciousness of sin and hell, of the fearful nature of our responsibilities and the savage character of our Taskmaster—these things had been lodged in the mind of a man of Fancy, whose fancy had straightway begun to take liberties and play tricks with them—to judge them (Heaven forgive him!) from the poetic and aesthetic point of view, the point of view of entertainment and irony." Hawthorne's temper led him to range across the whole spectrum of humor from innocent merriment to "the fiercer, deeper, and more tragic power of laughter" which he extolled in *The House of the Seven Gables* (1851). It was natural for him in his most somber novel, *The Scarlet Letter* (1850), to note with admirable historical accuracy that the earliest Puritans had brought an Elizabethan heritage of joy and mirth to New England, then add regretfully that subsequent generations had "darkened the national visage" and made it necessary "to learn again the forgotten art of gayety." Hawthorne's writings contributed to the educational process by merging the profound themes, psychological introspection, and humor of the Puritans with the fantasy and farce of American folk humor and the satire and earthiness of eighteenth-century English humor. Because Hawthorne's humor was often bent upon exposing those who had "gone astray from reason and common sense," because it was often either ironic as in "Mrs. Bullfrog" (1837) and "Feathertop" (1852) or satiric and sometimes macabre as in "The Wedding Knell" (1836) and "Governor Pyncheon" (1851), the lighter aspects of Hawthorne's writing have been unwarrantably overlooked. This was the unhappy fate of his Puritan ancestors, and equally unmerited. Tall tales, jokes, verbal horse-play, sexual innuendoes, ludicrous characters, and gross buffoonery impart a racy verve to his fiction. Hawthorne, like Melville and Poe, incorporated the American humorous traditions of his own and earlier centuries and pointed the way to such later masters as Henry James, William Faulkner, and Nathanael West.

TEXT: "Mrs. Bullfrog," *The Complete Works of Nathaniel Hawthorne* (Riverside Edition), Boston, Mass., 1883, II; "Governor Pyncheon," *The House of the Seven Gables*, Riverside Edition, III. COMMENTARY: Arlin Turner, *Nathaniel Hawthorne*, New York, 1961.

MRS. BULLFROG

It makes me melancholy to see how like fools some very sensible people act in the matter of choosing wives. They perplex their judgments by a most undue attention to little niceties of personal appearance, habits, disposition, and other trifles which concern nobody but the lady herself. An unhappy gentleman, resolving to wed nothing short of perfection, keeps his heart and hand till both get so old and withered that no tolerable woman will accept them. Now this is the very height of absurdity. A kind Providence has so skilfully adapted sex to sex and the mass of individuals to each other, that, with certain obvious exceptions, any male and female may be moderately happy in the married state. The true rule is to ascertain that the match is fundamentally a good one, and then to take it for granted that all minor objections, should there be such, will vanish, if you let them alone. Only put yourself beyond hazard as to the real basis of matrimonial bliss, and it is scarcely to be imagined what miracles, in the way of recognizing smaller incongruities, connubial love will effect.

For my own part I freely confess that, in my bachelorship, I was precisely such an over-curious simpleton as I now advise the reader not to be. My early habits had gifted me with a feminine sensibility and too exquisite refinement. I was the accomplished graduate of a dry goods store, where, by dint of ministering to the whims of fine ladies, and suiting silken hose to delicate limbs, and handling satins, ribbons, chintzes, calicoes, tapes, gauze, and cambric needles, I grew up a very ladylike sort of a gentleman. It is not assuming too much to affirm that the ladies themselves were hardly so ladylike as Thomas Bullfrog. So painfully acute was my sense of female imperfection, and such varied excellence did I require in the woman whom I could love, that there was an awful risk of my getting no wife at all, or of being driven to perpetrate matrimony with my own image in the looking-glass. Besides the fundamental principle already hinted at, I demanded the fresh bloom of youth, pearly teeth, glossy ringlets, and the whole list of lovely items, with the utmost delicacy of habits and sentiments, a silken texture of mind, and, above all, a virgin heart. In a word, if a young angel just from paradise, yet dressed in earthly fashion, had come and offered me her hand, it is by no means certain that I should have taken it. There was every chance of my becoming a most miserable old bachelor, when, by the best luck in the world, I made a journey into another state, and was smitten by, and smote again, and wooed, won, and married, the present Mrs. Bullfrog, all in the space of a fortnight. Owing to these extempore measures, I not only gave my bride credit for certain perfections which have not as yet come to light, but also overlooked a few trifling defects, which, however, glimmered on my perception long before the close of the honeymoon. Yet, as there was no mistake about the fundamental principle aforesaid, I soon learned, as will be seen, to estimate Mrs. Bullfrog's deficiencies and superfluities at exactly their proper value.

The same morning that Mrs. Bullfrog and I came together as a unit, we took two seats in the stage-coach and began our journey towards my place of business. There being no other passengers, we were as much alone and as free to give vent to our raptures as if I had hired a hack for the matrimonial jaunt. My bride looked charmingly in a green silk calash and riding habit of pelisse cloth; and whenever her red lips parted with a smile, each tooth appeared like an inestimable pearl. Such was my passionate warmth that—we had rattled out of the village, gentle reader, and were lonely as Adam and Eve in paradise—I plead guilty to no less freedom than a kiss. The gentle eye of Mrs. Bullfrog scarcely rebuked me for the profanation. Emboldened by her indulgence, I threw back the calash from her polished brow, and suffered my fingers, white and delicate as her own, to stray among those dark and glossy curls which realized my daydreams of rich hair.

"My love," said Mrs. Bullfrog, tenderly, "you will disarrange my curls."

"Oh, no, my sweet Laura!" replied I, still playing with the glossy ringlet. "Even your fair hand could not manage a curl more delicately than mine. I propose myself the pleasure of doing up your hair in papers every evening at the same time with my own."

"Mr. Bullfrog," repeated she, "you must not disarrange my curls."

This was spoken in a more decided tone than I had happened to hear, until then, from my gentlest of all gentle brides. At the same time she put up her hand and took mine prisoner; but merely drew it away from the forbidden ringlet, and then immediately released it. Now, I am a fidgety little man, and always love to have something in my fingers; so that, being debarred from my wife's curls, I looked about me for any other plaything. On the front seat of the coach there was one of those small baskets in which travelling ladies who are too delicate to appear at a public table generally carry a supply of gingerbread, biscuits and cheese, cold ham, and other light refreshments, merely to sustain nature to the journey's end. Such airy diet will sometimes keep them in pretty good flesh for a week together. Laying hold of this same little basket, I thrust my hand under the newspaper with which it was carefully covered.

"What's this, my dear?" cried I; for the black neck of a bottle had popped out of the basket.

"A bottle of Kalydor, Mr. Bullfrog," said my wife, coolly taking the basket from my hands and replacing it on the front seat.

There was no possibility of doubting my wife's word; but I never knew genuine Kalydor, such as I use for my own complexion, to smell so much like cherry brandy. I was about to express my fears that the lotion would injure her skin, when an accident occurred which threatened more than a skin-deep injury. Our Jehu had carelessly driven over a heap of gravel and fairly capsized the coach, with the wheels in the air and our heels where our heads should have been. What became of my wits I cannot imagine; they have always had a perverse trick of deserting me just when they were most needed; but so it chanced, that in the confusion of our overthrow I quite forgot that there was a Mrs. Bullfrog in the world. Like many men's wives, the good lady served her husband as a stepping-stone. I had scrambled out of the coach and was instinctively settling my cravat, when somebody brushed roughly by me, and I heard a smart thwack upon the coachman's ear.

"Take that, you villain!" cried a strange, hoarse voice. "You have ruined me, you blackguard! I shall never be the woman I have been!"

And then came a second thwack, aimed at the driver's other ear; but which missed it, and hit him on the nose, causing a terrible effusion of blood. Now, who or what fearful apparition was inflicting this punishment on the poor fellow remained an impenetrable mystery to me. The blows were given by a person of grisly aspect, with a head almost bald, and sunken cheeks, apparently of the feminine gender, though hardly to be classed in the gentler sex. There being no teeth to modulate the voice, it had a mumbled fierceness, not passionate, but stern, which absolutely made me quiver like calf's-foot jelly. Who could the phantom be? The most awful circumstance of the affair is yet to be told: for this ogre, or whatever it was, had a riding habit like Mrs. Bullfrog's, and also a green silk calash dangling down her back by the strings. In my terror and turmoil of mind I could imagine nothing less than that the Old Nick, at the moment of our overturn, had annihilated my wife and jumped into her petticoats. This idea seemed the more probable, since I could nowhere perceive Mrs. Bullfrog alive, nor, though I looked very sharply about the coach, could I detect any traces of that beloved woman's dead body. There would have been a comfort in giving her Christian burial.

"Come, sir, bestir yourself! Help this rascal to set up the coach," said the hobgoblin to me; then, with a terrific screech to three countrymen at a distance, "Here, you fellows, ain't you ashamed to stand off when a poor woman is in distress?"

The countrymen, instead of fleeing for their lives, came running at full speed, and laid hold of the topsy-turvy coach. I, also, though a small-sized man, went to work like a son of Anak. The coachman, too, with the blood still streaming from his nose, tugged and toiled most manfully, dreading, doubtless, that the next blow might break his head. And yet, bemauled as the poor fellow had been, he seemed to glance at me with an eye of pity, as if my case were more deplorable than his. But I cherished a hope that all would turn out a dream, and seized the opportunity, as we raised the coach, to jam two of my fingers under the wheel, trusting that the pain would awaken me.

"Why, here we are, all to rights again!" exclaimed a sweet voice behind. "Thank you for your assistance, gentlemen. My dear Mr. Bullfrog, how you perspire! Do let me wipe your face. Don't take this little accident too much to heart, good driver. We ought to be thankful that none of our necks are broken."

"We might have spared one neck out of the three," muttered the driver, rubbing his ear and pulling his nose, to ascertain whether he had been cuffed or not. "Why, the woman's a witch!"

I fear that the reader will not believe, yet it is positively a fact, that there stood Mrs. Bullfrog, with her glossy ringlets curling on her brow, and two rows of orient pearls gleaming between her parted lips, which wore a most angelic smile. She had regained her riding habit and calash from the grisly phantom, and was, in all respects, the lovely woman who had been sitting by my side at the instant of our overturn. How she had happened to disappear, and who had supplied her place, and whence she did now return, were problems too knotty for me to solve. There stood my wife. That was the one thing certain among a heap of mysteries. Nothing remained but to help her into the coach, and plod on, through the journey of the day and the journey of life, as comfortably as we could. As the driver closed the door upon us, I heard him whisper to the three countrymen,—

"How do you suppose a fellow feels shut up in the cage with a she tiger?"

Of course this query could have no reference to my situation. Yet, unreasonable as it may appear, I confess that my feelings were not altogether so ecstatic as when I first called Mrs. Bullfrog mine. True, she was a sweet woman and an angel of a wife; but what if a Gorgon should return, amid the transports of our connubial bliss, and take the angel's place. I recollected the tale of a fairy, who half the time was a beautiful woman and half the time a hideous monster. Had I taken that very fairy to be the wife of my bosom? While such whims and chimeras were flitting across my fancy I began to look askance at Mrs. Bullfrog, almost expecting that the transformation would be wrought before my eyes.

To divert my mind, I took up the newspaper which had covered the little basket of refreshments, and which now lay at the bottom of the coach, blushing with a deep-red stain and emitting a potent spirituous fume from the contents of the broken bottle of Kalydor. The paper was two or three years old, but contained an article of several columns, in which I soon grew wonderfully interested. It was the report of a trial for breach of promise of marriage, giving the testimony in full, with fervid extracts from both the gentleman's and lady's amatory correspondence.

The deserted damsel had personally appeared in court, and had borne energetic evidence to her lover's perfidy and the strength of her blighted affections. On the defendant's part there had been an attempt, though insufficiently sustained, to blast the plaintiff's character, and a plea, in mitigation of damages, on account of her unamiable temper. A horrible idea was suggested by the lady's name.

"Madam," said I, holding the newspaper before Mrs. Bullfrog's eyes,— and, though a small, delicate, and thin-visaged man, I feel assured that I looked very terrific,—"madam," repeated I, through my shut teeth, "were you the plaintiff in this cause?"

"Oh, my dear Mr. Bullfrog," replied my wife, sweetly, "I thought all the world knew that!"

"Horror! horror!" exclaimed I, sinking back on the seat.

Covering my face with both hands, I emitted a deep and deathlike groan, as if my tormented soul were rending me asunder—I, the most exquisitely fastidious of men, and whose wife was to have been the most delicate and refined of women, with all the fresh dew-drops glittering on her virgin rosebud of a heart!

I thought of the glossy ringlets and pearly teeth; I thought of the Kalydor; I thought of the coachman's bruised ear and bloody nose; I thought of the tender love secrets which she had whispered to the judge and jury and a thousand tittering auditors,—and gave another groan!

"Mr. Bullfrog," said my wife.

As I made no reply, she gently took my hands within her own, removed them from my face, and fixed her eyes steadfastly on mine.

"Mr. Bullfrog," said she, not unkindly, yet with all the decision of her strong character, "let me advise you to overcome this foolish weakness, and prove yourself, to the best of your ability, as good a husband as I will be a wife. You have discovered, perhaps, some little imperfections in your bride. Well, what did you expect? Women are not angels. If they were, they would go to heaven for husbands; or, at least, be more difficult in their choice on earth."

"But why conceal those imperfections?" interposed I, tremulously.

"Now, my love, are not you a most unreasonable little man?" said Mrs. Bullfrog, patting me on the cheek. "Ought a woman to disclose her frailties earlier than the wedding day? Few husbands, I assure you, make the discovery in such good season, and still fewer complain that these trifles are concealed too long. Well, what a strange man you are! Poh! you are joking."

"But the suit for breach of promise!" groaned I.

"Ah, and is that the rub?" exclaimed my wife. "Is it possible that you view that affair in an objectionable light? Mr. Bullfrog, I never could have dreamed it! Is it an objection that I have triumphantly defended myself against slander and vindicated my purity in a court of justice? Or do you complain because your wife has shown the proper spirit of a woman, and punished the villain who trifled with her affections?"

"But," persisted I, shrinking into a corner of the coach, however,—for I did not know precisely how much contradiction the proper spirit of a woman would endure,—"but, my love, would it not have been more dignified to treat the villain with the silent contempt he merited?"

"That is all very well, Mr. Bullfrog," said my wife, slyly; "but, in that case, where would have been the five thousand dollars which are to stock your dry goods store?"

"Mrs. Bullfrog, upon your honor," demanded I, as if my life hung upon her words, "is there no mistake about those five thousand dollars?"

"Upon my word and honor there is none," replied she. "The jury gave me every cent the rascal had; and I have kept it all for my dear Bullfrog."

"Then, thou dear woman," cried I, with an overwhelming gush of tenderness, "let me fold thee to my heart. The basis of matrimonial bliss is secure, and all thy little defects and frailties are forgiven. Nay, since the result has been so fortunate, I rejoice at the wrongs which drove thee to this blessed lawsuit. Happy Bullfrog that I am!"

.

GOVERNOR PYNCHEON

Judge Pyncheon, while his two relatives have fled away with such ill-considered haste, still sits in the old parlor, keeping house, as the familiar phrase is, in the absence of its ordinary occupants. To him, and to the venerable House of the Seven Gables, does our story now betake itself, like an owl, bewildered in the daylight, and hastening back to his hollow tree.

The Judge has not shifted his position for a long while now. He has not stirred hand or foot, nor withdrawn his eyes so much as a hair's-breadth from their fixed gaze towards the corner of the room, since the footsteps of Hepzibah and Clifford creaked along the passage, and the outer door was closed cautiously behind their exit. He holds his watch in his left hand, but clutched in such a manner that you cannot see the dial-plate. How profound a fit of meditation! Or, supposing him asleep, how infantile a quietude of conscience, and what wholesome order in the gastric region, are betokened by slumber so entirely undisturbed with starts, cramp, twitches, muttered dream-talk, trumpet-blasts through the nasal organ, or any the slightest irregularity of breath! You must hold your own breath, to satisfy yourself whether he breathes at all. It is quite inaudible. You hear the ticking of his watch; his breath you do not hear. A most refreshing slumber, doubtless! And yet, the Judge cannot be asleep. His eyes are open! A veteran politician, such as he, would never fall asleep with wide-open eyes, lest some enemy or mischief-maker, taking him thus at unawares, should peep through these windows into his consciousness, and make strange discoveries among the reminiscences, projects, hopes, apprehensions, weaknesses, and strong points, which he has heretofore shared with nobody. A cautious man is proverbially said to sleep with one eye open. That may be wisdom. But not with both; for this were heedlessness! No, no! Judge Pyncheon cannot be asleep.

It is odd, however, that a gentleman so burdened with engagements,—and noted, too, for punctuality,—should linger thus in an old lonely mansion, which he has never seemed very fond of visiting. The oaken chair, to be sure, may tempt him with its roominess. It is, indeed, a spacious, and, allowing for the rude age that fashioned it, a moderately easy seat, with capacity enough, at all events, and offering no restraint to the Judge's breadth of beam. A bigger man might find ample accommodation in it. His ancestor, now pictured upon the wall, with all his English beef about him, used hardly to present a front extending from elbow to elbow of this chair, or a base that would cover its whole cushion. But there are better chairs than this,—mahogany, black-walnut, rosewood, spring-seated and damask-cushioned, with varied slopes, and innumerable artifices to make them easy, and obviate the irksomeness of too tame an ease,—a score of such might be at Judge Pyncheon's service. Yes! in a score of drawing-rooms he would be more than welcome. Mamma would advance to meet him, with outstretched hand; the virgin daughter, elderly as he has now got to be,—an old widower, as he smilingly describes himself,—would shake up the cushion for the Judge, and do her pretty little utmost to make him comfortable. For the Judge is a prosperous man. He cherishes his schemes, moreover, like other people, and reasonably brighter than most others; or did so, at least, as he lay abed this morning, in an agreeable half-drowse, planning the business of the day, and speculating on the probabilities of the next fifteen years. With his firm health, and the little inroad that age has made upon him, fifteen years or twenty—yes, or perhaps five-and-twenty!—are no more than he may fairly call his own. Five-and-twenty years for the enjoyment of his real estate in town and country, his railroad, bank, and insurance shares, his United States stock,—his wealth, in short, however invested, now in possession, or soon to be acquired; together with the public honors that have fallen upon him, and the weightier ones that are yet to fall! It is good! It is excellent! It is enough!

Still lingering in the old chair! If the Judge has a little time to throw away, why does not he visit the insurance office, as is his frequent custom, and sit awhile in one of their leathern-cushioned arm-chairs, listening to the gossip of the day, and dropping some deeply designed chance-word, which will be certain to become the gossip of to-morrow! And have not the bank directors a meeting at which it was the Judge's purpose to be present, and his office to preside? Indeed they have; and the hour is noted on a card, which is, or ought to be, in Judge Pyncheon's right vest-pocket. Let him go thither, and loll at ease upon his money-bags! He has lounged long enough in the old chair!

This was to have been such a busy day! In the first place, the interview with Clifford. Half an hour, by the Judge's reckoning, was to suffice for that; it would probably be less, but—taking into consideration that Hepzibah was first to be dealt with, and that these women are apt to make many words where a few would do much better—it might be safest to allow half an hour. Half an hour? Why, Judge, it is already two hours, by your own undeviatingly accurate chronometer! Glance your eye down at it and see! Ah! he will not give himself the trouble either to bend his head, or elevate his hand, so as to bring the faithful time-keeper within his range of vision! Time, all at once, appears to have become a matter of no moment with the Judge!

And has he forgotten all the other items of his memoranda? Clifford's affair arranged, he was to meet a State Street broker, who has undertaken to procure a heavy percentage, and the best of paper, for a few loose thousands which the Judge happens to have by him, uninvested. The wrinkled note-shaver will have taken his railroad trip in vain. Half an hour later, in the street next to this, there was to be an auction of real estate, including a portion of the old Pyncheon property, originally belonging to Maule's garden-ground. It has been alienated from the Pyncheons these four-score years; but the Judge had kept it in his eye, and had set his heart on reannexing it to the small demesne still left around the Seven Gables; and now, during this odd fit of oblivion, the fatal hammer must have fallen, and transferred our ancient patrimony to some alien possessor! Possibly, indeed, the sale may have been postponed till fairer weather. If so, will the Judge make it convenient to be present, and favor the auctioneer with his bid, on the proximate occasion?

The next affair was to buy a horse for his own driving. The one heretofore his favorite stumbled, this very morning, on the road to town, and must be at once discarded. Judge Pyncheon's neck is too precious to be risked on such a contingency as a stumbling steed. Should all the above business be seasonably got through with, he might attend the meeting of a charitable society; the very name of which, however, in the multiplicity of his benevolence, is quite forgotten; so that this engagement may pass unfulfilled, and no great harm done. And if he have time, amid the press of more urgent matters, he must take measures for the renewal of Mrs. Pyncheon's tombstone, which, the sexton tells him, has fallen on its marble face, and is cracked quite in twain. She was a praise-worthy woman enough, thinks the Judge, in spite of her nervousness, and the tears that she was so oozy with, and her foolish behavior about the coffee; and as she took her departure so seasonably, he will not grudge the second tombstone. It is better, at least, than if she had never needed any! The next item on his list was to give orders for some fruit-trees, of a rare variety, to be deliverable at his country-seat, in the ensuing autumn. Yes, buy them, by all means; and may the peaches be luscious in your mouth, Judge Pyncheon! After this comes something more important. A committee of his political party has besought him for a hundred or two of dollars, in addition to his previous disbursements, towards carrying on the fall campaign. The Judge is a patriot; the fate of the country is staked on the November election; and besides, as will be shadowed forth in another paragraph, he has no trifling stake of his own in the same great game. He will do what the committee asks; nay, he will be liberal beyond their expectations; they shall have a check for five hundred dollars, and more anon, if it be needed. What next? A decayed widow, whose husband was Judge Pyncheon's early friend, has laid her case of destitution before him, in a very moving letter. She and her fair daughter have scarcely bread to eat. He partly intends to call on her, to-day,—perhaps so—perhaps not,—accordingly as he may happen to have leisure, and a small bank-note.

Another business, which, however, he puts no great weight on (it is well, you know, to be heedful, but not over-anxious, as respects one's personal health),—another business, then, was to consult his family physician. About what, for Heaven's sake? Why, it is rather difficult to describe the symptoms. A mere dimness of sight and dizziness of brain, was it?—or a disagreeable choking, or stifling, or gurgling, or bubbling, in the region of the thorax, as the anatomists say?—or was it a pretty severe throbbing and kicking of the heart, rather creditable to him than otherwise, as showing that the organ had not been left out of the Judge's physical contrivance? No matter what it was. The doctor, probably, would smile at the statement of such trifles to his professional ear; the Judge would smile in his turn; and meeting one another's eyes, they would enjoy a hearty laugh together! But a fig for medical advice! The Judge will never need it.

Pray, pray, Judge Pyncheon, look at your watch, now! What—not a glance! It is within ten minutes of the dinner-hour! It surely cannot have slipped your memory that the dinner of to-day is to be the most important, in its consequences, of all the dinners you ever ate. Yes, precisely the most important; although, in the course of your somewhat eminent career, you have been placed high towards the head of the table, at splendid banquets, and have poured out your festive eloquence to ears yet echoing with Webster's mighty organ-tones. No public dinner this, however. It is merely a gathering of some dozen or so of friends from several districts of the State; men of distinguished character and influence, assembling, almost casually, at the house of a common friend, likewise distinguished, who will make them welcome to a little better than his ordinary fare.

Nothing in the way of French cookery, but an excellent dinner neverthe-less. Real turtle, we understand, and salmon, tautog, canvas-backs, pig, English mutton, good roast-beef, or dainties of that serious kind, fit for substantial country gentlemen, as these honorable persons mostly are. The delicacies of the season, in short, and flavored by a brand of old Madeira which has been the pride of many seasons. It is the Juno brand; a glorious wine, fragrant, and full of gentle might; a bottled-up happi-ness, put up for use; a golden liquid, worth more than liquid gold; so rare and admirable, that veteran wine-bibbers count it among their epochs to have tasted it! It drives away the heart-ache, and substitutes no head-ache! Could the Judge but quaff a glass, it might enable him to shake off the unaccountable lethargy which (for the ten intervening min-utes, and five to boot, are already past) has made him such a laggard at this momentous dinner. It would all but revive a dead man! Would you like to sip it now, Judge Pyncheon?

Alas, this dinner! Have you really forgotten its true object? Then let us whisper it, that you may start at once out of the oaken chair, which really seems to be enchanted, like the one in Comus, or that in which Moll Pitcher imprisoned your own grandfather. But ambition is a talisman more powerful than witchcraft. Start up, then, and, hurrying through the streets, burst in upon the company, that they may begin before the fish is spoiled! They wait for you; and it is little for your interest that they should wait. These gentlemen—need you be told it?—have assembled, not without purpose, from every quarter of the State. They are practised politicians, every man of them, and skilled to adjust those preliminary measures which steal from the people, without its knowledge, the power of choosing its own rulers. The popular voice, at the next gubernatorial election, though loud as thunder, will be really but an echo of what these gentlemen shall speak, under their breath, at your friend's festive board. They meet to decide upon their candidate. This little knot of subtle schemers will control the convention, and, through it, dictate to the party. And what worthier candidate,—more wise and learned, more noted for philanthropic liberality, truer to safe principles, tried oftener by public trusts, more spotless in private character, with a larger stake in the com-mon welfare, and deeper grounded, by hereditary descent, in the faith and practice of the Puritans,—what man can be presented for the suffrage of the people, so eminently combining all these claims to the chief-rulership as Judge Pyncheon here before us?

Make haste, then! Do your part! The meed for which you have toiled, and fought, and climbed, and crept, is ready for your grasp! Be present at this dinner!—drink a glass or two of that noble wine!—make your pledges in as low a whisper as you will!—and you rise up from table virtually governor of the glorious old State! Governor Pyncheon of Mas-sachusetts!

And is there no potent and exhilarating cordial in a certainty like this? It has been the grand purpose of half your lifetime to obtain it. Now, when there needs little more than to signify your acceptance, why do you sit so lumpishly in your great-great-grandfather's oaken chair, as if preferring it to the gubernatorial one? We have all heard of King Log; but, in these jostling times, one of that royal kindred will hardly win the race for an elective chief-magistracy.

Well! it is absolutely too late for dinner! Turtle, salmon, tautog, woodcock, boiled turkey, South-Down mutton, pig, roast-beef, have vanished, or exist only in fragments, with lukewarm potatoes, and gravies crusted over with cold fat. The Judge, had he done nothing else, would have achieved wonders with his knife and fork. It was he, you know, of whom it used to be said, in reference to his ogre-like appetite, that his Creator made him a great animal, but that the dinner-hour made him a great beast. Persons of his large sensual endowments must claim indulgence, at their feeding-time. But, for once, the Judge is entirely too late for dinner! Too late, we fear, even to join the party at their wine! The guests are warm and merry; they have given up the Judge; and, concluding that the Free-Soilers have him, they will fix upon another candidate. Were our friend now to stalk in among them, with that wide-open stare, at once wild and stolid, his ungenial presence would be apt to change their cheer. Neither would it be seemly in Judge Pyncheon, generally so scrupulous in his attire, to show himself at a dinner-table with that crimson stain upon his shirt-bosom. By the by, how came it there? It is an ugly sight, at any rate; and the wisest way for the Judge is to button his coat closely over his breast, and, taking his horse and chaise from the livery-stable, to make all speed to his own house. There, after a glass of brandy and water, and a mutton-chop, a beefsteak, a broiled fowl, or some such hasty little dinner and supper all in one, he had better spend the evening by the fireside. He must toast his slippers a long while, in order to get rid of the chilliness which the air of this vile old house has sent curdling through his veins.

Up, therefore, Judge Pyncheon, up! You have lost a day. But tomorrow will be here anon. Will you rise, betimes, and make the most of it? To-morrow! To-morrow! To-morrow! We, that are alive, may rise betimes to-morrow. As for him that has died to-day, his morrow will be the resurrection morn.

Meanwhile the twilight is glooming upward out of the corners of the room. The shadows of the tall furniture grow deeper, and at first become more definite; then, spreading wider, they lose their distinctness of outline in the dark gray tide of oblivion, as it were, that creeps slowly over the various objects, and the one human figure sitting in the midst of them. The gloom has not entered from without; it has brooded here all day, and now, taking its own inevitable time, will possess itself of everything. The Judge's face, indeed, rigid, and singularly white, refuses to melt into this universal solvent. Fainter and fainter grows the light. It is as if another double-handful of darkness had been scattered through the air. Now it is no longer gray, but sable. There is still a faint appearance at the window; neither a glow, nor a gleam, nor a glimmer,—any phrase of light would express something far brighter than this doubtful perception, or sense, rather, that there is a window there. Has it yet vanished? No!—yes!—not quite! And there is still the swarthy whiteness, —we shall venture to marry these ill-agreeing words,—the swarthy whiteness of Judge Pyncheon's face. The features are all gone: there is only the paleness of them left. And how looks it now? There is no window! There is no face! An infinite, inscrutable blackness has annihilated sight! Where is our universe? All crumbled away from us; and we, adrift in chaos, may hearken to the gusts of homeless wind, that go sighing and murmuring about, in quest of what was once a world!

Is there no other sound? One other, and a fearful one. It is the ticking of the Judge's watch, which, ever since Hepzibah left the room in search of Clifford, he has been holding in his hand. Be the cause what it may, this little, quiet, never-ceasing throb of Time's pulse, repeating its small strokes with such busy regularity, in Judge Pyncheon's motionless hand, has an effect of terror, which we do not find in any other accompaniment of the scene.

But, listen! That puff of the breeze was louder; it had a tone unlike the dreary and sullen one which has bemoaned itself, and afflicted all mankind with miserable sympathy, for five days past. The wind has veered about! It now comes boisterously from the northwest, and, taking hold of the aged framework of the Seven Gables, gives it a shake, like a wrestler that would try strength with his antagonist. Another and another sturdy tussle with the blast! The old house creaks again, and makes a vociferous but somewhat unintelligible bellowing in its sooty throat (the big flue, we mean, of its wide chimney), partly in complaint at the rude wind, but rather, as befits their century and a half of hostile intimacy, in tough defiance. A rumbling kind of a bluster roars behind the fire-board. A door has slammed above stairs. A window, perhaps, has been left open, or else is driven in by an unruly gust. It is not to be conceived, beforehand, what wonderful wind-instruments are these old timber mansions, and how haunted with the strangest noises, which immediately begin to sing, and sigh, and sob, and shriek,—and to smite with sledge-hammers, airy but ponderous, in some distant chamber,—and to tread along the entries as with stately footsteps, and rustle up and down the staircase, as with silks miraculously stiff,—whenever the gale catches the house with a window open, and gets fairly into it. Would that we were not an attendant spirit here! It is too awful! This clamor of the wind through the lonely house; the Judge's quietude, as he sits invisible; and that pertinacious ticking of his watch!

As regards Judge Pyncheon's invisibility, however, that matter will soon be remedied. The northwest wind has swept the sky clear. The window is distinctly seen. Through its panes, moreover, we dimly catch the sweep of the dark, clustering foliage, outside, fluttering with a constant irregularity of movement, and letting in a peep of starlight, now here, now there. Oftener than any other object, these glimpses illuminate the Judge's face. But here comes more effectual light. Observe that silvery dance upon the upper branches of the pear-tree, and now a little lower, and now on the whole mass of boughs, while, through their shifting intricacies, the moonbeams fall aslant into the room. They play over the Judge's figure and show that he has not stirred throughout the hours of darkness. They follow the shadows, in changeful sport, across his unchanging features. They gleam upon his watch. His grasp conceals the dial-plate; but we know that the faithful hands have met; for one of the city clocks tells midnight.

A man of sturdy understanding, like Judge Pyncheon, cares no more for twelve o'clock at night than for the corresponding hour of noon. However just the parallel drawn, in some of the preceding pages, between his Puritan ancestor and himself, it fails in this point. The Pyncheon of two centuries ago, in common with most of his contemporaries, professed his full belief in spiritual ministrations, although reckoning them chiefly of a malignant character. The Pyncheon of to-night, who sits in yonder arm-chair, believes in no such nonsense. Such, at least, was his creed, some few hours since. His hair will not bristle, therefore, at the stories which—in times when chimney-corners had benches in them, where old people sat poking into the ashes of the past, and raking out traditions like live coals—used to be told about this very room of his ancestral house. In fact, these tales are too absurd to bristle even childhood's hair. What sense, meaning, or moral, for example, such as even ghost-stories should be susceptible of, can be traced in the ridiculous legend, that, at midnight, all the dead Pyncheons are bound to assemble in this parlor? And, pray, for what? Why, to see whether the portrait of their ancestor still keeps its place upon the wall, in compliance with his testamentary directions! Is it worth while to come out of their graves for that?

We are tempted to make a little sport with the idea. Ghost-stories are hardly to be treated seriously, any longer. The family-party of the defunct Pyncheons, we presume, goes off in this wise.

First comes the ancestor himself, in his black cloak, steeple-hat, and trunk-breeches, girt about the waist with a leathern belt, in which hangs his steel-hilted sword; he has a long staff in his hand, such as gentlemen in advanced life used to carry, as much for the dignity of the thing as for the support to be derived from it. He looks up at the portrait; a thing of no substance, gazing at its own painted image! All is safe. The picture is still there. The purpose of his brain has been kept sacred thus long after the man himself has sprouted up in graveyard grass. See! he lifts his ineffectual hand, and tries the frame. All safe! But is that a smile?—is it not, rather, a frown of deadly import, that darkens over the shadow of his features? The stout Colonel is dissatisfied! So decided is his look of discontent as to impart additional distinctness to his features; through which, nevertheless, the moonlight passes, and flickers on the wall beyond. Something has strangely vexed the ancestor! With a grim shake of the head, he turns away. Here come other Pyncheons, the whole tribe, in their half a dozen generations, jostling and elbowing one another, to reach the picture. We behold aged men and grandames, a clergyman with the Puritanic stiffness still in his garb and mien, and a red-coated officer of the old French war; and there comes the shop-keeping Pyncheon of a century ago, with the ruffles turned back from his wrists; and there the periwigged and brocaded gentleman of the artist's legend, with the beautiful and pensive Alice, who brings no pride out of her virgin grave. All try the picture-frame. What do these ghostly people seek? A mother lifts her child, that his little hands may touch it! There is evidently a mystery about the picture, that perplexes these poor Pyncheons when they ought to be at rest. In a corner, meanwhile, stands the figure of an elderly man, in a leather jerkin and breeches, with a carpenter's rule sticking out of his side pocket; he points his finger at the bearded Colonel and his descendants, nodding, jeering, mocking, and finally bursting into obstreperous, though inaudible laughter.

Indulging our fancy in this freak, we have partly lost the power of restraint and guidance. We distinguish an unlooked-for figure in our visionary scene. Among these ancestral people there is a young man, dressed in the very fashion of to-day: he wears a dark frock-coat, almost destitute of skirts, gray pantaloons, gaiter boots of patent leather, and has a finely wrought gold chain across his breast, and a little silver-headed whalebone stick in his hand. Were we to meet this figure at noonday, we should greet him as young Jaffrey Pyncheon, the Judge's only surviving child, who has been spending the last two years in foreign travel. If still in life, how comes his shadow hither? If dead, what a misfortune! The old Pyncheon property, together with the great estate acquired by the young man's father, would devolve on whom? On poor, foolish Clifford, gaunt Hepzibah, and rustic little Phœbe! But another and a greater marvel greets us! Can we believe our eyes? A stout, elderly gentleman has made his appearance; he has an aspect of eminent respectability, wears a black coat and pantaloons, of roomy width, and might be pronounced scrupulously neat in his attire, but for a broad crimson stain across his snowy neckcloth and down his shirt-bosom. Is it the Judge, or no? How can it be Judge

Pyncheon? We discern his figure, as plainly as the flickering moonbeams can show us anything, still seated in the oaken chair! Be the apparition whose it may, it advances to the picture, seems to seize the frame, tries to peep behind it, and turns away, with a frown as black as the ancestral one.

The fantastic scene just hinted at must by no means be considered as forming an actual portion of our story. We were betrayed into this brief extravagance by the quiver of the moonbeams; they dance hand-in-hand with shadows, and are reflected in the looking-glass, which, you are aware, is always a kind of window or doorway into the spiritual world. We needed relief, moreover, from our too long and exclusive contemplation of that figure in the chair. This wild wind, too, has tossed our thoughts into strange confusion, but without tearing them away from their one determined centre. Yonder leaden Judge sits immovably upon our soul. Will he never stir again? We shall go mad unless he stirs! You may the better estimate his quietude by the fearlessness of a little mouse, which sits on its hind legs, in a streak of moonlight, close by Judge Pyncheon's foot, and seems to meditate a journey of exploration over this great black bulk. Ha! what has startled the nimble little mouse? Is it the visage of grimalkin, outside of the window, where he appears to have posted himself for a deliberate watch. This grimalkin has a very ugly look. Is it a cat watching for a mouse, or the devil of a human soul? Would we could scare him from the window!

Thank Heaven, the night is wellnigh past! The moonbeams have no longer so silvery a gleam, nor contrast so strongly with the blackness of the shadows among which they fall. They are paler, now; the shadows look gray, not black. The boisterous wind is hushed. What is the hour? Ah! the watch has at last ceased to tick; for the Judge's forgetful fingers neglected to wind it up, as usual, at ten o'clock, being half an hour or so before his ordinary bedtime,—and it has run down, for the first time in five years. But the great world-clock of Time still keeps its beat. The dreary night—for, oh, how dreary seems its haunted waste, behind us!—gives place to a fresh, transparent cloudless morn. Blessed, blessed radiance! The day-beam—even what little of it finds its way into this always dusky parlor—seems part of the universal benediction, annulling evil, and rendering all goodness possible, and happiness attainable. Will Judge Pyncheon now rise up from his chair? Will he go forth, and receive the early sunbeams on his brow? Will he begin this new day,—which God has smiled upon, and blessed, and given to mankind,—will he begin it with better purposes than the many that have been spent amiss? Or are all the deep-laid schemes of yesterday as stubborn in his heart, and as busy in his brain, as ever?

In this latter case, there is much to do. Will the Judge still insist with Hepzibah on the interview with Clifford? Will he buy a safe, elderly gen-

tleman's horse? Will he persuade the purchaser of the old Pyncheon property to relinquish the bargain, in his favor? Will he see his family's physician, and obtain a medicine that shall preserve him, to be an honor and
blessing to his race, until the utmost term of patriarchal longevity? Will
Judge Pyncheon, above all, make due apologies to that company of honorable friends, and satisfy them that his absence from the festive board
was unavoidable, and so fully retrieve himself in their good opinion that
he shall yet be Governor of Massachusetts? And all these great purposes
accomplished, will he walk the streets again, with that dog-day smile of
elaborate benevolence, sultry enough to tempt flies to come and buzz in
it? Or will he, after the tomb-like seclusion of the past day and night, go
forth a humbled and repentant man, sorrowful, gentle, seeking no profit,
shrinking from worldly honor, hardly daring to love God, but bold to love
his fellowman, and to do him what good he may? Will he bear about with
him,—no odious grin of feigned benignity, insolent in its pretence, and
loathsome in its falsehood,—but the tender sadness of a contrite heart,
broken, at last, beneath its own weight of sin? For it is our belief, whatever show of honor he may have piled upon it, that there was heavy sin
at the base of this man's being.

Rise up, Judge Pyncheon! The morning sunshine glimmers through the
foliage, and, beautiful and holy as it is, shuns not to kindle up your face.
Rise up, thou subtle, worldly, selfish, iron-hearted hypocrite, and make
thy choice whether still to be subtle, worldly, selfish, iron-hearted, and
hypocritical, or to tear these sins out of thy nature, though they bring the
life-blood with them! The Avenger is upon thee! Rise up, before it be
too late!

What! Thou art not stirred by this last appeal? No, not a jot! And
there we see a fly,—one of your common house-flies, such as are always
buzzing on the window-pane,—which has smelt out Governor Pyncheon,
and alights, now on his forehead, now on his chin, and now, Heaven help
us! is creeping over the bridge of his nose, towards the would-be chief-
magistrate's wide-open eyes! Canst thou not brush the fly away? Art
thou too sluggish? Thou man, that hadst so many busy projects yesterday! Art thou too weak, that wast so powerful? Not brush away a fly?
Nay, then, we give thee up!

And hark! the shop-bell rings. After hours like these latter ones, through
which we have borne our heavy tale, it is good to be made sensible that
there is a living world, and that even this old, lonely mansion retains
some manner of connection with it. We breathe more freely, emerging
from Judge Pyncheon's presence into the street before the Seven Gables.

Oliver Wendell Holmes (1809–1894)

Though "Brahmin" Oliver Wendell Holmes distinguished himself as a medical scholar and teacher, he is better known as a popular man of letters, certainly the most famous light versifier of the nineteenth century. Holmes was a lifelong scoffer at Puritan theology. The sharp satire of "The Moral Bully" (1850) and the good-humored burlesque of "The Deacon's Masterpiece" (1858), a commentary on Jonathan Edwards' attempt in 1754 to salvage Puritanism with his treatise on the freedom of the will, illustrate Holmes' determination to eradicate his New England spiritual inheritance. Ironically enough, however, Holmes perpetuated the lighter strains of seventeenth-century Puritanism which also had flourished in early eighteenth-century Boston and would become more secularized in succeeding epochs. He claimed, for example, to be part of the humorous tradition in which Reverend Mather Byles had been a prominent participant. In *The Autocrat of the Breakfast Table* (1858), witty prose monologues sparkling with epigrammatic brilliance and clever observations of character and society, Holmes set forth a theory of mirth which he apparently didn't know had been delineated in 1707 by the Puritan minister Reverend Benjamin Colman (see pp. 1–2): "The ludicrous has its place in the universe; it is not a human invention, but one of the Divine ideas, illustrated in the practical jokes of kittens and monkeys long before Aristophanes and Shakespeare. How curious it is that we always consider solemnity and the absence of all gay surprises and encounter of wits as essential to the idea of the future life of those whom we thus deprive of half their faculties and then call *blessed!*"

Holmes's humor was most often genial, as in "My Aunt" (1831); in addition, he was naturally convivial and a lively speaker. As a result, many of his light pieces began their careers, to use the title of a verse written in 1873 for Phi Beta Kappa, as "A Poem Served to Order." His talent was fertile, however, and his humor remained inexhaustible despite the excessive demands put upon it in the course of his becoming the most sought-after of bards at dinners, meetings, and ceremonial occasions. No other light poet of the nineteenth century has left behind so many pieces, including "The Ballad of the Oysterman" (1830), "Aestivation" (1850), "Rip Van Winkle, M.D." (1870), "Dorothy Q." (1871), "Cacoethes Scribendi" (1890), "The Broomstick Train" (1890), and others, which deserve a place alongside the best light verse of T. S. Eliot and E. E. Cummings.

TEXT: *The Complete Poetical Works of Oliver Wendell Holmes*, ed. H. E. Scudder (Cambridge Edition), Boston, Mass., 1895.

MY AUNT

My aunt! my dear unmarried aunt!
   Long years have o'er her flown;
Yet still she strains the aching clasp
   That binds her virgin zone;
I know it hurts her,—though she looks
   As cheerful as she can;
Her waist is ampler than her life,
   For life is but a span.

My aunt! my poor deluded aunt!
   Her hair is almost gray;
Why will she train that winter curl
   In such a spring-like way?
How can she lay her glasses down,
   And say she reads as well,
When through a double convex lens
   She just makes out to spell?

Her father—grandpapa! forgive
   This erring lip its smiles—
Vowed she should make the finest girl
   Within a hundred miles;
He sent her to a stylish school;
   'Twas in her thirteenth June;
And with her, as the rules required,
   "Two towels and a spoon."

They braced my aunt against a board,
   To make her straight and tall;
They laced her up, they starved her down,
   To make her light and small;
They pinched her feet, they singed her hair,
   They screwed it up with pins;—
Oh, never mortal suffered more
   In penance for her sins.

So, when my precious aunt was done,
   My grandsire brought her back;
(By daylight, lest some rabid youth
   Might follow on the track;)

"Ah!" said my grandsire, as he shook
  Some powder in his pan,
"What could this lovely creature do
  Against a desperate man!"

Alas! nor chariot, nor barouche,
  Nor bandit cavalcade,
Tore from the trembling father's arms
  His all-accomplished maid.
For her how happy had it been!
  And Heaven had spared to me
To see one sad, ungathered rose
  On my ancestral tree.

THE MORAL BULLY

  Yon whey-faced brother, who delights to wear
A weedy flux of ill-conditioned hair,
Seems of the sort that in a crowded place
One elbows freely into smallest space;
A timid creature, lax of knee and hip,
Whom small disturbance whitens round the lip;
One of those harmless spectacled machines,
The Holy-Week of Protestants convenes;
Whom school-boys question if their walk transcends
The last advices of maternal friends;
Whom John, obedient to his master's sign,
Conducts, laborious, up to *ninety-nine*,
While Peter, glistening with luxurious scorn,
Husks his white ivories like an ear of corn;
Dark in the brow and bilious in the cheek,
Whose yellowish linen flowers but once a week,
Conspicuous, annual, in their threadbare suits,
And the laced high-lows which they call their boots,
Well mayst thou *shun* that dingy front severe,
But him, O stranger, him thou canst not *fear*!

  Be slow to judge, and slower to despise,
Man of broad shoulders and heroic size!
The tiger, writhing from the boa's rings,
Drops at the fountain where the cobra stings.
In that lean phantom, whose extended glove

Points to the text of universal love,
Behold the master that can tame thee down
To crouch, the vassal of his Sunday frown;
His velvet throat against thy corded wrist,
His loosened tongue against thy doubled fist!

The MORAL BULLY, though he never swears,
Nor kicks intruders down his entry stairs,
Though meekness plants his backward-sloping hat,
And non-resistance ties his white cravat,
Though his black broadcloth glories to be seen
In the same plight with Shylock's gaberdine,
Hugs the same passion to his narrow breast
That heaves the cuirass on the trooper's chest,
Hears the same hell-hounds yelling in his rear
That chase from port the maddened buccaneer,
Feels the same comfort while his acrid words
Turn the sweet milk of kindness into curds,
Or with grim logic prove, beyond debate,
That all we love is worthiest of our hate,
As the scarred ruffian of the pirate's deck,
When his long swivel rakes the staggering wreck!

Heaven keep us all! Is every rascal clown
Whose arm is stronger free to knock us down?
Has every scarecrow, whose cachectic soul
Seems fresh from Bedlam, airing on parole,
Who, though he carries but a doubtful trace
Of angel visits on his hungry face,
From lack of marrow or the coins to pay,
Has dodged some vices in a shabby way,
The right to stick us with his cutthroat terms,
And bait his homilies with his brother worms?

THE DEACON'S MASTERPIECE

Or, the Wonderful "One-Hoss Shay": a Logical Story

Have you heard of the wonderful one-hoss shay,
That was built in such a logical way
It ran a hundred years to a day,
And then, of a sudden, it—ah, but stay,

I'll tell you what happened without delay,
Scaring the parson into fits,
Frightening people out of their wits,—
Have you ever heard of that, I say?

Seventeen hundred and fifty-five.
Georgius Secundus was then alive,—
Snuffy old drone from the German hive.
That was the year when Lisbon-town
Saw the earth open and gulp her down,
And Braddock's army was done so brown,
Left without a scalp to its crown.
It was on the terrible Earthquake-day
That the Deacon finished the one-hoss shay.

Now in building of chaises, I tell you what
There is always *somewhere* a weakest spot,—
In hub, tire, felloe, in spring or thill,
In panel, or crossbar, or floor, or sill,
In screw, bolt, thoroughbrace,—lurking still,
Find it somewhere you must and will,—
Above or below, or within or without,—
And that's the reason, beyond a doubt,
That a chaise *breaks down*, but doesn't *wear out*.

But the Deacon swore (as Deacons do,
With an "I dew vum," or an "I tell *yeou*,")
He would build one shay to beat the taown
'N' the keounty 'n' all the kentry raoun';
It should be so built that it *couldn'* break daown:
"Fur," said the Deacon, " 't's mighty plain
Thut the weakes' place mus' stan' the strain;
'N' the way t' fix it, uz I maintain,
Is only jest
T' make that place uz strong uz the rest."

So the Deacon inquired of the village folk
Where he could find the strongest oak,
That couldn't be split nor bent nor broke,—
That was for spokes and floor and sills;
He sent for lancewood to make the thills;
The crossbars were ash, from the straightest trees;
The panels of white-wood, that cuts like cheese,
But last like iron for things like these;
The hubs of logs from the "Settler's ellum,"—
Last of its timber,—they couldn't sell 'em,

Never an axe had seen their chips,
And the wedges flew from between their lips,
Their blunt ends frizzled like celery-tips;
Step and prop-iron, bolt and screw,
Spring, tire, axle, and linchpin too,
Steel of the finest, bright and blue;
Thoroughbrace bison-skin, thick and wide;
Boot, top, dasher, from tough old hide
Found in the pit when the tanner died.
That was the way he "put her through."
"There!" said the Deacon, "naow she'll dew!"

Do! I tell you, I rather guess
She was a wonder, and nothing less!
Colts grew horses, beards turned gray,
Deacon and deaconess dropped away,
Children and grandchildren—where were they?
But there stood the stout old one-hoss shay
As fresh as on Lisbon-earthquake-day!

EIGHTEEN HUNDRED;—it came and found
The Deacon's masterpiece strong and sound.
Eighteen hundred increased by ten;—
"Hahnsum kerridge" they called it then.
Eighteen hundred and twenty came;—
Running as usual; much the same.
Thirty and forty at last arrive,
And then come fifty, and FIFTY-FIVE.

Little of all we value here
Wakes on the morn of its hundredth year
Without both feeling and looking queer.
In fact, there's nothing that keeps its youth,
So far as I know, but a tree and truth.
(This is a moral that runs at large;
Take it.—You're welcome.—No extra charge.)

FIRST OF NOVEMBER,—the Earthquake-day,—
There are traces of age in the one-hoss shay,
A general flavor of mild decay,
But nothing local, as one may say.
There couldn't be,—for the Deacon's art
Had made it so like in every part
That there wasn't a chance for one to start.
For the wheels were just as strong as the thills,
And the floor was just as strong as the sills,

And the panels just as strong as the floor,
And the whipple-tree neither less nor more,
And the back crossbar as strong as the fore,
And spring and axle and hub *encore*.
And yet, *as a whole*, it is past a doubt
In another hour it will be *worn out!*

First of November, 'Fifty-five!
This morning the parson takes a drive.
Now, small boys, get out of the way!
Here comes the wonderful one-hoss shay,
Drawn by a rat-tailed, ewe-necked bay.
"Huddup!" said the parson.—Off went they.
The parson was working his Sunday's text,—
He got to *fifthly*, and stopped perplexed
At what the—Moses—was coming next.
All at once the horse stood still,
Close by the meet'n'-house on the hill.
First a shiver, and then a thrill,
Then something decidedly like a spill,—
And the parson was sitting upon a rock,
At half-past nine by the meet'n'-house clock,—
Just the hour of the Earthquake shock!
What do you think the parson found,
When he got up and stared around?
The poor old chaise in a heap or mound,
As if it had been to the mill and ground!
You see, of course, if you're not a dunce,
How it went to pieces all at once,—
All at once and nothing first,—
Just as bubbles do when they burst.

End of the wonderful one-hoss shay.
Logic is logic. That's all I say.

Edgar Allan Poe (1809–1849)

Odd though it may seem to say so, Edgar Allan Poe is one of our major humorists. Misled by Poe's propensity for the dark and macabre, it has appeared to some that his work lacks humor. The truth, of course, is that in Poe's best tales of the grotesque and the arabesque the dark and the light are admirably integrated. Often it is the reader who willfully divides them and overlooks either one or the other. Poe's early fiction, written to entertain a popular magazine audience, contains his humor in a more obvious form than his later fiction. Nervous in tone, the early stories and sketches dealt wittily and ironically with aspects of American life and character, gibing away at an audience which he regarded as obtuse and deluded; in numerous burlesques and hoaxes he mocked popular fads and deeply cherished beliefs with unrelenting gusto. This early work seems to be the production of a jester such as Poe drew in "Hop-Frog" (1849), one of those bitter, unhappy " 'fools' who wore motley, with caps and bells, and who were expected to be always ready with sharp witticisms, at a moment's notice, in consideration of the crumbs that fell from the royal table." As jester or court fool Poe developed a style replete with jocular anecdotes, sly innuendoes, mock erudition, farcical characters, practical jokes, vulgarities, and verbal witticisms.

Poe's later work, more familiar to most readers than his earlier writings, retained his humorous equipment and fused it with the trappings of Gothic mystery and supernaturalism. At its peak the critically humorous spirit of Poe is disconcerting because it harks back to a darkness associated with Puritan orthodoxy, displays itself in fantastic grotesqueries abjured by a realistic temper, delights in blending humor with such abhorred topics as death and insanity in violation of a humanitarian spirit, and cavorts about with seemingly amoral unconcern over the fact that its grappling with evil and sadism is the sign of an unhealthy psyche. Disturbed and unhappy Poe undoubtedly was, yet he managed to sublimate his troubled emotions in such undeservedly neglected stories as "The System of Dr. Tarr and Prof. Fether" (1845). A work of his artistic maturity, it illustrates, as do such late masterpieces as "The Cask of Amontillado" (1846) and "Hop-Frog," how persistently and even sensibly Poe insisted upon the necessity for laughter in chambers of horror. Poe's approach to mental illness is more wholesome, less fearful, than that of his age and more akin to the modern post-Freudian belief that psychological disorder is surmountable and by no means evidence of innate evil. Apparently, too, Poe recognized sooner than most of his contemporaries how slight the barrier between sanity and insanity really is. The French, whose literature

Poe helped guide to symbolism and surrealism, honored him more than a decade ago by basing an eerily amusing film comedy on the events which occurred at the restless haven of Doctor Tarr and Professor Fether.

TEXT: *The Complete Works of Edgar Allan Poe*, ed. James A. Harrison (Virginia Edition), New York, 1902, VI. COMMENTARY: Edward H. Davidson, *Poe: A Critical Study*, Cambridge, Mass., 1957.

THE SYSTEM OF DR. TARR AND PROF. FETHER

During the autumn of 18—, while on a tour through the extreme Southern provinces of France, my route led me within a few miles of a certain *Maison de Santé*, or private Mad-House, about which I had heard much, in Paris, from my medical friends. As I had never visited a place of the kind, I thought the opportunity too good to be lost; and so proposed to my traveling companion, (a gentleman with whom I had made casual acquaintance a few days before,) that we should turn aside, for an hour or so, and look through the establishment. To this he objected—pleading haste, in the first place, and, in the second, a very usual horror at the sight of a lunatic. He begged me, however, not to let any mere courtesy toward himself interfere with the gratification of my curiosity, and said that he would ride on leisurely, so that I might overtake him during the day, or, at all events, during the next. As he bade me good-bye, I bethought me that there might be some difficulty in obtaining access to the premises, and mentioned my fears on this point. He replied that, in fact, unless I had personal knowledge of the superintendent, Monsieur Maillard, or some credential in the way of a letter, a difficulty might be found to exist, as the regulations of these private mad-houses were more rigid than the public hospital laws. For himself, he added, he had, some years since, made the acquaintance of Maillard, and would so far assist me as to ride up to the door and introduce me; although his feelings on the subject of lunacy would not permit of his entering the house.

I thanked him, and, turning from the main-road, we entered a grass-grown by-path, which, in half an hour, nearly lost itself in a dense forest, clothing the base of a mountain. Through this dank and gloomy wood we rode some two miles, when the *Maison de Santé* came in view. It was a fantastic *château*, much dilapidated, and indeed scarcely tenantable through age and neglect. Its aspect inspired me with absolute dread, and, checking my horse, I half resolved to turn back. I soon, however, grew ashamed of my weakness, and proceeded.

As we rode up to the gate-way, I perceived it slightly open, and the visage of a man peering through. In an instant afterward, this man came forth, accosted my companion by name, shook him cordially by the hand,

and begged him to alight. It was Monsieur Maillard himself. He was a portly, fine-looking gentleman of the old school, with a polished manner, and a certain air of gravity, dignity, and authority which was very impressive.

My friend, having presented me, mentioned my desire to inspect the establishment, and received Monsieur Maillard's assurance that he would show me all attention, now took leave, and I saw him no more.

When he had gone, the superintendent ushered me into a small and exceedingly neat parlor, containing, among other indications of refined taste, many books, drawings, pots of flowers, and musical instruments. A cheerful fire blazed upon the hearth. At a piano, singing an aria from Bellini, sat a young and very beautiful woman, who, at my entrance, paused in her song, and received me with graceful courtesy. Her voice was low, and her whole manner subdued. I thought, too, that I perceived the traces of sorrow in her countenance, which was excessively, although, to my taste, not unpleasingly pale. She was attired in deep mourning, and excited in my bosom a feeling of mingled respect, interest, and admiration.

I had heard, at Paris, that the institution of Monsieur Maillard was managed upon what is vulgarly termed the "system of soothing"—that all punishments were avoided—that even confinement was seldom resorted to—that the patients, while secretly watched, were left much apparent liberty, and that most of them were permitted to roam about the house and grounds, in the ordinary apparel of persons in right mind.

Keeping these impressions in view, I was cautious in what I said before the young lady; for I could not be sure that she was sane; and, in fact, there was a certain restless brilliancy about her eyes which half led me to imagine she was not. I confined my remarks, therefore, to general topics, and to such as I thought would not be displeasing or exciting even to a lunatic. She replied in a perfectly rational manner to all that I said; and even her original observations were marked with the soundest good sense; but a long acquaintance with the metaphysics of *mania*, had taught me to put no faith in such evidence of sanity, and I continued to practice, throughout the interview, the caution with which I commenced it.

Presently a smart footman in livery brought in a tray with fruit, wine, and other refreshments, of which I partook, the lady soon afterwards leaving the room. As she departed I turned my eyes in an inquiring manner toward my host.

"No," he said, "oh, no—a member of my family—my niece, and a most accomplished woman."

"I beg a thousand pardons for the suspicion," I replied, "but of course you will know how to excuse me. The excellent administration of your affairs here is well understood in Paris, and I thought it just possible, you know—"

"Yes, yes—say no more—or rather it is myself who should thank you for the commendable prudence you have displayed. We seldom find so much of forethought in young men; and, more than once, some unhappy *contre-temps* has occurred in consequence of thoughtlessness on the part of our visitors. While my former system was in operation, and my patients were permitted the privilege of roaming to and fro at will, they were often aroused to a dangerous frenzy by injudicious persons who called to inspect the house. Hence I was obliged to enforce a rigid system of exclusion; and none obtained access to the premises upon whose discretion I could not rely."

"While your *former* system was in operation!" I said, repeating his words—"do I understand you, then, to say that the 'soothing system' of which I have heard so much is no longer in force?"

"It is now," he replied, "several weeks since we have concluded to renounce it forever."

"Indeed! you astonish me!"

"We found it, sir," he said, with a sigh, "absolutely necessary to return to the old usages. The *danger* of the soothing system was, at all times, appalling; and its advantages have been much overrated. I believe, sir, that in this house it has been given a fair trial, if ever in any. We did every thing that rational humanity could suggest. I am sorry that you could not have paid us a visit at an earlier period, that you might have judged for yourself. But I presume you are conversant with the soothing practice—with its details."

"Not altogether. What I have heard has been at third or fourth hand."

"I may state the system, then, in general terms, as one in which the patients were *menagés*, humored. We contradicted *no* fancies which entered the brains of the mad. On the contrary, we not only indulged but encouraged them; and many of our most permanent cures have been thus effected. There is no argument which so touches the feeble reason of the madman as the *argumentum ad absurdum*. We have had men, for example, who fancied themselves chickens. The cure was, to insist upon the thing as a fact—to accuse the patient of stupidity in not sufficiently perceiving it to be a fact—and thus to refuse him any other diet for a week than that which properly appertains to a chicken. In this manner a little corn and gravel were made to perform wonders."

"But was this species of acquiescence all?"

"By no means. We put much faith in amusements of a simple kind, such as music, dancing, gymnastic exercises generally, cards, certain classes of books, and so forth. We affected to treat each individual as if for some ordinary physical disorder; and the word 'lunacy' was never employed. A great point was to set each lunatic to guard the actions of all the others. To repose confidence in the understanding or discretion of a madman, is to gain him body and soul. In this way we were enabled to dispense with an expensive body of keepers."

"And you had no punishments of any kind?"

"None."

"And you never confined your patients?"

"Very rarely. Now and then, the malady of some individual growing to a crisis, or taking a sudden turn of fury, we conveyed him to a secret cell, lest his disorder should infect the rest, and there kept him until we could dismiss him to his friends—for with the raging maniac we have nothing to do. He is usually removed to the public hospitals."

"And you have now changed all this—and you think for the better?"

"Decidedly. The system had its disadvantages, and even its dangers. It is now, happily, exploded throughout all the *Maisons de Santé* of France."

"I am very much surprised," I said, "at what you tell me; for I made sure that, at this moment, no other method of treatment for mania existed in any portion of the country."

"You are young yet, my friend," replied my host, "but the time will arrive when you will learn to judge for yourself of what is going on in the world, without trusting to the gossip of others. Believe nothing you hear, and only one-half that you see. Now about our *Maisons de Santé*, it is clear that some ignoramus has misled you. After dinner, however, when you have sufficiently recovered from the fatigue of your ride, I will be happy to take you over the house, and introduce to you a system which, in my opinion, and in that of every one who has witnessed its operation, is incomparably the most effectual as yet devised."

"Your own?" I inquired—"one of your own invention?"

"I am proud," he replied, "to acknowledge that it is—at least in some measure."

In this manner I conversed with Monsieur Maillard for an hour or two, during which he showed me the gardens and conservatories of the place.

"I cannot let you see my patients," he said, "just at present. To a sensitive mind there is always more or less of the shocking in such exhibitions; and I do not wish to spoil your appetite for dinner. We will dine. I can give you some veal *à la St. Menehoult*, with cauliflowers in *velouté* sauce—after that a glass [of] *Clos de* Vougeôt—then your nerves will be sufficiently steadied."

At six, dinner was announced; and my host conducted me into a large *salle à manger*, where a very numerous company were assembled—twenty-five or thirty in all. They were, apparently, people of rank—certainly of high breeding—although their habiliments, I thought, were extravagantly rich, partaking somewhat too much of the ostentatious finery of the *vieille cour*. I noticed that at least two-thirds of these guests were ladies; and some of the latter were by no means accoutred in what a Parisian would consider good taste at the present day. Many females, for example, whose age could not have been less than seventy, were bedecked with a profusion of jewelry, such as rings, bracelets, and ear-rings, and wore their bosoms and arms shamefully bare. I observed, too, that very few of the dresses were well made—or, at least, that very few of them fitted the wearers. In looking about, I discovered the inter-esting girl to whom Monsieur Maillard had presented me in the little parlor; but my surprise was great to see her wearing a hoop and far-thingale, with high-heeled shoes, and a dirty cap of Brussels lace, so much too large for her that it gave her face a ridiculously diminutive expression. When I had first seen her she was attired, most becomingly, in deep mourning. There was an air of oddity, in short, about the dress of the whole party, which, at first, caused me to recur to my original idea of the "soothing system," and to fancy that Monsieur Maillard had been willing to deceive me until after dinner, that I might experience no un-comfortable feelings during the repast, at finding myself dining with lunatics; but I remembered having been informed, in Paris, that the southern provincialists were a peculiarly eccentric people, with a vast number of antiquated notions; and then, too, upon conversing with sev-eral members of the company, my apprehensions were immediately and fully dispelled.

The dining-room itself, although perhaps sufficiently comfortable, and of good dimensions, had nothing too much of elegance about it. For example, the floor was uncarpeted; in France, however, a carpet is fre-quently dispensed with. The windows, too, were without curtains; the shutters, being shut, were securely fastened with iron bars, applied diag-onally, after the fashion of our ordinary shop-shutters. The apartment, I observed, formed, in itself, a wing of the *château*, and thus the windows were on three sides of the parallelogram, the door being at the other. There were no less than ten windows in all.

The table was superbly set out. It was loaded with plate, and more than loaded with delicacies. The profusion was absolutely barbaric. There were meats enough to have feasted the Anakim. Never, in all my life, had I witnessed so lavish, so wasteful an expenditure of the good things of life. There seemed very little taste, however, in the arrange-ments; and my eyes, accustomed to quiet lights, were sadly offended by the prodigious glare of a multitude of wax candles, which, in silver *can-delabra*, were deposited upon the table, and all about the room, wher-ever it was possible to find a place. There were several active servants in attendance; and, upon a large table, at the farther end of the apartment, were seated seven or eight people with fiddles, fifes, trombones, and a drum. These fellows annoyed me very much, at intervals, during the repast, by an infinite variety of noises, which were intended for music, and which appeared to afford much entertainment to all present, with the exception of myself.

Upon the whole, I could not help thinking that there was much of the *bizarre* about every thing I saw—but then the world is made up of all kinds of persons, with all modes of thought and all sorts of conventional customs. I had traveled so much as to be quite an adept in the *nil admirari*, so I took my seat very coolly at the right hand of my host, and, having an excellent appetite, did justice to the good cheer set before me.

The conversation, in the meantime, was spirited and general. The ladies, as usual, talked a great deal. I soon found that nearly all the company were well educated; and my host was a world of good-humored anecdote in himself. He seemed quite willing to speak of his position as superintendent of a *Maison de Santé*; and, indeed, the topic of lunacy was, much to my surprise, a favorite one with all present. A great many amusing stories were told, having reference to the *whims* of the patients.

"We had a fellow here once," said a fat little gentleman, who sat at my right,—"a fellow that fancied himself a tea-pot; and by the way, is it not especially singular how often this particular crotchet has entered the brain of the lunatic? There is scarcely an insane asylum in France which cannot supply a human tea-pot. *Our* gentleman was a Britannia-ware tea-pot, and was careful to polish himself every morning with buckskin and whiting."

"And then," said a tall man just opposite, "we had here, not long ago, a person who had taken it into his head that he was a donkey—which allegorically speaking, you will say, was quite true. He was a troublesome patient; and we had much ado to keep him within bounds. For a long time he would eat nothing but thistles; but of this idea we soon cured him by insisting upon his eating nothing else. Then he was perpetually kicking out his heels—so—so—"

"Mr. De Kock! I will thank you to behave yourself!" here interrupted an old lady, who sat next to the speaker. "Please keep your feet to yourself! You have spoiled my brocade! Is it necessary, pray, to illustrate a remark in so practical a style? Our friend here can surely comprehend you without all this. Upon my word, you are nearly as great a donkey as the poor unfortunate imagined himself. Your acting is very natural, as I live."

"*Mille pardons! Ma'm'selle!*" replied Monsieur De Kock, thus addressed—"a thousand pardons! I had no intention of offending. Ma'm'selle Laplace—Monsieur De Kock will do himself the honor of taking wine with you."

Here Monsieur De Kock bowed low, kissed his hand with much ceremony, and took wine with Ma'm'selle Laplace.

"Allow me, *mon ami*," now said Monsieur Maillard, addressing myself, "allow me to send you a morsel of this veal *à la* St. *Menehoult*—you
will find it particularly fine."

At this instant three sturdy waiters had just succeeded in depositing
safely upon the table an enormous dish, or trencher, containing what
I supposed to be the *"monstrum horrendum, informe, ingens, cui lumen
ademptum."* A closer scrutiny assured me, however, that it was only a
small calf roasted whole, and set upon its knees, with an apple in its
mouth, as is the English fashion of dressing a hare.

"Thank you, no," I replied; "to say the truth, I am not particularly
partial to veal *à la* St.——what is it?—for I do not find that it altogether
agrees with me. I will change my plate, however, and try some of the
rabbit."

There were several side-dishes on the table, containing what appeared
to be the ordinary French rabbit—a very delicious *morceau*, which I can
recommend.

"Pierre," cried the host, "change this gentleman's plate, and give him
a side-piece of this rabbit *au-chat*."

"This what?" said I.

"This rabbit *au-chat*."

"Why, thank you—upon second thoughts, no. I will just help myself
to some of the ham."

There is no knowing what one eats, thought I to myself, at the tables
of these people of the province. I will have none of their rabbit *au-chat*—
and, for the matter of that, none of their *cat-au-rabbit* either.

"And then," said a cadaverous looking personage, near the foot of the
table, taking up the thread of the conversation where it had been broken
off,—"and then, among other oddities, we had a patient, once upon a
time, who very pertinaciously maintained himself to be a Cordova
cheese, and went about, with a knife in his hand, soliciting his friends
to try a small slice from the middle of his leg."

"He was a great fool, beyond doubt," interposed some one, "but not
to be compared with a certain individual whom we all know, with the
exception of this strange gentleman. I mean the man who took himself
for a bottle of champagne, and always went off with a pop and a fizz, in
this fashion."

Here the speaker, very rudely, as I thought, put his right thumb in
his left cheek, withdrew it with a sound resembling the popping of a
cork, and then, by a dexterous movement of the tongue upon the teeth,
created a sharp hissing and fizzing, which lasted for several minutes, in
imitation of the frothing of champagne. This behavior, I saw plainly,

was not very pleasing to Monsieur Maillard; but that gentleman said nothing, and the conversation was resumed by a very lean little man in a big wig.

"And then there was an ignoramus," said he, "who mistook himself for a frog; which, by the way, he resembled in no little degree. I wish you could have seen him, sir,"—here the speaker addressed myself—"it would have done your heart good to see the natural airs that he put on. Sir, if that man was *not* a frog, I can only observe that it is a pity he was not. His croak thus—o-o-o-o-gh—o-o-o-o-gh! was the finest note in the world—B flat; and when he put his elbows upon the table thus—after taking a glass or two of wine—and distended his mouth, thus, and rolled up his eyes, thus, and winked them with excessive rapidity, thus, why then, sir, I take it upon myself to say, positively, that you would have been lost in admiration of the genius of the man."

"I have no doubt of it," I said.

"And then," said somebody else, "then there was Petit Gaillard, who thought himself a pinch of snuff, and was truly distressed because he could not take himself between his own finger and thumb."

"And then there was Jules Desoulières, who was a very singular genius, indeed, and went mad with the idea that he was a pumpkin. He persecuted the cook to make him up into pies—a thing which the cook indignantly refused to do. For my part, I am by no means sure that a pumpkin pie *à la Desoulières* would not have been very capital eating indeed!"

"You astonish me!" said I; and I looked inquisitively at Monsieur Maillard.

"Ha! ha! ha!" said that gentleman—"he! he! he!—hi! hi! hi!—ho! ho! ho!—hu! hu! hu!—very good indeed! You must not be astonished, *mon ami*; our friend here is a wit—a *drôle*—you must not understand him to the letter."

"And then," said some other one of the party,—"then there was Bouffon Le Grand—another extraordinary personage in his way. He grew deranged through love, and fancied himself possessed of two heads. One of these he maintained to be the head of Cicero; the other he imagined a composite one, being Demosthenes' from the top of the forehead to the mouth, and Lord Brougham's from the mouth to the chin. It is not impossible that he was wrong; but he would have convinced you of his being in the right; for he was a man of great eloquence. He had an absolute passion for oratory, and could not refrain from display. For example, he used to leap upon the dinner-table thus, and—and—"

Here a friend, at the side of the speaker, put a hand upon his shoulder and whispered a few words in his ear; upon which he ceased talking with great suddenness, and sank back within his chair.

"And then," said the friend who had whispered, "there was Boullard, the tee-totum. I call him the tee-totum because, in fact, he was seized with the droll, but not altogether irrational, crotchet, that he had been converted into a tee-totum. You would have roared with laughter to see him spin. He would turn round upon one heel by the hour, in this manner—so—"

Here the friend whom he had just interrupted by a whisper, performed an exactly similar office for himself.

"But then," cried the old lady, at the top of her voice, "your Monsieur Boullard was a madman, and a very silly madman at best; for who, allow me to ask you, ever heard of a human tee-totum? The thing is absurd. Madame Joyeuse was a more sensible person, as you know. She had a crotchet, but it was instinct with common sense, and gave pleasure to all who had the honor of her acquaintance. She found, upon mature deliberation, that, by some accident, she had been turned into a chicken-cock; but, as such, she behaved with propriety. She flapped her wings with prodigious effect—so—so—so—and, as for her crow, it was delicious! Cock-a-doodle-doo!—cock-a-doodle-doo!—cock-a-doodle-de-doo-doo-dooo-do-o-o-o-o-o-o—!"

"Madame Joyeuse, I will thank you to behave yourself!" here interrupted our host, very angrily. "You can either conduct yourself as a lady should do, or you can quit the table forthwith—take your choice."

The lady (whom I was much astonished to hear addressed as Madame Joyeuse, after the description of Madame Joyeuse she had just given) blushed up to the eyebrows, and seemed exceedingly abashed at the reproof. She hung down her head, and said not a syllable in reply. But another and younger lady resumed the theme. It was my beautiful girl of the little parlor.

"Oh, Madame Joyeuse *was* a fool!" she exclaimed, "but there was really much sound sense, after all, in the opinion of Eugénie Salsafette. She was a very beautiful and painfully modest young lady, who thought the ordinary mode of habiliment indecent, and wished to dress herself, always, by getting outside instead of inside of her clothes. It is a thing very easily done, after all. You have only to do so—and then so—so—so—and then so—so—so—and then—"

"Mon dieu! Ma'm'selle Salsafette!" here cried a dozen voices at once. "What *are* you about?—forbear!—that is sufficient!—we see, very plainly, how it is done!—hold! hold!" and several persons were already leaping from their seats to withhold Ma'm'selle Salsafette from putting herself upon a par with the Medicean Venus, when the point was very effectually and suddenly accomplished by a series of loud screams, or yells, from some portion of the main body of the *château*.

My nerves were very much affected, indeed, by these yells: but the rest of the company I really pitied. I never saw any set of reasonable people so thoroughly frightened in my life. They all grew as pale as so many corpses, and, shrinking within their seats, sat quivering and gibbering with terror, and listening for a repetition of the sound. It came again—louder and seemingly nearer—and then a third time *very* loud, and then a fourth time with a vigor evidently diminished. At this apparent dying away of the noise, the spirits of the company were immediately regained, and all was life and anecdote as before. I now ventured to inquire the cause of the disturbance.

"A mere *bagatelle*," said Monsieur Maillard. "We are used to these things, and care really very little about them. The lunatics, every now and then, get up a howl in concert; one starting another, as is sometimes the case with a bevy of dogs at night. It occasionally happens, however, that the *concerto* yells are succeeded by a simultaneous effort at breaking loose; when, of course, some little danger is to be apprehended."

"And how many have you in charge?"

"At present we have not more than ten, altogether."

"Principally females, I presume?"

"Oh, no—every one of them men, and stout fellows, too, I can tell you."

"Indeed! I have always understood that the majority of lunatics were of the gentler sex."

"It is generally so, but not always. Some time ago, there were about twenty-seven patients here; and, of that number, no less than eighteen were women; but, lately, matters have changed very much, as you see."

"Yes—have changed very much, as you see," here interrupted the gentleman who had broken the shins of Ma'm'selle Laplace.

"Yes—have changed very much, as you see!" chimed in the whole company at once.

"Hold your tongues, every one of you!" said my host, in a great rage. Whereupon the whole company maintained a dead silence for nearly a minute. As for one lady, she obeyed Monsieur Maillard to the letter, and thrusting out her tongue, which was an excessively long one, held it very resignedly, with both hands, until the end of the entertainment.

"And this gentlewoman," said I, to Monsieur Maillard, bending over and addressing him in a whisper—"this good lady who has just spoken, and who gives us the cock-a-doodle-de-doo—she, I presume, is harmless—quite harmless, eh?"

"Harmless!" ejaculated he, in unfeigned surprise, "why—why, what *can* you mean?"

"Only slightly touched?" said I, touching my head. "I take it for granted that she is not particularly—not dangerously affected, eh?"

"*Mon dieu!* what *is* it you imagine? This lady, my particular old friend, Madame Joyeuse, is as absolutely sane as myself. She has her little eccentricities, to be sure—but then, you know, all old women—all *very* old women—are more or less eccentric!"

"To be sure," said I,—"to be sure—and then the rest of these ladies and gentlemen—"

"Are my friends and keepers," interrupted Monsieur Maillard, drawing himself up with *hauteur*,—"my very good friends and assistants."

"What! all of them?" I asked,—"the women and all?"

"Assuredly," he said,—"we could not do at all without the women; they are the best lunatic-nurses in the world; they have a way of their own, you know; their bright eyes have a marvellous effect;—something like the fascination of the snake, you know."

"To be sure," said I,—"to be sure! They behave a little odd, eh?— they are a little *queer*, eh?—don't you think so?"

"Odd!—queer!—why, do you *really* think so? We are not very prudish, to be sure, here in the South—do pretty much as we please—enjoy life, and all that sort of thing, you know—"

"To be sure," said I,—"to be sure."

"And then, perhaps, this *Clos de Vougeôt* is a little heady, you know —a little *strong*—you understand, eh?"

"To be sure," said I,—"to be sure. By the bye, Monsieur, did I understand you to say that the system you have adopted, in place of the celebrated soothing system, was one of very rigorous severity?"

"By no means. Our confinement is necessarily close; but the treatment—the medical treatment, I mean—is rather agreeable to the patients than otherwise."

"And the new system is one of your own invention?"

"Not altogether. Some portions of it are referable to Professor Tarr, of whom you have, necessarily, heard; and, again, there are modifications in my plan which I am happy to acknowledge as belonging of right to the celebrated Fether, with whom, if I mistake not, you have the honor of an intimate acquaintance."

"I am quite ashamed to confess," I replied, "that I have never even heard the names of either gentleman before."

"Good heavens!" ejaculated my host, drawing back his chair abruptly, and uplifting his hands. "I surely do not hear you aright! You did not intend to say, eh? that you had never *heard* either of the learned Doctor Tarr, or of the celebrated Professor Fether?"

"I am forced to acknowledge my ignorance," I replied; "but the truth should be held inviolate above all things. Nevertheless, I feel humbled to the dust, not to be acquainted with the works of these, no doubt, extraordinary men. I will seek out their writings forthwith, and peruse them with deliberate care. Monsieur Maillard, you have really—I must confess it—you have *really*—made me ashamed of myself!"

And this was the fact.

"Say no more, my good young friend," he said kindly, pressing my hand,—"join me now in a glass of Sauterne."

We drank. The company followed our example without stint. They chatted—they jested—they laughed—they perpetrated a thousand absurdities—the fiddles shrieked—the drum row-de-dowed—the trombones bellowed like so many brazen bulls of Phalaris—and the whole scene, growing gradually worse and worse, as the wines gained the ascendancy, became at length a sort of Pandemonium *in petto*. In the meantime, Monsieur Maillard and myself, with some bottles of Sauterne and Vougeôt between us, continued our conversation at the top of the voice. A word spoken in an ordinary key stood no more chance of being heard than the voice of a fish from the bottom of Niagara Falls.

"And, sir," said I, screaming in his ear, "you mentioned something before dinner about the danger incurred in the old system of soothing. How is that?"

"Yes," he replied, "there was, occasionally, very great danger indeed. There is no accounting for the caprices of madmen; and, in my opinion as well as in that of Doctor Tarr and Professor Fether, it is *never* safe to permit them to run at large unattended. A lunatic may be 'soothed,' as it is called, for a time, but, in the end, he is very apt to become obstreperous. His cunning, too, is proverbial and great. If he has a project in view, he conceals his design with a marvellous wisdom; and the dexterity with which he counterfeits sanity, presents, to the metaphysician, one of the most singular problems in the study of mind. When a madman appears *thoroughly* sane, indeed, it is high time to put him in a straitjacket."

"But the *danger*, my dear sir, of which you were speaking, in your own experience—during your control of this house—have you had practical reason to think liberty hazardous in the case of a lunatic?"

"Here?—in my own experience?—why, I may say, yes. For example: —no *very* long while ago, a singular circumstance occurred in this very house. The 'soothing system,' you know, was then in operation, and the patients were at large. They behaved remarkably well—especially so— any one of sense might have known that some devilish scheme was brewing from that particular fact, that the fellows behaved so *remarkably* well. And, sure enough, one fine morning the keepers found themselves pinioned hand and foot, and thrown into the cells, where they were attended, as if *they* were the lunatics, by the lunatics themselves, who had usurped the offices of the keepers."

"You don't tell me so! I never heard of any thing so absurd in my life!"

"Fact—it all came to pass by means of a stupid fellow—a lunatic— who, by some means, had taken it into his head that he had invented a better system of government than any ever heard of before—of lunatic government, I mean. He wished to give his invention a trial, I suppose, and so he persuaded the rest of the patients to join him in a conspiracy for the overthrow of the reigning powers."

"And he really succeeded?"

"No doubt of it. The keepers and kept were soon made to exchange places. Not that exactly either—for the madmen had been free, but the keepers were shut up in cells forthwith, and treated, I am sorry to say, in a very cavalier manner."

"But I presume a counter-revolution was soon effected. This condition of things could not have long existed. The country people in the neighborhood—visiters coming to see the establishment—would have given the alarm."

"There you are out. The head rebel was too cunning for that. He admitted no visiters at all—with the exception, one day, of a very stupid-looking young gentleman of whom he had no reason to be afraid. He let him in to see the place—just by way of variety,—to have a little fun with him. As soon as he had gammoned him sufficiently, he let him out, and sent him about his business."

"And *how* long, then, did the madmen reign?"

"Oh, a very long time, indeed—a month certainly—how much longer I can't precisely say. In the meantime, the lunatics had a jolly season of it—that you may swear. They doffed their own shabby clothes, and made free with the family wardrobe and jewels. The cellars of the *château* were well stocked with wine; and these madmen are just the devils that know how to drink it. They lived well, I can tell you."

"And the treatment—what was the particular species of treatment which the leader of the rebels put into operation?"

"Why, as for that, a madman is not necessarily a fool, as I have already observed; and it is my honest opinion that his treatment was a much better treatment than that which it superseded. It was a very capital system indeed—simple—neat—no trouble at all—in fact it was delicious —it was—"

Here my host's observations were cut short by another series of yells, of the same character as those which had previously disconcerted us. This time, however, they seemed to proceed from persons rapidly approaching.

"Gracious heavens!" I ejaculated—"the lunatics have most undoubtedly broken loose."

"I very much fear it is so," replied Monsieur Maillard, now becoming excessively pale. He had scarcely finished the sentence, before loud shouts and imprecations were heard beneath the windows; and, immediately afterward, it became evident that some persons outside were endeavoring to gain entrance into the room. The door was beaten with what appeared to be a sledge-hammer, and the shutters were wrenched and shaken with prodigious violence.

A scene of the most terrible confusion ensued. Monsieur Maillard, to my excessive astonishment, threw himself under the side-board. I had expected more resolution at his hands. The members of the orchestra, who, for the last fifteen minutes, had been seemingly too much intoxicated to do duty, now sprang all at once to their feet and to their instruments, and, scrambling upon their table, broke out, with one accord, into, "Yankee Doodle," which they performed, if not exactly in tune, at least with an energy superhuman, during the whole of the uproar.

Meantime, upon the main dining-table, among the bottles and glasses, leaped the gentleman who, with such difficulty, had been restrained from leaping there before. As soon as he fairly settled himself, he commenced an oration, which, no doubt, was a very capital one, if it could only have been heard. At the same moment, the man with the tee-totum predilection, set himself to spinning around the apartment, with immense energy, and with arms outstretched at right angles with his body; so that he had all the air of a tee-totum in fact, and knocked everybody down that happened to get in his way. And now, too, hearing an incredible popping and fizzing of champagne, I discovered at length, that it proceeded from the person who performed the bottle of that delicate drink during dinner. And then, again, the frog-man croaked away as if the salvation of his soul depended upon every note that he uttered. And, in the midst of all this, the continuous braying of a donkey arose over all. As for my old friend, Madame Joyeuse, I really could have wept for the poor lady, she appeared so terribly perplexed. All she did, however, was to stand up in a corner, by the fireplace, and sing out incessantly at the top of her voice, "Cock-a-doodle-de-dooooooh!"

And now came the climax—the catastrophe of the drama. As no resistance, beyond whooping and yelling and cock-a-doodleing, was offered to the encroachments of the party without, the ten windows were very speedily, and almost simultaneously, broken in. But I shall never forget the emotions of wonder and horror with which I gazed, when, leaping through these windows, and down among us *pêle-mêle*, fighting, stamping, scratching, and howling, there rushed a perfect army of what I took to be Chimpanzees, Ourang-Outangs, or big black baboons of the Cape of Good Hope.

I received a terrible beating—after which I rolled under a sofa and lay still. After lying there some fifteen minutes, during which time I listened with all my ears to what was going on in the room, I came to same satisfactory *dénouement* of this tragedy. Monsieur Maillard, it appeared, in giving me the account of the lunatic who had excited his fellows to rebellion, had been merely relating his own exploits. This gentleman had, indeed, some two or three years before, been the superintendent of the establishment; but grew crazy himself, and so became a patient. This fact was unknown to the travelling companion who introduced me. The keepers, ten in number, having been suddenly overpowered, were first well tarred, then carefully feathered, and then shut up in underground cells. They had been so imprisoned for more than a month, during which period Monsieur Maillard had generously allowed them not only the tar and feathers (which constituted his "system"), but some bread and abundance of water. The latter was pumped on them daily. At length, one escaping through a sewer, gave freedom to all the rest.

The "soothing system," with important modifications, has been resumed at the *château*; yet I cannot help agreeing with Monsieur Maillard, that his own "treatment" was a very capital one of its kind. As he justly observed, it was "simple—neat—and gave no trouble at all—not the least."

I have only to add that, although I have searched every library in Europe for the works of Doctor *Tarr* and Professor *Fether*, I have, up to the present day, utterly failed in my endeavors at procuring an edition.

Frances Miriam Whitcher (1811–1852)

Frances Miriam Whitcher, who spent her life in central New York, was born in the Mohawk Valley town of Whitesboro and later lived with her clergyman husband in Elmira. Her humorous monologues first appeared in a Rome, New York, newspaper. After the satirist Joseph C. Neal began to print her work in his *Saturday Gazette* in 1846, Mrs. Whitcher became extremely popular and remained so for the rest of the nineteenth century. David Ross Locke ("Petroleum V. Nasby") (pp. 343–45) dramatized her *Widow Bedott Papers* in 1879, and many performances of the play were given during the 1880's. Frances Whitcher was an acute observer of New York village folk and skillfully drew their lineaments in her expert sketches; many neighbors resented her alleged portraits of themselves. Her major characters are highly individualized and Mrs. Whitcher had more than one attitude towards them. The gossipy, loquacious, and self-deceiving "Widow Bedott" is treated with a mild irony much like that of Sarah Orne Jewett (pp. 410–20); on the other hand, "Aunt Maguire" is permitted to look rather tartly on man and society with a tone anticipating the best stories of Mary Wilkins Freeman (pp. 421–32). A good deal of Mrs. Whitcher's humor arises from funny names ("Reverend Sniffles," "Podunk," "Wiggletown," "Meddleville"), malapropisms, doggerel poetry, phonetic spellings, and ludicrous situations such as "Widow Bedott's" difficulties in her hunt for a second husband. But like the local colorists with whom Mrs. Whitcher's work has many affinities and whom she probably influenced, Mrs. Whitcher was not satisfied with surface effects. No tragedies such as those of Miss Jewett and Mrs. Freeman turn up in the *Widow Bedott Papers*; yet Mrs. Whitcher was critical of the dulling monotony of village life and character. A village's parsimonious treatment of its young clergyman and his family, a pious busybody's bearing of false witness, a literary circle's naïveté and sentimentality—all these are laughed at good-naturedly but with unmistakable social and moral implications.

TEXT: *The Widow Bedott Papers*, New York, 1856.

HEZEKIAH BEDOTT

He was a wonderful hand to moralize, husband was, 'specially after he begun to enjoy poor health. He made an observation once when he was in one of his poor turns, that I never shall forget the longest day I live. He says to me one winter evenin' as we was a settin' by the fire, I was a knittin' (I was always a wonderful great knitter) and he was a smokin' (he was a master hand to smoke, though the doctor used to tell him he'd be better off to let tobacker alone; when he was well, used to take his pipe and smoke a spell after he'd got the chores done up, and when he wa'n't well, used to smoke the biggest part o' the time). Well, he took his pipe out of his mouth and turned toward me, and I knowed something was comin', for he had a pertikkeler way of lookin' round when he was gwine to say any thing oncommon. Well, he says to me, says he, "Silly," (my name was Prissilly naterally, but he ginerally called me "Silly," cause 'twas handier, you know.) Well, he says to me, says he, "Silly," and he looked pretty sollem, I tell you, he had a sollem countenance naterally—and after he got to be deacon 'twas more so, but since he'd lost his health he looked sollemer than ever, and certingly you wouldent wonder at it if you knowed how much he underwent. He was troubled with a wonderful pain in his chest, and amazin' weakness in the spine of his back, besides the pleurissy in the side, and having the ager a considerable part of the time, and bein' broke of his rest o' nights 'cause he was so put to 't for breath when he laid down. Why its an onaccountable fact that when that man died he hadent seen a well day in fifteen year, though when he was married and for five or six year after I shouldent desire to see a ruggeder man than what he was. But the time I'm speakin' of he'd been out o' health nigh upon ten year, and O dear sakes! how he had altered since the first time I ever see him! That was to a quiltin' to Squire Smith's a spell afore Sally was married. I'd no idee then that Sal Smith was a gwine to be married to Sam Pendergrass. She'd ben keepin' company with Mose Hewlitt, for better'n a year, and every body said *that* was a settled thing, and lo and behold! all of a sudding she up and took Sam Pendergrass. Well, that was the first time I ever see my husband, and if any body'd a told me then that I should ever marry him, I should a said—but lawful sakes! I most forgot, I was gwine to tell you what he said to me that evenin', and when a body begins to tell a thing I believe in finishin' on 't some time or other. Some folks have a way of talkin' round and round and round for evermore, and never comin' to the pint. Now there's Miss Jinkins, she that was Poll Bingham afore she was married, she is the tejusest individooal to tell a story that ever I see in all my born days. But I was a gwine to tell you what husband said. He says to me says he, "Silly," says I, "What?" I dident say "What, Hezekier?" for I dident like his name. The first time I ever heard it I near killed myself a laffin. "Hezekier Bedott," says I, "well, I would give up if I had sich a name," but then you know I had no more idee o' marryin' the feller than you have this minnit o' marryin' the governor. I s'pose you think it's curus we should a named our oldest son Hezekier. Well, we done it to please father and mother Bedott, it's father Bedott's name, and he and mother Bedott both used to think that names had ought to go down from gineration to gineration. But we always called him Kier, you know. Speakin' o' Kier, he *is* a blessin', ain't he? and I ain't the only one that thinks so, I guess. Now don't you never tell nobody that I said so, but between you and me I rather guess that if Kezier Winkle thinks she is gwine to ketch Kier Bedott she is a *leetle* out of her reckonin'. But I was going to tell what husband said. He says to me, says he, "Silly," I says, says I, "What?" If I dident say "what" when he said "Silly," he'd a kept on saying "Silly," from time to eternity. He always did, because, you know, he wanted me to pay pertikkeler attention, and I ginerally did; no woman was ever more attentive to her husband than what I was. Well, he says to me, says he, "Silly." Says I, "What?" though I'd no idee what he was gwine to say, dident know but what 'twas something about his sufferings, though he wa'n't apt to complain, but he frequently used to remark that he wouldent wish his worst enemy to suffer one minnit as he did all the time, but that can't be called grumblin'—think it can? Why, I've seen him in sitivations when you'd a thought no mortal could a helped grumblin', but *he* dident. He and me went once in the dead o' winter in a one hoss slay out to Boonville to see a sister o' hisen. You know the snow is amazin' deep in that section o' the kentry. Well, the hoss got stuck in one o' them are flambergasted snow-banks, and there we sot, onable to stir, and to cap all, while we was a sittin' there, husband was took with a dretful crick in his back. Now *that* was what I call a *perdickerment*, don't you? Most men would a swore, but husband dident. He only said, says he, "Consarn it." How did we get out, did you ask? Why we might a been sittin' there to this day fur as I know, if there hadent a happened to come along a mess o' men in a double team and they hysted us out. But I was gwine to tell you that observation o' hisen. Says he to me, says he, "Silly," (I could see by the light o' the fire, there dident happen to be no candle burnin', if I don't disremember, though my memory is sometimes ruther forgitful, but I know we wa'n't apt to burn candles exceptin' when we had company) I could see by the light of the fire that his mind was oncommon solemnized. Says he to me, says he, "Silly." I says to him, says I, "What?" He says to me, says he, "*We're all poor critters!*"

T. B. Thorpe (1815–1878)

T. B. Thorpe's "The Big Bear of Arkansas" (1841) marks a stage in the development of "frontier" or "Southwestern" humor which carried it beyond Augustus B. Longstreet's sketches of man in society. With the acceleration of American expansion westward, "frontier" humorists such as Thorpe began to concern themselves with man in nature. Painter, newspaper editor, politician, Union officer, and United States government official, Thorpe was born in Massachusetts but spent most of his life in Louisiana and territories farther west. "The Big Bear of Arkansas" was one of the sketches of Far Western sportsmen, scenery, and sporting activity which Thorpe contributed to the *Spirit of the Times*, a widely circulated New York sporting periodical edited by W. T. Porter from 1831 to 1856 and of which Thorpe became part-owner in 1859. The *Spirit* fostered the growth of "frontier" humor by encouraging Western sportsmen and adventurers to contribute anecdotes or yarns of their experiences. These itinerant correspondents emulated the more polished writing of such men as Thorpe and Johnson J. Hooper, and in turn encouraged those more talented writers to take over the amateurs' exaggerative techniques as well as other elements of the oral humorous tradition developing in the West. The result was a fruitful cross-fertilization which did much to make "frontier" humor a distinctive achievement combining elements of folk culture and high culture. Its typical central character is masculine, shrewd, and heroic, intuitively capable of outwitting both man and nature; his bragging reflects the vastness of the wilderness he is subduing, and at times he almost assumes the character of a demigod. The sentimentality inherent in this primitivist glorification of the natural barbarian is balanced by the braggart hero's ironic revelations of his petty frailties, which make him a comic human figure after all. Thorpe's "Big Bear" contains epic overtones which resemble those in Melville's *Moby-Dick* and Faulkner's "The Bear." Reprinted in *The Big Bear of Arkansas* (1845), Porter's first popular anthology of *Spirit* humor, the sketch soon became one of the most famous of American tall stories.

TEXT: T. B. Thorpe, *The Spirit of the Times*, Vol. XI (March 27, 1841).
COMMENTARY: Norris W. Yates, *William T. Porter and the "Spirit of the Times": A Study of the "Big Bear" School of Humor*, Baton Rouge, La., 1957.

THE BIG BEAR OF ARKANSAS

A steamboat on the Mississippi frequently, in making her regular trips, carries between places varying from one to two thousand miles apart; and as these boats advertise to land passengers and freight at "all intermediate landings," the heterogeneous character of the passengers of one of these up-country boats can scarcely be imagined by one who has never seen it with his own eyes. Starting from New Orleans in one of these boats, you will find yourself associated with men from every state in the Union, and from every portion of the globe; and a man of observation need not lack for amusement or instruction in such a crowd, if he will take the trouble to read the great book of character so favorably opened before him. Here may be seen jostling together the wealthy Southern planter, and the pedlar of tin-ware from New England—the Northern merchant, and the Southern jockey—a venerable bishop, and a desperate gambler —the land speculator, and the honest farmer—professional men of all creeds and characters—Wolvereens, Suckers, Hoosiers, Buckeyes, and Corn-crackers, besides a "plentiful sprinkling" of the half-horse and half-alligator species of men, who are peculiar to "old Mississippi," and who appear to gain a livelihood simply by going up and down the river. In the pursuit of pleasure or business, I have frequently found myself in such a crowd.

On one occasion, when in New Orleans, I had occasion to take a trip of a few miles up the Mississippi, and I hurried on board the well-known "high-pressure-and-beat-every-thing" steamboat *Invincible*, just as the last note of the last bell was sounding; and when the confusion and bustle that is natural to a boat's getting under way had subsided, I discovered that I was associated in as heterogeneous a crowd as was ever got to-gether. As my trip was to be of a few hours' duration only, I made no endeavors to become acquainted with my fellow passengers, most of whom would be together many days. Instead of this, I took out of my pocket the "latest paper," and more critically than usual examined its contents; my fellow passengers at the same time disposed of themselves in little groups. While I was thus busily employed in reading, and my com-panions were more busily still employed in discussing such subjects as suited their humors best, we were startled most unexpectedly by a loud In-dian whoop, uttered in the "social hall," that part of the cabin fitted off for a bar; then was to be heard a loud crowing, which would not have continued to have interested us—such sounds being quite common in that *place of spirits*—had not the hero of these windy accomplishments stuck his head into the cabin and hallooed out, "Hurra for the Big Bar of Arkansaw!" and then might be heard a confused hum of voices, unin-telligible, save in such broken sentences as "horse," "screamer," "lightning is slow," &c. As might have been expected, this continued interruption attracted the attention of every one in the cabin; all conversation dropped, and in the midst of this surprise the "Big Bar" walked into the cabin, took a chair, put his feet on the stove, and looking back over his shoulder, passed the general and familiar salute of "Strangers, how are you?" He then expressed himself as much at home as if he had been at "the Forks of Cypress," and "prehaps a little more so." Some of the company at this familiarity looked a little angry, and some astonished; but in a moment every face was wreathed in a smile. There was something about the intruder that won the heart on sight. He appeared to be a man enjoying perfect health and contentment: his eyes were as sparkling as diamonds, and good-natured to simplicity. Then his perfect confidence in himself was irresistibly droll. "Prehaps," said he, "gentlemen," running on without a person speaking, "prehaps you have been to New Orleans often; I never made *the first visit before,* and I don't intend to make another in a crow's life. I am thrown away in that ar place, and useless, that ar a fact. Some of the gentlemen thar called me *green*—well, prehaps I am, said I, *but I arn't so at home;* and if I ain't off my trail much, the heads of them perlite chaps themselves weren't much the hardest; for according to my notion, they were *real know-nothings,* green as a pumpkin vine—couldn't, in farming, I'll bet, raise a crop of turnips: and as for shooting, they'd miss a barn if the door was swinging, and that, too, with the best rifle in the country. And then they talked to me 'bout hunting, and laughed at my calling the principal game in Arkansaw poker, and high-low-jack. 'Prehaps,' said I, 'you prefer chickens and rolette'; at this they laughed harder than ever, and asked me if I lived in the woods, and didn't know what *game* was? At this I rather think I laughed. 'Yes,' I roared, and says, 'Strangers, if you'd asked me *how we got our meat* in Arkansaw, I'd a told you at once, and given you a list of varmints that would make a caravan, beginning with the bar, and ending off with the cat; that's *meat* though, not game.' Game, indeed that's what city folks call it; and with them it means chippen-birds and shite-pokes; maybe such trash live in my diggins, but I arn't noticed them yet: a bird any way is too trifling. I never did shoot at but one, and I'd never forgiven myself for that, had it weighed less than forty pounds. I wouldn't draw a rifle on any thing less than that; and when I meet with another wild turkey of the same weight I will drap him."

"A wild turkey weighing forty pounds!" exclaimed twenty voices in the cabin at once.

"Yes, strangers, and wasn't it a whopper? You see, the thing was so fat that it couldn't fly far; and when he fell out of the tree, after I shot him, on striking the ground he bust open behind, and the way the pound gobs of tallow rolled out of the opening was perfectly beautiful."

"Where did all that happen?" asked a cynical-looking Hoosier.

"Happen! happened in Arkansaw: where else could it have happened, but in the creation state, the finishing-up country—a state where the *sile* runs down to the centre of the 'arth, and government gives you a title to every inch of it? Then its airs—just breathe them, and they will make you snort like a horse. It's a state without a fault, it is."

"Excepting mosquitoes," cried the Hoosier.

"Well, stranger, except them; for it ar a fact that they are rather *enormous*, and do push themselves in somewhat troublesome. But, stranger, they never stick twice in the same place; and give them a fair chance for a few months, and you will get as much above noticing them as an alligator. They can't hurt my feelings, for they lay under the skin; and I never knew but one case of injury resulting from them, and that was to a Yankee: and they take worse to foreigners, any how, than they do to natives. But the way they used that fellow up! first they punched him until he swelled up and busted; then he su-per-a-ted, as the doctor called it, until he was as raw as beef; then he took the ager, owing to the warm weather, and finally he took a steamboat and left the country. He was the only man that ever took mosquitoes to heart that I know of. But mosquitoes is natur, and I never find fault with her. If they ar large, Arkansaw is large, her varmints ar large, her trees ar large, her rivers ar large, and a small mosquito would be of no more use in Arkansaw than preaching in a cane-brake."

This knock-down argument in favor of big mosquitoes used the Hoosier up, and the logician started on a new track, to explain how numerous bear were in his "diggins," where he represented them to be "about as plenty as blackberries, and a little plentifuler."

Upon the utterance of this assertion, a timid little man near me inquired if the bear in Arkansaw ever attacked the settlers in numbers.

"No," said our hero, warming with the subject, "no, stranger, for you see it ain't the natur of bar to go in droves; but the way they squander about in pairs and single ones is edifying. And then the way I hunt them the old black rascals know the crack of my gun as well as they know a pig's squealing. They grow thin in our parts, it frightens them so, and they do take the noise dreadfully, poor things. That gun of mine is a perfect *epidemic among bar*; if not watched closely, it will go off as quick on a warm scent as my dog Bowie-knife will: and then that dog—whew! why the fellow thinks that the world is full of bar, he finds them so easy. It's lucky he don't talk as well as think; for with his natural modesty, if he should suddenly learn how much he is acknowledged to be ahead of all other dogs in the universe, he would be astonished to death in two minutes. Strangers, the dog knows a bar's way as well as a horse-jockey knows a woman's: he always barks at the right time, bites at the exact place, and whips without getting a scratch. I never could tell whether he was made expressly to hunt bar, or whether bar was made expressly for him to hunt: any way, I believe they were ordained to go together as naturally as Squire Jones says a man and woman is, when he moralizes in marrying a couple. In fact, Jones once said, said he, 'Marriage according to law is a civil contract of divine origin; it's common to all countries as well as Arkansaw, and people take to it as naturally as Jim Doggett's Bowie-knife takes to bar.'"

"What season of the year do your hunts take place?" inquired a gentlemanly foreigner, who, from some peculiarities of his baggage, I suspected to be an Englishman, on some hunting expedition, probably at the foot of the Rocky Mountains.

"The season for bar hunting, stranger," said the man of Arkansaw, "is generally all the year round, and the hunts take place about as regular. I read in history that varmints have their fat season, and their lean season. That is not the case in Arkansaw, feeding as they do upon the *spontenacious* productions of the sile, they have one continued fat season the year round: though in winter things in this way is rather more greasy than in summer, I must admit. For that reason bar with us run in warm weather, but in winter, they only waddle. Fat, fat! it's an enemy to speed; it tames everything that has plenty of it. I have seen wild turkeys, from its influence, as gentle as chickens. Run a bar in this fat condition, and the way it improves the critter for eating is amazing; it sort of mixes the ile up with the meat, until you can't tell t'other from which. I've done this often. I recollect one perty morning in particular, of putting an old he fellow on the stretch, and considering the weight he carried, he run well. But the dogs soon tired him down, and when I came up with him wasn't he in a beautiful sweat—I might say fever; and then to see his tongue sticking out of his mouth a few feet, and his sides sinking and opening like a bellows, and his cheeks so fat he couldn't look cross. In this fix I blazed at him, and pitch me naked into a briar patch if the steam didn't come out of the bullet-hole ten foot in a straight line. The fellow, I reckon, was made on the high-pressure system, and the lead sort of bust his biler."

"That column of steam was rather curious, or else the bear must have been *warm*," observed the foreigner, with a laugh.

"Stranger, as you observe, that bar was WARM, and the blowing off of the steam show'd it, and also how hard the varmint had been run. I have no doubt if he had kept on two miles farther his insides would have been stewed; and I expect to meet with a varmint yet of extra bottom, who will run himself into a skinfull of bar's grease: it is possible, much onlikelier things have happened."

"Whereabouts are these bears so abundant?" inquired the foreigner, with increasing interest.

"Why, stranger, they inhabit the neighborhood of my settlement, one of the prettiest places on old Mississippi—a perfect location, and no mistake; a place that had some defects until the river made the 'cut-off' at 'Shirt-tail bend,' and that remedied the evil, as it brought my cabin on the edge of the river—a great advantage in wet weather, I assure you, as you can now roll a barrel of whiskey into my yard in high water from a boat, as easy as falling off a log. It's a great improvement, as toting it by land in a jug, as I used to do, *evaporated* it too fast, and it became expensive. Just stop with me, stranger, a month or two, a year if you like, and you will appreciate my place. I can give you plenty to eat; for beside hog and hominy, you can have bar-ham, and bar sausages, and a mattrass of bar-skins to sleep on, and a wildcat-skin, pulled off hull, stuffed with corn-shucks, for a pillow. That bed would put you to sleep if you had the rheumatics in every joint in your body. I call that ar bed a *quietus*. Then look at my land—the government ain' got another such a piece to dispose of. Such timber, and such bottom land, why you can't preserve any thing natural you plant in it unless you pick it young, things thar will grow out of shape so quick. I once planted in those diggins a few potatoes and beets: they took a fine start, and after that an ox team couldn't have kept them from growing. About that time I went off to old Kentuck on bisiness, and did not hear from them things in three months, when I accidentally stumbled on a fellow who had stopped at my place, with an idea of buying me out. 'How did you like things?' said I. 'Pretty well,' said he; 'the cabin is convenient, and the timber land is good; but that bottom land ain't worth the first red cent.' 'Why?' said I. ' 'Cause,' said he. ' 'Cause what?' said I. ' 'Cause it's full of cedar stumps and Indian mounds,' said he, *'and it can't be cleared.'* 'Lord,' said I, 'them ar "cedar stumps" is beets, and them ar "Indian mounds" ar tater hills.' As I expected, the crop was overgrown and useless: the sile is too rich, *and planting in Arkansaw is dangerous.* I had a good-sized sow killed in that same bottom land. The old thief stole an ear of corn, and took it down where she slept at night to eat. Well, she left a grain or two on the ground, and lay down on them: before morning the corn shot up, and the percussion killed her dead. I don't plant any more; natur intended Arkansaw for a hunting ground, and I go according to natur."

The questioner who thus elicited the description of our hero's settlement, seemed to be perfectly satisfied, and said no more; but the "Big Bar of Arkansaw" rambled on from one thing to another with a volubility perfectly astonishing, occasionally disputing with those around him, particularly with a "live Sucker" from Illinois, who had the daring to say that our Arkansaw friend's stories "smelt rather tall."

In this manner the evening was spent; but conscious that my own association with so singular a personage would probably end before morning, I asked him if he would not give me a description of some particular bear hunt; adding that I took great interest in such things, though I was no sportsman. The desire seemed to please him, and he squared himself round towards me, saying, that he could give me an idea of a bar hunt that was never beat in this world, or in any other. His manner was so singular, that half of his story consisted in his excellent way of telling it, the great peculiarity of which was, the happy manner he had of emphasizing the prominent parts of his conversation. As near as I can recollect, I have italicized them, and given the story in his own words.

"Stranger," said he, "in bar hunts *I am numerous*, and which particular one, as you say, I shall tell, puzzles me. There was the old she devil I shot at the Hurricane last fall—then there was the old hog thief I popped over at the Bloody Crossing, and then—Yes, I have it! I will give you an idea of a hunt, in which the greatest bar was killed that ever lived, *none excepted*; about an old fellow that I hunted, more or less, for two or three years; and if that ain't a *particular bar hunt*, I ain't got one to tell. But in the first place, stranger, let me say, I am pleased with you, because you ain't ashamed to gain information by asking, and listening, and that's what I say to Countess's pups every day when I'm home; and I have got great hopes of them ar pups, because they are continually *nosing* about; and though they stick it sometimes in the wrong place, they gain experience any how, and may learn something useful to boot. Well, as I was saying about this big bar, you see when I and some more first settled in our region, we were driven to hunting naturally; we soon liked it, and after that we found it an easy matter to make the thing our business. One old chap who had pioneered 'afore us, gave us to understand that we had settled in the right place. He dwelt upon its merits until it was affecting, and showed us, to prove his assertions, more marks on the sassafras trees than I ever saw on a tavern door 'lection time. 'Who keeps that ar reckoning?' said I. 'The bar,' said he. 'What for?' said I. 'Can't tell,' said he; 'but so it is: the bar bite the bark and wood too, at the highest point from the ground they can reach, and you can tell, by the marks,' said he, 'the length of the bar to an inch.' 'Enough,' said I; 'I've learned something here a'ready, and I'll put it in practice.'

"Well, stranger, just one month from that time I killed a bar, and told its exact length before I measured it, by those very marks; and when I did that, I swelled up considerable—I've been a prouder man ever since. So I went on, larning something every day, until I was reckoned a buster, and allowed to be decidedly the best bar hunter in my district; and that is a reputation as much harder to earn than to be reckoned first man in Congress, as an iron ramrod is harder than a toadstool. Did the varmints grow over-cunning by being fooled with by green-horn hunters, and by this means get troublesome, they send for me as a matter of course; and thus I do my own hunting, and most of my neighbors'. I walk into the varmints though, and it has become about as much the same to me as drinking. It is told in two sentences—a bar is started, and he is killed. The thing is somewhat monotonous now—I know just how much they will run, where they will tire, how much they will growl, and what a thundering time I will have in getting them home. I could give you this history of the chase with all the particulars at the commencement, I know the signs so well—*Stranger, I'm certain.* Once I met a match though, and I will tell you about it; for a common hunt would not be worth relating.

"On a fine fall day, long time ago, I was trailing about for bar, and what should I see but fresh marks on the sassafras trees, about eight inches above any in the forests that I knew of. Says I, 'them marks is a hoax, or it indicates the d——t bar that was ever grown.' In fact, stranger, I couldn't believe it was real, and I went on. Again I saw the same marks, at the same height, and I *knew the thing lived.* That conviction came home to my soul like an earthquake. Says I, 'here is something a-purpose for me; that bar is mine, or I give up the hunting business.' The very next morning what should I see but a number of buzzards hovering over my cornfield. 'The rascal has been there,' said I, 'for that sign is certain': and, sure enough, on examining, I found the bones of what had been as beautiful a hog the day before, as was ever raised by a Buckeye. Then I tracked the critter out of the field to the woods, and all the marks he left behind, showed me that he was *the bar.*

"Well, stranger, the first fair chase I ever had with that big critter, I saw him no less than three distinct times at a distance: the dogs run him over eighteen miles and broke down, my horse gave out, and I was as nearly used up as a man can be, made on *my* principle, *which is patent.* Before this adventure, such things were unknown to me as possible; but, strange as it was, that bar got me used to it before I was done with him; for he got so at last, that he would leave me on a long chase *quite easy.* How he did it, I never could understand. That a bar runs at all, is puzzling; but how this one could tire down and bust up a pack of hounds and a horse, that were used to overhauling everything they started after in no time, was past my understanding. Well, stranger, that bar finally got so sassy, that he used to help himself to a hog off my premises whenever he wanted one;—the buzzards followed after what he left, and so between *bar and buzzard,* I rather think I was *out of pork.*

"Well, missing that bar so often took hold of my vitals, and I wasted away. The thing had been carried too far, and it reduced me in flesh faster than an ager. I would see that bar in every thing I did: *he hunted me,* and that, too, like a devil, which I began to think he was. While in this fix, I made preparations to give him a last brush, and be done with it. Having completed every thing to my satisfaction, I started at sunrise, and to my great joy, I discovered from the way the dogs run, that they were near him; finding his trail was nothing, for that had become as plain to the pack as a turnpike road. On we went, and coming to an open country, what should I see but the bar very leisurely ascending a hill, and the dogs close at his heels, either a match for him in speed, or else he did not care to get out of their way—I don't know which. But wasn't he a beauty, though? I loved him like a brother.

"On he went, until he came to a tree, the limbs of which formed a crotch about six feet from the ground. Into this crotch he got and seated himself, the dogs yelling all around it; and there he sat eyeing them as quiet as a pond in low water. A green-horn friend of mine, in company, reached shooting distance before me, and blazed away, hitting the critter in the centre of his forehead. The bar shook his head as the ball struck it, and then walked down from that tree as gently as a lady would from a carriage. 'Twas a beautiful sight to see him do that—he was in such a rage that he seemed to be as little afraid of the dogs as if they had been sucking pigs; and the dogs warn't slow in making a ring around him at a respectful distance, I tell you; even Bowie-knife, himself, stood off. Then the way his eyes flashed—why the fire of them would have singed a cat's hair; in fact that bar was *wrath all over*. Only one pup came near him, and he was brushed out so totally with the bar's left paw, that he entirely disappeared; and that made the old dogs more cautious still. In the mean time, I came up, and taking deliberate aim as a man should do, at his side, just back of his foreleg, *if my gun did not snap*, call me a coward, and I won't take it personal. Yes, stranger, *it snapped*, and I could not find a cap about my person. While in this predicament, I turned round to my fool friend—says I, 'Bill,' says I, 'you're an ass—you're a fool —you might as well have tried to kill that bar by barking the tree under his belly, as to have done it by hitting him in the head. Your shot has made a tiger of him, and blast me, if a dog gets killed or wounded when they come to blows, I will stick my knife into your liver, I will—' my wrath was up. I had lost my caps, my gun had snapped, the fellow with me had fired at the bar's head, and I expected every moment to see him close in with the dogs, and kill a dozen of them at least. In this thing I was mistaken, for the bar leaped over the ring formed by the dogs, and giving a fierce growl, was off—the pack, of course, in full cry after him. The run this time was short, for coming to the edge of a lake the varmint jumped in, and swam to a little island in the lake, which it reached just a moment before the dogs. 'I'll have him now,' said I, for I had found my caps in the *lining of my coat*—so, rolling a log into the lake, I paddled myself across to the island, just as the dogs had cornered the bar in a thicket. I rushed up and fired—at the same time the critter leaped over the dogs and came within three feet of me, running like mad; he jumped into the lake, and tried to mount the log I had just deserted, but every time he got half his body on it, it would roll over and send him under; the dogs, too, got around him, and pulled him about, and finally Bowie-knife clenched with him, and they sunk into the lake together. Stranger, about this time, I was excited, and I stripped off my coat, drew my knife, and intended to have taken a part with Bowie-knife myself, when the bar rose to the surface. But the varmint staid under—Bowie-knife came up alone, more dead than alive, and with the pack came ashore. 'Thank God,' said I, 'the old villain has got his deserts at last.' Determined to have the body, I cut a grape-vine for a rope, and dove down where I could see the bar in the water, fastened my queer rope to his leg, and fished him, with great difficulty, ashore. Stranger, may I be chawed to death by young alligators, if the thing I looked at wasn't a *she bar, and not the old critter after all.* The way matters got mixed on that island was onaccountably curious, and thinking of it made me more than ever convinced that I was hunting the devil himself. I went home that night and took to my bed— the thing was killing me. The entire team of Arkansaw in bar-hunting, acknowledged himself used up, and the fact sunk into my feelings like a snagged boat will in the Mississippi. I grew as cross as a bar with two cubs and a sore tail. The thing got out 'mong my neighbours, and I was asked how come on that individu-al that never lost a bar when once started? and if that same individu-al didn't wear telescopes when he turned a she bar, of ordinary size, into an old he one, a little larger than a horse? 'Prehaps,' said I, 'friends'—getting wrathy—'prehaps you want to call somebody a liar.' 'Oh, no,' said they, 'we only heard such things as being *rather common* of late, but we don't believe one word of it; oh, no,' —and then they would ride off and laugh like so many hyenas over a dead nigger. It was too much, and I determined to catch that bar, go to Texas, or die,—and I made my preparations accordin'. I had the pack shut up and rested. I took my rifle to pieces and iled it. I put caps in every pocket about my person, *for fear of the lining.* I then told my neighbours, that on Monday morning—naming the day—I would start THAT BAR, and bring him home with me, or they might divide my settlement among them, the owner having disappeared. Well, stranger, on the morning previous to the great day of my hunting expedition, I went into the woods near my house, taking my gun and Bowie-knife along, just *from habit,* and there sitting down also from habit, what should I see, getting over my fence, but *the bar!* Yes, the old varmint was within a hundred yards of me, and the way he walked *over that fence*—stranger, he loomed up like a *black mist,* he seemed so large, and he walked right towards me. I raised myself, took deliberate aim, and fired. Instantly the varmint wheeled, gave a yell, and *walked through the fence* like a falling tree would through a cobweb. I started after, but was tripped up by my inexpressibles, which either from habit, or the excitement of the moment, were about my heels, and before I had really gathered myself up, I heard the old varmint groaning in a thicket near by, like a thousand sinners, and by the time I reached him he was a corpse. Stranger, it took five niggers and myself to put that carcase on a mule's back and old long-ears waddled under the load, as if he was foundered in every leg of his body, and with a common whopper of a bar, he would have trotted off, and enjoyed himself. 'Twould astonish you to know how big he was: I made a *bed-spread of his skin,* and the way it used to cover my bar mattress, and leave several feet on each side to tuck up, would have delighted you. It was in fact a creation bar, and if it had lived in Samson's time, and had met him, in a fair fight, it would have licked him in the twinkling of a dice-box. But, strangers, I never like the way I hunted, and *missed him*. There is something curious about it, I could never understand,—and I never was satisfied at his giving in *so easy at last*. Perhaps, he had heard of my preparations to hunt him the next day, so he jist come in, like Capt. Scott's coon, to save his wind to grunt with in dying; but that ain't likely. My private opinion is, that that bar was an *unhuntable bar, and died when his time come*."

When the story was ended, our hero sat some minutes with his auditors in a grave silence; I saw there was a mystery to him connected with the bear whose death he had just related, that had evidently made a strong impression on his mind. It was also evident that there was some superstitious awe connected with the affair,—a feeling common with all "children of the wood," when they meet with any thing out of their everyday experience. He was the first one, however, to break the silence, and jumping up, he asked all present to "liquor" before going to bed,—a thing which he did, with a number of companions, evidently to his heart's content.

Long before day, I was put ashore at my place of destination, and I can only follow with the reader, in imagination, our Arkansas friend, in his adventures at the "Forks of Cypress" on the Mississippi.

Johnson J. Hooper (1815–1863)

Johnson J. Hooper's *Some Adventures of Captain Simon Suggs* (1845) is a comic picaresque novel whose hero is so inventive and unabashed a rogue that his moral turpitude becomes a subject for laughter. Designed to read as if it were a campaign biography, Hooper's novel satirizes democracy as Brackenridge's *Modern Chivalry* had done earlier and specifically ridicules such contemporary political figures as Andrew Jackson and James K. Polk. Hooper was an Alabama lawyer, judge, newspaper editor, and politician whose first Simon Suggs sketch appeared in the La Fayette (Ala.) *East Alabamian* in 1844; the characteristics of Simon Suggs were modeled upon those of an Alabama gentleman notorious for escapades as amusing as the Captain's. Hooper won great popularity for his Suggs pieces and other humorous writings. His novel, like Longstreet's *Georgia Scenes*, was reprinted in numerous editions during the nineteenth century and in this century as recently as 1928. The chapter below has been said to have influenced Mark Twain's camp meeting scene in the *Adventures of Huckleberry Finn*.

TEXT: *Simon Suggs' Adventures and Travels* . . . , Philadelphia, Pa., 1858. COMMENTARY: W. Stanley Hoole, *Alias Simon Suggs: The Life and Times of Johnson Jones Hooper*, Tuscaloosa, Ala., 1952.

THE CAPTAIN ATTENDS A CAMP-MEETING

Captain Suggs found himself as poor at the conclusion of the Creek war as he had been at its commencement. Although no "arbitrary," "despotic," "corrupt," and "unprincipled" judge had fined him a thousand dollars for his proclamation of martial law at Fort Suggs, or the enforcement of its rules in the case of Mrs. Haycock; yet somehow—the thing is alike inexplicable to him and to us—the money which he had contrived, by various shifts, to obtain, melted away and was gone forever. To a man like the Captain, of intense domestic affections, this state of destitution was most distressing. "He could stand it himself—didn't care a d——n for it, no way," he observed, "but the old woman and the children; *that* bothered him!"

As he sat one day, ruminating upon the unpleasant condition of his "financial concerns," Mrs. Suggs informed him that "the sugar and the coffee was nigh about out," and that there were not "a dozen j'ints and middlins, *all put together*, in the smoke-house." Suggs bounced up on the instant, exclaiming, "D——n it! *somebody* must suffer!" But whether this remark was intended to convey the idea that he and his family were about to experience the want of the necessaries of life; or that some other, and as yet unknown, individual should "suffer" to prevent that prospective exigency, must be left to the commentators, if perchance any of that ingenious class of persons should hereafter see proper to write notes for this history. It is enough for us that we give all the facts in this connection, so that ignorance of the subsequent conduct of Captain Suggs may not lead to an erroneous judgment in respect to his words.

Having uttered the exclamation we have repeated—and perhaps, hurriedly walked once or twice across the room—Captain Suggs drew on his famous old green-blanket overcoat, and ordered his horse, and within five minutes was on his way to a camp-meeting, then in full blast on Sandy Creek, twenty miles distant, where he hoped to find amusement, at least. When he arrived there, he found the hollow square of the encampment filled with people, listening to the mid-day sermon, and its dozen accompanying "exhortations." A half-dozen preachers were dispensing the word; the one in the pulpit, a meek-faced old man, of great simplicity and benevolence. His voice was weak and cracked, notwithstanding which, however, he contrived to make himself heard occasionally, above the din of the exhorting, the singing, and the shouting which were going on around him. The rest were walking to and fro (engaged in the other exercises we have indicated), among the "mourners"—a host of whom occupied the seat set apart for their especial use—or made personal appeals to the mere spectators. The excitement was intense. Men and women rolled about on the ground, or lay sobbing or shouting in promiscuous heaps. More than all, the negroes sang and screamed and prayed. Several, under the influence of what is technically called "the jerks," were plunging and pitching about with convulsive energy. The great object of all seemed to be, to see who could make the greatest noise—

> "And each—for madness ruled the hour—
> Would try his own expressive power."

"Bless my poor old soul!" screamed the preacher in the pulpit; "ef yonder aint a squad in that corner that we aint got one outen yet! It'll never do"—raising his voice—"you must come outen that! Brother Fant, fetch up that youngster in the blue coat! I see the Lord's a-workin' upon him! Fetch him along—glory—yes!—hold to him!"

"Keep the thing warm!" roared a sensual seeming man, of stout mould and florid countenance, who was exhorting among a bevy of young women, upon whom he was lavishing caresses. "Keep the thing warm, breethring! —come to the Lord, honey!" he added, as he vigorously hugged one of the damsels he sought to save.

"Oh, I've got him!" said another man in exulting tones, as he led up a gawky youth among the mourners—"I've got him—he tried to git off, but—ha! Lord!"—shaking his head as much as to say, it took a smart fellow to escape him—"ha! Lord!"—and he wiped the perspiration from his face with one hand, and with the other, patted his neophyte on the shoulder—"he couldn't do it! No! Then he tried to argy wi' me—but bless the Lord!—he couldn't do that nother! Ha! Lord! I tuk him, fust in the Old Testament—bless the Lord!—and I argyed him all thro' Kings—then I throwed him into Proverbs,—and from that, here we had it up and down, kleer down to the New Testament, and then I begun to see it work him! —then we got into Matthy, and from Matthy right straight along to Acts; and *thar* I throwed him! Y-e-s—L-o-r-d!"—assuming the nasal twang and high pitch which are, in some parts, considered the perfection of rhetorical art—"Y-e-s—L-o-r-d! and h-e-r-e he is! Now g-i-t down thar," addressing the subject, "and s-e-e ef the L-o-r-d won't do somethin' f-o-r you!" Having thus deposited his charge among the mourners, he started out, summarily to convert another soul!

"Gl-o-r*ee!*" yelled a huge, greasy negro woman, as in a fit of the jerks, she threw herself convulsively from her feet, and fell "like a thousand of brick," across a diminutive old man in a little round hat, who was squeaking consolation to one of the mourners.

"Good Lord, have mercy!" ejaculated the little man earnestly and unaffectedly, as he strove to crawl from under the sable mass which was crushing him.

In another part of the square a dozen old women were singing. They were in a state of absolute ecstasy, as their shrill pipes gave forth.

> "I rode on the sky,
> Quite ondestified I,
> And the moon it was under my feet!"

Near these last, stood a delicate woman in that hysterical condition in which the nerves are incontrollable, and which is vulgarly—and almost blasphemously—termed the "holy laugh." A hideous grin distorted her mouth, and was accompanied with a maniac's chuckle; while every muscle and nerve of her face twitched and jerked in horrible spasms.[1]

Amid all this confusion and excitement Suggs stood unmoved. He viewed the whole affair as a grand deception—a sort of "opposition line" running against his own, and looked on with a sort of professional jealousy. Sometimes he would mutter running comments upon what passed before him.

"Well now," said he, as he observed the full-faced brother who was

[1] The reader is requested to bear in mind, that the scenes described in this story are not *now* to be witnessed. Eight or ten years ago, all classes of population of the Creek country were very different from what they now are. Of course no disrespect is intended to any denomination of Christians. We believe that camp meetings are not peculiar to any church, though most usual in the Methodist—a denomination whose respectability in Alabama is attested by the fact, that *very many* of its worthy clergymen and lay members, hold honourable and profitable offices in the gift of the state legislature; of which, indeed, almost a controlling portion are themselves Methodists.

"officiating" among the women, "that ere feller takes *my* eye!—thar he's been this half-hour, a-figurin amongst them galls, and's never said the fust word to nobody else. Wonder what's the reason these here preachers never hugs up the old ugly women? Never seed one do it in my life—the sperrit never moves 'em that way! It's nater tho'; and the women, *they* never flocks round one o' the old dried-up breethring—bet two to one old splinter-legs thar,"—nodding at one of the ministers—"won't git a chance to say turkey to a good-lookin gall to-day! Well! who blames 'em? Nater will be nater, all the world over; and I judge ef I was a preacher, I should save the purtiest souls fust, myself!"

While the Captain was in the middle of this conversation with himself, he caught the attention of the preacher in the pulpit, who inferring from an indescribable something about his appearance that he was a person of some consequence, immediately determined to add him at once to the church if it could be done; and to that end began a vigorous, direct personal attack.

"Breethring," he exclaimed, "I see yonder a man that's a sinner; I *know* he's a sinner! Thar he stands," pointing at Simon, "a missubble old crittur, with his head a-blossomin for the grave! A few more short years, and d-o-w-n he'll go to perdition, lessen the Lord have mer-cy on him! Come up here, you old hoary-headed sinner, a-n-d git down upon your knees, a-n-d put up your cry for the Lord to snatch you from the bottomless pit! You're ripe for the devil—you're b-o-u-n-d for hell, and the Lord only knows what'll become on you!"

"D——n it," thought Suggs, "ef I only had you down in the krick swamp for a minit or so, *I'd* show you who's *old!* I'd alter your tune *mighty* sudden, you sassy, 'saitful old rascal!" But he judiciously held his tongue and gave no utterance to the thought.

The attention of many having been directed to the Captain by the preacher's remarks, he was soon surrounded by numerous well-meaning, and doubtless very pious persons, each one of whom seemed bent on the application of his own particular recipe for the salvation of souls. For a long time the Captain stood silent, or answered the incessant stream of exhortations only with a sneer; but at length, his countenance began to give token of inward emotion. First his eye-lids twitched—then his upper lip quivered—next a transparent drop formed on one of his eye-lashes, and a similar one on the tip of his nose—and, at last, a sudden bursting of air from nose and mouth, told that Captain Suggs was overpowered by his emotions. At the moment of the explosion, he made a feint as if to rush from the crowd, but he was in experienced hands, who well knew that the battle was more than half won.

"Hold to him!" said one—"it's a-workin in him as strong as a Dick horse!"

"Pour it into him," said another, "it'll all come right directly!"

"That's the way I love to see 'em do," observed a third; "when you begin to draw the water from their eyes, taint gwine to be long afore you'll have 'em on their knees!"

And so they clung to the Captain manfully, and half dragged, half led him to the mourner's bench; by which he threw himself down, altogether unmanned, and bathed in tears. Great was the rejoicing of the brethren, as they sang, shouted, and prayed round him—for by this time it had come to be generally known that the "convicted" old man was Captain Simon Suggs, the very "chief of sinners" in all that region.

The Captain remained grovelling in the dust during the usual time, and gave vent to even more than the requisite number of sobs, and groans, and heart-piercing cries. At length, when the proper time had arrived, he bounced up, and with a face radiant with joy, commenced a series of vaultings and tumblings, which "laid in the shade" all previous performances of the sort at that camp-meeting. The brethren were in ecstasies at this demonstrative evidence of completion of the work; and whenever Suggs shouted "Gloree!" at the top of his lungs, every one of them shouted it back, until the woods rang with echoes.

The effervescence having partially subsided, Suggs was put upon his pins to relate his experience, which he did somewhat in this style—first brushing the tear-drops from his eyes, and giving the end of his nose a preparatory wring with his fingers, to free it of the superabundant moisture:

"Friends," he said, "it don't take long to curry a short horse, accordin' to the old sayin', and I'll give you the perticklers of the way I was 'brought to a knowledge' "—here the Captain wiped his eyes, brushed the tip of his nose and snuffled a little—"in less'n no time."

"Praise the Lord!" ejaculated a bystander.

"You see I come here full o' romancin' and devilment, and jist to make game of all the purceedins. Well, sure enough, I done so for some time, and was a-thinkin how I should play some trick—"

"Dear soul alive! *don't* he talk sweet!" cried an old lady in black silk— "Whar's John Dobbs? You Sukey!" screaming at a negro woman on the other side of the square—"ef you don't hunt up your mass John in a minute, and have him here to listen to this 'sperience, I'll tuck you up when I git home and give you a hundred and fifty lashes, madam!—see ef I don't! Blessed Lord!"—referring again to the Captain's relation—"ain't it a *precious* 'scource!"

"I was jist a-thinkin' how I should play some trick to turn it all into redecule, when they began to come round me and talk. Long at fust I didn't mind it, but arter a little that brother"—pointing to the reverend gentleman who had so successfully carried the unbeliever through the Old and New Testament, and who Simon was convinced was the "big dog of the tanyard"—"that brother spoke a word that struck me kleen to the heart, and run all over me, like fire in dry grass—"

"*I-I-I* can bring 'em!" cried the preacher alluded to, in a tone of exultation—"Lord thou knows ef thy servant can't stir 'em up, nobody else needn't try—but the glory aint mine! I'm a poor worrum of the dust," he added, with ill-managed affectation.

"And so from that I felt somethin' a-pullin' me inside—"

"Grace! grace! nothin' but grace!" exclaimed one; meaning that "grace" had been operating in the Captain's gastric region.

"And then," continued Suggs, "I wanted to git off, but they hilt me, and bimeby I felt so missuble, I had to go yonder"—pointing to the mourner's seat—"and when I lay down thar it got wuss and wuss, and 'peared like somethin' was a-mashin' down on my back—"

"That was his load o' sin," said one of the brethren—"never mind, it'll tumble off presently, see ef it don't!" and he shook his head professionally and knowingly.

"And it kept a-gittin heavier and heavier, ontwell it looked like it might be a four year old steer, or a big pine log, or somethin' of that sort—"

"Glory to my soul," shouted Mrs. Dobbs, "it's the sweetest talk I *ever* hearn! You Sukey! ain't you got John yit? never mind, my lady, *I'll* settle wi' you!" Sukey quailed before the finger which her mistress shook at her.

"And arter awhile," Suggs went on, " 'peared like I fell into a trance, like, and I seed—"

"Now we'll git the good on it!" cried one of the sanctified.

"And I seed the biggest, longest, rip-roarenest, blackest, scaliest—" Captain Suggs paused, wiped his brow, and ejaculated, "Ah, L-o-r-d!" so as to give full time for curiosity to become impatience to know what he saw.

"*Sarpent!* warn't it?" asked one of the preachers.

"No, not a sarpent," replied Suggs, blowing his nose.

"Do tell us *what* it war, soul alive!—whar *is* John?" said Mrs. Dobbs.

"Allegator!" said the Captain.

"Alligator!" repeated every woman present, and screamed for very life. Mrs. Dobbs's nerves were so shaken by the announcement, that after repeating the horrible word, she screamed to Sukey, "You Sukey, I say, you Su-u-ke-e-y! ef you let John come a-nigh this way, whar the dreadful alliga—shaw! what am I thinkin' 'bout? 'Twarn't nothin' but a vishin!"

"Well," said the Captain in continuation, "the allegator kept a-comin' an a-comin' to'ards me, with his great long jaws a-gapin' open like a ten-foot pair o' tailor's shears—"

"Oh! oh! oh! Lord! gracious above!" cried the women.

"Satan!" was the laconic ejaculation of the oldest preacher present, who thus informed the congregation that it was the devil which had attacked Suggs in the shape of an alligator.

"And then I concluded the jig was up, 'thout I could block his game some way; for I seed his idee was to snap off my head—"

The women screamed again.

"So I fixed myself jist like I was purfectly willin' for him to take my head, and rather he'd do it as not"—here the women shuddered perceptibly—"and so I hilt my head straight out"—the Captain illustrated by elongating his neck—"and when he come up and was a gwine to *shet down* on it, I jist pitched in a big rock which choked him to death, and that minit I felt the weight slide off, and I had the best feelins—sorter like you'll have from *good* sperrits—any body ever had!"

"Didn't I *tell* you so? Didn't I *tell* you so?" asked the brother who had predicted the off-tumbling of the load of sin. "Ha, Lord! fool *who!* I've been *all* along thar!—yes, *all along thar!* and I know every inch of the way jist as good as I do the road home!"—and then he turned round and round, and looked at all, to receive a silent tribute to his superior penetration.

Captain Suggs was now the "lion of the day." Nobody could pray so well, or exhort so movingly, as "brother Suggs." Nor did his natural modesty prevent the proper performance of appropriate exercises. With the reverend Bela Bugg (him to whom, under providence, he ascribed his conversion) he was a most especial favorite. They walked, sang, and prayed together for hours.

"Come, come up; thar's room for all!" cried brother Bugg, in his evening exhortation. "Come to the 'seat,' and ef you won't pray yourselves, let *me* pray for you!"

"Yes!" said Simon, by way of assisting his friend; "it's a game that all can win at! Ante up! ante up, boys—friends I mean—don't back out!"

"Thar aint a sinner here," said Bugg, "no matter ef his soul's black as a nigger, but what thar's room for him!"

"No matter what sort of a hand you've got," added Simon in the fulness of his benevolence; "take stock! Here am *I*, the wickedest and blindest of sinners—has spent my whole life in the sarvice of the devil—has come now in on *narry pair* and won a *pile!*" and the Captain's face beamed with holy pleasure.

"D-o-n-'t be afeared!" cried the preacher; "come along! the meanest won't be turned away! humble yourselves and come!"

"No!" said Simon, still indulging in his favourite style of metaphor; "the bluff game aint played here! No runnin' of a body off! Every body holds four aces, and when you bet, you win!"

And thus the Captain continued, until the services were concluded, to assist in adding to the number at the mourners' seat; and up to the hour of retiring, he exhibited such enthusiasm in the cause, that he was unanimously voted to be the most efficient addition the church had made during that meeting.

The next morning, when the preacher of the day first entered the pulpit, he announced that "brother Simon Suggs," mourning over his past iniquities, and desirous of going to work in the cause as speedily as possible, would take up a collection to found a church in his own neighbourhood, at which he hoped to make himself useful as soon as he could prepare himself for the ministry, which the preacher didn't doubt, would be in a very few weeks, as brother Suggs was "a man of mighty good judgment, and of a great discorse." The funds were to be collected by "brother Suggs," and held in trust by brother Bela Bugg, who was the financial officer of the circuit, until some arrangement could be made to build a suitable house.

"Yes, breethring," said the Captain, rising to his feet; "I want to start a little 'sociation close to me, and I want you all to help. I'm mighty poor myself, as poor as any of you—don't leave, breethring"—observing that several of the well-to-do were about to go off—"don't leave; ef you aint able to afford any thing, jist give us your blessin' and it'll be all the same!"

This insinuation did the business, and the sensitive individuals reseated themselves.

"It's mighty little of this world's goods I've got," resumed Suggs, pulling off his hat and holding it before him; "but I'll bury *that* in the cause any how," and he deposited his last five-dollar bill in the hat.

There was a murmur of approbation at the Captain's liberality throughout the assembly.

Suggs now commenced collecting, and very prudently attacked first the gentlemen who had shown a disposition to escape. These, to exculpate themselves from anything like poverty, contributed handsomely.

"Look here, breethring," said the Captain, displaying the bank-notes thus received, "brother Snooks has drapt a five wi' me, and brother Snodgrass a ten! In course 'taint expected that you *that aint as well off as them*, will give *as much*; let every one give *accordin'* to ther means."

This was another chain-shot that raked as it went! "Who so low" as not to be able to contribute as much as Snooks and Snodgrass?

"Here's all the *small* money I've got about me," said a burly old fellow, ostentatiously handing to Suggs, over the heads of a half dozen, a ten dollar bill.

"That's what I call maganimus!" exclaimed the Captain; "that's the way *every* rich man ought to do!"

These examples were followed, more or less closely, by almost all present, for Simon had excited the pride of purse of the congregation, and a very handsome sum was collected in a very short time.

The reverend Mr. Bugg, as soon as he observed that our hero had obtained all that was to be had at that time, went to him and inquired what amount had been collected. The Captain replied that it was still uncounted, but that it couldn't be much under a hundred.

"Well, brother Suggs, you'd better count it and turn it over to me now. I'm goin' to leave presently."

"No!" said Suggs—"can't do it!'

"Why?—what's the matter?" inquired Bugg.

"It's got to be *prayed over*, fust!" said Simon, a heavenly smile illuminating his whole face.

"Well," replied Bugg, "les go one side and do it!"

"No!" said Simon, solemnly.

Mr. Bugg gave a look of inquiry.

"You see that krick swamp?" asked Suggs—"I'm gwine down in *thar*, and I'm gwine to lay this money down *so*"—showing how he would place it on the ground—"and I'm gwine to git on these here knees"—slapping the right one—"and I'm *n-e-v-e-r* gwine to quit the grit ontwell I feel it's got the blessin'! And nobody ain't got to be thar but me!"

Mr. Bugg greatly admired the Captain's fervent piety, and bidding him God-speed, turned off.

Captain Suggs "struck for" the swamp sure enough, where his horse was already hitched. "Ef them fellers aint done to a cracklin," he muttered to himself as he mounted, "I'll never bet on two pair again! They're peart at the snap game, theyselves; but they're badly lewed this hitch! Well! Live and let live is a good old motter, and it's my sentiments adzactly!" And giving the spur to his horse, off he cantered.

George Washington Harris (1814–1869)

Sut Lovingood is the most fully developed humorous character in American literature prior to the appearance of Mark Twain's Tom Sawyer and Huck Finn. Sut's creator, George Washington Harris of Tennessee, is in turn the greatest of the "frontier" humorists who preceded Mark Twain. Harris' imagination, language, ribaldry, and mirthfulness possess an intensity which few American writers of humor but Herman Melville, Mark Twain, S. J. Perelman, and William Faulkner have equalled. Not surprisingly, Harris is one of Faulkner's favorite writers. Hillbilly Sut lives somewhere in the Southern Appalachians. With sure comic insight, Harris created a character who boasts of his scariness, his tendency to flee from the very whiff of trouble, his "natural born durned fool" spirit, his petty trickiness, and his conscienceless infliction of pain and discomfiture. Yet out of the seeming chaos and meanness of Sut's personality and actions there gradually arises a superstructure revealing that a morality and a philosophy have been in existence always; that they contain, ironically enough, numerous traditional and wholesome values. Ultimately the mythic universalities such as heroism, fertility, masculinity, and femininity emerge over a bedrock of elemental human values which Sut has carved out in the course of his adventures, values such as love, joy, truth, and justice. These are only some of the positive concepts which Sut has admired and championed, and it is no small feat that they emerge from behind a protagonist who ironically has been deprecated by his creator. This is humor on a grand scale. Harris's monologues brought the vernacular style to a level of poetry and psychological subtlety which makes his prose the equal of Melville's in some respects and the most accomplished of its kind before Mark Twain's. Unfortunately, Harris' "yarns" are not easy to read. The popular success of the "literary comedians" (see Charles Farrar Browne, pp. 339–42) encouraged Harris to blur his sensitive rendition of folk speech with the misspellings, mispronunciations, and other superficialities of the comedians. Mark Twain discarded these cheap tricks in Huckleberry Finn and it may be that Harris would have done so too had he not been disoriented by the Civil War and dead shortly after its end. A 1954 edition of Harris' writings makes them available without the unnecessary obstacles to reading which have prevented Harris from achieving the wide recognition he merits.

TEXT: Sut Lovingood, New York, 1867. Sut Lovingood, ed. Brom Weber, New York, 1954, includes most of the 1867 edition and three political satires printed elsewhere.

RARE RIPE GARDEN-SEED

"I tell yu now, I minds my fust big skeer jis' es well as rich boys minds thar fust boots, ur seein the fust spotted hoss sirkis. The red top ove them boots am still a rich red stripe in thar minds, an' the burnin red ove my fust skeer hes lef es deep a scar ontu my thinkin works. Mam hed me a standin atwixt her knees. I kin feel the knobs ove her jints a-rattlin a-pas' my ribs yet. She didn't hev much petticoats tu speak ove, an' I hed but one, an' hit wer calliker slit frum the nap ove my naik tu the tail, hilt tugether at the top wif a draw-string, an' at the bottom by the hem; hit wer the handiest close I ever seed, an' wud be pow'ful cumfurtin in summer if hit warn't fur the flies. Ef they was good tu run in, I'd war one yet. They beats pasted shuts, an' britches, es bad es a feather bed beats a bag ove warnut shells fur sleepin on.

"Say, George, wudn't yu like tu see me intu one 'bout haf fadid, slit, an' a-walkin jis' so, up the middil street ove yure city chuch, a-aimin fur yure pew pen, an' hit chock full ove yure fine city gal friends, jis' arter the peopil hed sot down frum the fust prayer, an' the orgin beginin tu groan; what wud yu du in sich a margincy? say hoss?"

"Why, I'd shoot you dead, Monday morning before eight o'clock," was my reply.

"Well, I speck yu wud; but yu'd take a rale ole maid faint fus, rite amung them ar gals. Lordy! wudn't yu be shamed ove me! Yit why not ten chuch in sich a suit, when yu hesn't got no store clothes?

"Well, es I wer sayin, mam wer feedin us brats ontu mush an' milk, wifout the milk, an' es I wer the baby then, she hilt me so es tu see that I got my sheer. Whar thar ain't enuf feed, big childer roots littil childer outen the troff, an' gobbils up thar part. Jis' so the yeath over: bishops eats elders, elders eats common peopil; they eats sich cattil es me, I eats possums, possums eats chickins, chickins swallers wums, an' wums am content tu eat dus, an' the dus am the aind ove hit all. Hit am all es regilur es the souns frum the tribil down tu the bull base ove a fiddil in good tchune, an' I speck hit am right, ur hit wudn't be 'lowed.

"'The sheriff!' his'd mam in a keen trimblin whisper; hit sounded tu me like the skreech ove a hen when she sez 'hawk,' tu her little roun-sturn'd fuzzy, bead-eyed, stripid-backs.

"I actid jis' adzacly as they dus; I darted on all fours onder mam's petticoatails, an' thar I met, face tu face, the wooden bowl, an' the mush, an' the spoon what she slid onder frum tuther side. I'se mad at myself yet, fur rite thar I show'd the fust flash ove the nat'ral born durn fool what I now is. I orter et hit all up, in jestis tu my stumick an' my growin, while the sheriff wer levyin ontu the bed an' the cheers. Tu this day, ef enybody sez 'sheriff,' I feels skeer, an' ef I hears constabil men-shun'd, my laigs goes thru runnin moshuns, even ef I is asleep. Did yu ever watch a dorg dreamin ove rabbit huntin? Thems the moshuns, an' the feelin am the rabbit's.

"Sherifs am orful 'spectabil peopil; everybody looks up tu em. I never adzacly seed the 'spectabil part mysef. I'se too fear'd ove em, I reckon, tu 'zamin fur hit much. One thing I knows, no country atwix yere an' Tophit kin ever 'lect me tu sell out widders' plunder, ur poor men's co'n, an' the tho'ts ove hit gins me a good feelin; hit sorter flashes thru my heart when I thinks ove hit. I axed a passun onst, whan hit cud be, an' he pernounced hit tu be *onregenerit pride*, what I orter squelch in prayer, an' in tendin chuch on colleckshun days. I wer in hopes hit mout be 'ligion, ur sence, a-soakin intu me; hit feels good, enyhow, an' I don't keer ef every suckit rider outen jail knows hit. Sheriffs' shuts allers hes nettil dus ur fleas inside ove em when they lies down tu sleep, an' I'se glad ove hit, fur they'se allers discumfortin me, durn em. I scarcely ever git tu drink a ho'n, ur eat a mess in peace. I'll hurt one sum day, see ef I don't. Show me a sheriff a-steppin softly roun, an' a-sorter sightin at me, an' I'll show yu a far sampil ove the speed ove a express ingine, fired up wif rich, dry, rosiny skeers. They don't ketch me *much*, usin only human laigs es wepuns.

"Ole John Doltin wer a 'spectabil sheriff, monsusly so, an' hed the bes' scent fur poor fugatif devils, an' wimen, I ever seed; he were sure fire. Well, he toted a warrun fur this yere skinful ove durn'd fool, 'bout that ar misfortnit nigger meetin bisness, ontil he wore hit intu six seperit squar bits, an' hed wore out much shoe leather a-chasin ove me. I'd foun a doggery in full milk, an' hated pow'ful bad tu leave that settilment while hit suck'd free; so I sot intu sorter try an' wean him off frum botherin me so much. I suckseedid so well that he not only quit racin ove me, an' wimen, but he wer tetotaly spiled es as a sheriff, an' los' the 'spectabil seckshun ove his karacter. Tu make yu fool fellers onderstan how hit wer done, I mus' interjuice yure minds tu one Wat Mastin, a bullit-headed yung blacksmith.

"Well, las' year—no hit wer the year afore las'—in struttin an' gob-blin time, Wat felt his keepin right warm, so he sot intu bellerin an' pawin up dus in the neighborhood roun the ole widder McKildrin's. The more dus he flung up, the wus he got, ontil at las' he jis cudn't stan the ticklin sensashuns anuther minnit; so he put fur the county court clark's offis, wif his hans sock'd down deep intu his britchis pockets, like he wer fear'd ove pick-pockets, his back roach'd roun, an' a-chompin his teef ontil he sploch'd his whiskers wif foam. Oh! he wer yearnis' hot, an' es restless es a cockroach in a hot skillit."

"What was the matter with this Mr. Mastin? I cannot understand you, Mr. Lovingood; had he hydrophobia?" remarked a man in a square-tail coat, and cloth gaiters, who was obtaining subscribers for some forth-coming Encyclopedia of Useful Knowledge, who had quartered at our camp, uninvited, and really unwanted.

"What du yu mean by high-dry-foby?" and Sut looked puzzled.

"A madness produced by being bit by some rabid animal," explained Square-tail, in a pompous manner.

"Yas, hoss, he hed high-dry-foby *orful*, an' Mary McKildrin, the wid-der McKildrin's only darter, hed gin him the complaint; I don't know whether she bit 'im ur not; he mout a-cotch hit frum her bref, an' he wer now in the roach back, chompin stage ove the sickness, so he wer arter the clark fur a tickit tu the hospital. Well, the clark sole 'im a piece ove paper, part printin an' part ritin, wif a picter ove two pigs' hearts, what sum boy hed shot a arrer thru, an' lef hit stickin, printed at the top. That paper were a splicin pass—sum calls hit a par ove licins —an' that very nite he tuck Mary, fur better, fur wus, tu hev an' tu hole tu him his heirs, an'——"

"Allow me to interrupt you," said our guest; "you do not quote the marriage ceremony correctly."

"Yu go tu *hell*, mistofer; yu bothers me."

This outrageous rebuff took the stranger all aback, and he sat down.

"Whar wer I? Oh yas, he married Mary tight an' fas', an' nex day he wer abil tu be about. His coat tho', an' his trousis look'd jis' a skrimshun too big, loose like, an' heavy tu tote. I axed him ef he felt soun. He sed yas, but he'd welded a steamboat shaftez the day afore, an' were sorter tired like. Thar he tole a durn lie, fur he'd been a-ho'nin up dirt mos' ove the day, roun the widder's garden, an' bellerin in the orchard. Mary an' him sot squar intu hous'-keepin, an' 'mung uther things he bot a lot ove *rar ripe garden-seed*, frum a Yankee peddler. Rar ripe co'n, rar ripe peas, rar ripe taters, rar ripe everything, an' the two yung durn'd fools wer dreadfully exercis'd 'bout hit. Wat sed he ment tu git him a rar ripe hammer an' anvil, an' Mary vow'd tu grashus, that she'd hev a rar ripe wheel an' loom, ef money wud git em. Purty soon arter he hed made the garden, he tuck a noshun tu work a spell down tu Ataylanty, in the railroad shop, es he sed he hed a sorter ailin in his back, an' he tho't weldin rail car-tire an' ingine axiltrees, wer lighter work nur sharpinin plows, an' puttin lap-links in trace-chains. So down he went, an' foun hit agreed wif him, fur he didn't cum back ontil the middil ove August. The fust thing he seed when he landid intu his cabin-door, wer a shoebox wif rockers onder hit, an' the nex thing he seed, wer Mary hersef, propped up in bed, an' the nex thing he seed arter that, wer a par ove littil rat-eyes a-shinin abuv the aind ove the quilt, ontu Mary's arm, an' the nex an' las' thing he seed wer the two littil rat-eyes aforesed, a-turnin intu two hundred thousand big green stars,

an' a-swingin roun an' roun the room, faster an' faster, ontil they mix'd
intu one orful green flash. He drap't intu a limber pile on the floor. The
durn'd fool what hed weldid the steamboat shaftez hed fainted safe
an' soun es a gal skeered at a mad bull. Mary fotch a weak cat-scream,
an' kivered her head, an' sot intu work ontu a whifflin dry cry, while
littil Rat-eyes gin hissef up tu suckin. Cryin an' suckin bof at onst
ain't far; mus' cum pow'ful strainin on the wet seckshun ove an' 'oman's
constitushun; yet hit am ofen dun, an' more too. Ole Missis McKildrin,
what wer a-nussin Mary, jis' got up frum knittin, an' flung a big gourd
ove warter squar intu Wat's face, then she fotch a glass bottil ove swell-
skull whisky outen the three-cornered cupboard, an' stood furnint Wat,
a-holdin hit in wun han, an' the tin-cup in tuther, waitin fur Wat tu
cum to. She wer the piusses lookin ole 'oman jis' then, yu ever seed
outside ove a prayer-meetin. Arter a spell, Wat begun tu move, twitchin
his fingers, an' battin his eyes, sorter 'stonished like. That pius lookin
statue sed tu him:

" 'My son, jis' take a drap ove sperrits, honey. Yu'se very sick, dumplin,
don't take on darlin, ef yu kin help hit, ducky, fur poor Margarit Jane
am mons'ous ailin, an' the leas' nise ur takin on will kill the poor sufferin dear, an' yu'll loose yure tuckil ducky duv ove a sweet wifey, arter
all she's dun gone thru fur yu. My dear son Watty, yu mus' consider
her feelins a littil.' Sez Wat, a-turnin up his eyes at that vartus ole rel-
ick, sorter sick like—

" 'I is a-considerin em a heap, rite now.'

" 'Oh that's right, my good kine child.'

"Oh dam ef ole muther-in-lors can't plaster humbug over a feller,
jis' es saft an' easy es they spreads a camrick hanketcher over a three
hour ole baby's face; yu don't feel hit at all, but hit am thar, a plum
inch thick, an' stickin fas es court-plaster. She raised Wat's head, an'
sot the aidge ove the tin cup agin his lower teef, an' turned up the
bottim slow an' keerful, a-winkin at Mary, hu wer a-peepin over the
aidge ove the coverlid, tu see ef Wat *tuck the perskripshun,* fur a heap
ove famerly cumfort 'pended on that ar ho'n ove sperrits. *Wun* ho'n
allers saftens a man, the yeath over. Wat keep a-battin his eyes, wus
nur a owl in daylight; at las' he raised hissef ontu wun elbow, an' rested
his head in that han, sorter weak like. Sez he, mons'ous trimblin an'
slow: 'Aprile—May—June—July—an' mos'—haf—ove—August,' a-countin
the munths ontu the fingers ove tuther han, wif the thumb, a-shakin
ove his head, an' lookin at his spread fingers like they warn't his'n, ur
they were nastied wif sumfin. Then he counted em agin, slower, Aprile
—May—June—July—an', mos' haf ove August, an' he run his thumb
atwixt his fingers, es meanin mos' haf ove August, an' look'd at the
pint ove hit, like hit mout be a snake's head. He raised his eyes tu the
widder's face, who wer standin jis' es steady es a hitchin pos', an' still

a-warin that pius 'spression ontu her pussonal feturs, an' a flood ove saft luv fur Wat, a-shinin strait frum her eyes intu his'n. Sez he, 'That jis' makes four munths, an' mos' a half, don't hit, Missis McKildrin?' She never sed one word. Wat reached fur the hath, an' got a dead fire-coal; then he made a mark clean acrost a floorplank. Sez he, 'Aprile,' a-holdin down the coal ontu the aind ove the mark, like he were fear'd hit mout blow away afore he got hit christened Aprile. Sez he, 'May' —an' he marked across the board agin; then he counted the marks, one, two, a-dottin at em wif the coal. 'June,' an' he marked agin, one, two, three; counted wif the pint ove the coal. He scratched his head wif the littil finger ove the han holdin the charcoal, an' he drawed hit slowly acrost the board agin, peepin onder his wrist tu see when hit reached the crack, an' sez he 'July,' es he lifted the coal; 'one, two, three, four,' countin frum lef tu right, an' then frum right tu lef. 'That haint but four, no way I kin fix hit. Ole Pike hissef cudn't make hit five, ef he wer tu sifer ontu hit ontil his laigs turned intu figger eights.' Then he made a mark, haf acrost a plank, spit on his finger, an' rubbed off a haf inch ove the aind, an' sez he, 'Mos' haf ove August.' He looked up at the widder, an' thar she wer, same es ever, still a-holdin the flask agin her bussum, an' sez he 'Four months, an' mos' a haf. *Haint enuf, is hit mammy?* hits jis' 'bout (lackin a littil) *haf enuf*, haint hit, mammy?'

"Missis McKildrin shuck her head sorter onsartin like, an' sez she, 'Take a drap more sperrits, Watty, my dear pet; dus yu mine buyin that ar rar ripe seed, frum the peddler?' Wat nodded his head, an' looked 'what ove hit,' but didn't say hit.

" 'This is what cums ove hit, an' four months an' a haf am rar ripe time fur babys, adzackly. Tu be sure, hit lacks a day ur two, but Margarit Jane wer allers a pow'ful interprizin gal, an' a yearly rizer.' Sez Wat,

" 'How about the 'taters?'

" 'Oh, *we* et 'taters es big es goose aigs, afore ole Missis Collinze's blossomed.'

" 'How 'bout co'n?'

" 'Oh, we shaved down roasin years afore hern tassel'd——'

" 'An' peas?'

" 'Yes son, we hed gobs an' lots in three weeks. Everything cums in adzackly half the time that hit takes the ole sort, an' yu *knows*, my darlin son, yu planted hit waseful. I tho't then yu'd rar ripe everything on the place. Yu planted *often*, too, didn't yu luv? fur fear hit wudn't cum up.'

" 'Ye-ye-s-s he—he did,' sed Mary a-cryin. Wat studied pow'ful deep a spell, an' the widder jis' waited. Widders allers wait, an' allers win. At las, sez he, 'Mammy.' She looked at Mary, an' winked these yere words at her, es plain es she cud a-talked em. 'Yu hearn him call me *mammy twiste*. I'se *got him* now. His back-bone's a-limberin fas', he'll own the baby yet, see ef he don't. Jis' hole still my darter, an' let yer mammy knead this dough, then yu may bake hit es brown es yu please.'

" 'Mammy, when I married on the fust day ove Aprile'—— The widder look'd oneasy; she tho't he mout be a-cupplin that day, his weddin, an' the idear, dam fool, together. But he warn't, fur he sed 'That day I gin ole man Collins my note ove han fur a hundred dullars, jew in one year arter date, the balluns on this lan. Dus yu think that ar seed will change the *time* eny, ur will hit alter the *amount?*' An' Wat looked at her powerful ankshus. She raised the whisky bottil way abuv her head, wif her thumb on the mouf, an' fotch the bottim down ontu her han, spat. Sez she, 'Watty, my dear b'lovid son, pripar tu pay *two* hundred dullars 'bout the fust ove October, fur hit'll be jew jis' then, *es* sure es that littil black-eyed angel in the bed thar, am yer darter.'

"Wat drap't his head, an' sed, '*Then hits a dam sure thing.*' Rite yere, the baby fotch a rattlin loud squall, (I speck Mary wer sorter figetty jis' then, an' hurt hit.) 'Yas,' sez Wat, a-wallin a red eye to'ards the bed; 'my littil she—what wer hit yu called her name, mammy?' 'I called her a sweet littil angel, an' she is wun, es sure es yu're her daddy, my b'loved son.' 'Well,' sez Wat, 'my littil sweet, patent rar ripe she angel, ef yu lives tu marryin time, yu'll 'stonish sum man body outen his shut, ef yu don't rar ripe lose hits vartu arter the fust plantin, that's all.' He rared up on aind, wif his mouf pouch'd out. He had a pow'ful forrid, fur-reachin, bread funnel, enyhow—cud a-bit the aigs outen a catfish, in two-foot warter, wifout wettin his eyebrows. 'Dod durn rar ripe seed, an' rar ripe pedlers, an' rar ripe notes tu the hottes' corner ove——'

" 'Stop Watty, *darlin*, don't swar; 'member yu belongs tu meetin.'

" 'My blacksmith's fire,' ainded Wat, an' he studied a long spell; sez he,

" 'Did you save eny ove that infunnel doubil-trigger seed?' 'Yas,' sez the widder, 'thar in that bag by the cupboard.' Wat got up ofen the floor, tuck a countin sorter look at the charcoal marks, an' reached down the bag; he went tu the door an' called 'Suke, muley! Suke, Suke, cow, chick, chick, chicky chick.' 'What's yu gwine tu du now, my dear son?' sed Missis McKildrin. 'I'se jis' gwine tu feed this actif *smart* truck tu the cow, an' the hens, that's what I'se gwine tu du. Ole muley haint hed a calf in two years, an' I'll eat sum rar ripe aigs.' Mary now venter'd tu speak: 'Husban, I ain't sure hit'll work on hens; cum an' kiss me my luv.' 'I haint sure hit'll work on hens, either,' sed Wat. 'They's powerful onsartin in thar ways, well es wimen,' an' he flung out a hanful spiteful like. 'Takin the rar ripe invenshun all tugether, frum 'taters an' peas tu notes ove han, an' childer, I can't say I likes hit much,' an' he flung out anuther hanful. 'Yer mam hed thuteen the ole way, an' ef this truck stays 'bout the hous', yu'se good fur twenty-six, maybe thuty, fur yu'se a pow'ful interprizin gal, yer mam sez,' an' he flung out anuther hanful, overhandid, es hard es ef he wer flingin rocks at a stealin sow. 'Make yere mine easy,' sed the widder; 'hit never works on married folks only the fust time.' 'Say them words agin,' sed Wat, 'I'se glad tu hear em. Is hit the same way wif notes ove han?' 'I speck hit am,' answer'd the widder, wif jis' a taste ove strong vinegar in the words, es she sot the flask in the cupboard wif a push.

"Jis' then ole Doltin, the sheriff, rid up, an' started 'stonished when he seed Wat, but he, quick es an 'oman kin hide a strange hat, drawed the puckerin-string ove that legil face ove his'n, an' fotch hit up tu the 'know'd yu wer at home,' sorter look, an' wishin Wat much joy, sed he'd fotch the baby a present, a par ove red shoes, an' a calliker dress, fur the luv he bore hits granmam. Missis McKildrin tole him what the rar ripe hed dun, an' he swore hit allers worked jis' that way, an' wer 'stonished at Wat's not knowin hit; an' they talked so fas', an' so much, that the more Wat listened the less he know'd.

"Arter the sheriff lef, they onrolled the bundil, an' Wat straitched out the calliker in the yard. He step't hit off keerfully, ten yards, an a littil the rise. He puss'd up his mouf, an' blow'd out a whistil seven foot long, lookin up an' down the middil stripe ove the drygoods, frum aind tu aind. Sez he, 'Missis McKildrin, that'll make Rar Ripe a good *full* frock, won't hit?' 'Y-a-s,' sed she, wif her hans laid up along her jaw, like she wer studyin the thing keerfully. 'My son, I thinks hit will, an' I wer jis' a-thinkin ef hit wer cut tu 'vantage, thar *mout* be nuff lef, squeezed out tu make yu a Sunday shutin shut, makin the ruffils an' ban outen sumthin else.' 'Put hit in the bag what the rar ripe wer in, an' by mornin thar'll be nuff fur the ruffils an' bans, an' yu mout make the tail tu drag the yeath, wifout squeezin ur pecin,' sez Wat, an' he put a few small wrinkils in the pint ove his nose, what seemed tu bother the widder tu make out the meanin ove; they look'd mons'ous like the outward signs ove an onb'lever. Jis' then his eyes sot fas' ontu sumthin a-lyin on the groun whar he'd onrolled the bundil; he walk'd up tu hit slow, sorter like a feller goes up tu a log, arter he thinks he seed a snake run onder. He walk'd clean roun hit twiste, never takin his eyes ofen hit. At las' he lifted hit on his instep, an' hilt out his laig strait at that widdered muther-in-lor ove his'n. Sez he, 'What mout yu call that? Red baby's shoes don't giner'lly hev teeth, dus they?' 'Don't yu *know* hits a tuckin comb, Watty? The store-keeper's made a sorter blunder, I speck,' sed that vartus petti-coatful ove widderhood. 'Maybe he hes; I'se durn sure I *hes*,' sed Wat, an' he wrinkil'd his nose agin, mons'ous botherinly tu that watchful widder. He scratched his head a spell; sez he, 'Ten yards an' the rise fur a baby's frock, *an' hit rar ripe at that, gits me*; an' that ar tuckin comb gits me wus.' 'Oh, fiddlesticks an' flusterashun,' sez she. 'Save the comb; baby'll soon want hit.' 'That's so, mammy, I'm dam ef hit don't,' an' he slip't his foot frum onder hit, an hit scarcely totch the yeath afore he stomp't hit, an' the teeth flew all over the widder. He look'd like he'd been stompin a blowin adder, an' went apas' the 'oman intu the cabin, in a rale Aprile tucky gobbler strut. When he tore the rapper off the sheriff's present, I seed a littil bit ove white paper fall out. On-benowenst tu enybody, I sot my foot ontu hit, an' when they went in I socked hit deep intu my pocket, an' went over tu the still-'ous. I tuck Jim Dunkin out, an' arter swarin 'im wif a uplifted han', tu keep dark, got him tu read hit tu me, ontil hit wer printed on the mindin seckshun ove my brain. Hit run jis' so:

"My sweet Mary:

I mayn't git the chance tu talk eny tu yu, so when Wat gits home, an' axes enything 'bout the *comb* an' *calliker*, yu tell him yer mam foun the bundil in the road. She'll back yu up in that ar statement, ontil thar's enuf white fros' in hell tu kill snap-beans.

Notey Beney.—I hope Wat'll stay in Atlanty ontil the merlenium, don't yu, my dear duv?

Yures till deth,

Doltin

An' tu that ar las' remark he'd sot a big D. I reckon he ment that fur dam Wat.

"Now, I jis' know'd es long es I hed that paper, I hilt four aces ontu the sheriff, an' I ment tu bet on the han, an' *go halves wif Wat*, fur I wer sorry fur him, he wer so infunely 'posed upon. I went tu school tu Sicily Burns, tu larn 'oman tricks, an' I tuck a dirplomer, I did, an' now I'd jes' like tu see the pussonal feeters ove the she 'oman what cud stock rar ripe kerds on me, durn'd fool es I is. I hed a talk wif Wat, an' soon foun out that his mine hed simmer'd down intu a strong belief that the sheriff an' Mary wer doin thar weavin in the same loom.

"Then I show'd him my four aces, an' that chip made the pot bile over, an' he jis' 'greed tu be led by me, spontanashusly.

"Jis' think on that fac' a minnit boys; a man what hed sense enuf tu turn a hoss shoe, an' then nail hit on toe aind foremos', bein led by me, looks sorter like a plum tree barin tumil bug-balls, but hit wer jis' so, an' durn my pictur, ef I didn't lead him tu victory, strait along.

"Wat narrated hit, that he b'leved strong in rar ripe, frum beans, thru notes ove han, plum tu babys, an' that his cabin shud never be wifout hit. The widder wer cheerful, Mary wer luvin, an' the sheriff wer told on the sly, by ole Mister McKildrin's remainin, an' mos' pius she half, that Wat wer es plum blind es ef his eyes wer two tuckil aigs. So the wool grow'd over *his* eyes, ontil hit wer fit tu shear, an' *dam ef I warn't at the shearin.*

"Things, tharfore, went smoof, an' es quiet es a greased waggin, runnin in san. Hits allers so, jis' afore a tarin big storm.

"By the time littil Rar Ripe wer ten weeks ole, Doltin begun tu be pow'ful plenty in the neighborhood. Even the brats know'd his hoss's tracks, an' go whar he wud, the road led ni ontu Wat's, ur the widder's, tu git thar. My time tu play my four aces hed 'bout cum."

"And so has orderly bed time. I wish to repose," remarked the man of Useful Knowledge, in the squaretail coat, and cloth gaiters.

Sut opened his eyes in wonder.

"Yu wish tu du what?"

"I wish to go to sleep."

"Then why the h—l didn't yu say so? Yu mus' talk Inglish tu me, ur not git yersef onderstood. I warn't edikated at no Injun ur nigger school. Say, bunty, warn't yu standid deep in sum creek, when the taylure man put the string to yu, fur that ar cross atwix a rounabout an' a flour barril, what yu'se got on in place of a coat?"

My self-made guest looked appealingly at me, as he untied his gaiters, evidently deeply insulted. I shook my head at Sut, who was lying on his breast, with his arms crossed for a pillow, but with head elevated like a lizard's, watching the traveler's motions with great interest.

"Say, George, what dus repose mean? That wurd wer used at me jis' now."

"Repose means rest."

"Oh, the devil hit dus! I'se glad tu hear hit, I tho't hit wer pussonal. I kin repose now, mysef. Say, ole Onsightly Peter, repose sum tu, ef yu kin in that flour barril. I ain't gwine tu hunt fur yure har ontil mor——" and Sut slept. When morning broke, the Encyclopedia, or Onsightly Peter as Sut pronounced it, had

> "Folded his tent like the Arab,
> And as silently stole away."

CONTEMPT OF COURT—ALMOST

"Ole Onsightly Peter tuck his squar-tail cackus kiver away frum this yere horspitable camp, wifout axin fur his bill, ur even sayin 'mornin' tu us. Le's look roun a littil; I bet he'se stole sumfin. Fellers ove his stripe allers dus. They never thinks a night's lodgin cumplete, onless they hooks a bed-quilt, ur a candilstick, ur sum sichlike. I hates ole Onsightly Peter, jis' caze he didn't seem tu like tu hear me narrate las' night; that's human nater the yeath over, an' yere's more univarsal onregenerit human nater: ef ever yu dus enything tu enybody wifout cause, yu hates em allers arterwards, an' sorter wants tu hurt em agin. An' yere's anuther human nater: ef enything happens sum feller, I don't keer ef he's yure bes' frien, an' I don't keer how sorry yu is fur him, thar's a streak ove satisfackshun 'bout like a sowin thread a-runnin all thru yer sorrer. Yu may be shamed ove hit, but durn me ef hit ain't thar. Hit will show like the white cottin chain in mean cassinett; brushin hit onder only hides hit. An' yere's a littil more; no odds now good yu is tu yung things, ur how kine yu is in treatin em, when yu sees a littil long laiged lamb a-shakin hits tail, an' a-dancin staggerinly onder hits mam a-huntin fur the tit, ontu hits knees, yer fingers *will* itch tu seize that ar tail, an' fling the littil ankshus son ove a mutton over the fence amung the blackberry briars, not tu hurt hit, but jis' tu disapint hit. Ur say, a littil calf, a-buttin fas' under the cow's fore-laigs, an' then the hine, wif the pint ove hits tung stuck out, makin suckin moshuns, not yet old enuf tu know the bag aind ove hits mam frum the hookin aind, don't yu want tu kick hit on the snout, hard enough tu send hit backwards, say fifteen foot, jis' tu show hit that buttin won't allers fetch milk? Ur a baby even, rubbin hits heels apas' each uther, a-rootin an' a-snifflin arter the breas', an' the mam duin her bes' tu git hit out, over the hem ove her clothes, don't yu feel hungry tu gin hit jis' one 'cussion cap slap, rite ontu the place what sum day'll fit a saddil, ur a sowin cheer, tu show hit what's atwixt hit an' the grave; that hit stans a pow'ful chance not tu be fed every time hits hungry, ur in a hurry? An' agin: ain't thar sum grown up babys what yu meets, that the moment yer eyes takes em in, yer toes itch tu tetch thar starns, jis' 'bout es saftly es a muel kicks in playin; a histin kine ove a tetch, fur the way they wares thar har, hat, ur watchchain, the shape ove thar nose, the cut ove thar eye, ur sumthin ove a like littil natur. Jis' tu show the idear, a strange fellow onst cum intu a doggery whar I wer buzzy a-raisin steam, an' had got hit a few poun abuv a bladder bustin pint.

"He tuck off his gloves, slow an' keerful, a-lookin at me like I mout smell bad. Then he flattened em ontu the counter, an' laid em in the crown ove his hat, like he wer packin shuts in a trunk. Then sez he—

" 'Baw-keepaw, ole Champaigne Brandy, vintage ove thuty-eight, ef yu please, aw.'

"He smelt hit slow, a-lookin at hissef in the big lookin-glass ahine the counter, shook his head, an' turned up his mustachus, sorter like a goat hists hits tail.

"Mustachus am pow'ful holesum things I speck, tu them what hes the stumick tu wear em. Bes' buttermilk strainers on yeath. All the scrimpshuns ove butter lodges in the har, an' rubbed in makes it grow, like chicken dung dus inyuns. Strains whisky powerful good, what hes dead flies in hit, an' then yu kin comb em off ur let em stay, 'cordin tu yer taste. They changes the taste ove a kiss clear over; makes hit tas' an' smell like a mildew'd saddil-blankit, arter hit hed been rid on a sore-back hoss three hundred miles in August, an' increases yer appertite fur sich things 'cordinly. I seed a blue-bird devil a feller onst, all one spring, a-tryin tu git intu his mouf tu bild a nestes, an' the durn'd fool wer proud ove the bird's preferens, but wudn't let hit git in.

"Rite then, I thought, well, durn yure artifishul no-count soul, an' my toes begun tu tingle. He tuck four trials, a-pourin back an' forrid, afore he got his dram the right depth, a-lookin thru the tumbler like he spected tu see a minner, ur a warter-mockasin in hit. Then he drunk hit, like hit wer caster ile, the infunel fool. Lordy crimminy! how bad my toes wer itchin now. He lit a seegar, cocked hit up to'ards one eye, an' looked at me agin thru the smoke, while he shook his hat over ontu one ove his years. Sez I, 'Mornin mister.'

"He never sed a word, but turned an' started fur the door. When he got six foot nine inches distunt, (that's my bes' kickin range,) the durned agravatin toe itch overcum me, an' I let one ove these yere hoss-hide boots *go arter 'im*; hit imejuntly cotch up wif the fork ove his coattail, an' went outen my sight, mos' up tu the straps. He went flyin outen the doggery door, over the hoss-rack. While he wer in the air, he turned plum roun an' lit facin me wif a cock't Derringer, a-starin me squar in the face. I tho't I seed the bullit in hit lookin es big es a hen's aig. Es I dodged, hit plowed a track acrost the door-jam, jis' es high es my eye-brows. I wer one hundred an' nineteen yards deep in the wheat-field when I hearn hits mate bark, an' he wer a pow'rful quick moshun'd man wif shootin irons.

"I wer sorter fooled in the nater ove that feller, that's a fac'. The idear ove Derringers, an' the melt tu use em, bein mix't up wif es much durned finekey fool es he show'd, never struck me at all, but I made my pint on 'im, I cured my toe itch.

"Well, I allers tuck the cumplaint every time I seed ole Jedge Smarty, but I dusn't try tu cure hit on him, an' so hit jis' hed tu run hits course, onless I met sumthin I cud kick.

"Wirt Staples got him onst, bad; 'stonished the ole bag ove lor amos' outen his dignity, dam ef he didn't, an' es Wirt tuck a skeer in what's tu cum ove my narashun about the consekinses ove foolin wif uther men's wives, I'll tell yu how he 'stonished ole Smarty, an' then yu'll better onderstand me when I cums tu tell yu how he help't tu 'stonish ole Doltin.

"Wirt hed changed his grocery range, an' the sperrits at the new lick-log hed more scrimmage seed an' raise-devil intu hit than the old biled drink he wer used tu, an' three ho'ns histed his tail, an' sot his bristils 'bout es stiff es eight ove the uther doggery juice wud. So when cort sot at nine o'clock, Wirt wer 'bout es fur ahead as cleaving, ur half pas' that.

"The hollerin stage ove the disease now struck him, so he roar'd one good year-quiverin roar, an' riz three foot inside the doggery door, an' lit nine more out in the mud, sploshin hit all over the winders, tuther side the street. He hed a dried venerson ham in one han, an' a ten-year old he nigger by hits gallus-crossin in tuther. He waved fus' the nigger an' then the venerson over his head, steppin short an' high, like ontu a bline hoss, an lookin squar atwixt his shoe-heels, wif his shoulders hump'd hi up. Sez he,

"'Hu—wee,' clear an' loud es a tin ho'n, 'run onder the hen, yere's the blue-tail hawk, an' he's a-flyin low. The Devil's grist mill-dam's broke; take tu yer canoes.' Then he roared a time ur two, an' look'd up an' down the street, like a bull looks fur tuther one, when he thinks he hearn a beller. He riz ontu his tip-toes, an' finished a good loud 'Hu-wee.' Es he drap't ontu his heels agin, he yelled so hard his head shook an' his long black har quivered agin; he then shook hit outen his eyes, wipin the big draps ove sweat ofen his snout wif his shut-sleeve, still hangin tu the venerson an' the nigger. Sez he,

"'Look out fur the ingine when yu hears hit whistil; hits a-whistilin rite now. Nineteen hundred an' eighty pouns tu the squar scrimpshun by golly, an' eighty-nine miles in the shake ove a lamb's tail. Purfeckly clear me jis' ten acres tu du my gesterin on, yu durned Jews, tape-sellers, gentiles, an' jackasses, I'se jis' a mossel ove the bes' man what ever laid a shadder ontu this dirt. Hit wilts grass, my breff pizins skeeters, my yell breaks winders, an' my tromp gits yeathquakes. I kin bust the bottom outen a still by blowin in at the wum, I kin addil a room full ove goose aigs by peepin in at the key-hole, an' *I kin spit a blister ontu a washpot, ontil the flies blow hit.* Listen tu me, oh yu dam puney, panady eatin siterzens, an' soujourners in this half-stock't town, I'se in yearnis' now.' Then he reared a few times agin, an' cut the pidgeon-wing three foot high, finished off wif 'bout haf ove a ho'n-pipe, keepin time abuv his head wif the venerson an' the littil son ove midnite. He hilt em straight out at arm's laingth, leaned way back, an' lookin straight up at the sky, sung 'bout es loud es a cow bellers, one vearse ove the sixteen hundred an' ninety-ninth hyme—

> 'The martins bilds in boxis,
>   The foxis dens in holes,
> The sarpints crawls in rocksis,
>   The yeath's the home ove moles.
>   Cock a-doodil-do, hits movin,
>   An' dram time's cum agin.

'Yere's what kin jis' sircumstansully flax out that ar court-hous' full tu the chimbly tops, ove bull-dorgs, Bengal tigers, an' pizen bitin things, wif that ar pusley-gutted, leather whisky jug ove a jedge, tu laig fur em. Cum out yere, yu ole false apostil ove lor, yu cussed, termatis-nosed desipil ove supeners, an' let me gin *yu* a charge. I'll bet high hit busts yu plum open, frum fork tu forrid, yu hary, sulky, choliky durn'd son ove a slush-tub. Cum out yere, oh yu coward's skeer, yu widder's night-mar, yu poor man's heart ache, yu constabil's god, yu lawyer's king, yu treasury's tape-wum, yer wife's dam barril ove soap-grease, saften'd wif unbought whisky.'

"Thinks I, *that's hit*; now Wirt yu'se draw'd an ace kerd at las', fur the winders wer histed an' the cort hearn every word.

"Wirt wer bilin hot; nobody tu gainsay him, hed made him piedied all over; he wer plum pizen. So arter finishin his las' narashun, aim'd at Jedge Smarty, he tuck a vigrus look at the yung nigger, what he still hilt squirmin an' twistin his face, what warn't eyes, glazed all over wif tears, an' starch outen his nose, an' sez he, 'Go.' He flung hit up'ards, an' es hit cum down, hit met one ove Wirt's boots. Away hit flew, spread like ontu a flyin squirrel, smash thru a watch-tinker's winder, totin in broken sash, an' glass, an' bull's-eye watches, an' sasser watches, an' spoons, an' doll heads, an' clay pipes, an' fishin reels, an' sum noise. A ole ball-headed cuss wer a-sittin a-peepin intu a ole watch, arter spiders, wif a thing like a big black wart kiverin one eye, when the smashery cum, an' the fus' thing he knowed, he wer flat ove his back, wif a small, pow'fully skeer'd, ash-culler'd nigger, a-straddil his naik, littil brass wheels spinnin on the floor, an' watches singin like rattil-snakes all roun. I wer a-peepin outen the ole doggery door, an' thinks I, thar, by jingo, Wirt, yu'se draw'd *anuther ace*, an' ef yu hilt enything ove a han afore, yu hes got a sure thing now; so better bet fas', ole feller, fur I rather think the jedge'll 'call yu' purty soon. Wirt seed me, an' ove course tho't ove whisky that moment; so he cum over tu lay on a littil more kindlin wood. I'll swar, tu look at him, yu cudn't think fur the life ove yu, that he hed over-bragged a single word. His britches wer buttoned tite roun his loins, an' stuffed 'bout half intu his boots, his shut bagg'd out abuv, an' wer es white es milk, his sleeves wer rolled up tu his arm-pits, an' his collar wer es wide open es a gate, the mussils on his arms moved about like rabbits onder the skin, an' ontu his hips an' thighs they play'd like the swell on the river, his skin wer clear red an' white, an' his eyes a deep, sparklin, wickid blue, while a smile fluttered like a hummin bird roun his mouf all the while. When the State-fair offers a premin fur *men* like they now dus fur jackasses, I means tu enter Wirt Staples, an' I'll git hit, ef thar's five thousand entrys. I seed ole Doltin cumin waddlin outen the court-hous', wif a paper in his han, an' a big stick onder his arm, lookin to'ards the doggery wif his mouf puss'd up, an' his brows draw'd down. Sez I, 'Wirt, look thar, thar's a "herearter" a-huntin yu; du yu see hit? whar's yer hoss?' He tuck one wickid, blazin look, an' slip't intu the stret wif his arms folded acrost his venerson laig.

"Now Wirt wer Wat Mastin's cuzzin, *an' know'd all about the rar ripe bisness*, an' tuck sides wif Wat strong. I'd show'd him the sheriff's note tu Mary, an' he hed hit by heart. The crowd wer now follerin Doltin tu see the fun. When he got in about ten steps, sez Wirt:

"'Stop rite thar; ef yu don't, thar's *no calliker ur combs in Herrin's store*, ef I don't make yu fear'd ove lightnin. I'll stay wif yu till *thar's enuf fros' in hell tu kill snap-beans.*'

"When Wirt menshun'd snap-beans, I seed the sheriff sorter start, an git pale ahine the years.

" 'Git intu that ar hog-pen, quick,' (a-pintin at the court-hous' wif the venerson laig,) 'ur I'll split yer head plum tu the swaller wif this yere buck's laig, yu durn'd ole skaley-heel'd, bob-tail old muley bull; I'll spile yer appertite fur the grass in uther men's pasturs.'

" 'Don't talk so loud, Mister Staples; hit discomboberates the court. I hes no papers agin yu. Jis' keep quiet,' sez Doltin, aidgin up slow, an' two ur three depertys sorter flankin.

"Wirt seed the signs. He jis' roared 'the lion's loose! Shet yer doors.' I seed his har a-flyin es he sprung, an' I hearn a soun like smashin a dry gourd. Thar wer a rushin tugether ove depertys an' humans, an' hit look'd like bees a-swarmin. Yere cum Wirt, mowin his way outen the crowd, wif his venerson, an' sprung ontu his hoss. Thar lay Doltin, flat ove his back, his belly pintin up like a big tater-hill, an' eight ur nine more in es many shapes, lyin all about, every durned wun a-holdin his head, 'sceptin Doltin, an' he wer plum limber. Wirt hed a pow'ful fine hoss, an' he rid 'im roun that crowd like a Cumanche Injun, ur a suckis, es fas' es quarter racin, jis' bustin his froat a-hollerin. Then he went fur the court-hous', rid in at one door, an' out at tuther. Es he went, he flung that mortul buck's hine laig at the jedge's head, sayin:

" 'Thar's a dried supeaner fur yu, yu dam ole cow's paunch.'

"Es hit cum hit hit the tabil afore him, an' sent a head ove hit, the broken glass ove a big inkstand, an' a half pint ove ink, intu the face ove the court, then glancin up, hit tuck a par ove specks what hed been rared back ontu his head, outen the winder wif hit. Ole Smarty hes a mity nice idear ove when tu duck his head, even ef a rain-storm ove ink am cumin upwards intu his face. Warn't that mons'ous nigh bein a case ove contempt ove court?"

Henry David Thoreau (1817–1862)

The sculptured truths embodied in Henry David Thoreau's *Walden* (1854) are so apt that it is a rare reader who is not inspired to explore more keenly both himself and his world. But many leave *Walden* too quickly, too often with a somber spirit such as Thoreau deplored, having missed the intense *joie de vivre* which he believed was prerequisite for regeneration. "I do not propose to write an ode to dejection, but to brag as lustily as chanticleer in the morning, standing on his roost, if only to wake up my neighbors." That exuberant crow might have been shouted out by a character in the humorous writings of Augustus B. Longstreet, George Washington Harris, T. B. Thorpe, or Mark Twain (see "Frescoes from the Past," pp. 350–60), for the image of a boastful bird—eagle or rooster—recurs frequently in popular American humorous literature. Actually the lines, borrowed from Chapter 2 of *Walden*, appeared as an epigraph on the title page of the first edition; it is surely in violation of Thoreau's spirit and intention that they have been omitted from almost all subsequent editions. Thoreau meant all to know that he had determined to engage his neighbors' hearts and minds with more than dead seriousness, that he wished to exhort them pleasurably. Though *Walden* as a result is richly stuffed with ironic, ludicrous, and satirical passages, it does not sport all of the broad and earthy humor Thoreau revealed in *A Week on the Concord and Merrimack Rivers* (1849), his letters and Cape Cod essays, and most magnificently in the anecdotal and character sketches of his posthumously published private journals. To some extent Thoreau was a victim of the disease of taste which afflicted Emerson, the belief that common physical experiences were vulgar and should be kept private. Consequently, the many revisions which *Walden* underwent before publication refined its humor and made it more literary and esoteric. "Brute Neighbors" displays the wit and mirth of Thoreau in his formal mood. The pretended dialogue between two parts of his personality and the burlesque battle of the ants which satirizes militarism are finely polished bits of humor. More intricately ironic is the concluding account of Thoreau's fascinated preoccupation with the indomitable "silly loon" and his unquenchable "wild laugh"; Thoreau's proud identification of himself with the bird and of his writings with the bird's cry echoes the humorous exultation of the epigraph to *Walden*.

TEXT: "The Respectable Folks" and "Conscience," *A Week on the Concord and Merrimack Rivers, The Writings of Henry David Thoreau* (Riverside Edition), Boston, Mass., 1893, I; "Brute Neighbors," *Walden,* Riverside Edition, II. COMMENTARY: Walter Harding, *A Thoreau Hand-*

book, New York, 1959; J. Golden Taylor, *Neighbor Thoreau's Critical Humor*, Logan, Utah, 1958.

THE RESPECTABLE FOLKS

The respectable folks,—
Where dwell they?
They whisper in the oaks,
And they sigh in the hay;
Summer and winter, night and day,
Out on the meadow, there dwell they.
They never die,
Nor snivel nor cry,
Nor ask our pity
With a wet eye.
A sound estate they ever mend,
To every asker readily lend;
To the ocean wealth,
To the meadow health,
To Time his length,
To the rocks strength,
To the stars light,
To the weary night,
To the busy day,
To the idle play;
And so their good cheer never ends,
For all are their debtors, and all their friends.

CONSCIENCE

Conscience is instinct bred in the house,
Feeling and Thinking propagate the sin
By an unnatural breeding in and in.
I say, Turn it out doors,
Into the moors.
I love a life whose plot is simple,
And does not thicken with every pimple,
A soul so sound no sickly conscience binds it,
That makes the universe no worse than't finds it.
I love an earnest soul,

Whose mighty joy and sorrow
Are not drowned in a bowl,
And brought to life to-morrow;
That lives one tragedy,
And not seventy;
A conscience worth keeping,
Laughing not weeping;
A conscience wise and steady,
And forever ready;
Not changing with events,
Dealing in compliments;
A conscience exercised about
Large things, where one *may* doubt.
I love a soul not all of wood,
Predestinated to be good,
But true to the backbone
Unto itself alone,
And false to none;
Born to its own affairs,
Its own joys and own cares;
By whom the work which God begun
Is finished, and not undone;
Taken up where he left off,
Whether to worship or to scoff;
If not good, why then evil,
If not good god, good devil.
Goodness! you hypocrite, come out of that,
Live your life, do your work, then take your hat.
I have no patience towards
Such conscientious cowards.
Give me simple laboring folk,
Who love their work,
Whose virtue is a song
To cheer God along.

BRUTE NEIGHBORS

Sometimes I had a companion in my fishing, who came through the village to my house from the other side of the town, and the catching of the dinner was as much a social exercise as the eating of it.

Hermit. I wonder what the world is doing now. I have not heard so much as a locust over the sweet-fern these three hours. The pigeons are all asleep upon their roosts,—no flutter from them. Was that a farmer's noon horn which sounded from beyond the woods just now? The hands are coming in to boiled salt beef and cider and Indian bread. Why will men worry themselves so? He that does not eat need not work. I wonder how much they have reaped. Who would live there where a body can never think for the barking of Bose? And O, the housekeeping! to keep bright the devil's door-knobs, and scour his tubs this bright day! Better not keep a house. Say, some hollow tree; and then for morning calls and dinner-parties! Only a woodpecker tapping. O, they swarm; the sun is too warm there; they are born too far into life for me. I have water from the spring, and a loaf of brown bread on the shelf.—Hark! I hear a rustling of the leaves. Is it some ill-fed village hound yielding to the instinct of the chase? or the lost pig which is said to be in these woods, whose tracks I saw after the rain? It comes on apace; my sumachs and sweetbriers tremble.—Eh, Mr. Poet, is it you? How do you like the world to-day?

Poet. See those clouds; how they hang! That's the greatest thing I have seen to-day. There's nothing like it in old paintings, nothing like it in foreign lands,—unless when we were off the coast of Spain. That's a true Mediterranean sky, I thought, as I have my living to get, and have not eaten to-day, that I might go a-fishing. That's the true industry for poets. It is the only trade I have learned. Come, let's along.

Hermit. I cannot resist. My brown bread will soon be gone. I will go with you gladly soon, but I am just concluding a serious meditation. I think that I am near the end of it. Leave me alone, then, for a while. But that we may not be delayed, you shall be digging the bait meanwhile. Angleworms are rarely to be met with in these parts, where the soil was never fattened with manure; the race is nearly extinct. The sport of digging the bait is nearly equal to that of catching the fish, when one's appetite is not too keen; and this you may have all to yourself to-day. I would advise you to set in the spade down yonder among the groundnuts, where you see the johnswort waving. I think that I may warrant you one worm to every three sods you turn up, if you look well in among the roots of the grass, as if you were weeding. Or, if you choose to go farther, it will not be unwise, for I have found the increase of fair bait to be very nearly as the squares of the distances.

Hermit alone. Let me see; where was I? Methinks I was nearly in this frame of mind; the world lay about at this angle. Shall I go to heaven or a-fishing? If I should soon bring this meditation to an end, would another so sweet occasion be likely to offer? I was as near being resolved into the essence of things as ever I was in my life. I fear my thoughts will not come back to me. If it would do any good, I would whistle for them. When they make us an offer, is it wise to say, We will think of it? My thoughts have let no track, and I cannot find the path again. What was it that I was thinking of? It was a very hazy day. I will just try these three sentences of Confut-see; they may fetch that state about again. I know not whether it was the dumps or a budding ecstasy. Mem. There never is but one opportunity of a kind.

Poet. How now, Hermit, is it too soon? I have got just thirteen whole ones, beside several which are imperfect or undersized; but they will do for the smaller fry; they do not cover up the hook so much. Those village worms are quite too large; a shiner may make a meal off one without finding the skewer.

Hermit. Well, then, let's be off. Shall we to the Concord? There's good sport there if the water be not too high.

Why do precisely these objects which we behold make a world? Why has man just these species of animals for his neighbors; as if nothing but a mouse could have filled this crevice? I suspect that Pilpay & Co. have put animals to their best use, for they are all beasts of burden, in a sense, made to carry some portion of our thoughts.

The mice which haunted my house were not the common ones, which are said to have been introduced into the country, but a wild native kind not found in the village. I sent one to a distinguished naturalist, and it interested him much. When I was building, one of these had its nest underneath the house, and before I had laid the second floor, and swept out the shavings, would come out regularly at lunch time and pick up the crumbs at my feet. It probably had never seen a man before; and it soon became quite familiar, and would run over my shoes and up my clothes. It could readily ascend the sides of the room by short impulses, like a squirrel, which it resembled in its motions. At length, as I leaned with my elbow on the bench one day, it ran up my clothes, and along my sleeve, and round and round the paper which held my dinner, while I kept the latter close, and dodged and played at bopeep with it; and when at last I held still a piece of cheese between my thumb and finger, it came and nibbled it, sitting in my hand, and afterward cleaned its face and paws, like a fly, and walked away.

A phœbe soon built in my shed, and a robin for protection in a pine which grew against the house. In June the partridge (*Tetrao umbellus*), which is so shy a bird, led her brood past my windows, from the woods in the rear to the front of my house, clucking and calling to them like a hen, and in all her behavior proving herself the hen of the woods. The young suddenly disperse on your approach, at a signal from the mother, as if a whirlwind had swept them away, and they so exactly resemble the dried leaves and twigs that many a traveller has placed his foot in the midst of a brood, and heard the whir of the old bird as she flew off, and her anxious calls and mewing, or seen her trail her wings to attract his attention, without suspecting their neighborhood. The parent will sometimes roll and spin round before you in such a dishabille, that you cannot, for a few moments, detect what kind of creature it is. The young squat still and flat, often running their heads under a leaf, and mind only their mother's directions given from a distance, nor will your approach make them run again and betray themselves. You may even tread on them, or have your eyes on them for a minute, without discovering them. I have held them in my open hand at such a time, and still their only care, obedient to their mother and their instinct, was to squat there without fear or trembling. So perfect is this instinct, that once, when I had laid them on the leaves again, and one accidentally fell on its side, it was found with the rest in exactly the same position ten minutes afterward. They are not callow like the young of most birds, but more perfectly developed and precocious even than chickens. The remarkably adult yet innocent expression of their open and serene eyes is very memorable. All intelligence seems reflected in them. They suggest not merely the purity of infancy, but a wisdom clarified by experience. Such an eye was not born when the bird was, but is coeval with the sky it reflects. The woods do not yield another such a gem. The traveller does not often look into such a limpid well. The ignorant or reckless sportsman often shoots the parent at such a time, and leaves these innocents to fall a prey to some prowling beast or bird, or gradually mingle with the decaying leaves which they so much resemble. It is said that when hatched by a hen they will directly disperse on some alarm, and so are lost, for they never hear the mother's call which gathers them again. These were my hens and chickens.

It is remarkable how many creatures live wild and free though secret in the woods, and still sustain themselves in the neighborhood of towns, suspected by hunters only. How retired the otter manages to live here! He grows to be four feet long, as big as a small boy, perhaps without any human being getting a glimpse of him. I formerly saw the raccoon in the woods behind where my house is built, and probably still heard their whinnering at night. Commonly I rested an hour or two in the shade at noon, after planting, and ate my lunch, and read a little by a spring which was the source of a swamp and of a brook, oozing from under Brister's Hill, half a mile from my field. The approach to this was through a succession of descending grassy hollows, full of young pitch pines, into a larger wood about the swamp. There, in a very secluded and shaded spot, under a spreading white pine, there was yet a clean, firm sward to sit on. I had dug out the spring and made a well of clear gray water, where I could dip up a pailful without roiling it, and thither I went for this purpose almost every day in midsummer, when the pond was warmest. Thither, too, the woodcock led her brood, to probe the mud for worms, flying but a foot above them down the bank, while they ran in a troop beneath; but at last, spying me, she would leave her young and circle round and round me, nearer and nearer till within four or five feet, pretending broken wings and legs, to attract my attention, and get off her young, who would already have taken up their march, with faint, wiry peep, single file through the swamp, as she directed. Or I heard the peep of the young when I could not see the parent bird. There too the turtle doves sat over the spring, or fluttered from bough to bough of the soft white pines over my head; or the red squirrel, coursing down the nearest bough, was particularly familiar and inquisitive. You only need sit still long enough in some attractive spot in the woods that all its inhabitants may exhibit themselves to you by turns.

I was witness to events of a less peaceful character. One day when I went out to my wood-pile, or rather my pile of stumps, I observed two large ants, the one red, the other much larger, nearly half an inch long, and black, fiercely contending with one another. Having once got hold they never let go, but struggled and wrestled and rolled on the chips incessantly. Looking farther, I was surprised to find that the chips were covered with such combatants, that it was not a *duellum*, but a *bellum*, a war between two races of ants, the red always pitted against the black, and frequently two red ones to one black. The legions of these Myrmidons covered all the hills and vales in my wood-yard, and the ground was already strewn with the dead and dying, both red and black. It was the only battle which I have ever witnessed, the only battle-field I ever trod while the battle was raging; internecine war; the red republicans on the one hand, and the black imperialists on the other. On every side they were engaged in deadly combat, yet without any noise that I could hear, and human soldiers never fought so resolutely. I watched a couple that were fast locked in each other's embraces, in a little sunny valley amid the chips, now at noonday prepared to fight till the sun went down, or life went out. The smaller red champion had fastened himself like a vice to his adversary's front, and through all the tumblings on that field never for an instant ceased to gnaw at one of his feelers near the root, having already caused the other to go by the board; while the stronger black one dashed him from side to side, and, as I saw on looking nearer, had already divested him of several of his members. They fought with more pertinacity than bulldogs. Neither manifested the least disposition to retreat. It was evident that their battle-cry was "Conquer or die." In the meanwhile there came along a single red ant on the hillside of this valley, evidently full of excitement, who either had despatched his foe, or had not yet taken part in the battle; probably the latter, for he had lost none of his limbs; whose mother had charged him to return with his shield or upon it. Or perchance he was some Achilles, who had nourished his wrath apart, and had now come to avenge or rescue his Patroclus. He saw this unequal combat from afar,—for the blacks were nearly twice the size of the red,—he drew near with rapid pace till he stood on his guard within half an inch of the combatants; then, watching his opportunity, he sprang upon the black warrior, and commenced his operations near the root of his right fore leg, leaving the foe to select among his own members; and so there were three united for life, as if a new kind of attraction had been invented which put all other locks and cements to shame. I should not have wondered by this time to find that they had their respective musical bands stationed on some eminent chip, and playing their national airs the while, to excite the slow and cheer the dying combatants. I was myself excited somewhat even as if they had been men. The more you think of it, the less the difference. And certainly there is not the fight recorded in Concord history, at least, if in the history of America, that will bear a moment's comparison with this, whether for the numbers engaged in it, or for the patriotism and heroism displayed. For numbers and for carnage it was an Austerlitz or Dresden. Concord Fight! Two killed on the patriots' side, and Luther Blanchard wounded! Why here every ant was a Buttrick,—"Fire! for God's sake fire!"—and thousands shared the fate of Davis and Hosmer. There was not one hireling there. I have no doubt that it was a principle they fought for, as much as our ancestors, and not to avoid a three-penny tax on their tea; and the results of this battle will be as important and memorable to those whom it concerns as those of the battle of Bunker Hill, at least.

I took up the chip on which the three I have particularly described were struggling, carried it into my house, and placed it under a tumbler on my window-sill, in order to see the issue. Holding a microscope to the first-mentioned red ant, I saw that, though he was assiduously gnawing at the near fore leg of his enemy, having severed his remaining feeler, his own breast was all torn away, exposing what vitals he had there to the jaws of the black warrior, whose breastplate was apparently too thick for him to pierce; and the dark carbuncles of the sufferer's eyes shone with ferocity such as war only could excite. They struggled half an hour longer under the tumbler, and when I looked again the black soldier had severed the heads of his foes from their bodies, and the still living heads were hanging on either side of him like ghastly trophies at his saddle-bow, still apparently as firmly fastened as ever, and he was endeavoring with feeble struggles, being without feelers and with only the remnant of a leg, and I know not how many other wounds, to divest himself of them; which at length, after half an hour more, he accomplished. I raised the glass, and he went off over the window-sill in that crippled state. Whether he finally survived that combat, and spent the remainder of his days in some Hôtel des Invalides, I do not know; but I thought that his industry would not be worth much thereafter. I never learned which party was victorious, nor the cause of the war; but I felt for the rest of that day as if I had had my feelings excited and harrowed by witnessing the struggle, the ferocity and carnage, of a human battle before my door.

Kirby and Spence tell us that the battles of ants have long been celebrated and the date of them recorded, though they say that Huber is the only modern author who appears to have witnessed them. "Æneas Sylvius," say they, "after giving a very circumstantial account of one contested with great obstinacy by a great and small species on the trunk of a pear tree," adds that " 'this action was fought in the pontificate of Eugenius the Fourth, in the presence of Nicholas Pistoriensis, an eminent lawyer, who related the whole history of the battle with the greatest fidelity.' A similar engagement between great and small ants is recorded by Olaus Magnus, in which the small ones, being victorious, are said to have buried the bodies of their own soldiers, but left those of their giant enemies a prey to the birds. This event happened previous to the expulsion of the tyrant Christiern the Second from Sweden." The battle which I witnessed took place in the Presidency of Polk, five years before the passage of Webster's Fugitive-Slave Bill.

Many a village Bose, fit only to course a mud-turtle in a victualling cellar, sported his heavy quarters in the woods, without the knowledge of his master, and ineffectually smelled at old fox burrows and wood-chucks' holes; led perchance by some slight cur which nimbly threaded the wood, and might still inspire a natural terror in its denizens;—now far behind his guide, barking like a canine bull toward some small squirrel which had treed itself for scrutiny, then, cantering off, bending the bushes with his weight, imagining that he is on the track of some stray member of the jerbilla family. Once I was surprised to see a cat walking along the stony shore of the pond, for they rarely wander so far from home. The surprise was mutual. Nevertheless the most domestic cat, which has lain on a rug all her days, appears quite at home in the woods, and, by her sly and stealthy behavior, proves herself more native there than the regular inhabitants. Once, when berrying, I met with a cat with young kittens in the woods, quite wild, and they all, like their mother, had their backs up and were fiercely spitting at me. A few years before I lived in the woods there was what was called a "winged cat" in one of the farm-houses in Lincoln nearest the pond, Mr. Gilian Baker's. When I called to see her in June, 1842, she was gone a-hunting in the woods, as was her wont (I am not sure whether it was a male or female, and so use the more common pronoun), but her mistress told me that she came into the neighborhood a little more than a year before, in April, and was finally taken into their house; that she was of a dark brownish-gray color, with a white spot on her throat, and white feet, and had a large bushy tail like a fox; that in the winter the fur grew thick and flatted out along her sides, forming strips ten or twelve inches long by two and a half wide, and under her chin like a muff, the upper side loose, the under matted like felt, and in the spring these appendages dropped off. They gave me a pair of her "wings," which I keep still. There is no appearance of a membrane about them. Some thought it was part flying squirrel or some other wild animal, which is not impossible, for, according to naturalists, prolific hybrids have been produced by the union of the marten and domestic cat. This would have been the right kind of cat for me to keep, if I had kept any; for why should not a poet's cat be winged as well as his horse?

In the fall the loon (*Colymbus glacialis*) came, as usual, to moult and bathe in the pond, making the woods ring with his wild laughter before I had risen. At rumor of his arrival all the Mill-dam sportsmen are on the alert, in gigs and on foot, two by two and three by three, with patent rifles and conical balls and spy-glasses. They come rustling through the woods like autumn leaves, at least ten men to one loon. Some station themselves on this side of the pond, some on that, for the poor bird cannot be omnipresent; if he dive here he must come up there. But now the kind October wind rises, rustling the leaves and rippling the surface of the water, so that no loon can be heard or seen, though his foes sweep the pond with spy-glasses, and make the woods resound with their discharges. The waves generously rise and dash angrily, taking sides with all water-fowl, and our sportsmen must beat a retreat to town and shop and unfinished jobs. But they were too often successful. When I went to get a pail of water early in the morning I frequently saw this stately bird sailing out of my cove within a few rods. If I endeavored to overtake him in a boat, in order to see how he would manœuvre, he would dive and be completely lost, so that I did not discover him again, sometimes, till the latter part of the day. But I was more than a match for him on the surface. He commonly went off in a rain.

As I was paddling along the north shore one very calm October afternoon, for such days especially they settle on to the lakes, like the milkweed down, having looked in vain over the pond for a loon, suddenly one, sailing out from the shore toward the middle a few rods in front of me, set up his wild laugh and betrayed himself. I pursued with a paddle and he dived, but when he came up I was nearer than before. He dived again, but I miscalculated the direction he would take, and we were fifty rods apart when he came to the surface this time, for I had helped to widen the interval; and again he laughed long and loud, and with more reason than before. He manœuvred so cunningly that I could not get within half a dozen rods of him. Each time, when he came to the surface, turning his head this way and that, he coolly surveyed the water and the land, and apparently chose his course so that he might come up where there was the widest expanse of water and at the greatest distance from the boat. It was surprising how quickly he made up his mind and put his resolve into execution. He led me at once to the widest part of the pond, and could not be driven from it. While he was thinking one thing in his brain, I was endeavoring to divine his thought in mine. It was a pretty game, played on the smooth surface of the pond, a man against a loon. Suddenly your adversary's checker disappears beneath the board, and the problem is to place yours nearest to where his will appear again. Sometimes he would come up unexpectedly on the opposite side of me, having apparently passed directly under the boat. So long-winded was he and so unweariable, that when he had swum farthest he would immediately plunge again, nevertheless; and then no wit could divine where in the deep pond, beneath the smooth surface, he might be speeding his way like a fish, for he had time and ability to visit the bottom of the pond in its deepest part. It is said that loons have been caught in the New York lakes eighty feet beneath the surface, with hooks set for trout,—though Walden is deeper than that. How surprised must the fishes be to see this ungainly visitor from another sphere speeding his way amid their schools! Yet he appeared to know his course as surely under water as on the surface, and swam much faster there. Once or twice I saw a ripple where he approached the surface, just put his head out to reconnoitre, and instantly dived again. I found that it was as well for me to rest on my oars and wait his reappearing as to endeavor to calculate where he would rise; for again and again, when I was straining my eyes over the surface one way, I would suddenly be startled by his unearthly laugh behind me. But why, after displaying so much cunning, did he invariably betray himself the moment he came up by that loud laugh? Did not his white breast enough betray him? He was indeed a silly loon, I thought. I could commonly hear the plash of the water when he came up, and so also detected him. But after an hour he seemed as fresh as ever, dived as willingly, and swam yet farther than at first. It was surprising to see how serenely he sailed off with unruffled breast when he came to the surface, doing all the work with his webbed feet beneath. His usual note was this demoniac laughter, yet somewhat like that of a water-fowl; but occasionally, when he had balked me most successfully and come up a long way off, he uttered a long-drawn unearthly howl, probably more like that of a wolf than any bird; as when a beast puts his muzzle to the ground and deliberately howls. This was his looning,—perhaps the wildest sound that is ever heard here, making the woods ring far and wide. I concluded that he laughed in derision of my efforts, confident of his own resources. Though the sky was by this time overcast, the pond was so smooth that I could see where he broke the surface when I did not hear him. His white breast, the stillness of the air, and the smoothness of the water were all against him. At length, having come up fifty rods off, he uttered one of those prolonged howls, as if calling on the god of loons to aid him, and immediately there came a wind from the east and rippled the surface, and filled the whole air with misty rain, and I was impressed as if it were the prayer of the loon answered, and his god was angry with me; and so I left him disappearing far away on the tumultuous surface.

For hours, in fall days, I watched the ducks cunningly tack and veer and hold the middle of the pond, far from the sportsman; tricks which they will have less need to practise in Louisiana bayous. When compelled to rise they would sometimes circle round and round and over the pond at a considerable height, from which they could easily see to other ponds and the river, like black motes in the sky; and, when I thought they had gone off thither long since, they would settle down by a slanting flight of a quarter of a mile on to a distant part which was left free; but what beside safety they got by sailing in the middle of Walden I do not know, unless they love its water for the same reason that I do.

James Russell Lowell (1819–1891)

It is as a short-lived satiric humorist who briefly demonstrated the literary vitality of American humor and language that James Russell Lowell no doubt will be remembered longest. His other achievements as editor, teacher, critic, politician, ambassador, social commentator, "serious" poet, and Brahmin dignitary will probably grow less and less memorable. Gifted with verbal wit, knowledge of New England's folklore and colloquial speech, Puritan conscience, and humanitarian impulses, Lowell contributed greatly to the development of American humorous literature. *The Biglow Papers* (1848), which first appeared in a Boston newspaper in 1846, were designed to arouse antislavery and anti-imperialist sentiment; they were widely read, enjoyed as much for their flavorsome language and sharp humor as for their political message. Lowell's skill as a humorous poet was also manifest in his nondialect *Fable for Critics* (1848), a satirical survey of contemporary American letters and publishing. Thereafter, however, most of the vivid humor and idiom of Lowell's early poetry disappeared from his writing. Though "Fitz Adam's Story" was printed in the *Atlantic* in 1867, for example, the section dealing with Deacon Bitters and the Devil apparently had been written as early as 1850. Lowell's opening apology for the "coarse" humor and "common" characters of this poem does much to explain his rejection of his past. The same ambivalence is to be found in his preface to the second series of the *Biglow Papers* (1867), written from 1862 to 1866. Having become a Harvard professor and *Atlantic* editor after the 1840's, Lowell apparently smarted under the thought that he might be regarded as a literary comedian (see Charles Farrar Browne, pp. 339–42) and insisted upon his essential seriousness: "If I put on the cap and bells and made myself one of the court-fools of King Demos, it was less to make his majesty laugh than to win a passage to his royal ears for certain serious things which I had deeply at heart." He defended his use of "Yankee dialect" because "our popular idiom is racy with life and vigor and originality" and "it is only from its roots in the living generations of men that a language can be reinforced with fresh vigor for its needs." Yet he self-consciously proceeded to prove the dignity of "Yankee dialect" by showing that its apparent linguistic flaws were really virtues since they were also to be found in English speech and literature. The post-Civil War genteel tradition which Lowell helped create would discourage the vigorous American humor which had flourished in the North and South during his youth.

TEXT: "The Pious Editor's Creed," *The Biglow Papers, The Writings of James Russell Lowell* (Riverside Edition), Boston, Mass., 1890, VIII; "Self-

Portrait," A *Fable for Critics*, Riverside Edition, IX; "Deacon Bitters and
the Devil," "Fitz Adam's Story," Riverside Edition, X. COMMENTARY:
Leon Howard, *Victorian Knight-Errant*, Berkeley, Calif., 1952.

THE PIOUS EDITOR'S CREED

I du believe in Freedom's cause,
    Ez fur away ez Payris is;
I love to see her stick her claws
    In them infarnal Phayrisees;
It's wal enough agin a king
    To dror resolves an' triggers,—
But libbaty 's a kind o' thing
    Thet don't agree with niggers.

I du believe the people want
    A tax on teas an' coffees,
Thet nothin' aint extravygunt,—
    Purvidin' I'm in office;
Fer I hev loved my country sence
    My eye-teeth filled their sockets,
An' Uncle Sam I reverence,
    Partic'larly his pockets.

I du believe in *any* plan
    O' levyin' the texes,
Ez long ez, like a lumberman,
    I git jest wut I axes;
I go free-trade thru thick an' thin,
    Because it kind o' rouses
The folks to vote,—an' keeps us in
    Our quiet custom-houses.

I du believe it's wise an' good
    To sen' out furrin missions,
Thet is, on sartin understood
    An' orthydox conditions;—
I mean nine thousan' dolls. per anñ.,
    Nine thousan' more fer outfit,
An' me to recommend a man
    The place 'ould jest about fit.

I du believe in special ways
    O' prayin' an' convartin';

The bread comes back in many days,
   An' buttered, tu, fer sartin;
I mean in preyin' till one busts
   On wut the party chooses,
An' in convartin' public trusts
   To very privit uses.

I du believe hard coin the stuff
   Fer 'lectioneers to spout on;
The people's ollers soft enough
   To make hard money out on;
Dear Uncle Sam pervides fer his,
   An' gives a good-sized junk to all,—
I don't care *how* hard money is,
   Ez long ez mine's paid punctooal.

I du believe with all my soul
   In the gret Press's freedom,
To pint the people to the goal
   An' in the traces lead 'em;
Palsied the arm thet forges yokes
   At my fat contracts squintin',
An' withered be the nose thet pokes
   Inter the gov'ment printin'!

I du believe thet I should give
   Wut's his'n unto Cæsar,
Fer it's by him I move an' live,
   Frum him my bread an' cheese air;
I du believe thet all o' me
   Doth bear his superscription,—
Will, conscience, honor, honesty,
   An' things o' thet description.

I du believe in prayer an' praise
   To him thet hez the grantin'
O' jobs,—in every thin' thet pays,
   But most of all in CANTIN';
This doth my cup with marcies fill,
   This lays all thought o' sin to rest,—
I *don't* believe in princerple,
   But oh, I *du* in interest.

I du believe in bein' this
   Or thet, ez it may happen

One way or t' other hendiest is
    To ketch the people nappin';
It aint by princerples nor men
    My preudunt course is steadied,—
I scent wich pays the best, an' then
    Go into it baldheaded.

I du believe thet holdin' slaves
    Comes nat'ral to a Presidunt,
Let 'lone the rowdedow it saves
    To hev a wal-broke precedunt;
Fer any office, small or gret,
    I couldn't ax with no face,
'uthout I'd ben, thru dry an' wet,
    Th' unrizzest kind o' doughface.

I du believe wutever trash
    'll keep the people in blindness,—
Thet we the Mexicuns can thrash
    Right inter brotherly kindness,
Thet bombshells, grape, an' powder 'n' ball
    Air good-will's strongest magnets,
Thet peace, to make it stick at all,
    Must be druv in with bagnets.

In short, I firmly du believe
    In Humbug generally,
Fer it's a thing thet I perceive
    To hev a solid vally;
This heth my faithful shepherd ben,
    In pasturs sweet heth led me,
An' this'll keep the people green
    To feed ez they hev fed me.

SELF-PORTRAIT

    There is Lowell, who's striving Parnassus to climb
With a whole bale of *isms* tied together with rhyme,
He might get on alone, spite of brambles and boulders,
But he can't with that bundle he has on his shoulders,
The top of the hill he will ne'er come nigh reaching
Till he learns the distinction 'twixt singing and preaching;

His lyre has some chords that would ring pretty well,
But he'd rather by half make a drum of the shell,
And rattle away till he's old as Methusalem,
At the head of a march to the last new Jerusalem

DEACON BITTERS AND THE DEVIL

" 'T was there I caught from Uncle Reuben's lips,
In dribbling monologue 'twixt whiffs and sips,
The story I so long have tried to tell;
The humor coarse, the persons common,—well,
From Nature only do I love to paint,
Whether she send a satyr or a saint;
To me Sincerity's the one thing good,
Soiled though she be and lost to maidenhood.
Quompegan is a town some ten miles south
From Jethro, at Nagumscot river-mouth,
A seaport town, and makes its title good
With lumber and dried fish and eastern wood.
Here Deacon Bitters dwelt and kept the Store,
The richest man for many a mile of shore;
In little less than everything dealt he,
From meeting-houses to a chest of tea;
So dextrous therewithal a flint to skin,
He could make profit on a single pin;
In business strict, to bring the balance true
He had been known to bite a fig in two,
And change a board-nail for a shingle-nail.
All that he had he ready held for sale,
His house, his tomb, whate'er the law allows,
And he had gladly parted with his spouse.
His one ambition still to get and get,
He would arrest your very ghost for debt.
His store looked righteous, should the Parson come,
But in a dark back-room he peddled rum,
And eased Ma'am Conscience, if she e'er would scold,
By christening it with water ere he sold.
A small, dry man he was, who wore a queue,
And one white neckcloth all the week-days through,—
On Monday white, by Saturday as dun
As that worn homeward by the prodigal son.
His frosted earlocks, striped with foxy brown,

Were braided up to hide a desert crown;
His coat was brownish, black perhaps of yore;
In summer-time a banyan loose he wore;
His trousers short, through many a season true,
Made no pretence to hide his stockings blue;
A waistcoat buff his chief adornment was,
Its porcelain buttons rimmed with dusky brass.
A deacon he, you saw it in each limb,
And well he knew to deacon-off a hymn,
Or lead the choir through all its wandering woes
With voice that gathered unction in his nose,
Wherein a constant snuffle you might hear,
As if with him 't were winter all the year.
At pew-head sat he with decorous pains,
In sermon-time could foot his weekly gains,
Or, with closed eyes and heaven-abstracted air,
Could plan a new investment in long-prayer.
A pious man, and thrifty too, he made
The psalms and prophets partners in his trade,
And in his orthodoxy straitened more
As it enlarged the business at his store;
He honored Moses, but, when gain he planned,
Had his own notion of the Promised Land.

"Soon as the winter made the sledding good,
From far around the farmers hauled him wood,
For all the trade had gathered 'neath his thumb.
He paid in groceries and New England rum,
Making two profits with a conscience clear,—
Cheap all he bought, and all he paid with dear.
With his own mete-wand measuring every load,
Each somehow had diminished on the road;
An honest cord in Jethro still would fail
By a good foot upon the Deacon's scale,
And, more to abate the price, his gimlet eye
Would pierce to cat-sticks that none else could spy;
Yet none dared grumble, for no farmer yet
But New Year found him in the Deacon's debt.

"While the first snow was mealy under feet,
A team drawled creaking down Quompegan street
Two cords of oak weighed down the grinding sled,
And cornstalk fodder rustled overhead;
The oxen's muzzles, as they shouldered through,
Were silver-fringed; the driver's own was blue

As the coarse frock that swung below his knee.
Behind his load for shelter waded he;
His mittened hands now on his chest he beat,
Now stamped the stiffened cowhides of his feet,
Hushed as a ghost's; his armpit scarce could hold
The walnut whipstock slippery-bright with cold.
What wonder if, the tavern as he past,
He looked and longed, and stayed his beasts at last,
Who patient stood and veiled themselves in steam
While he explored the bar-room's ruddy gleam?

"Before the fire, in want of thought profound,
There sat a brother-townsman weather-bound:
A sturdy churl, crisp-headed, bristly-eared,
Red as a pepper; 'twixt coarse brows and beard
His eyes lay ambushed, on the watch for fools,
Clear, gray, and glittering like two bay-edged pools;
A shifty creature, with a turn for fun,
Could swap a poor horse for a better one,—
He'd a high-stepper always in his stall;
Liked far and near, and dreaded therewithal.
To him the in-comer, 'Perez, how d' ye do?'
'Jest as I 'm mind to, Obed; how do you?'
Then, his eyes twinkling such swift gleams as run
Along the levelled barrel of a gun
Brought to his shoulder by a man you know
Will bring his game down, he continued, 'So,
I s'pose you're haulin' wood? But you're too late
The Deacon's off; Old Splitfoot couldn't wait;
He made a bee-line las' night in the storm
To where he won't need wood to keep him warm.
'Fore this he's treasurer of a fund to train
Young imps as missionaries; hopes to gain
That way a contract that he has in view
For fireproof pitchforks of a pattern new.
It must have tickled him, all drawbacks weighed,
To think he stuck the Old One in a trade;
His soul, to start with, wasn't worth a carrot,
And all he'd left 'ould hardly serve to swear at.'

"By this time Obed had his wits thawed out,
And, looking at the other half in doubt,
Took off his fox-skin cap to scratch his head,
Donned it again, and drawled forth, 'Mean he's dead?'
'Jesso; he's dead and t' other *d* that follers

With folks that never love a thing but dollars.
He pulled up stakes last evening, fair and square,
And ever since there's been a row Down There.
The minute the old chap arrived, you see,
Comes the Boss-devil to him, and says he,
"What are you good at? Little enough, I fear;
We callilate to make folks useful here."
"Well," says old Bitters, "I expect I can
Scale a fair load of wood with e'er a man."
"Wood we don't deal in; but perhaps you'll suit,
Because we buy our brimstone by the foot:
Here, take this measurin'-rod, as smooth as sin,
And keep a reckonin' of what loads comes in.
You'll not want business, for we need a lot
To keep the Yankees that you send us hot;
At firin' up they're barely half as spry
As Spaniards or Italians, though they're dry;
As first we have to let the draught on stronger,
But, heat 'em through, they seem to hold it longer."

   " 'Bitters he took the rod, and pretty soon
A teamster comes, whistling an ex-psalm tune.
A likelier chap you wouldn't ask to see,
No different, but his limp, from you or me'—
'No different, Perez! Don't your memory fail?
Why, where in thunder was his horns and tail?'
'They're only worn by some old-fashioned pokes;
They mostly aim at looking just like folks.
Sech things are scarce as queues and top-boots here;
'T would spoil their usefulness to look too queer.
Ef you could always know 'em when they come,
They'd get no purchase on you: now be mum.
On come the teamster, smart as Davy Crockett,
Jinglin' the red-hot coppers in his pocket,
And clost behind, ('t was gold-dust, you'd ha' sworn,)
A load of sulphur yallower 'n seed-corn;
To see it wasted as it is Down There
Would make a Friction-Match Co. tear its hair!
"Hold on!" says Bitters, "stop right where you be;
You can't go in athout a pass from me."
"All right," says t' other, "only step round smart;
I must be home by noon-time with the cart."
Bitters goes round it sharp-eyed as a rat,
Then with a scrap of paper on his hat

Pretends to cipher. "By the public staff,
That load scarce rises twelve foot and a half."
"There's fourteen foot and over," says the driver,
"Worth twenty dollars, ef it's worth a stiver;
Good fourth-proof brimstone, that'll make 'em squirm,—
I leave it to the Headman of the Firm;
After we masure it, we always lay
Some on to allow for settlin' by the way.
Imp and full-grown, I've carted sulphur here,
And gi'n fair satisfaction, thirty year."
With that they fell to quarrellin' so loud
That in five minutes they had drawed a crowd,
And afore long the Boss, who heard the row,
Comes elbowin' in with "What's to pay here now?"
Both parties heard, the measurin'-rod he takes,
And of the load a careful survey makes.
"Sence I have bossed the business here," says he,
"No fairer load was ever seen by me."
Then, turnin' to the Deacon, "You mean cus,
None of your old Quompegan tricks with us!
They won't do here: we're plain old-fashioned folks,
And don't quite understand that kind o' jokes.
I know this teamster, and his pa afore him,
And the hard-working Mrs. D. that bore him;
He wouldn't soil his conscience with a lie,
Though he might get the custom-house thereby.
Here, constable, take Bitters by the queue,
And clap him into furnace ninety-two,
And try this brimstone on him; if he's bright,
He'll find the masure honest afore night.
He isn't worth his fuel, and I'll bet
The parish oven has to take him yet!" ' "

Herman Melville (1819–1891)

The revivification of Herman Melville's reputation in the 1920's and 1930's tended paradoxically to obscure his multifarious humor. Critics almost unanimously stressed his skill as a novelist, the philosophical depth of his mind, the Shakespearean quality of his language, and the worth of his cultural criticism. Now that Melville is firmly established as a major artist, therefore, it is essential to recognize the organic significance of humor in his best work, that published in the 1840's and 1850's. In *Moby-Dick* (1851), for example, humor plays so important a role that to excise it by neglect or misunderstanding is truly to violate the work and turn it into the shambles which some of his insensitive contemporaries believed it to be. The comic horseplay, bawdy puns, low characters, and tall tales intermesh successfully with the hyperbolic rhetoric, metaphysical conceits, social satire, philosophical ponderings, and intellectually-rich comic scenes and dialogues to transform the whaling ship into a universe tragic for Ahab but, in a religious and physical sense, comic and hopeful for Ishmael. The novel is economically structured and executed in great part because its humorous elements have been integrated rather than thrown in merely for comic relief. Like Mark Twain, Melville drew heavily from popular American folk humor and humorous literature. Unlike Mark Twain, however, he was also inspired by Rabelais, Shakespeare, Smollett, Sterne, Dickens, Carlyle, and other European creators of great humor.

TEXT: *White-Jacket*, New York, 1850; "The Cassock," *Moby-Dick*, New York, 1851; "Cock-A-Doodle-Doo!," *Harper's New Monthly Magazine*, VIII (December, 1853). COMMENTARY: Richard Chase, *Herman Melville: A Critical Study*, New York, 1949; Leon Howard, *Herman Melville: A Biography*, Berkeley, Calif., 1951; Edward H. Rosenberry, *Melville and the Comic Spirit*, Cambridge, Mass., 1955.

COCK-A-DOODLE-DOO! OR, THE CROWING OF THE NOBLE COCK BENEVENTANO

In all parts of the world many high-spirited revolts from rascally despotisms had of late been knocked on the head; many dreadful casualties, by locomotive and steamer, had likewise knocked hundreds of high-spirited travelers on the head (I lost a dear friend in one of them); my own private affairs were also full of despotisms, casualties, and knockings on the head, when early one morning in spring, being too full of hypoes to sleep, I sallied out to walk on my hillside pasture.

It was a cool and misty, damp, disagreeable air. The country looked underdone, its raw juices squirting out all round. I buttoned out this squitchy air as well as I could with my lean, double-breasted dress-coat—my overcoat being so long-skirted I only used it in my wagon—and spitefully thrusting my crab-stick into the oozy sod, bent my blue form to the steep ascent of the hill. This toiling posture brought my head pretty well earthward, as if I were in the act of butting it against the world. I marked the fact, but only grinned at it with a ghastly grin.

All round me were tokens of a divided empire. The old grass and the new grass were striving together. In the low wet swales the verdure peeped out in vivid green; beyond, on the mountains, lay light patches of snow, strangely relieved against their russet sides; all the humped hills looked like brindled kine in the shivers. The woods were strewn with dry dead boughs, snapped off by the riotous winds of March, while the young trees skirting the woods were just beginning to show the first yellowish tinge of the nascent spray.

I sat down for a moment on a great rotting log nigh the top of the hill, my back to a heavy grove, my face presented toward a wide sweeping circuit of mountains enclosing a rolling, diversified country. Along the base of one long range of heights ran a lagging, fever-and-agueish river, over which was a duplicate stream of dripping mist, exactly corresponding in every meander with its parent water below. Low down, here and there, shreds of vapor listlessly wandered in the air, like abandoned or helmless nations or ships—or very soaky towels hung on criss-cross clothes-lines to dry. Afar, over a distant village lying in a bay of the plain formed by the mountains, there rested a great flat canopy of haze, like a pall. It was the condensed smoke of the chimneys, with the condensed, exhaled breath of the villagers, prevented from dispersion by the imprisoning hills. It was too heavy and lifeless to mount of itself; so there it lay, between the village and the sky, doubtless hiding many a man with the mumps, and many a queasy child.

My eye ranged over the capacious rolling country, and over the mountains, and over the village, and over a farmhouse here and there, and over woods, groves, streams, rocks, fells—and I thought to myself, what a slight mark, after all, does man make on this huge great earth. Yet the earth makes a mark on him. What a horrid accident was that on the Ohio, where my good friend and thirty other good fellows were sloped into eternity at the bidding of a thick-headed engineer, who knew not a valve from a flue. And that crash on the railroad just over yon mountains there, where two infatuate trains ran pell-mell into each other, and climbed and clawed each other's backs; and one locomotive was found fairly shelled, like a chick, inside of a passenger car in the antagonist train; and near a score of noble hearts, a bride and her groom, and an innocent little infant, were all disembarked into the grim hulk of Charon, who ferried them over, all baggageless, to some clinkered iron-foundry country or other. Yet what's the use of complaining? What justice of the peace will right the matter? Yea, what's the use of bothering the very heavens about it? Don't the heavens themselves ordain these things—else they could not happen?

A miserable world! Who would take the trouble to make a fortune in it, when he knows not how long he can keep it, for the thousand villains and asses who have the management of railroads and steamboats, and innumerable other vital things in the world. If they would make me Dictator in North America a while I'd string them up! and hang, draw, and quarter; fry, roast and boil; stew, grill, and devil them like so many turkey-legs—the rascally numskulls of stokers; I'd set them to stokering in Tartarus—I would.

Great improvements of the age! What! to call the facilitation of death and murder an improvement! Who wants to travel so fast? My grandfather did not, and he was no fool. Hark! here comes that old dragon again—that gigantic gadfly of a Moloch—snort! puff! scream!—here he comes straight-bent through these vernal woods, like the Asiatic cholera cantering on a camel. Stand aside! Here he comes, the chartered murderer! the death monopolizer! judge, jury, and hangman all together, whose victims die always without benefit of clergy. For two hundred and fifty miles that iron fiend goes yelling through the land, crying "More! more! more!" Would fifty conspiring mountains would fall atop of him! And, while they were about it, would they would also fall atop of that smaller dunning fiend, my creditor, who frightens the life out of me more than any locomotive—a lantern-jawed rascal, who seems to run on a railroad track too, and duns me even on Sunday, all the way to church and back, and comes and sits in the same pew with me, and pretending to be polite and hand me the prayer book opened at the proper place, pokes his pesky bill under my nose in the very midst of my devotions, and so shoves himself between me and salvation; for how can one keep his temper on such occasions?

I can't pay this horrid man, and yet they say money was never so plentiful—a drug on the market; but blame me if I can get any of the drug, though there never was a sick man more in need of that particular sort of medicine. It's a lie; money ain't plenty—feel of my pocket. Ha! here's a powder I was going to send to the sick baby in yonder hovel, where the Irish ditcher lives. That baby has the scarlet fever. They say the measles are rife in the country too, and the varioloid, and the chicken-pox, and it's bad for teething children. And after all, I suppose many of the poor little ones, after going through all this trouble, snap off short;

and so they had the measles, mumps, croup, scarlet fever, chicken-pox, cholera-morbus, summer-complaint, and all else, in vain! Ah! there's that twinge of the rheumatics in my right shoulder. I got it one night on the North River, when, in a crowded boat, I gave up my berth to a sick lady, and staid on deck till morning in drizzling weather. There's the thanks one gets for charity! Twinge! Shoot away, ye rheumatics! Ye couldn't lay on worse if I were some villain who had murdered the lady instead of befriending her. Dyspepsia too—I am troubled with that.

Hallo! here come the calves, the two-year-olds, just turned out of the barn into the pasture, after six months of cold victuals. What a miserable-looking set, to be sure! A breaking up of a hard winter, that's certain; sharp bones sticking out like elbows; all quilted with a strange stuff dried on their flanks like layers of pancakes. Hair worn quite off too, here and there; and where it ain't pancaked, or worn off, looks like the rubbed sides of mangy old hair-trunks. In fact, they are not six two-year-olds, but six abominable old hair-trunks wandering about here in this pasture.

Hark! By Jove, what's that? See! the very hair-trunks prick their ears at it, and stand and gaze away down into the rolling country yonder. Hark again! How clear! how musical! how prolonged! What a triumphant thanksgiving of a cock-crow! *"Glory be to God in the highest!"* It says those very words as plain as ever cock did in this world. Why, why, I began to feel a little in sorts again. It ain't so very misty, after all. The sun yonder is beginning to show himself; I feel warmer.

Hark! there again! Did ever such a blessed cock-crow so ring out over the earth before! Clear, shrill, full of pluck, full of fire, full of fun, full of glee. It plainly says—*"Never say die!"* My friends, it is extraordinary, is it not?

Unwittingly, I found that I had been addressing the two-year-olds—the calves—in my enthusiasm; which shows how one's true nature will betray itself at times in the most unconscious way. For what a very two-year-old, and calf, I had been to fall into the sulks, on a hill-top too, when a cock down in the lowlands there, without discourse of reason, and quite penniless in the world, and with death hanging over him at any moment from his hungry master, sends up a cry like a very laureate celebrating the glorious victory of New Orleans.

Hark! there it goes again! My friends, that must be a Shanghai; no domestic-born cock could crow in such prodigious exulting strains. Plainly, my friends, a Shanghai of the Emperor of China's breed.

But my friends, the hair-trunks, fairly alarmed at last by such clamorously-victorious tones, were now scampering off, with their tails flirting in the air, and capering with their legs in clumsy enough sort of style, sufficiently evincing that they had not freely flourished them for the six months last past.

Hark! there again! Whose cock is that? Who in this region can afford to buy such an extraordinary Shanghai? Bless me—it makes my blood bound—I feel wild. What? jumping on this rotten old log here, to flap my elbows and crow too? And just now in the doleful dumps. And all this from the simple crow of a cock. Marvelous cock! But soft—this fellow now crows most lustily; but it's only morning; let's see how he'll crow about noon, and towards nightfall. Come to think of it, cocks crow mostly in the beginning of the day. Their pluck ain't lasting, after all. Yes, yes; even cocks have to succumb to the universal spell of tribulation: jubilant in the beginning, but down in the mouth at the end.

> . . . Of fine mornings,
> We fine lusty cocks begin our crows in gladness;
> But when the eve does come we don't crow quite so much,
> For then cometh despondency and madness.

The poet had this very Shanghai in mind when he wrote that. But stop. There he rings out again, ten times richer, fuller, longer, more obstreperously exulting than before! Why, this is equal to hearing the great bell of St. Paul's rung at a coronation! In fact, that bell ought to be taken down, and this Shanghai put in its place. Such a crow would jollify all London, from Mile-End (which is no end) to Primrose Hill (where there ain't any primroses), and scatter the fog.

Well, I have an appetite for my breakfast this morning, if I have not had it for a week before. I meant to have only tea and toast; but I'll have coffee and eggs—no, brown stout and a beefsteak. I want something hearty. Ah, here comes the down-train: white cars, flashing through the trees like a vein of silver. How cheerfully the steam-pipe chirps! Gay are the passengers. There waves a handkerchief—going down to the city to eat oysters, and see their friends, and drop in at the circus. Look at the mist yonder; what soft curls and undulations round the hills, and the sun weaving his rays among them. See the azure smoke of the village, like the azure tester over a bridal-bed. How bright the country looks there where the river overflowed the meadows. The old grass has to knock under to the new. Well, I feel the better for this walk. Home now, and walk into that steak and crack that bottle of brown stout; and by the time that's drank—a quart of stout—by that time, I shall feel about as stout as Samson. Come to think of it, that dun may call, though. I'll just visit the woods and cut a club. I'll club him, by Jove, if he duns me this day.

Hark! there goes Shanghai again. Shanghai says, "Bravo!" Shanghai says, "Club him!"

Oh, brave cock!

I felt in rare spirits the whole morning. The dun called about eleven. I had the boy Jake send the dun up. I was reading *Tristram Shandy*, and could not go down under the circumstances. The lean rascal (a lean farmer, too—think of that!) entered, and found me seated in an armchair, with my feet on the table, and the second bottle of brown stout handy, and the book under eye.

"Sit down," said I, "I'll finish this chapter, and then attend to you. Fine morning. Ha! ha!—this is a fine joke about my Uncle Toby and the Widow Wadman! Ha! ha! ha! let me read this to you."

"I have no time; I've got my noon *chores* to do."

"To the deuce with your *chores!*" said I. "Don't drop your old tobacco about here, or I'll turn you out."

"Sir!"

"Let me read you this about the Widow Wadman. Said the Widow Wadman——"

"There's my bill, sir."

"Very good. Just twist it up, will you—it's about my smoking-time; and hand a coal, will you, from the hearth yonder!"

"My bill, sir!" said the rascal, turning pale with rage and amazement at my unwonted air (formerly I had always dodged him with a pale face), but too prudent as yet to betray the extremity of his astonishment. "My bill, sir"—and he stiffly poked it at me.

"My friend," said I, "what a charming morning! How sweet the country looks! Pray, did you hear that extraordinary cock-crow this morning? Take a glass of my stout!"

"*Yours?* First pay your debts before you offer folks *your* stout!"

"You think, then, that, properly speaking, I have no *stout*," said I, deliberately rising. "I'll undeceive you. I'll show you stout of a superior brand to Barclay and Perkins."

Without more ado, I seized that insolent dun by the slack of his coat —(and, being a lean, shad-bellied wretch, there was plenty of slack to it) —I seized him that way, tied him with a sailor-knot, and, thrusting his bill between his teeth, introduced him to the open country lying round about my place of abode.

"Jake," said I, "you'll find a sack of blue-nosed potatoes lying under the shed. Drag it here, and pelt this pauper away; he's been begging pence of me, and I know he can work, but he's lazy. Pelt him away, Jake!"

Bless my stars, what a crow! Shanghai sent up such a perfect pæan and *laudamus*—such a trumpet blast of triumph, that my soul fairly snorted in me. Duns!—I could have fought an army of them! Plainly, Shanghai was of the opinion that duns only came into the world to be kicked, hanged, bruised, battered, choked, walloped, hammered, drowned, clubbed!

Returning indoors, when the exultation of my victory over the dun had a little subsided, I fell to musing over the mysterious Shanghai. I had no idea I would hear him so nigh my house. I wondered from what rich gentleman's yard he crowed. Nor had he cut short his crows so easily as I had supposed he would. This Shanghai crowed till midday, at least. Would he keep a-crowing all day? I resolved to learn. Again I ascended the hill. The whole country was now bathed in a rejoicing sunlight. The warm verdure was bursting all round me. Teams were a-field. Birds, newly arrived from the South, were blithely singing in the air. Even the crows cawed with a certain unction, and seemed a shade or two less black than usual.

Hark! there goes the cock! How shall I describe the crow of the Shanghai at noontide! His sunrise crow was a whisper to it. It was the loudest, longest and most strangely musical crow that ever amazed mortal man. I had heard plenty of cock-crows before, and many fine ones;—but this one! so smooth and flute-like in its very clamor—so self-possessed in its very rapture of exultation—so vast, mounting, swelling, soaring, as if spurted out from a golden throat, thrown far back. Nor did it sound like the foolish, vain-glorious crow of some young sophomorean cock, who knew not the world, and was beginning life in audacious gay spirits, because in wretched ignorance of what might be to come. It was the crow of a cock who crowed not without advice; the crow of a cock who knew a thing or two; the crow of a cock who had fought the world and got the better of it and was resolved to crow, though the earth should heave and the heavens should fall. It was a wise crow; an invincible crow; a philosophic crow; a crow of all crows.

I returned home once more full of reinvigorated spirits, with a dauntless sort of feeling. I thought over my debts and other troubles, and over the unlucky risings of the poor oppressed *peoples* abroad, and over the railroad and steamboat accidents, and even over the loss of my dear friend, with a calm, good-natured rapture of defiance, which astounded myself. I felt as though I could meet Death, and invite him to dinner, and toast the Catacombs with him, in pure overflow of self-reliance and a sense of universal security.

Toward evening I went up to the hill once more to find whether, indeed, the glorious cock would prove game even from the rising of the sun unto the going down thereof. Talk of Vespers or Curfew!—the evening crow of the cock went out of his mighty throat all over the land and inhabited it, like Xerxes from the East with his double-winged host. It was miraculous. Bless me, what a crow! The cock went game to roost that night, depend upon it, victorious over the entire day, and bequeathing the echoes of his thousand crows to night.

After an unwontedly sound, refreshing sleep I rose early, feeling like a carriage-spring—light—elliptical—airy—buoyant as sturgeon-nose—and, like a foot-ball, bounded up the hill. Hark! Shanghai was up before me. The early bird that caught the worm—crowing like a bugle worked by an engine—lusty, loud, all jubilation. From the scattered farmhouses a multitude of other cocks were crowing, and replying to each other's crows. But they were as flageolets to a trombone. Shanghai would suddenly break in, and overwhelm all their crows with his one domineering blast.

He seemed to have nothing to do with any other concern. He replied to no other crow, but crowed solely by himself, on his own account, in solitary scorn and independence.

Oh, brave cock!—oh, noble Shanghai!—oh, bird rightly offered up by the invincible Socrates, in testimony of his final victory over life.

As I live, thought I, this blessed day, will I go and seek out the Shanghai, and buy him, if I have to clap another mortgage on my land.

I listened attentively now, striving to mark from what direction the crow came. But it so charged and replenished, and made bountiful and overflowing all the air, that it was impossible to say from what precise point the exultation came. All that I could decide upon was this: the crow came from out of the East, and not from out of the West. I then considered with myself how far a cock-crow might be heard. In this still country, shut in, too, by mountains, sounds were audible at great distances. Besides, the undulations of the land, the abuttings of the mountains into the rolling hill and valley below, produced strange echoes, and reverberations, and multiplications, and accumulations of resonance, very remarkable to hear, and very puzzling to think of. Where lurked this valiant Shanghai —this bird of cheerful Socrates—the game-fowl Greek who died unappalled? Where lurked he? Oh, noble cock, where are you? Crow once more, my Bantam! my princely, my imperial Shanghai! my bird of the Emperor of China! Brother of the sun! Cousin of great Jove! where are you?—one crow more, and tell me your number!

Hark! like a full orchestra of the cocks of all nations, forth burst the crow. But where from? There it is; but where? There was no telling, further than it came from out of the East.

After breakfast I took my stick and sallied down the road. There were many gentlemen's seats dotting the neighboring country, and I made no doubt that some of these opulent gentlemen had invested a hundred dollar bill in some royal Shanghai recently imported in the ship *Trade Wind*, or the ship *White Squall*, or the ship *Sovereign of the Seas*; for it must needs have been a brave ship with a brave name which bore the fortunes of so brave a cock. I resolved to walk the entire country, and find this noble foreigner out; but thought it would not be amiss to inquire on the way at the humblest homesteads, whether, peradventure, they had heard of a lately-imported Shanghai belonging to any of the gentlemen settlers from the city; for it was plain that no poor farmer, no poor man of any sort, could own such an Oriental trophy—such a Great Bell of St. Paul's swung in a cock's throat.

I met an old man, plowing, in a field nigh the road-side fence.

"My friend, have you heard an extraordinary cock-crow of late?"

"Well, well," he drawled, "I don't know—the Widow Crowfoot has a cock—and Squire Squaretoes has a cock— and I have a cock, and they all crow. But I don't know of any on 'em with 'straordinary crows."

"Good-morning to you," said I, shortly; "it's plain that you have not heard the crow of the Emperor of China's chanticleer."

Presently I met another old man mending a tumble-down old rail-fence. The rails were rotten, and at every move of the old man's hand they crumbled into yellow ochre. He had much better let the fence alone, or else get him new rails. And here I must say, that one cause of the sad fact why idiocy more prevails among farmers than any other class of people, is owing to their undertaking the mending of rotten rail-fences in warm, relaxing spring weather. The enterprise is a hopeless one. It is a laborious one; it is a bootless one. It is an enterprise to make the heart break. Vast pains squandered upon a vanity. For how can one make rotten rail-fences stand up on their rotten pins? By what magic put pitch into sticks which have lain freezing and baking through sixty consecutive winters and summers? This it is, this wretched endeavor to mend rotten rail-fences with their own rotten rails, which drives many farmers into the asylum.

On the face of the old man in question incipient idiocy was plainly marked. For, about sixty rods before him extended one of the most unhappy and desponding broken-hearted Virginia rail-fences I ever saw in my life. While in a field behind, were a set of young steers, possessed as by devils, continually butting at this forlorn old fence, and breaking through it here and there, causing the old man to drop his work and chase them back within bounds. He would chase them with a piece of rail huge as Goliath's beam, but as light as cork. At the first flourish, it crumbled into powder.

"My friend," said I, addressing this woeful mortal, "have you heard an extraordinary cock-crow of late?"

I might as well as have asked him if he had heard the death-tick. He stared at me with a long, bewildered, doleful, and unutterable stare, and without reply resumed his unhappy labors.

What a fool, thought I, to have asked such an uncheerful and uncheerable creature about a cheerful cock!

I walked on. I had now descended the high land where my house stood, and being in a low tract could not hear the crow of the Shanghai, which doubtless overshot me there. Besides, the Shanghai might be at lunch of corn and oats, or taking a nap, and so interrupted his jubilations for a while.

At length, I encountered riding along the road, a portly gentleman—nay, a *pursy* one—of great wealth, who had recently purchased him some noble acres, and built him a noble mansion, with a goodly fowl-house attached, the fame whereof spread through all the country. Thought I, Here now is the owner of the Shanghai.

"Sir," said I, "excuse me, but I am a countryman of yours, and would ask, if so be you own any Shanghais?"

"Oh, yes; I have ten Shanghais."

"Ten!" exclaimed I, in wonder; "and do they all crow?"

"Most lustily; every soul of them; I wouldn't own a cock that wouldn't crow."

"Will you turn back, and show me those Shanghais?"

"With pleasure: I am proud of them. They cost me, in the lump, six hundred dollars."

As I walked by the side of his horse, I was thinking to myself whether possibly I had not mistaken the harmoniously combined crowing of ten Shanghais in a squad, for the supernatural crow of a single Shanghai by himself.

"Sir," said I, "is there one of your Shanghais which far exceeds all the others in the lustiness, musicalness, and inspiring effects of his crow?"

"They crow pretty much alike, I believe," he courteously replied. "I really don't know that I could tell their crow apart."

I began to think that after all my noble chanticleer might not be in the possession of this wealthy gentleman. However, we went into his fowl-yard, and saw his Shanghais. Let me say that hitherto I had never clapped eye on this species of imported fowl. I had heard what enormous prices were paid for them, and also that they were of an enormous size, and had somehow fancied they must be of a beauty and brilliancy proportioned both to size and price. What was my surprise, then, to see ten carrot-colored monsters, without the smallest pretension to effulgence of plumage. Immediately, I determined that my royal cock was neither among these, nor could possibly be a Shanghai at all; if these gigantic gallows-bird fowl were fair specimens of the true Shanghai.

I walked all day, dining and resting at a farmhouse, inspecting various fowl-yards, interrogating various owners of fowls, hearkening to various crows, but discovered not the mysterious chanticleer. Indeed, I had wandered so far and deviously, that I could not hear his crow. I began to suspect that this cock was a mere visitor in the country, who had taken his departure by the eleven o'clock train for the South, and was now crowing and jubilating somewhere on the verdant banks of Long Island Sound.

But next morning, again I heard the inspiring blast, again felt my blood bound in me, again felt superior to all the ills of life, again felt like turning my dun out of doors. But displeased with the reception given him at his last visit, the dun staid away. Doubtless being in a huff; silly fellow that he was to take a harmless joke in earnest.

Several days passed, during which I made sundry excursions in the regions roundabout, but in vain sought the cock. Still, I heard him from the hill, and sometimes from the house, and sometimes in the stillness of the night. If at times I would relapse into my doleful dumps, straightway at the sound of the exultant and defiant crow, my soul, too, would turn chanticleer, and clap her wings, and throw back her throat, and breathe forth a cheerful challenge to all the world of woes.

At last, after some weeks I was necessitated to clap another mortgage on my estate, in order to pay certain debts, and among others the one I owed the dun, who of late had commenced a civil-process against me. The way the process was served was a most insulting one. In a private room I had been enjoying myself in the village tavern over a bottle of Philadelphia porter, and some Herkimer cheese, and a roll, and having apprised the landlord who was a friend of mine, that I would settle with him when I received my next remittances, stepped to the peg where I had hung my hat in the bar-room, to get a choice cigar I had left in the hall, when lo! I found the civil-process enveloping the cigar. When I unrolled the cigar, I unrolled the civil-process, and the constable standing by rolled out, with a thick tongue, "Take notice!" and added, in a whisper, "Put that in your pipe and smoke it!"

I turned short round upon the gentlemen then and there present in that bar-room. Said I, "Gentlemen, is this an honorable—nay, is this a lawful way of serving a civil-process? Behold!"

One and all they were of opinion, that it was a highly inelegant act in the constable to take advantage of a gentleman's lunching on cheese and porter, to be so uncivil as to slip a civil-process into his hat. It was ungenerous; it was cruel; for the sudden shock of the thing coming in-stanter upon the lunch, would impair the proper digestion of the cheese, which is proverbially not so easy of digestion as *blanc-mange*.

Arrived at home I read the process, and felt a twinge of melancholy. Hard world! hard world! Here I am, as good a fellow as ever lived—hos-pitable—open-hearted—generous to a fault; and the Fates forbid that I should possess the fortune to bless the country with my bounteousness. Nay, while many a stingy curmudgeon rolls in idle gold, I, heart of nobleness as I am, I have civil-processes served on me! I bowed my head, and felt forlorn—unjustly used—abused—unappreciated—in short, misera-ble.

Hark! like a clarion! yea, like a bolt of thunder with bells to it—came the all-glorious and defiant crow! Ye gods, how it set me up again! Right on my pins! Yes, verily on stilts!

Oh, noble cock!

Plain as cock could speak, it said, "Let the world and all aboard of it go to pot. Do you be jolly, and never say die! What's the world compared to you? What is it, anyhow, but a lump of loam? Do you be jolly!"

Oh, noble cock!

"But my dear and glorious cock," mused I, upon second thought, "one can't so easily send this world to pot; one can't so easily be jolly with civil-processes in his hat or hand."

Hark! the crow again. Plain as cock could speak, it said: "Hang the process, and hang the fellow that sent it! If you have not land or cash, go and thrash the fellow, and tell him you never mean to pay him. Be jolly!"

Now this was the way—through the imperative intimations of the cock —that I came to clap the added mortgage on my estate; paid all my debts by fusing them into this one added bond and mortgage. Thus made at ease again, I renewed my search for the noble cock. But in vain, though I heard him every day. I began to think there was some sort of deception in this mysterious thing: some wonderful ventriloquist prowled around my barns, or in my cellar, or on my roof, and was minded to be gayly mischievous. But no—what ventriloquist could so crow with such an heroic and celestial crow?

At last, one morning there came to me a certain singular man, who had sawed and split my wood in March—some five-and-thirty cords of it —and now he came for his pay. He was a singular man, I say. He was tall and spare, with a long saddish face, yet somehow a latently joyous eye, which offered the strangest contrast. His air seemed staid, but un-depressed. He wore a long, gray, shabby coat, and a big battered hat. This man had sawed my wood at so much a cord. He would stand and saw all day in a driving snow-storm, and never wink at it. He never spoke unless spoken to. He only sawed. Saw, saw, saw—snow, snow, snow. The saw and the snow went together like two natural things. The first day this man came, he brought his dinner with him, and volunteered to eat it sitting on his buck in the snow-storm. From my window, where I was reading Burton's *Anatomy of Melancholy*, I saw him in the act. I burst out of doors bareheaded. "Good heavens!" cried I; "what are you doing? Come in. *This* your dinner!"

He had a hunk of stale bread and another hunk of salt beef, wrapped in a wet newspaper, and washed his morsels down by melting a handful of fresh snow in his mouth. I took this rash man indoors, planted him by the fire, gave him a dish of hot pork and beans, and a mug of cider.

"Now," said I, "don't you bring any of your damp dinners here. You work by the job, to be sure, but I'll dine you for all that."

He expressed his acknowledgements in a calm, proud, but not un-grateful way, and dispatched his meal with satisfaction to himself, and me also. It afforded me pleasure to perceive that he quaffed down his mug of cider like a man. I honored him. When I addressed him in the way of business at his buck, I did so in a guardedly respectful and defer-ential manner. Interested in his singular aspect, struck by his wondrous intensity of application at his saw—a most wearisome and disgustful occu-pation to most people—I often sought to gather from him who he was, what sort of a life he led, where he was born, and so on. But he was mum. He came to saw my wood, and eat my dinners—if I chose to offer them—but not to gabble. At first, I somewhat resented his sullen silence under the circumstances. But better considering it, I honored him the more. I increased the respectfulness and deferentialness of my address toward him. I concluded within myself that this man had experienced hard times; that he had had many sore rubs in the world; that he was of a solemn disposition; that he was of the mind of Solomon; that he lived calmly, decorously, temperately; and though a very poor man, was, nevertheless, a highly respectable one. At times I imagined that he might even be an elder or deacon of some small country church. I thought it would not be a bad plan to run this excellent man for President of the United States. He would prove a great reformer of abuses.

His name was Merrymusk. I had often thought how jolly a name for so unjolly a wight. I inquired of people whether they knew Merrymusk. But it was some time before I learned much about him. He was by birth a Marylander, it appeared, who had long lived in the country round about; a wandering man; until within some ten years ago, a thriftless man, though perfectly innocent of crime; a man who would work hard a month with surprising soberness, and then spend all his wages in one riotous night. In youth he had been a sailor, and run away from his ship at Batavia, where he caught the fever, and came nigh dying. But he rallied, reshipped, landed home, found all his friends dead, and struck for the Northern interior, where he had since tarried. Nine years back he had married a wife, and now had four children. His wife was become a perfect invalid; one child had the white-swelling and the rest were rickety. He and his family lived in a shanty on a lonely barren patch nigh the railroad track, where it passed close to the base of the mountain. He had bought a fine cow to have plenty of wholesome milk for his children; but the cow died during an accouchement, and he could not afford to buy another. Still, his family never suffered for lack of food. He worked hard and brought it to them.

Now, as I said before, having long previously sawed my wood, this Merrymusk came for his pay.

"My friend," said I, "do you know of any gentleman hereabouts who owns an extraordinary cock?"

The twinkle glittered quite plain in the wood sawyer's eye.

"I know of no *gentleman*," he replied, "who has what might well be called an extraordinary cock."

Oh, thought I, this Merrymusk is not the man to enlighten me. I am afraid I shall never discover this extraordinary cock.

Not having the full change to pay Merrymusk, I gave him his due, as nigh as I could make it, and told him that in a day or two I would take a walk and visit his place, and hand him the remainder. Accordingly one fine morning I sallied forth upon the errand. I had much ado finding the best road to the shanty. No one seemed to know where it was exactly.

It lay in a very lonely part of the country, a densely-wooded mountain on one side (which I call October Mountain, on account of its bannered aspect in that month), and a thicketed swamp on the other, the railroad cutting the swamp. Straight as a die the railroad cut it; many times a day tantalizing the wretched shanty with the sight of all the beauty, rank, fashion, health, trunks, silver and gold, dry-goods and groceries, brides and grooms, happy wives and husbands, flying by the lonely door—no time to stop—flash! here they are—and there they go! out of sight at both ends—as if that part of the world were only made to fly over, and not to settle upon. And this was about all the shanty saw of what people call "life."

Though puzzled somewhat, yet I knew the general direction where the shanty lay, and on I trudged. As I advanced, I was surprised to hear the mysterious cock crow with more and more distinctness. Is it possible, thought I, that any gentleman owning a Shanghai can dwell in such a lonesome, dreary region? Louder and louder, nigher and nigher, sounded the glorious and defiant clarion. Though somehow I may be out of the track to my wood-sawyer's, I said to myself, yet, thank heaven, I seem to be on the way toward that extraordinary cock. I was delighted with this auspicious accident. On I journeyed; while at intervals the crow sounded most invitingly, and jocundly, and superbly; and the last crow was ever nigher than the former one. At last, emerging from a thicket of elders, straight before me I saw the most resplendent creature that ever blessed the sight of man.

A cock, more like a golden eagle than a cock. A cock, more like a field marshal than a cock. A cock, more like Lord Nelson with all his glittering arms on, standing on the *Vanguard's* quarter-deck going into battle, than a cock. A cock, more like the Emperor Charlemagne in his robes at Aix le Chapelle, than a cock.

Such a cock!

He was of a haughty size, stood haughtily on his haughty legs. His colors were red, gold, and white. The red was on his crest, along which was a mighty and symmetric crest, like unto Hector's helmet, as delineated on antique shields. His plumage was snowy, traced with gold. He walked in front of the shanty, like a peer of the realm; his crest lifted, his chest heaved out, his embroidered trappings flashing in the light. His pace was wonderful. He looked like some Oriental king in some magnificent Italian opera.

Merrymusk advanced from the door.

"Pray is not that the Signor Beneventano?"

"Sir!"

"That's the cock," said I, a little embarrassed. The truth was, my enthusiasm had betrayed me into a rather silly inadvertence. I had made a somewhat learned sort of allusion in the presence of an unlearned man.

Consequently, upon discovering it by this honest stare, I felt foolish; but carried it off by declaring that *this was the cock*.

Now, during the preceding autumn I had been to the city, and had chanced to be present at a performance of the Italian Opera. In that opera figured in some royal character, a certain Signor Beneventano—a man of a tall, imposing person, clad in rich raiment, like to plumage, and with a most remarkable, majestic, scornful stride. The Signor Beneventano seemed on the point of tumbling over backward with exceeding haughtiness. And for all the world, the proud pace of the cock seemed the very stage-pace of the Signor Beneventano.

Hark! suddenly the cock paused, lifted his head still higher, ruffled his plumes, seemed inspired, and sent forth a lusty crow. October Mountain echoed it; other mountains sent it back; still others rebounded it; it overran the country round. Now I plainly perceived how it was I had chanced to hear the gladdening sound on my distant hill.

"Good heavens! do you own the cock? Is that cock yours?"

"Is it my cock!" said Merrymusk, looking slyly gleeful out of the corner of his long, solemn face.

"Where did you get it?"

"It chipped the shell here. I raised it."

"You?"

Hark? Another crow. It might have raised the ghosts of all the pines and hemlocks ever cut down in that country. Marvelous cock! Having crowed, he strode on again, surrounded by a bevy of admiring hens.

"What will you take for Signor Beneventano?"

"Sir?"

"That magic cock—what will you take for him?"

"I won't sell him."

"I will give you fifty dollars."

"Pooh!"

"One hundred!"

"Pish!"

"Five hundred!"

"Bah!"

"And you a poor man."

"No; don't I own that cock, and haven't I refused five hundred dollars for him?"

"True," said I, in profound thought; "that's a fact. You won't sell him, then?"

"No."

"Will you give him?"

"No."

"Will you *keep* him, then!" I shouted, in a rage.

"Yes."

I stood awhile admiring the cock, and wondering at the man. At last I felt a redoubled admiration of the one, and a redoubled deference for the other.

"Won't you step in?" said Merrymusk.

"But won't the cock be prevailed upon to join us?" said I.

"Yes. Trumpet! hither, boy! hither!"

The cock turned round, and strode up to Merrymusk.

"Come!"

The cock followed us into the shanty.

"Crow!"

The roof jarred.

Oh, noble cock!

I turned in silence upon my entertainer. There he sat on an old battered chest, in his old battered gray coat, with patches at his knees and elbows, and a deplorably bunged hat. I glanced round the room. Bare rafters overhead, but solid junks of jerked beef hanging from them. Earth floor, but a heap of potatoes in one corner, and a sack of Indian meal in another. A blanket was strung across the apartment at the further end, from which came a woman's ailing voice and the voices of ailing children. But somehow in the ailing of these voices there seemed no complaint.

"Mrs. Merrymusk and children?"

"Yes."

I looked at the cock. There he stood majestically in the middle of the room. He looked like a Spanish grandee caught in a shower, and standing under some peasant's shed. There was a strange supernatural look of contrast about him. He irradiated the shanty; he glorified its meanness. He glorified the battered chest, and tattered gray coat, and the bunged hat. He glorified the very voices which came in ailing tones from behind the screen.

"Oh, father," cried a little sickly voice, "let Trumpet sound again."

"Crow," cried Merrymusk.

The cock threw himself into a posture.

The roof jarred.

"Does not this disturb Mrs. Merrymusk and the sick children?"

"Crow again, Trumpet."

The roof jarred.

"It does not disturb them, then?"

"Didn't you hear 'em *ask* for it?"

"How is it, that your sick family like this crowing?" said I. "The cock is a glorious cock, with a glorious voice, but not exactly the sort of thing for a sick chamber, one would suppose. Do they really like it?"

"Don't *you* like it? Don't it do *you* good? Ain't it inspiring? Don't it impart pluck? give stuff against despair?"

"All true," said I, removing my hat with profound humility before the brave spirit disguised in the base coat.

"But then," said I, still with some misgivings, "so loud, so wonderfully clamorous a crow, methinks might be amiss to invalids, and retard their convalescence."

"Crow your best now, Trumpet!"

I leaped from my chair. The cock frightened me, like some overpowering angel in the Apocalypse. He seemed crowing over the fall of wicked Babylon, or crowing over the triumph of righteous Joshua in the vale of Askelon. When I regained my composure somewhat, an inquisitive thought occurred to me. I resolved to gratify it.

"Merrymusk, will you present me to your wife and children?"

"Yes. Wife, the gentleman wants to step in."

"He is very welcome," replied a weak voice.

Going behind the curtain, there lay a wasted, but strangely cheerful human face; and that was pretty much all; the body, hid by the counterpane and an old coat, seemed too shrunken to reveal itself through such impediments. At the bedside sat a pale girl, ministering. In another bed lay three children, side by side: three more pale faces.

"Oh, father, we don't mislike the gentleman, but let us see Trumpet too."

At a word, the cock strode behind the screen, and perched himself on the children's bed. All their wasted eyes gazed at him with a wild and spiritual delight. They seemed to sun themselves in the radiant plumage of the cock.

"Better than a 'pothecary, eh," said Merrymusk. "This is Dr. Cock himself."

We retired from the sick ones, and I reseated myself again, lost in thought, over this strange household.

"You seem a glorious independent fellow," said I.

"And I don't think you a fool, and never did. Sir, you are a trump."

"Is there any hope of your wife's recovery?" said I, modestly seeking to turn the conversation.

"Not the least."

"The children?"

"Very little."

"It must be a doleful life, then, for all concerned. This lonely solitude —this shanty—hard work—hard times."

"Haven't I Trumpet? He's the cheerer. He crows through all; crows at the darkest: Glory to God in the highest! Continually he crows it."

"Just the import I first ascribed to his crow, Merrymusk, when first I heard it from my hill. I thought some rich nabob owned some costly Shanghai; little weening any such poor man as you owned this lusty cock of a domestic breed."

"*Poor* man like *me*? Why call *me* poor? Don't the cock I own glorify this otherwise inglorious, lean, lantern-jawed land? Didn't *my* cock encourage *you*? And *I* give you all this glorification away gratis. I am a great philanthropist. I am a rich man—a very rich man, and a very happy one. Crow, Trumpet."

The roof jarred.

I returned home in a deep mood. I was not wholly at rest concerning the soundness of Merrymusk's views of things, though full of admiration for him. I was thinking on the matter before my door, when I heard the cock crow again. Enough. Merrymusk is right.

Oh, noble cock! oh, noble man!

I did not see Merrymusk for some weeks after this; but hearing the glorious and rejoicing crow, I supposed that all went as usual with him. My own frame of mind remained a rejoicing one. The cock still inspired me. I saw another mortgage piled on my plantation; but only bought another dozen of stout, and a half-dozen of Philadelphia porter. Some of my relatives died; I wore no mourning, but for three days drank stout in preference to porter, stout being of the darker color. I heard the cock crow the instant I received the unwelcome tidings.

"Your health in this stout, oh, noble cock!"

I thought I would call on Merrymusk again, not having seen or heard of him for some time now. Approaching the place, there were no signs of motion about the shanty. I felt a strange misgiving. But the cock crew from within doors, and the boding vanished. I knocked at the door. A feeble voice bade me enter. The curtain was no longer drawn; the whole house was a hospital now. Merrymusk lay on a heap of old clothes; wife and children were all in their beds. The cock was perched on an old hogshead hoop, swung from the ridge-pole in the middle of the shanty.

"You are sick, Merrymusk," said I mournfully.

"No, I am well," he feebly answered.—"Crow, Trumpet."

I shrunk. The strong soul in the feeble body appalled me.

But the cock crew.

The roof jarred.

"How is Mrs. Merrymusk?"

"Well."

"And the children?"

"Well. All well."

The last two words he shouted forth in a kind of wild ecstasy of triumph over ill. It was too much. His head fell back. A white napkin seemed dropped upon his face. Merrymusk was dead.

An awful fear seized me.

But the cock crew.

The cock shook his plumage as if each feather were a banner. The cock hung from the shanty roof as erewhile the trophied flags from the dome of St. Paul's. The cock terrified me with exceeding wonder.

I drew nigh the bedsides of the woman and children. They marked my look of strange affright; they knew what had happened.

"My good man is just dead," breathed the woman lowly. "Tell me true?"

"Dead," said I.

The cock crew.

She fell back, without a sigh, and through long-loving sympathy was dead.

The cock crew.

The cock shook sparkles from his golden plumage. The cock seemed in a rapture of benevolent delight. Leaping from the hoop, he strode up majestically to the pile of old clothes, where the wood-sawyer lay, and planted himself, like an armorial supporter, at his side. Then raised one long, musical, triumphant, and final sort of crow, with throat heaved far back, as if he meant the blast to waft the wood-sawyer's soul sheer up to the seventh heavens. Then he strode, king-like, to the woman's bed. Another upturned and exultant crow, mated to the former.

The pallor of the children was changed to radiance. Their faces shone celestially through grime and dirt. They seemed children of emperors and kings, disguised. The cock sprang upon their bed, shook himself, and crowed, and crowed again, and still and still again. He seemed bent upon crowing the souls of the children out of their wasted bodies. He seemed bent upon rejoining instanter this whole family in the upper air. The children seemed to second his endeavors. Far, deep, intense longings for release transfigured them into spirits before my eyes. I saw angels where they lay.

They were dead.

The cock shook his plumage over them. The cock crew. It was now like a Bravo! like a Hurrah! like a Three-times-three! hip! hip! He strode out of the shanty. I followed. He flew upon the apex of the dwelling, spread wide his wings, sounded one supernatural note, and dropped at my feet.

The cock was dead.

If now you visit that hilly region, you will see, nigh the railroad track, just beneath October Mountain, on the other side of the swamp—there you will see a gravestone, not with skull and cross-bones, but with a lusty cock in act of crowing, chiseled on it, with the words beneath:

> O death, where is thy sting?
> O grave, where is thy victory?

The wood-sawyer and his family, with the Signor Beneventano, lie in that spot; and I buried them, and planted the stone, which was a stone made to order; and never since then have I felt the doleful dumps, but under all circumstances crow late and early with a continual crow.

Cock-A-Doodle-Doo!—oo!—oo!—oo!—oo!

THE CASSOCK

Had you stepped on board the Pequod at a certain juncture of this post-mortemizing of the whale; and had you strolled forward nigh the windlass, pretty sure am I that you would have scanned with no small curiosity a very strange, enigmatical object, which you would have seen there, lying along lengthwise in the lee scuppers. Not the wondrous cistern in the whale's huge head; not the prodigy of his unhinged lower jaw; not the miracle of his symmetrical tail; none of these would so surprise you, as half a glimpse of that unaccountable cone,—longer than a Kentuckian is tall, nigh a foot in diameter at the base, and jet-black as Yojo, the ebony idol of Queequeg. And an idol, indeed, it is; or, rather, in old times, its likeness was. Such an idol as that found in the secret groves of Queen Maachah in Judea; and for worshipping which, king Asa, her son, did depose her, and destroyed the idol, and burnt it for an abomination of the brook Kedron, as darkly set forth in the 15th chapter of the first book of Kings.

Look at the sailor, called the mincer, who now comes along, and as-sisted by two allies, heavily backs the grandissimus, as the mariners call it, and with bowed shoulders, staggers off with it as if he were a grenadier carrying a dead comrade from the field. Extending it upon the forecastle deck, he now proceeds cylindrically to remove its dark pelt, as an African hunter the pelt of a boa. This done he turns the pelt inside out, like a pantaloon leg; gives it a good stretching, so as almost to double its diameter; and at last hangs it, well spread, in the rigging, to dry. Ere long, it is taken down; when removing some three feet of it, towards the pointed extremity, and then cutting two slits for arm-holes at the other end, he lengthwise slips himself bodily into it. The mincer now stands before you invested in the full canonicals of his calling. Immemorial to all his order, this investiture alone will adequately protect him, while employed in the peculiar functions of his office.

That office consists in mincing the horse-pieces of blubber for the pots; an operation which is conducted at a curious wooden horse, planted end-wise against the bulwarks, and with a capacious tub beneath it, into which the minced pieces drop, fast as the sheets from a rapt orator's desk. Ar-rayed in decent black; occupying a conspicuous pulpit; intent on bible leaves; what a candidate for an archbishoprick, what a lad for a Pope were this mincer! *

* Bible leaves! Bible leaves! This is the invariable cry from the mates to the mincer. It enjoins him to be careful, and cut his work into as thin slices as possible, inasmuch as by so doing the business of boiling out the oil is much accelerated, and its quantity considerably increased, besides perhaps improving it in quality.

From WHITE-JACKET

CHAPTER LXI

The Surgeon of the Fleet

Cadwallader Cuticle, M.D., and Honorary Member of the most distinguished Colleges of Surgeons both in Europe and America, was our Surgeon of the Fleet. Nor was he at all blind to the dignity of his position; to which, indeed, he was rendered peculiarly competent, if the reputation he enjoyed was deserved. He had the name of being the foremost surgeon in the Navy, a gentleman of remarkable science, and a veteran practitioner.

He was a small, withered man, nearly, perhaps quite, sixty years of age. His chest was shallow, his shoulders bent, his pantaloons hung round skeleton legs, and his face was singularly attenuated. In truth, the corporeal vitality of this man seemed, in a good degree, to have died out of him. He walked abroad, a curious patchwork of life and death, with a wig, one glass eye, and a set of false teeth, while his voice was husky and thick; but his mind seemed undebilitated as in youth; it shone out of his remaining eye with basilisk brilliancy.

Like most old physicians and surgeons who have seen much service, and have been promoted to high professional place for their scientific attainments, this Cuticle was an enthusiast in his calling. In private, he had once been heard to say, confidentially, that he would rather cut off a man's arm than dismember the wing of the most delicate pheasant. In particular, the department of morbid anatomy was his peculiar love; and in his state-room below he had a most unsightly collection of Parisian casts, in plaster and wax, representing all imaginable malformations of the human members, both organic and induced by disease. Chief among these was a cast, often to be met with in the anatomical museums of Europe, and no doubt an unexaggerated copy of a genuine original; it was the head of an elderly woman, with an aspect singularly gentle and meek, but at the same time wonderfully expressive of a gnawing sorrow, never to be relieved. You would almost have thought it the face of some abbess, for some unspeakable crime voluntarily sequestered from human society, and leading a life of agonized penitence without hope; so marvellously sad and tearfully pitiable was this head. But when you first beheld it, no such emotions ever crossed your mind. All your eyes and all your horrified soul were fast fascinated and frozen by the sight of a hideous, crumpled horn, like that of a ram, downward growing out from the forehead, and partly shadowing the face; but as you gazed, the freezing fascination of its horribleness gradually waned, and then your whole heart burst with sorrow, as you contemplated those aged features, ashy pale and wan. The horn seemed the mark of a curse for some mysterious sin, conceived and committed before the spirit had entered the flesh. Yet that sin seemed something imposed, and not voluntarily sought; some sin growing out of the heartless necessities of the predestination of things; some sin under which the sinner sank in sinless woe.

But no pang of pain, not the slightest touch of concern, ever crossed the bosom of Cuticle when he looked on this cast. It was immovably fixed to a bracket, against the partition of his stateroom, so that it was the first object that greeted his eyes when he opened them from his nightly sleep. Nor was it to hide the face, that upon retiring he always hung his Navy cap upon the upward curling extremity of the horn, for that obscured it but little.

The surgeon's cot-boy, the lad who made up his winging bed and took care of his room, often told us of the horror he sometimes felt when he would find himself alone in his master's retreat. At times he was seized with the idea that Cuticle was a preternatural being; and once entering his room in the middle watch of the night, he started at finding it enveloped in a thick, bluish vapour, and stifling with the odors of brimstone. Upon hearing a low groan from the smoke, with a wild cry he darted from the place, and, rousing the occupants of the neighbouring staterooms, it was found, that the vapour proceeded from smoldering bunches of Lucifer matches, which had become ignited through the carelessness of the surgeon. Cuticle, almost dead, was dragged from the suffocating atmosphere, and it was several days ere he completely recovered from its effects. This accident took place immediately over the powder magazine; but as Cuticle, during his sickness, paid dearly enough for transgressing the laws prohibiting combustibles in the gun room, the captain contented himself with privately remonstrating with him.

Well knowing the enthusiasm of the surgeon for all specimens of morbid anatomy, some of the ward-room officers used to play upon his credulity, though, in every case, Cuticle was not long in discovering their deceptions. Once, when they had some sago pudding for dinner, and Cuticle chanced to be ashore, they made up a parcel of this bluish-white, firm, jelly-like preparation, and placing it in a tin box, carefully sealed with wax, they deposited it on the gunroom table, with a note, purporting to come from an eminent physician in Rio, connected with the Grand National Museum on the Praca d'Acclamacao, begging leave to present to the scientific Senhor Cuticle—with the donor's compliments—an uncommonly fine specimen of a cancer.

Descending to the ward-room, Cuticle spied the note, and no sooner read it, than, clutching the case, he opened it, and exclaimed, 'Beautiful! splendid! I have never seen a finer specimen of this most interesting disease.'

'What have you there, Surgeon Cuticle?' said a lieutenant, advancing.

'Why, sir, look at it; did you ever see anything more exquisite?'

'Very exquisite, indeed; let me have a bit of it, will you, Cuticle?'

'Let you have a bit of it!' shrieked the surgeon, starting back. 'Let you have one of my limbs! I wouldn't mar so large a specimen for a hundred dollars; but what can you want of it? You are not making collections!'

'I'm fond of the article,' said the lieutenant; 'it's a fine cold relish to bacon or ham. You know, I was in New Zealand last cruise, Cuticle, and got into sad dissipation there among the cannibals; come, let's have a bit, if it's only a mouthful.'

'Why, you infernal Feejee!' shouted Cuticle, eyeing the other with a profound expression; 'you don't really mean to eat a piece of this cancer?'

'Hand it to me, and see whether I will not,' was the reply.

'In God's name, take it!' cried the surgeon, putting the case into his hands, and then standing with his own uplifted.

'Steward!' cried the lieutenant, 'the castor—quick! I always use plenty of pepper with this dish, Surgeon; it's oystery. Ah! this is really delicious,' he added, smacking his lips over a mouthful. 'Try it now, Surgeon, and you'll never keep such a fine dish as this, lying uneaten on your hands, as a mere scientific curiosity.'

Cuticle's whole countenance changed; and, slowly walking up to the table, he put his nose close to the tin case, then touched its contents with his finger and tasted it. Enough. Buttoning up his coat, in all the tremblings of an old man's rage, he burst from the ward-room, and, calling for a boat, was not seen again for twenty-four hours.

But though, like all other mortals, Cuticle was subject at times to these fits of passion—at least under outrageous provocation—nothing could exceed his coolness when actually employed in his imminent vocation. Surrounded by moans and shrieks, by features distorted with anguish inflicted by himself, he yet maintained a countenance almost supernaturally calm; and unless the intense interest of the operation flushed his wan face with a momentary tinge of professional enthusiasm, he toiled away, untouched by the keenest misery coming under a fleet-surgeon's eye. Indeed, long habituation to the dissecting-room and the amputation-table had made him seemingly impervious to the ordinary emotions of humanity. Yet you could not say that Cuticle was essentially a cruel-hearted man. His apparent heartlessness must have been of a purely scientific origin. It is not to be imagined even that Cuticle would have harmed a fly, unless he could procure a microscope powerful enough to assist him in experimenting on the minute vitals of the creature.

But notwithstanding his marvellous indifference to the sufferings of his patients, and spite even of his enthusiasm in his vocation—not cooled by frosting old age itself—Cuticle, on some occasions, would affect a certain disrelish of his profession, and declaim against the necessity that forced a man of his humanity to perform a surgical operation. Especially was it apt to be thus with him, when the case was one of more than ordinary interest. In discussing it, previous to setting about it, he would veil his eagerness under an aspect of great circumspection, curiously marred, however, by the continual sallies of unsuppressible impatience. But the knife once in his hand, the compassionless surgeon himself, undisguised, stood before you. Such was Cadwallader Cuticle, our Surgeon of the Fleet.

CHAPTER LXII

A *Consultation of Man-of-war Surgeons*

It seems customary for the Surgeon of the Fleet, when any important operation in his department is on the anvil and there is nothing to absorb professional attention from it, to invite his brother surgeons, if at hand at the time, to a ceremonious consultation upon it. And this, in courtesy, his brother surgeons expect.

In pursuance of this custom, then, the surgeons of the neighbouring American ships of war were requested to visit the *Neversink* in a body, to advise concerning the case of the topman, whose situation had now become critical. They assembled on the half-deck, and were soon joined by their respected senior, Cuticle. In a body they bowed as he approached, and accosted him with deferential regard.

'Gentlemen,' said Cuticle, unostentatiously seating himself on a camp-stool, handed him by his cot-boy, 'we have here an extremely interesting case. You have all seen the patient, I believe. At first I had hopes that I should have been able to cut down to the ball, and remove it; but the state of the patient forbade. Since then, the inflammation and sloughing of the part has been attended with a copious suppuration, great loss of substance, extreme debility and emaciation. From this, I am convinced that the ball has shattered and deadened the bone, and now lies impacted in the medullary canal. In fact, there can be no doubt that the wound is incurable, and that amputation is the only resource. But, gentlemen, I find myself placed in a very delicate predicament. I assure you I feel no professional anxiety to perform the operation. I desire your advice, and if you will now again visit the patient with me, we can then return here, and decide what is best to be done. Once more, let me say, that I feel no personal anxiety whatever to use the knife.'

The assembled surgeons listened to this address with the most serious attention, and, in accordance with their superior's desire, now descended to the sick-bay, where the patient was languishing. The examination concluded, they returned to the half-deck, and the consultation was renewed.

'Gentlemen,' began Cuticle, again seating himself, 'you have now just inspected the limb; you have seen that there is no resource but amputation; and now, gentlemen, what do you say? Surgeon Bandage, of the *Mohawk*, will you express your opinion?'

'The wound is a very serious one,' said Bandage—a corpulent man, with a high German forehead—shaking his head solemnly.

'Can anything save him but amputation?' demanded Cuticle.

'His constitutional debility is extreme,' observed Bandage, 'but I have seen more dangerous cases.'

'Surgeon Wedge, of the *Malay*,' said Cuticle, in a pet, 'be pleased to give *your* opinion; and let it be definitive, I entreat': this was said with a severe glance toward Bandage.

'If I thought,' began Wedge, a very spare, tall man, elevating himself still higher on his toes, 'that the ball had shattered and divided the whole *femur*, including the *Greater* and *Lesser Trochanter*, the *Linear aspera*, the *Digital fossa*, and the *Intertrochanteric*, I should certainly be in favor of amputation; but that, sir, permit me to observe, is not my opinion.'

'Surgeon Sawyer, of the *Buccaneer*,' said Cuticle, drawing in his thin lower lip with vexation, and turning to a round-faced, florid, frank, sensible-looking man, whose uniform coat very handsomely fitted him, and was adorned with an unusual quantity of gold lace; 'Surgeon Sawyer, of the *Buccaneer*, let us now hear *your* opinion, if you please. Is not amputation the only resource, sir?'

'Excuse me,' said Sawyer, 'I am decidedly opposed to it; for if hitherto the patient has not been strong enough to undergo the extraction of the ball, I do not see how he can be expected to endure a far more severe operation. As there is no immediate danger of mortification, and you say the ball cannot be reached without making large incisions, I should support him, I think, for the present, with tonics, and gentle antiphlogistics, locally applied. On no account would I proceed to amputation until further symptoms are exhibited.'

'Surgeon Patella, of the *Algerine*,' said Cuticle, in an ill-suppressed passion, abruptly turning round on the person addressed, 'will *you* have the kindness to say whether *you* do not think that amputation is the only resource?'

Now Patella was the youngest of the company, a modest man, filled with a profound reverence for the science of Cuticle, and desirous of gaining his good opinion, yet not wishing to commit himself altogether by a decided reply, though, like Surgeon Sawyer, in his own mind he might have been clearly against the operation.

'What you have remarked, Mr. Surgeon of the Fleet,' said Patella, respectfully hemming, 'concerning the dangerous condition of the limb, seems obvious enough; amputation would certainly be a cure to the wound; but then, as, notwithstanding his present debility, the patient seems to have a strong constitution, he might rally as it is, and by your scientific treatment, Mr. Surgeon of the Fleet'—bowing—'be entirely made whole, without risking an amputation. Still, it is a very critical case, and amputation may be indispensable; and, if it *is* to be performed, there ought to be no delay whatever. That is my view of the case, Mr. Surgeon of the Fleet.'

'Surgeon Patella, then, gentlemen,' said Cuticle, turning round triumphantly, 'is clearly of opinion that amputation should be immediately performed. For my own part—individually, I mean, and without respect to the patient—I am sorry to have it so decided. But this settles the question, gentlemen—in my own mind, however, it was settled before. At ten o'clock to-morrow morning the operation will be performed. I shall be happy to see you all on the occasion, and also your juniors' (alluding to the absent *Assistant Surgeons*). 'Good morning, gentlemen; at ten o'clock, remember.'

And Cuticle retreated to the ward-room.

CHAPTER LXIII

The Operation

Next morning, at the appointed hour, the surgeons arrived in a body. They were accompanied by their juniors, young men ranging in age from nineteen years to thirty. Like the senior surgeons, these young gentlemen were arrayed in their blue navy uniforms, displaying a profusion of bright buttons, and several broad bars of gold lace about the wristbands. As in honour of the occasion, they had put on their best coats; they looked exceedingly brilliant.

The whole party immediately descended to the half-deck, where preparations had been made for the operation. A large garrison-ensign was stretched across the ship by the mainmast, so as completely to screen the space behind. This space included the whole extent aft to the bulkhead of the commodore's cabin, at the door of which the marine orderly paced, in plain sight, cutlass in hand.

Upon two gun-carriages, dragged amidships, the Death-board (used for burials at sea) was horizontally placed, covered with an old royal-stun'-sail. Upon this occasion, to do duty as an amputation-table, it was widened by an additional plank. Two match-tubs, near by, placed one upon another, at either end supported another plank, distinct from the table, whereon was exhibited an array of saws and knives of various and peculiar shapes and sizes; also, a sort of steel, something like the dinner-table implement, together with long needles, crooked at the end for taking up the arteries, and large darning needles, thread, and beeswax, for sewing up a wound.

At the end nearest the larger table was a tin basin of water, surrounded by small sponges, placed at mathematical intervals. From the long hori-

zontal pole of a great-gun rammer—fixed in its usual place overhead—
hung a number of towels, with 'U. S.' marked in the corners.

All these arrangements had been made by the 'surgeon's steward,' a
person whose important functions in a man-of-war will, in a future chapter,
be entered upon at large. Upon the present occasion, he was bustling
about, adjusting and readjusting the knives, needles, and carver, like an
over-conscientious butler fidgeting over a dinner-table just before the
convivialists enter.

But by far the most striking object to be seen behind the ensign was a
human skeleton, whose every joint articulated with wires. By a rivet at the
apex of the skull, it hung dangling from a hammock hook fixed in a beam
above. Why this object was here, will presently be seen; but why it was
placed immediately at the foot of the amputation-table, only Surgeon
Cuticle can tell.

While the final preparations were being made, Cuticle stood conversing
with the assembled surgeons and assistant surgeons, his invited guests.

'Gentlemen,' said he, taking up one of the glittering knives and
artistically drawing the steel across it; 'Gentlemen, though these scenes
are very unpleasant, and in some moods, I may say, repulsive to me—yet
how much better for our patient to have the contusions and lacerations
of his present wound—with all its dangerous symptoms—converted into
a clean incision, free from these objections, and occasioning so much less
subsequent anxiety to himself and the surgeon! Yes,' he added, tenderly
feeling the edge of his knife, 'amputation is our only resource. Is it not so,
Surgeon Patella?' turning toward that gentleman, as if relying upon some
sort of an assent, however clogged with conditions.

'Certainly,' said Patella, 'amputation is your only resource, Mr. Surgeon
of the Fleet; that is, I mean, if you are fully persuaded of its necessity.'

The other surgeons said nothing, maintaining a somewhat reserved air,
as if conscious that they had no positive authority in the case, whatever
might be their own private opinions; but they seemed willing to behold,
and, if called upon, to assist at the operation, since it could not now be
averted.

The young men, their assistants, looked very eager, and cast frequent
glances of awe upon so distinguished a practitioner as the venerable
Cuticle.

'They say he can drop a leg in one minute and ten seconds from the
moment the knife touches it,' whispered one of them to another.

'We shall see,' was the reply; and the speaker clapped his hand to his
fob, to see if his watch would be forthcoming when wanted.

'Are you all ready here?' demanded Cuticle, now advancing to his
steward; 'have not those fellows got through yet?' pointing to three men of
the carpenter's gang, who were placing bits of wood under the gun-
carriages supporting the central table.

'They are just through, sir,' respectfully answered the steward, touching his hand to his forehead, as if there were a cap-front there.

'Bring up the patient, then,' said Cuticle.

'Young gentlemen,' he added, turning to the row of assistant surgeons, 'seeing you here reminds me of the classes of students once under my instruction at the Philadelphia College of Physicians and Surgeons. Ah, those were happy days!' he sighed, applying the extreme corner of his handkerchief to his glass eye. 'Excuse an old man's emotions, young gentlemen; but when I think of the numerous cases that then came under my treatment, I cannot but give way to my feelings. The town, the city, the metropolis, young gentlemen, is the place for you students; at least in these dull times of peace, when the Army and Navy furnish no inducements for a youth ambitious of rising in our honourable profession. Take an old man's advice, and if the war now threatening between the States and Mexico should break out, exchange your Navy commissions for commissions in the Army. From having no military marine herself, Mexico has always been backward in furnishing subjects for the amputation-tables of foreign navies. The cause of science has languished in her hands. The Army, young gentlemen, is your best school; depend upon it. You will hardly believe it, Surgeon Bandage,' turning to that gentleman, 'but this is my first important case of surgery in a nearly three years' cruise. I have been almost wholly confined in this ship to doctor's practice—prescribing for fevers and fluxes. True, the other day a man fell from the mizzen-topsail-yard; but that was merely an aggravated case of dislocations, and bones splintered and broken. No one, sir, could have made an amputation of it, without severely contusing his conscience. And mine—I may say it, gentlemen, without ostentation—is peculiarly susceptible.'

And so saying, the knife and carver touchingly dropped to his sides, and he stood for a moment fixed in a tender reverie. But a commotion being heard beyond the curtain, he started, and, briskly crossing and re-crossing the knife and carver, exclaimed, 'Ah, here comes our patient; surgeons, this side of the table, if you please; young gentlemen, a little further off, I beg. Steward, take off my coat—so; my neckerchief now; I must be perfectly unencumbered, Surgeon Patella, or I can do nothing whatever.'

These articles being removed, he snatched off his wig, placing it on the gun-deck capstan; then took out his set of false teeth, and placed it by the side of the wig; and, lastly, putting his forefinger to the inner angle of his blind eye, spirted out the glass optic with professional dexterity, and deposited that, also, next to the wig and false teeth.

Thus divested of nearly all inorganic appurtenances, what was left of the surgeon slightly shook itself, to see whether anything more could be spared to advantage.

'Carpenter's mates,' he now cried, 'will you never get through with that job?'

'Almost through, sir—just through,' they replied, staring round in search of the strange, unearthly voice that addressed them; for the absence of his teeth had not at all improved the conversational tones of the Surgeon of the Fleet.

With natural curiosity, these men had purposely been lingering, to see all they could; but now, having no further excuse, they snatched up their hammers and chisels, and—like the stage-builders decamping from a public meeting at the eleventh hour, after just completing the rostrum in time for the first speaker—the carpenter's gang withdrew.

The broad ensign now lifted, revealing a glimpse of the crowd of man-of-war's men outside, and the patient, borne in the arms of two of his mess-mates, entered the place. He was much emaciated, weak as an infant, and every limb visibly trembled, or rather jarred, like the head of a man with the palsy. As if an organic and involuntary apprehension of death had seized the wounded leg, its nervous motions were so violent that one of the messmates was obliged to keep his hand upon it.

The topman was immediately stretched upon the table, the attendants steadying his limbs, when, slowly opening his eyes, he glanced about at the glittering knives and saws, the towels and sponges, the armed sentry at the commodore's cabin-door, the row of eager-eyed students, the meagre death's-head of a Cuticle, now with his shirt-sleeves rolled up upon his withered arms and knife in hand, and, finally, his eye settled in horror upon the skeleton, slowly vibrating and jingling before him, with the slow, slight roll of the frigate in the water.

'I would advise perfect repose of your every limb, my man,' said Cuticle, addressing him; 'the precision of an operation is often impaired by the inconsiderate restlessness of the patient. But if you consider, my good fellow,' he added, in a patronizing and almost sympathetic tone, and slightly pressing his hand on the limb, 'if you consider how much better it is to live with three limbs than to die with four, and especially if you but knew to what torments both sailors and soldiers were subjected before the time of Celsus, owing to the lamentable ignorance of surgery then prevailing, you would certainly thank God from the bottom of your heart that *your* operation has been postponed to the period of this enlightened age, blessed with a Bell, a Brodie, and a Lally. My man, before Celsus's time, such was the general ignorance of our noble science, that, in order to prevent the excessive effusion of blood, it was deemed indispensable to operate with a red-hot knife'—making a professional movement toward the thigh—'and pour scalding oil upon the parts'—elevating his elbow, as if with a teapot in his hand—'still further to sear them, after amputation had been performed.'

'He is fainting!' said one of his messmates; 'quick! some water!' The steward immediately hurried to the topman with the basin.

Cuticle took the topman by the wrist, and feeling it a while, observed, 'Don't be alarmed, men,' addressing the two messmates; 'he'll recover presently; this fainting very generally takes place.' And he stood for a moment, tranquilly eyeing the patient.

Now the Surgeon of the Fleet and the topman presented a spectacle which, to a reflecting mind, was better than a churchyard sermon on the mortality of man.

Here was a sailor, who, four days previous, had stood erect—a pillar of life—with an arm like a royal-mast, and a thigh like a windlass. But the slightest conceivable finger-touch of a bit of crooked trigger had eventuated in stretching him out, more helpless than an hour-old babe, with a blasted thigh, utterly drained of its brawn. And who was it that now stood over him like a superior being, and, as if clothed himself with the attributes of immortality, indifferently discoursed of carving up his broken flesh, and thus piecing out his abbreviated days? Who was it, that, in capacity of Surgeon, seemed enacting the part of a Regenerator of life? The withered, shrunken, one-eyed, toothless, hairless Cuticle; with a trunk half dead—a *memento mori* to behold!

And while, in those soul-sinking and panic-striking premonitions of speedy death which almost invariably accompany a severe gun-shot wound, even with the most intrepid spirits; while thus drooping and dying, this once robust topman's eye was now waning in his head like a Lapland moon being eclipsed in clouds—Cuticle, who for years had still lived in his withered tabernacle of a body—Cuticle, no doubt sharing in the common self-delusion of old age—Cuticle must have felt his hold of life as secure as the grim hug of a grizzly bear. Verily, Life is more awful than Death; and let no man, though his live heart beat in him like a cannon—let him not hug his life to himself; for, in the predestinated necessities of things, that bounding life of his is not a whit more secure than the life of a man on his death-bed. To-day we inhale the air with expanding lungs, and life runs through us like a thousand Niles; but to-morrow we may collapse in death, and all our veins be dry as the brook Kedron in a drought.

'And now, young gentlemen,' said Cuticle, turning to the assistant surgeons, 'while the patient is coming to, permit me to describe to you the highly interesting operation I am about to perform.'

'Mr. Surgeon of the Fleet,' said Surgeon Bandage, 'if you are about to lecture, permit me to present you with your teeth; they will make your discourse more readily understood.' And so saying, Bandage, with a bow, placed the two semicircles of ivory into Cuticle's hands.

'Thank you, Surgeon Bandage,' said Cuticle, and slipped the ivory into its place.

'In the first place, now, young gentlemen, let me direct your attention to the excellent preparation before you. I have had it unpacked from its case, and set up here from my stateroom, where it occupies the spare berth; and all this for your express benefit, young gentlemen. This skeleton I procured in person from the Hunterian Department of the Royal College of Surgeons in London. It is a masterpiece of art. But we have no time to examine it now. Delicacy forbids that I should amplify at a juncture like this'—casting an almost benignant glance toward the patient, now beginning to open his eyes; 'but let me point out to you upon this thigh-bone'—disengaging it from the skeleton, with a gentle twist—'the precise place where I propose to perform the operation. *Here*, young gentlemen, *here* is the place. You perceive it is very near the point of articulation with the trunk.'

'Yes,' interposed Surgeon Wedge, rising on his toes, 'yes, young gentlemen, the point of articulation with the *acetabulum* of the *os innominatum*.'

'Where's your "Bell on Bones," Dick?' whispered one of the assistants to the student next him. 'Wedge has been spending the whole morning over it, getting out the hard names.'

'Surgeon Wedge,' said Cuticle, looking round severely, 'we will dispense with your commentaries, if you please, at present. Now, young gentlemen, you cannot but perceive, that the point of operation being so near the trunk and the vitals, it becomes an unusually beautiful one, demanding a steady hand and a true eye; and, after all, the patient may die under my hands.'

'Quick, steward! water, water; he's fainting again!' cried the two messmates.

'Don't be alarmed for your comrade, men,' said Cuticle, turning round. 'I tell you it is not an uncommon thing for the patient to betray some emotion upon these occasions—most usually manifested by swooning; it is quite natural it should be so. But we must not delay the operation. Steward, that knife—no, the next one—there, that's it. He is coming to, I think'—feeling the topman's wrist. 'Are you all ready, sir?'

This last observation was addressed to one of the *Neversink's* assistant surgeons, a tall, lank, cadaverous young man, arrayed in a sort of shroud of white canvas, pinned about his throat, and completely enveloping his person. He was seated on a match-tub—the skeleton swinging near his head —at the foot of the table, in readiness to grasp the limb, as when a plank is being severed by a carpenter and his apprentice.

'The sponges, steward,' said Cuticle, for the last time taking out his teeth, and drawing up his shirt sleeve still further. Then, taking the patient by the wrist, 'Stand by, now, you messmates; keep hold of his arms; pin him down. Steward, put your hand on the artery; I shall commence as soon as his pulse begins to—*now, now!*' Letting fall the wrist, feeling the thigh carefully, and bowing over it an instant, he drew the fatal knife unerringly across the flesh. As it first touched the part, the row of surgeons simultaneously dropped their eyes to the watches in their hands, while the patient lay, with eyes horribly distended, in a kind of waking trance. Not a breath was heard; but as the quivering flesh parted in a long, lingering gash, a spring of blood welled up between the living walls of the wound, and two thick streams, in opposite directions, coursed down the thigh. The sponges were instantly dipped in the purple pool; every face present was pinched to a point with suspense; the limb writhed; the man shrieked; his messmates pinioned him; while round and round the leg went the unpitying cut.

'The saw!' said Cuticle.

Instantly it was in his hand.

Full of the operation, he was about to apply it, when, looking up, and turning to the assistant surgeons, he said, 'Would any of you young gentlemen like to apply the saw? A splendid subject!'

Several volunteered; when, selecting one, Cuticle surrendered the instrument to him, saying, 'Don't be hurried, now; be steady.'

While the rest of the assistants looked upon their comrade with glances of envy, he went rather timidly to work; and Cuticle, who was earnestly regarding him, suddenly snatched the saw from his hand. 'Away, butcher! you disgrace the profession. Look at *me!*'

For a few moments the thrilling rasping sound was heard; and then the topman seemed parted in twain at the hip, as the leg slowly slid into the arms of the pale, gaunt man in the shroud, who at once made away with it, and tucked it out of sight under one of the guns.

'Surgeon Sawyer,' now said Cuticle, courteously turning to the surgeon of the *Buccaneer*, 'would you like to take up the arteries? They are quite at your service, sir.'

'Do, Sawyer; be prevailed upon,' said Surgeon Bandage.

Sawyer complied; and while, with some modesty, he was conducting the operation, Cuticle, turning to the row of assistants, said, 'Young gentlemen, we will now proceed with our illustration. Hand me that bone, steward.' And taking the thighbone in his still bloody hands, and holding it conspicuously before his auditors, the Surgeon of the Fleet began:

'Young gentlemen, you will perceive that precisely at this spot—*here*—to which I previously directed your attention—at the corresponding spot precisely—the operation has been performed. About here, young gentlemen, *here*'—lifting his hand some inches from the bone—'about *here* the great artery was. But you noticed that I did not use the tourniquet; I never do. The forefinger of my steward is far better than a tourniquet, being so much more manageable, and leaving the smaller veins uncompressed. But I have been told, young gentlemen, that a certain Seignior Seignioroni, a surgeon of Seville, has recently invented an admirable substitute for the clumsy, old-fashioned tourniquet. As I understand it, is is something like a pair of *calipers*, working with a small Archimedes screw—a very clever invention, according to all accounts. For the padded points at the end of the arches'—arching his forefinger and thumb—'can be so worked as to approximate in such a way, as to—but you don't attend to me, young gentlemen,' he added, all at once starting.

Being more interested in the active proceedings of Surgeon Sawyer, who was now threading a needle to sew up the overlapping of the stump, the young gentlemen had not scrupled to turn away their attention altogether from the lecturer.

A few moments more, and the topman, in a swoon, was removed below into the sick-bay. As the curtain settled again after the patient had disappeared, Cuticle, still holding the thighbone of the skeleton in his ensanguined hands, proceeded with his remarks upon it; and having concluded them, added, 'Now, young gentlemen, not the least interesting consequence of this operation will be the finding of the ball, which, in case of nonamputation, might have long eluded the most careful search. That ball, young gentlemen, must have taken a most circuitous route. Nor, in cases where the direction is oblique, is this at all unusual. Indeed, the learned Henner gives us a most remarkable—I had almost said an incredible—case of a soldier's neck, where the bullet, entering at the part called Adam's Apple——'

'Yes,' said Surgeon Wedge, elevating himself, 'the *pomum Adami*.'

'Entering the point called *Adam's Apple*,' continued Cuticle, severely emphasizing the last two words, 'ran completely round the neck, and, emerging at the same hole it had entered, shot the next man in the ranks. It was afterward extracted, says Henner, from the second man, and pieces of the other's skin were found adhering to it. But examples of foreign substances being received into the body with a ball, young gentlemen, are frequently observed. Being attached to a United States ship at the time, I happened to be near the spot of the battle of Ayacucho, in Peru. The day after the action, I saw in the barracks of the wounded a trooper, who having been severely injured in the brain, went crazy, and, with his own holster-pistol, committed suicide in the hospital. The ball drove inward a portion of his woolen nightcap——'

'In the form of a *cul-de-sac*, doubtless,' said the undaunted Wedge.

'For once, Surgeon Wedge, you use the only term that can be employed; and let me avail myself of this opportunity to say to you, young gentlemen, that a man of true science'—expanding his shallow chest a little—'uses but few hard words, and those only when none other will answer his purpose; whereas the smatterer in science'—slightly glancing toward Wedge—'thinks, that by mouthing hard words, he proves that he understands hard things. Let this sink deep in your minds, young gentlemen; and, Surgeon Wedge'—with a stiff bow—'permit me to submit the reflection to yourself. Well, young gentlemen, the bullet was afterward extracted by pulling upon the external parts of the *cul-de-sac*—a simple, but exceedingly beautiful operation. There is a fine example, somewhat similar, related in Guthrie; but, of course, you must have met with it, in so well-known a work as his Treatise upon Gun-shot Wounds. When, upward of twenty years ago, I was with Lord Cochrane, then admiral of the fleets of this very country'—pointing shoreward, out of a port-hole—'a sailor of the vessel to which I was attached, during the blockade of Bahia, had his leg——' But by this time the fidgets had completely taken possession of his auditors, especially of the senior surgeons; and turning upon them abruptly, he added, 'But I will not detain you longer, gentlemen'—turning round upon all the surgeons—'your dinners must be waiting you on board your respective ships. But, Surgeon Sawyer, perhaps you may desire to wash your hands before you go. There is the basin, sir; you will find a clean towel on the rammer. For myself, I seldom use them'—taking out his handkerchief. 'I must leave you now, gentlemen,'—bowing. 'To-morrow, at ten, the limb will be upon the table, and I shall be happy to see you all upon the occasion. Who's there?' turning to the curtain, which then rustled.

'Please, sir,' said the steward, entering, 'the patient is dead.'

'The body, also, gentlemen, at ten precisely,' said Cuticle, once more turning round upon his guests. 'I predicted that the operation might prove fatal; he was very much run down. Good morning'; and Cuticle departed.

'He does not, surely, mean to touch the body?' exclaimed Surgeon Sawyer, with much excitement.

'Oh, no!' said Patella, 'that's only his way; he means, doubtless, that it may be inspected previous to being taken ashore for burial.'

The assemblage of gold-laced surgeons now ascended to the quarter-deck; the second cutter was called away by the bugler, and, one by one, they were dropped aboard of their respective ships.

The following evening the messmates of the topman rowed his remains ashore, and buried them in the ever-vernal Protestant cemetery, hard by the Beach of the Flamingoes, in plain sight from the bay.

Emily Dickinson (1830–1886)

Though Emily Dickinson spent her life as an often unhappy recluse in Amherst, Massachusetts, she did not lose her wry sense of humor. The brilliant little poems published after her death present a fusion of serious theme and playful treatment such as few American poets but the Puritans and Walt Whitman had yet compounded. From girlhood on Miss Dickinson was apparently steeped in the varieties of humor popular in her day, that of the "frontier" as well as that of New England. Before creating the poems which brought her posthumous fame, she wrote humorous prose and verse revealing considerable verbal skill; burlesque sermon, tall tale, and parody were among the forms with which she experimented. The flashes of wit which vivify her mature poetry were characteristic of her speech and letters too. Deeply introspective, concerned with large matters such as death and immortality, Emily Dickinson was also an acute observer of man and nature. But if her vision was profound and wide-ranging, it was also exultantly merry. Her poems seem to be patterned not only upon Protestant hymns but upon nursery rhymes as well; their deceptively simple stanzas, language, and imagery present rich and delightful incongruities.

TEXT: *The Poems of Emily Dickinson*, ed. Thomas H. Johnson, Cambridge, Mass., 1955. COMMENTARY: George F. Whicher, *This Was a Poet: A Critical Biography of Emily Dickinson*, New York, 1938; Charles R. Anderson, *Emily Dickinson's Poetry*, New York, 1960.

214

I taste a liquor never brewed–
From Tankards scooped in Pearl–
Not all the Vats upon the Rhine
Yield such an Alcohol!

Inebriate of Air–am I–
And Debauchee of Dew–
Reeling–thro endless summer days–
From inns of Molten Blue–

When "Landlords" turn the drunken Bee
Out of the Foxglove's door–
When Butterflies–renounce their "drams"–
I shall but drink the more!

Till Seraphs swing their snowy Hats–
And Saints–to windows run–
To see the little Tippler
Leaning against the–Sun–

288

I'm Nobody! Who are you?
Are you–Nobody–too?
Then there's a pair of us!
Dont tell! they'd banish us–you know!

How dreary–to be–Somebody!
How public–like a Frog–
To tell your name–the livelong June
To an admiring Bog!

520

I started Early–Took my Dog–
And visited the Sea–
The Mermaids in the Basement
Came out to look at me–

And Frigates–in the Upper Floor
Extended Hempen Hands–
Presuming Me to be a Mouse–
Aground–upon the Sands–

But no Man moved Me–till the Tide
Went past my simple Shoe–
And past my Apron–and my Belt
And past my Boddice–too–

And made as He would eat me up–
As wholly as a Dew
Upon a Dandelion's Sleeve–
And then–I started–too–

And He–He followed–close behind–
I felt His Silver Heel
Upon my Ancle–Then my Shoes
Would overflow with Pearl–

Until We met the Solid Town–
No One He seemed to know–
And bowing–with a Mighty look–
At me–The Sea withdrew–

712

Because I could not stop for Death–
He kindly stopped for me–
The Carriage held but just Ourselves–
And Immortality.

We slowly drove–He knew no haste
And I had put away
My labor and my leisure too,
For His Civility–

We passed the School, where Children strove
At Recess–in the Ring–
We passed the Fields of Gazing Grain–
We passed the Setting Sun–

Or rather–He passed Us–
The Dews drew quivering and chill–
For only Gossamer, my Gown–
My Tippet–only Tulle–

We paused before a House that seemed
A Swelling of the Ground–
The Roof was scarcely visible–
The Cornice–in the Ground–

Since then–'tis Centuries–and yet
Feels shorter than the Day
I first surmised the Horses Heads
Were toward Eternity–

1207

He preached upon "Breadth" till it argued him narrow–
The Broad are too broad to define
And of "Truth" until it proclaimed him a Liar–
The Truth never flaunted a Sign–

Simplicity fled from his counterfeit presence
As Gold the Pyrites would shun–
What confusion would cover the innocent Jesus
To meet so enabled a Man!

Charles Farrar Browne (1834–1867)

Known to most readers as "Artemus Ward," Charles Farrar Browne was one of the "literary comedians" providing the mass of the American people with laughs during the second half of the nineteenth century. The best of these writers—Browne, David Ross Locke ("Petroleum V. Nasby"), and Samuel L. Clemens ("Mark Twain")—began their careers as small-town newspaper journalists and printers. They steeped themselves in humor regularly clipped from exchange newspapers in order to fill their own columns. They were familiar with the popular humor of almanac and stage comedy. As soon as they had written and printed several comic pieces which attracted favorable attention, the erstwhile amateurs assumed the role of professional humorist. Earlier humorous writers had interwoven humor with other effects and were not professional humorists. The professional humorist was a new cultural phenomenon. He aimed only to amuse and the means had to be unambiguous. Therefore, he tended to use humorous gambits which had already successfully aroused his audience's laughter. The resultant guaranteed humor was generally superficial, repetitive, and lucrative. Since the professional humorist was essentially a broad comic rather than a self-conscious literary artist, he easily assumed a comic folk guise which obliterated his own identity as an artist. Earlier humorous rustics and villagers had spoken in a crude and ungrammatical but also fresh and vivid language. The literary comedian strove to purvey a humor of absurdity, anticlimax, verbal wit, and realistic grammatical misconstruction, but his skill and imagination often flagged and he soon specialized in a corrupted folk language with chaotic misspellings whose limited humorous appeal was merely visual. The gulf between the literary humorist at whose work one laughs and the comic actor ("phunny phellow") at whose personal performance one also laughs was destroyed by the literary comedian, who inevitably mounted the stage as a comic "lecturer." The literary vaudevillians were highly popular and mistakenly assumed to be significant creators of American literary humor.

Browne's comic mask resembled the itinerant showman who had appeared in Hawthorne's "Ethan Brand" and would reappear in Mark Twain's *Huckleberry Finn*. Shrewd, ignorant Artemus Ward travelled from village to village with a wagon-load of live animals and diverse waxwork figures including George Washington, John Bunyan, and several "celebrated piruts & murders." The ironic contrast between Artemus Ward's professedly "moral" purposes and the greedy self-interest he revealed in his proud, illiterate accounts was and still is a source of some amusement. But the moral satire was "jenial" rather than searching;

the character of Artemus Ward was never developed and the action was never complicated. As a moral commentator on American follies, Artemus Ward reflected the dominant opinion of his age, lightly satirizing minority fads such as free love, Shakerism, and spiritualism; when the majority favored abolition of slavery he shifted from ridicule to eulogy of the Negro. Even Browne's effectively absurd mockeries of sentimental fiction, written in conventional English, were not amusing lessons to society but rather complacent confirmations of prevalent taste. Browne and Artemus Ward are no longer read much. This seems to be the inevitable fate of the literary comedian. His successors exploit the advantage of familiarity with the popular taste, risibility, and topical concerns of their times in the same way that the forgotten literary comedian capitalized on the superficialities of his own vanished age.

TEXT: *Artemus Ward: His Book*, New York, 1862.

AMONG THE FREE LOVERS *

Some years ago I pitched my tent and onfurled my banner to the breeze, in Berlin Hites, Ohio. I had hearn that Berlin Hites was ockepied by a extensive seck called Free Lovers, who beleeved in affinertys and sich, goin back on their domestic ties without no hesitation whatsomever. They was likewise spirit rappers and high presher reformers on gineral principles. If I can improve these 'ere misgided peple by showin them my onparalleld show at the usual low price of admitants, methunk, I shall not hav lived in vane! But bitterly did I cuss the day I ever sot foot in the retchid place. I sot up my tent in a field near the Love Cure, as they called it, and bimeby the free lovers begun for to congregate around the door. A ornreer set I have never sawn. The men's faces was all covered with hare and they lookt half-starved to deth. They didn't wear no weskuts for the purpuss (as they sed) of allowin the free air of hevun to blow onto their boozums. Their pockets was filled with tracks and pamplits and they was bare-footed. They sed the Postles didn't wear boots, & why should they? That was their stile of argyment. The wimin was wuss than the men. They wore trowsis, short gownds, straw hats with green ribbins, and all carried bloo cotton unbrellers.

Presently a perfeckly orful lookin female presented herself at the door. Her gownd was skanderlusly short and her trowsis was shameful to behold.

She eyed me over very sharp, and then startin back she sed, in a wild voice:

---

* Some queer people, calling themselves "Free Lovers," and possessing very original ideas about life and morality established themselves at Berlin Heights, in Ohio, a few years since. Public opinion was resistlessly against them, however, and the association was soon disbanded.

"Ah, can it be?"

"Which?" sed I.

"Yes, 'tis troo, O 'tis troo!"

"15 cents, marm," I anserd.

She bust out a cryin & sed:

"And so I hav found you at larst—at larst, O at larst!"

"Yes," I anserd, "you have found me at larst, and you would have found me at fust, if you had cum sooner."

She grabd me vilently by the coat collar, and brandishin her umbreller wildly round, exclaimed:

"Air you a man?"

Sez I, "I think I air, but if you doubt it, you can address Mrs. A. Ward, Baldinsville, Injianny, postage pade, & she will probly giv you the desired informashun."

"Then thou ist what the cold world calls marrid?"

"Madam, I istest!"

The exsentric female then clutched me franticly by the arm and hollerd:

"You air mine, O you air mine!"

"Scacely," I sed, endeverin to git loose from her. But she clung to me and sed:

"You air my Affinerty!"

"What upon arth is that?" I shouted.

"Dost thou not know?"

"No, I dostent!"

"Listen man, & I'll tell ye!" sed the strange female; "for years I hav yearned for thee. I knowd thou wast in the world, sumwhares, tho I didn't know whare. My hart sed he would cum and I took courage. He *has* cum—he's here—you air him—you air my Affinerty! O 'tis too mutch! too mutch!" and she sobbed agin.

"Yes," I anserd, "I think it is a darn site too mutch!"

"Hast thou not yearned for me?" she yelled, ringin her hands like a female play acter.

"Not a yearn!" I bellerd at the top of my voice, throwin her away from me.

The free lovers who was standin round obsarvin the scene commenst for to holler "shame!" "beast," etsettery, etsettery.

I was very mutch riled, and fortifyin myself with a spare tent stake, I addrest them as follers: "You pussylanermus critters, go way from me and take this retchid woman with you. I'm a law-abidin man, and bleeve in good, old-fashioned institutions. I am marrid & my orfsprings resemble me if I am a showman! I think your Affinity bizniss is cussed noncents, besides bein outrajusly wicked. Why don't you behave desunt like other folks? Go to work and earn a honist livin and not stay round here in this lazy, shiftless way, pizenin the moral atmosphere with your pestifrous idees! You wimin folks go back to your lawful husbands if you've got any, and take orf them skanderlous gownds and trowsis, and dress respectful like other wimin. You men folks, cut orf them pirattercal whiskers, burn up them infurnel pamplits, put sum weskuts on, go to work choppin wood, splittin fence rales, or tillin the sile. I pored 4th my indignashun in this way till I got out of breth, when I stopt. I shant go to Berlin Hites agin, not if I live to be as old as Methooseler.

David Ross Locke (1833–1888)

The acrid satire of literary comedian David Ross Locke was so powerful that Lincoln's secretary of the treasury ascribed the winning of the
Civil War to the army, the navy, and Locke's "Petroleum Vesuvius
Nasby" letters. Locke, along with Artemus Ward, also provided Lincoln
with comic relief before, during, and after cabinet meetings and other
affairs of state. A copy of *The Nasby Papers*, Locke's first collection,
found on Lincoln's desk after his assassination, showed that he had in-
advertently blotted a letter on one of the pages containing the account of
Nasby's visit with the President. No well-known Southern satirist other
than George Washington Harris was either as caustic or as mirthful as
Locke. The Copperhead Democrat he created as a comic mask is one of
the greatest unredeemable scoundrels in American humorous literature:
a vicious, corrupt, Scripture-quoting Ohioan who betrayed the Northern
cause and ironically sullied the Southern cause he championed. Petroleum
V. Nasby deserted from both armies, ordained himself as a minister,
swindled his friends, tormented the weak, sought unrelentingly for whiskey, money, and political office; his only virtue was his insistence upon
wearing clean shirts even if he had to steal them.

TEXT: *The Nasby Papers: Letters and Sermons*, Indianapolis, Ind., 1864.

SHOWS WHY HE SHOULD NOT BE DRAFTED

August 6, 1862

I see in the papers last nite, that the Government hez institooted a
draft, and that in a few weeks, sum hunderds uv thousands uv peeseable
citizens will be dragged to the tented feeld. I know not wat uthers may
do, but ez fer me, I can't go. Upon a rigid eggsaminashen uv my fizzlekle
man, I find it wood be wus ner madnis fer me 2 undertake a campane, to-
wit:

1. I'm bald-headid, and hev bin obliged to ware a wig these 22 yeres.
2. I hev dandruff in wat scanty hair still hangs around my venerable
temples.
3. I hev a chronic katarr.
4. I hev lost, sence Stanton's order to draft, the use uv wun eye entirely, and hev cronic inflammashen in the other.
5. My teeth is all unsound, my palit aint eggsactly rite, and I hev hed
bronkeetis 31 yeres last Joon. At present I hev a koff, the paroxisms uv
wich is friteful 2 behold.

6. I'm holler-chestid, am short-winded, and hev alluz hed panes in my back and side.

7. I am afflictid with kronic diarrear and kostivniss. The money I hev paid fer Jayneses karminnytiv balsam and pills wood astonish almost ennybody.

8. I am rupcherd in 9 places, and am entirely enveloped with trusses.

9. I hev verrykose vanes, hev a white swellin on wun leg and a fever sore on the uther—also wun leg is shorter than tother, though I handle it so expert that noboddy never noticed it.

10. I hev korns and bunyons on both feet, wich wood prevent me from marchin.

I dont suppose that my political opinions, wich are ferninst the prossekooshn uv this unconstooshnel war, wood hev any wate with a draftin orfiser, but the above reesons why I cant go, will, I maik no doubt, be suffishent.

Petroleum V. *Nasby*

TRIES AN EXPERIMENT

Church uv the Slawterd Innocents,⎫
(*Lait St. Valandigum,*) Dec. 25, '63⎬

Mankind is the most perverse and onrezonable beins uv the human family. Wile they assent 2 a principple, they never will put it into practis ef it bares hard onto em ez indivijjles, to-wit:

I had bin for sevral weeks deliverin a coarse uv lekters on the divinnity uv slaivry. I argood that the institooshn wuz based upon the infeeriority uv wun man 2 another—that it wuz not only a wise but a bootiful pervision uv nacher that the strong shood hev charge uv the week, a guidin, and protektin and a workin uv em. The idee plezed my congregashen vastly, and fifteen or twenty uv the strongest perposed that it shood be put into praktis, jest 2 show the world that the grate doctrine cood be carried out jest as well in the North as in the South. To wich I assented to-wunst, and at the next biznis meetin, the follerin plan wuz adoptid: The members uv the congregashen shood try ther strength, and them as cood lift 600 shood own and possess, in fee simple, all them ez coodent.

The trial wuz hed, the divizshen maid, and I wuz happy at bein the umble instrooment uv plantin the grate institooshen on Northrin sile.

But alas, owin 2 the perversity uv the human mind, aforesaid, it dident work. Old John Podhammer razed his 600 with the gratest eeze, wile Bill Sniffles, who wuz a workin fer him fer 12 dolers a munth coodent fetch it. Podhammer went over to Bill's cabin, the next mornin, and sez he, "Wilyum, frum this time hentz4th, and furever yoo air my man. As all a slaiv has is his masters, the 18 dolers I owe yoo, or that I did owe yoo afore this blessid system wuz establisht, I shel kepe, and as yoo hev moar furnytoor than befits yoor lowly condishen, I will send a teem over to-morrer, and taik yer bewrow and stand, and bedstids up to my house, and—"

At this junctur in cums Mrs. Sniffles, who kin lift 600 with old Pod-hammer on the top uv it, and it wuz no time afore she diskivered wat his biznis wuz. She turnd red in the fais. Sed she:

"Yoor goin to take my furnytoor?"

"Certingly."

"And we air yoor slaivs?"

"Uv coarse."

"And yoo kin sell my children?"

"Naterally."

"And yoo kin maik me yoor conkebine?"

"Ef I wish?"

"Yoo old beest!" shreckt the infooriated femail chattel, forgettin her normal condishn, "yoo sell my babies, yoo taik my furnytoor, drat ye, I'll giv ye sum uv it now," whereupon she hurled a chare, wich laid him prostrait on the flore, wen she pickt him up and flung him out the dore.

It did not end here: Podhammer hed in his hand a patch-work coverlid, wich he thot he wood taik with him, and wen he cum to he walked off with it, whereupon Mrs. Sniffles hed him took up on a charge uv steelin, and he wuz actooaly tride, found gilty, and sent to jail fer 30 daze. How kin we establish Dimocratic institooshens, wen the corts won't recognize the laws of nacher. The experiment, for the present, hez the apperentz of a failyer.

Petroleum V. Nasby,
Paster uv sed Church, in charge

Mark Twain (1835–1910)

The name "Mark Twain" epitomizes American humor throughout the world. In actuality, of course, American humor is much too complex and diversified for any one writer to be fully representative of it. Yet Samuel L. Clemens (or Mark Twain, the pseudonym by which the world knows him) certainly encompassed more elements of popular nineteenth-century humor than did any other American writer. On this ground Mark Twain is properly honored as a representative figure. Born in Hannibal, Missouri, a village still harboring memories of the frontier, he began to write humor as a self-taught newspaperman. In later years his journalistic career took him to other parts of the United States—the South, the Far West, the East—and abroad to the South Seas, Europe, and the Near East. Writing primarily to please a popular audience and familiar with the work of his popular predecessors and contemporaries, Mark Twain perpetuated many existing humorous traditions and devices. "The Blue-Jay Yarn," for example, is in the tradition of the tall tale and the animal fable. Some scenes and characters in George Washington Harris's Sut Lovingood yarns were to reappear in *The Adventures of Tom Sawyer* (1876). But Mark Twain did more than pillage and refine existing literary resources. Gifted with an unusually sensitive ear for the nuances and imagery of the American vernacular language, he became a self-conscious artist whose *Adventures of Huckleberry Finn* (1885), to single out only one work, would influence such diverse writers as Sherwood Anderson, T. S. Eliot, Ernest Hemingway, and William Faulkner. As a mind, furthermore, Mark Twain merits praise for the critical temper which invigorated his satiric and ironic visions of man and society. Though he was attracted to the simple faith in progress of his age, such caustic masterpieces as "The Man That Corrupted Hadleyburg" (1900) and *Huckleberry Finn* reveal that for Mark Twain the art of humor provided opportunity to explore not only that which gave immediate pleasure but also the most disagreeable of realities.

TEXT: "The Blue-Jay Yarn," A *Tramp Abroad*, Hartford, Conn., 1880; "Frescoes from the Past," *Life on the Mississippi*, Boston, Mass., 1883. COMMENTARY: Gladys C. Bellamy, *Mark Twain as Literary Artist*, Norman, Okla., 1950; Walter Blair, *Mark Twain & Huck Finn*, Berkeley, Calif., 1960; Bernard DeVoto, *Mark Twain's America*, Boston, Mass., 1932; Kenneth S. Lynn, *Mark Twain and Southwestern Humor*, Boston, Mass., 1960.

THE BLUE-JAY YARN

Animals talk to each other, of course. There can be no question about that; but I suppose there are very few people who can understand them. I never knew but one man who could. I knew he could, however, because he told me so himself. He was a middle-aged, simple-hearted miner who had lived in a lonely corner of California, among the woods and mountains, a good many years, and had studied the ways of his only neighbors, the beasts and the birds, until he believed he could accurately translate any remark which they made. This was Jim Baker. According to Jim Baker, some animals have only a limited education, and use only very simple words, and scarcely ever a comparison or a flowery figure; whereas, certain other animals have a large vocabulary, a fine command of language and a ready and fluent delivery; consequently these latter talk a great deal; they like it; they are conscious of their talent, and they enjoy "showing off." Baker said, that after long and careful observation, he had come to the conclusion that the blue-jays were the best talkers he had found among birds and beasts. Said he:—

"There's more *to* a blue-jay than any other creature. He has got more moods, and more different kinds of feelings than other creatures; and mind you, whatever a blue-jay feels, he can put into language. And no mere commonplace language, either, but rattling, out-and-out booktalk —and bristling with metaphor, too—just bristling! And as for command of language—why *you* never see a blue-jay get stuck for a word. No man ever did. They just boil out of him! And another thing: I've noticed a good deal, and there's no bird, or cow, or anything that uses as good grammar as a blue-jay. You may say a cat uses good grammar. Well, a cat does—but you let a cat get excited, once; you let a cat get to pulling fur with another cat on a shed, nights, and you'll hear grammar that will give you the lockjaw. Ignorant people think it's the *noise* which fighting cats make that is so aggravating, but it ain't so; it's the sickening grammar they use. Now I've never heard a jay use bad grammar but very seldom; and when they do, they are as ashamed as a human; they shut right down and leave.

"You may call a jay a bird. Well, so he is, in a measure—because he's got feathers on him, and don't belong to no church, perhaps; but otherwise he is just as much a human as you be. And I'll tell you for why. A jay's gifts, and instincts, and feelings, and interests, cover the whole ground. A jay hasn't got any more principle than a Congressman. A jay will lie, a jay will steal, a jay will deceive, a jay will betray; and four times out of five, a jay will go back on his solemnest promise. The sacredness of an obligation is a thing which you can't cram into no blue-jay's head. Now on top of all this, there's another thing: a jay can out-swear any gentleman in the mines. You think a cat can swear. Well, a cat can; but you give a blue-jay a subject that calls for his reserve-powers, and where is your cat? Don't talk to *me*—I know too much about this thing. And there's yet another thing: in the one little particular of scolding—just good, clean, out-and-out scolding—a blue-jay can lay over anything, human or divine. Yes, sir, a jay is everything that a man is. A jay can cry, a jay can laugh, a jay can feel shame, a jay can reason and plan and discuss, a jay likes gossip and scandal, a jay has got a sense of humor, a jay knows when he is an ass just as well as you do—maybe better. If a jay ain't human, he better take in his sign, that's all. Now I'm going to tell you a perfectly true fact about some blue-jays.

"When I first begun to understand jay language correctly, there was a little incident happened here. Seven years ago, the last man in this region but me, moved away. There stands his house,—been empty ever since; a long house, with a plank roof—just one big room, and no more; no ceiling—nothing between the rafters and the floor. Well, one Sunday morning I was sitting out here in front of my cabin, with my cat, taking the sun, and looking at the blue hills, and listening to the leaves rustling so lonely in the trees, and thinking of the home away yonder in the States, that I hadn't heard from in thirteen years, when a blue jay lit on that house, with an acorn in his mouth, and says, 'Hello, I reckon I've struck something.' When he spoke, the acorn dropped out of his mouth and rolled down the roof, of course, but he didn't care; his mind was all on the thing he had struck. It was a knot-hole in the roof. He cocked his head to one side, shut one eye and put the other one to the hole, like a 'possum looking down a jug; then he glanced up with his bright eyes, gave a wink or two with his wings—which signifies gratification, you understand,—and says, 'It looks like a hole, it's located like a hole,—blamed if I don't believe it *is* a hole!'

"Then he cocked his head down and took another look; he glances up perfectly joyful, this time; winks his wings and his tail both, and says, 'O, no, this ain't no fat thing, I reckon! If I ain't in luck!—why it's a perfectly elegant hole!' So he flew down and got that acorn, and fetched it up and dropped it in, and was just tilting his head back, with the heavenliest smile on his face, when all of a sudden he was paralyzed into a listening attitude and that smile faded gradually out of his countenance like breath off'n a razor, and the queerest look of surprise took its place. Then he says, 'Why I didn't hear it fall!' He cocked his eye at the hole again, and took a long look; raised up and shook his head; stepped around to the other side of the hole and took another look from that side; shook his head again. He studied a while, then he just went into the details—walked round and round the hole and spied into it from every point of the compass. No use. Now he took a thinking attitude on the comb of the roof and scratched the back of his head with his right foot a minute, and finally says, 'Well, it's too many for *me*, that's certain; must be a mighty long hole; however, I ain't got no time to fool around here, I got to 'tend to business; I reckon it's all right—chance it, anyway.'

"So he flew off and fetched another acorn and dropped it in, and tried to flirt his eye to the hole quick enough to see what become of it, but he was too late. He held his eye there as much as a minute; then he raised up and sighed, and says, 'Consound it, I don't seem to understand this thing, no way; however, I'll tackle her again.' He fetched another acorn, and done his level best to see what become of it, but he couldn't. He says, 'Well, I never struck no such a hole as this, before; I'm of the opinion it's a totally new kind of a hole.' Then he begun to get mad. He held in for a spell, walking up and down the comb of the roof and shaking his head and muttering to himself; but his feelings got the upper hand of him, presently, and he broke loose and cussed himself black in the face. I never see a bird take on so about a little thing. When he got through he walks to the hole and looks in again for half a minute; then he says, 'Well, you're a long hole, and a deep hole, and a mighty singular hole altogether—but I've started in to fill you, and I'm d——d if I *don't* fill you, if it takes a hundred years!'

"And with that, away he went. You never see a bird work so since you was born. He laid into his work like a nigger, and the way he hove acorns into that hole for about two hours and a half was one of the most exciting and astonishing spectacles I ever struck. He never stopped to take a look any more—he just hove 'em in and went for more. Well at last he could hardly flop his wings, he was so tuckered out. He comes a-drooping down, once more, sweating like an ice-pitcher, drops his acorn in and says, 'Now I guess I've got the bulge on you by this time!' So he bent down for a look. If you'll believe me, when his head come up again he was just pale with rage. He says, 'I've shoveled acorns enough in there to keep the family thirty years, and if I can see a sign of one of 'em I wish I may land in a museum with a belly full of sawdust in two minutes!'

"He just had strength enough to crawl up on to the comb and lean his back agin the chimbly, and then he collected his impressions and begun to free his mind. I see in a second that what I had mistook for profanity in the mines was only just the rudiments, as you may say.

"Another jay was going by, and heard him doing his devotions, and stops to inquire what was up. The sufferer told him the whole circumstances, and says, 'Now yonder's the hole, and if you don't believe me, go and look for yourself.' So this fellow went and looked, and comes back and says, 'How many did you say you put in there?' 'Not any less than two tons,' says the sufferer. The other jay went and looked again. He couldn't seem to make it out, so he raised a yell, and three more jays come. They all examined the hole, they all made the sufferer tell it over again, then they all discussed it, and got off as many leather-headed opinions about it as an average crowd of humans could have done.

"They called in more jays; then more and more, till pretty soon this whole region 'peared to have a blue flush about it. There must have been five thousand of them; and such another jawing and disputing and ripping and cussing, you never heard. Every jay in the whole lot put his eye to the hole and delivered a more chuckle-headed opinion about the mystery than the jay that went there before him. They examined the house all over, too. The door was standing half open, and at last one old jay happened to go and light on it and look in. Of course that knocked the mystery galley-west in a second. There lay the acorns, scattered all over the floor. He flopped his wings and raised a whoop. 'Come here!' he says, 'Come here, everybody; hang'd if this fool hasn't been trying to fill up a house with acorns!' They all came a-swooping down like a blue cloud, and as each fellow lit on the door and took a glance, the whole absurdity of the contract that that first jay had tackled hit him home and he fell over backwards suffocating with laughter, and the next jay took his place and done the same.

"Well, sir, they roosted around here on the house-top and the trees for an hour, and guffawed over that thing like human beings. It ain't any use to tell me a blue-jay hasn't got a sense of humor, because I know better. And memory, too. They brought jays here from all over the United States to look down that hole, every summer for three years. Other birds too. And they could all see the point, except an owl that come from Nova Scotia to visit the Yo Semite, and he took this thing in on his way back. He said he couldn't see anything funny in it. But then he was a good deal disappointed about Yo Semite, too."

FRESCOES FROM THE PAST

. . . . By way of illustrating keelboat talk and manners, and that now departed and hardly remembered raft life, I will throw in, in this place, a chapter from a book which I have been working at, by fits and starts, during the past five or six years, and may possibly finish in the course of five or six more. The book is a story which details some passages in the life of an ignorant village boy, Huck Finn, son of the town drunkard of my time out West, there. He has run away from his persecuting father, and from a persecuting good widow who wishes to make a nice, truth-telling, respectable boy of him; and with him a slave of the widow's has also escaped. They have found a fragment of a lumber-raft (it is high-water and dead-summer time), and are floating down the river by night, and hiding in the willows by day—bound for Cairo, whence the negro will seek freedom in the heart of the free states. But, in a fog, they pass Cairo without knowing it. By and by they begin to suspect the truth, and Huck Finn is persuaded to end the dismal suspense by swimming down to a huge raft which they have seen in the distance ahead of them, creeping aboard under cover of the darkness, and gathering the needed information by eavesdropping:

But you know a young person can't wait very well when he is impatient to find a thing out. We talked it over, and by and by Jim said it was such a black night, now, that it wouldn't be no risk to swim down to the big raft and crawl aboard and listen—they would talk about Cairo, because they would be calculating to go ashore there for a spree, maybe; or anyway they would send boats ashore to buy whisky or fresh meat or something. Jim had a wonderful level head, for a nigger: he could most always start a good plan when you wanted one.

I stood up and shook my rags off and jumped into the river, and struck out for the raft's light. By and by, when I got down nearly to her, I eased up and went slow and cautious. But everything was all right—nobody at the sweeps. So I swum down along the raft till I was most abreast the camp-fire in the middle, then I crawled aboard and inched along and got in among some bundles of shingles on the weather side of the fire. There was thirteen men there—they was the watch on deck of course. And a mighty rough-looking lot, too. They had a jug, and tin cups, and they kept the jug moving. One man was singing—roaring, you may say; and it wasn't a nice song—for a parlor, anyway. He roared through his nose, and strung out the last word of every line very long. When he was done they all fetched a kind of Injun war-whoop, and then another was sung. It begun:

> "There was a woman in our towdn,
> In our towdn did dwed'l [dwell],
> She loved her husband dear-i-lee,
> But another man twyste as wed'l.

> "Singing too, riloo, riloo, riloo,
> Ri-too, riloo, rilay—e,
> She loved her husband dear-i-lee,
> But another man twyste as wed'l."

And so on—fourteen verses. It was kind of poor, and when he was going to start on the next verse one of them said it was the tune the old cow died on; and another one said: "Oh, give us a rest!" And another one told him to take a walk. They made fun of him till he got mad and jumped up and begun to cuss the crowd, and said he could lam any thief in the lot.

They was all about to make a break for him, but the biggest man there jumped up and says:

"Set whar you are, gentlemen. Leave him to me; he's my meat."

Then he jumped up in the air three times, and cracked his heels together every time. He flung off a buckskin coat that was all hung with fringes, and says, "You lay thar tell the chawin-up's done"; and flung his hat down, which was all over ribbons, and says, "You lay thar tell his sufferin's is over."

Then he jumped up in the air and cracked his heels together again, and shouted out:

"Whoo-oop! I'm the old original iron-jawed, brass-mounted, copperbellied corpse-maker from the wilds of Arkansaw! Look at me! I'm the man they call Sudden Death and General Desolation! Sired by a hurricane, dam'd by an earthquake, half-brother to the cholera, nearly related to the smallpox on the mother's side! Look at me! I take nineteen alligators and a bar'l of whisky for breakfast when I'm in robust health, and a bushel of rattlesnakes and a dead body when I'm ailing. I split the everlasting rocks with my glance, and I squench the thunder when I speak! Whoo-oop! Stand back and give me room according to my strength! Blood's my natural drink, and the wails of the dying is music to my ear. Cast your eye on me, gentlemen! and lay low and hold your breath, for I'm 'bout to turn myself loose!"

All the time he was getting this off, he was shaking his head and looking fierce, and kind of swelling around in a little circle, tucking up his wristbands, and now and then straightening up and beating his breast with his fist, saying, "Look at me, gentlemen!" When he got through, he jumped up and cracked his heels together three times, and let off a roaring "Whoo-oop! I'm the bloodiest son of a wildcat that lives!"

Then the man that had started the row tilted his old slouch hat down over his right eye; then he bent stooping forward, with his back sagged and his south end sticking out far, and his fists a-shoving out and drawing in in front of him, and so went around in a little circle about three times, swelling himself up and breathing hard. Then he straightened, and jumped up and cracked his heels together three times before he lit again (that made them cheer), and he began to shout like this:

"Whoo-oop! bow your neck and spread, for the kingdom of sorrow's a-coming! Hold me down to the earth, for I feel my powers a-working! Whoo-oop! I'm a child of sin, *don't* let me get a start! Smoked glass, here, for all! Don't attempt to look at me with the naked eye, gentlemen! When I'm playful I use the meridians of longitude and parallels of latitude for a seine and drag the Atlantic Ocean for whales! I scratch my head with the lightning and purr myself to sleep with the thunder! When I'm cold, I bile the Gulf of Mexico and bathe in it; when I'm hot I fan myself with an equinoctial storm; when I'm thirsty I reach up and suck a cloud dry like a sponge; when I range the earth hungry, famine follows in my tracks! Whoo-oop! Bow your neck and spread! I put my hand on the sun's face and make it night in the earth; I bite a piece out of the moon and hurry the seasons; I shake myself and crumble the mountains! Contemplate me through leather—*don't* use the naked eye! I'm the man with a petrified heart and biler-iron bowels! The massacre of isolated communities is the pastime of my idle moments, the destruction of nationalities the serious business of my life! The boundless vastness of the great American desert is my enclosed property, and I bury my dead on my own premises!" He jumped up and cracked his heels together three times before he lit (they cheered him again), and as he come down he shouted out: "Whoo-oop! bow your neck and spread, for the Pet Child of Calamity's a-coming!"

Then the other one went to swelling around and blowing again—the first one—the one they called Bob; next, the Child of Calamity chipped in again, bigger than ever; then they both got at it at the same time, swelling round and round each other and punching their fists most into each other's faces, and whooping and jawing like Injuns; then Bob called the Child names, and the Child called him names back again; next, Bob called him a heap rougher names, and the Child come back at him with the very worst kind of language; next, Bob knocked the Child's hat off, and the Child picked it up and kicked Bob's ribbony hat about six foot; Bob went and got it and said never mind, this warn't going to be the last of this thing, because he was a man that never forgot and never forgive, and so the Child better look out, for there was a time a-coming, just as sure as he was a living man, that he would have to answer to him with the best blood in his body. The Child said no man was willinger than he for that time to come, and he would give Bob fair warning, *now*, never to cross his path again, for he could never rest till he had waded in his blood, for such was his nature, though he was sparing him now on account of his family, if he had one.

Both of them was edging away in different directions, growling and shaking their heads and going on about what they was going to do; but a little black-whiskered chap skipped up and says:

"Come back here, you couple of chicken-livered cowards, and I'll trash the two of ye!"

And he done it, too. He snatched them, he jerked them this way and that, he booted them around, he knocked them sprawling faster than they could get up. Why, it warn't two minutes till they begged like dogs—and how the other lot did yell and laugh and clap their hands all the way through, and shout, "Sail in, Corpse-Maker!" "Hi! at him again, Child of Calamity!" "Bully for you, little Davy!" Well, it was a perfect pow-wow for a while. Bob and the Child had red noses and black eyes when they got through. Little Davy made them own up that they was sneaks and cowards and not fit to eat with a dog or drink with a nigger; then Bob and the Child shook hands with each other, very solemn, and said they had always respected each other and was willing to let bygones be bygones. So then they washed their faces in the river; and just then there was a loud order to stand by for a crossing, and some of them went forward to man the sweeps there, and the rest went aft to handle the after sweeps.

I lay still and waited for fifteen minutes, and had a smoke out of a pipe that one of them left in reach; then the crossing was finished, and they stumped back and had a drink around and went to talking and singing again. Next they got out an old fiddle, and one played, and another patted juba, and the rest turned themselves loose on a regular old-fashioned keelboat breakdown. They couldn't keep that up very long without getting winded, so by and by they settled around the jug again.

They sung "Jolly, Jolly Raftsman's the Life for Me," with a rousing chorus, and then they got to talking about differences betwixt hogs, and their different kind of habits; and next about women and their different ways; and next about the best ways to put out houses that was afire; and the next about what ought to be done with the Injuns; and the next about what a king had to do, and how much he got; and next about how to make cats fight; and next about what to do when a man has fits; and next about differences betwixt clear-water rivers and muddy-water ones. The man they called Ed said the muddy Mississippi water was wholesomer to drink than the clear water of the Ohio; he said if you let a pint of this yaller Mississippi water settle, you would have about a half to three-quarters of an inch of mud in the bottom, according to the stage of the river, and then it warn't no better than Ohio water—what you wanted to do was to keep it stirred up—and when the river was low, keep mud on hand to put in and thicken the water up the way it ought to be.

The Child of Calamity said that was so; he said there was nutritiousness in the mud, and a man that drunk Mississippi water could grow corn in his stomach if he wanted to. He says:

"You look at the graveyards; that tells the tale. Trees won't grow worth shucks in a Cincinnati graveyard, but in a Sent Louis graveyard they grow upwards of eight hundred foot high. It's all on account of the water the people drunk before they laid up. A Cincinnati corpse don't richen a soil any."

And they talked about how Ohio water didn't like to mix with Mississippi water. Ed said if you take the Mississippi on a rise when the Ohio is low, you'll find a wide band of clear water all the way down the east side of the Mississippi for a hundred mile or more, and the minute you get out a quarter of a mile from shore and pass the line, it is all thick and yaller the rest of the way across. Then they talked about how to keep tobacco from getting moldy, and from that they went into ghosts and told about a lot that other folks had seen; but Ed says:

"Why don't you tell something that you've seen yourselves? Now let me have a say. Five years ago I was on a raft as big as this, and right along here it was a bright moonshiny night, and I was on watch and boss of the stabboard oar forrard, and one of my pards was a man named Dick Allbright, and he come along to where I was sitting, forrard—gaping and stretching, he was—and stooped down on the edge of the raft and washed his face in the river, and come and set down by me and got out his pipe, and had just got it filled, when he looks up and says:

" 'Why looky-here,' he says, 'ain't that Buck Miller's place, over yander in the bend?'

" 'Yes,' says I, 'it is—why?' He laid his pipe down and leaned his head on his hand, and says:

" 'I thought we'd be furder down.' I says:

" 'I thought it, too, when I went off watch'—we was standing six hours on and six off—'but the boys told me,' I says, 'that the raft didn't seem to hardly move, for the last hour,' says I, 'though she's a-slipping along all right now,' says I. He give a kind of groan, and says:

" 'I've seed a raft act so before, along here,' he says, ' 'pears to me the current has most quit above the head of this bend durin' the last two years,' he says.

"Well, he raised up two or three times, and looked away off and around on the water. That started me at it, too. A body is always doing what he sees somebody else doing, though there mayn't be no sense in it. Pretty soon I see a black something floating on the water away off to stabboard and quartering behind us. I see he was looking at it, too. I says:

" 'What's that?' He says, sort of pettish:

" ' 'Tain't nothing but an old empty bar'l.'

" 'An empty bar'l!' says I, 'why,' says I, 'a spy-glass is a fool to your eyes. How can you tell it's an empty bar'l?' He says:

" 'I don't know; I reckon it ain't a bar'l, but I thought it might be,' says he.

" 'Yes,' I says, 'so it might be, and it might be anything else, too; a body can't tell nothing about it, such a distance as that,' I says.

"We hadn't nothing else to do, so we kept watching it. By and by I says:

" 'Why looky-here, Dick Allbright, that thing's a-gaining on us, I believe.'

"He never said nothing. The thing gained and gained, and I judged it must be a dog that was about tired out. Well, we swung down into the crossing, and the thing floated across the bright streak of the moonshine, and by George, it was a bar'l. Says I:

" 'Dick Allbright, what made you think that thing was a bar'l, when it was half a mile off?' says I. Says he:

" 'I don't know.' Says I:

" 'You tell me, Dick Allbright.' Says he:

" 'Well, I knowed it was a bar'l; I've seen it before; lots has seen it; they says it's a ha'nted bar'l.'

"I called the rest of the watch, and they come and stood there, and I told them what Dick said. It floated right along abreast, now, and didn't gain any more. It was about twenty foot off. Some was for having it aboard, but the rest didn't want to. Dick Allbright said rafts that had fooled with it had got bad luck by it. The captain of the watch said he didn't believe in it. He said he reckoned the bar'l gained on us because it was in a little better current than what we was. He said it would leave by and by.

"So then we went to talking about other things, and we had a song, and then a breakdown; and after that the captain of the watch called for another song; but it was clouding up now, and the bar'l stuck right thar in the same place, and the song didn't seem to have much warm-up to it, somehow, and so they didn't finish it, and there warn't any cheers, but it sort of dropped flat, and nobody said anything for a minute. Then everybody tried to talk at once, and one chap got off a joke, but it warn't no use, they didn't laugh, and even the chap that made the joke didn't laugh at it, which ain't usual. We all just settled down glum, and watched the bar'l, and was oneasy and oncomfortable. Well, sir, it shut down black and still, and the wind began to moan around, and next the lightning began to play and the thunder to grumble. And pretty soon there was a regular storm, and in the middle of it a man that was running aft stumbled and fell and sprained his ankle so that he had to lay up. This made the boys shake their heads. And every time the lightning come, there was that bar'l with the blue lights winking around it. We was always on the lookout for it. But by and by, towards dawn, she was gone. When the day come we couldn't see her anywhere, and we warn't sorry, either.

"But the next night about half past nine, when there was songs and high jinks going on, here she comes again, and took her old roost on the stabboard side. There warn't no more high jinks. Everybody got solemn; nobody talked; you couldn't get anybody to do anything but set around moody and look at the bar'l. It begun to cloud up again. When the watch changed, the off watch stayed up, 'stead of turning in. The storm ripped and roared around all night, and in the middle of it another man tripped and sprained his ankle, and had to knock off. The bar'l left towards day, and nobody see it go.

"Everybody was sober and down in the mouth all day. I don't mean the kind of sober that comes of leaving liquor alone—not that. They was quiet, but they all drunk more than usual—not together, but each man sidled off and took it in private, by himself.

"After dark the off watch didn't turn in; nobody sung, nobody talked; the boys didn't scatter around, neither; they sort of huddled together, forrard; and for two hours they set there, perfectly still, looking steady in the one direction, and heaving a sigh once in a while. And then, here comes the bar'l again. She took up her old place. She stayed there all night; nobody turned in. The storm come on again, after midnight. It got awful dark; the rain poured down; hail, too; the thunder boomed and roared and bellowed; the wind blowed a hurricane; and the lightning spread over everything in big sheets of glare, and showed the whole raft as plain as day; and the river lashed up white as milk as far as you could see for miles, and there was that bar'l jiggering along, same as ever. The captain ordered the watch to man the after sweeps for a crossing, and nobody would go—no more sprained ankles for them, they said. They wouldn't even *walk aft*. Well, then, just then the sky split wide open, with a crash, and the lightning killed two men of the after watch, and crippled two more. Crippled them how, say you? Why, *sprained their ankles!*

" 'The bar'l left in the dark betwixt lightnings, toward dawn. Well, not a body eat a bite at breakfast that morning. After that the men loafed around, in twos and threes, and talked low together. But none of them herded with Dick Allbright. They all give him the cold shake. If he come around where any of the men was, they split up and sidled away. They wouldn't man the sweeps with him. The captain had all the skiffs hauled up on the raft, alongside of his wigwam, and wouldn't let the dead men be took ashore to be planted; he didn't believe a man that got ashore would come back; and he was right.

"After night come, you could see pretty plain that there was going to be trouble if that bar'l come again; there was such a muttering going on. A good many wanted to kill Dick Allbright, because he'd seen the bar'l on other trips, and that had an ugly look. Some wanted to put him ashore. Some said: 'Let's all go ashore in a pile, if the bar'l comes again.'

"This kind of whispers was still going on, the men being bunched together forrard watching for the bar'l, when lo and behold you! here she comes again. Down she comes, slow and steady, and settles into her old tracks. You could 'a' heard a pin drop. Then up comes the captain, and says:

" 'Boys, don't be a pack of children and fools; I don't want this bar'l to be dogging us all the way to Orleans, and *you* don't: Well, then, how's the best way to stop it? Burn it up—that's the way. I'm going to fetch it aboard,' he says. And before anybody could say a word, in he went.

"He swum to it, and as he come pushing it to the raft, the men spread to one side. But the old man got it aboard and busted in the head, and there was a baby in it! Yes, sir; a stark-naked baby. It was Dick Allbright's baby; he owned up and said so.

" 'Yes,' he says, a-leaning over it, 'yes, it is my own lamented darling, my poor lost Charles William Allbright deceased,' says he—for he could curl his tongue around the bulliest words in the language when he was a mind to, and lay them before you without a jint started anywheres. Yes, he said, he used to live up at the head of this bend, and one night he choked his child, which was crying, not intending to kill it—which was prob'ly a lie—and then he was scared, and buried it in a bar'l, before his wife got home, and off he went, and struck the northern trail and went to rafting; and this was the third year that the bar'l had chased him. He said the bad luck always begun light, and lasted till four men was killed, and then the bar'l didn't come any more after that. He said if the men would stand it one more night—and was a-going on like that—but the men had got enough. They started to get out a boat to take him ashore and lynch him, but he grabbed the little child all of a sudden and jumped overboard with it, hugged up to his breast and shedding tears, and we never seed him again in this life, poor old suffering soul, nor Charles William neither."

"*Who* was shedding tears?" says Bob; "was it Allbright or the baby?"

"Why, Allbright, of course; didn't I tell you the baby was dead? Been dead three years—how could it cry?"

"Well, never mind how it could cry—how could it *keep* all that time?" says Davy. "You answer me that."

"I don't know how it done it," says Ed. "It done it, though—that's all I know about it."

"Say—what did they do with the bar'l?" says the Child of Calamity.

"Why, they hove it overboard, and it sunk like a chunk of lead."

"Edward, did the child look like it was choked?" says one.

"Did it have its hair parted?" says another.

"What was the brand on that bar'l, Eddy?" says a fellow they called Bill.

"Have you got the papers for them statistics, Edmund?" says Jimmy.

"Say, Edwin, was you one of the men that was killed by the lightning?" says Davy.

"Him? Oh, no! he was both of 'em," says Bob. Then they all hawhawed.

"Say, Edward, don't you reckon you'd better take a pill? You look bad—don't you feel pale?" says the Child of Calamity.

"Oh, come, now, Eddy," says Jimmy, "show up; you must 'a' kept part of that bar'l to prove the thing by. Show us the bunghole—*do*—and we'll all believe you."

"Say, boys," says Bill, "less divide it up. Thar's thirteen of us. I can swaller a thirteenth of the yarn, if you can worry down the rest."

Ed got up mad and said they could all go to some place which he ripped out pretty savage, and then walked off aft, cussing to himself, and they yelling and jeering at him, and roaring and laughing so you could hear them a mile.

"Boys, we'll split a watermelon on that," says the Child of Calamity; and he come rummaging around in the dark amongst the shingle bundles where I was, and put his hand on me. I was warm and soft and naked; so he says "Ouch!" and jumped back.

"Fetch a lantern or a chunk of fire here, boys—there's a snake here as big as a cow!"

So they run there with a lantern, and crowded up and looked in on me.

"Come out of that, you beggar!" says one.

"Who are you?" says another.

"What are you after here? Speak up prompt, or overboard you go."

"Snake him out, boys. Snatch him out by the heels."

I began to beg, and crept out amongst them trembling. They looked me over, wondering, and the Child of Calamity says:

"A cussed thief! Lend a hand and less heave him overboard!"

"No," says Big Bob, "less get out the paint-pot and paint him a sky-blue all over from head to heel, and *then* heave him over."

"Good! that's it. Go for the paint, Jimmy."

When the paint come, and Bob took the brush and was just going to begin, the others laughing and rubbing their hands, I begun to cry, and that sort of worked on Davy, and he says:

" 'Vast there. He's nothing but a cub. I'll paint the man that teches him!"

So I looked around on them, and some of them grumbled and growled, and Bob put down the paint, and the others didn't take it up.

"Come here to the fire, and less see what you're up to here," says Davy. "Now set down there and give an account of yourself. How long have you been aboard here?"

"Not over a quarter of a minute, sir," says I.

"How did you get dry so quick?"

"I don't know, sir. I'm always that way, mostly."

"Oh, you are, are you? What's your name?"

I warn't going to tell my name. I didn't know what to say, so I just says: "Charles William Allbright, sir."

Then they roared—the whole crowd; and I was mighty glad I said that, because maybe laughing would get them in a better humor.

When they got done laughing, Davy says:

"It won't hardly do, Charles William. You couldn't have growed this much in five year, and you was a baby when you come out of the bar'l, you know, and dead at that. Come, now, tell a straight story, and nobody'll hurt you, if you ain't up to anything wrong. What *is* your name?"

"Aleck Hopkins, sir. Aleck James Hopkins."

"Well, Aleck, where did you come from, here?"

"From a trading-scow. She lays up the bend yonder. I was born on her. Pap has traded up and down here all his life; and he told me to swim off here, because when you went by he said he would like to get some of you to speak to a Mr. Jonas Turner, in Cairo, and tell him——"

"Oh, come!"

"Yes, sir, it's as true as the world. Pap he says——"

"Oh, your grandmother!"

They all laughed, and I tried again to talk, but they broke in on me and stopped me.

"Now, looky-here," says Davy; "you're scared, and so you talk wild. Honest, now, do you live in a scow, or is it a lie?"

"Yes, sir, in a trading-scow. She lays up at the head of the bend. But I warn't born in her. It's our first trip."

"Now you're talking! What did you come aboard here for? To steal?"

"No, sir, I didn't. It was only to get a ride on the raft. All boys does that."

"Well, I know that. But what did you hide for?"

"Sometimes they drive the boys off."

"So they do. They might steal. Looky-here; if we let you off this time, will you keep out of these kind of scrapes hereafter?"

" 'Deed I will, boss. You try me."

"All right, then. You ain't but little ways from shore. Overboard with you, and don't you make a fool of yourself another time this way. Blast it, boy, some raftsmen would rawhide you till you were black and blue!"

I didn't wait to kiss good-by, but went overboard and broke for shore. When Jim come along by and by, the big raft was away out of sight around the point. I swum out and got aboard, and was mighty glad to see home again.

The boy did not get the information he was after, but his adventure has furnished the glimpse of the departed raftsman and keelboatman which I desire to offer in this place.

Henry Adams (1838–1918)

Henry Adams' interest in manners led him to note some malicious gossip about the younger sister of his heroine in *Democracy* (1880): "People who envied her smile said that she cultivated a sense of humor in order to show her teeth." Adams, of course, was referring to feminine wiles alone, but he might just as easily have been describing his own literary style, whose amusing, ironic charm only faintly conceals an unusually keen intellectual bite. The urbane irony of Adams pervades almost all of his writings, whether history, biography, fiction, letters, or the autobiography which is virtually a novel: *The Education of Henry Adams* (1906). Compared to other political satires which attacked the administrations of Presidents Grant and Hayes, such as Mark Twain and Richard Watson Gilder's *The Gilded Age* (1873) or John W. De Forest's *Honest John Vane* (1874), *Democracy* is lacking in sordid detail and extravagant humor. Yet Adams' novel has urbane virtues of its own which are revealed in the unsentimental deflation of Mrs. Lee, where Adams' ironic satire is focused upon the social and cultural inadequacies of America's appallingly innocent post-Civil War élite.

TEXT: *Democracy*, New York, 1880. COMMENTARY: J. C. Levenson, *The Mind and Art of Henry Adams*, Boston, Mass., 1958.

MRS. LIGHTFOOT LEE

For reasons which many persons thought ridiculous, Mrs. Lightfoot Lee decided to pass the winter in Washington. She was in excellent health, but she said that the climate would do her good. In New York she had troops of friends, but she suddenly became eager to see again the very small number of those who lived on the Potomac. It was only to her closest intimates that she honestly acknowledged herself to be tortured by *ennui*. Since her husband's death, five years before, she had lost her taste for New York society; she had felt no interest in the price of stocks, and very little in the men who dealt in them; she had become serious. What was it all worth, this wilderness of men and women as monotonous as the brown stone houses they lived in? In her despair she had resorted to desperate measures. She had read philosophy in the original German, and the more she read, the more she was disheartened that so much culture should lead to nothing—nothing. After talking of Herbert Spencer for an entire evening with a very literary transcendental commission-merchant, she could not see that her time had been better employed than when in former days she had passed it in flirting with a very agreeable young stock-broker; indeed, there was an evident proof to the contrary, for the flirtation might lead to something—had, in fact, led to marriage; while the philosophy could lead to nothing, unless it were perhaps to another evening of the same kind, because transcendental philosophers are mostly elderly men, usually married, and, when engaged in business, somewhat apt to be sleepy towards evening. Nevertheless Mrs. Lee did her best to turn her study to practical use. She plunged into philanthrophy, visited prisons, inspected hospitals, read the literature of pauperism and crime, saturated herself with the statistics of vice, until her mind had nearly lost sight of virtue. At last it rose in rebellion against her, and she came to the limit of her strength. This path, too, seemed to lead nowhere. She declared that she had lost the sense of duty, and that, so far as concerned her, all the paupers and criminals in New York might henceforward rise in their majesty and manage every railway on the continent. Why should she care? What was the city to her? She could find nothing in it that seemed to demand salvation. What gave peculiar sanctity to numbers? Why were a million people, who all resembled each other, any more interesting than one person? What aspiration could she help to put into the mind of this great million-armed monster that would make it worth her love or respect? Religion? A thousand powerful churches were doing their best, and she could see no chance for a new faith of which she was to be the inspired prophet. Ambition? High popular ideals? Passion for whatever is lofty and pure? The very words irritated her. Was she not herself devoured of ambition, and was she not now eating her heart out because she could find no one object worth sacrifice?

Was it ambition—real ambition—or was it mere restlessness that made Mrs. Lightfoot Lee so bitter against New York and Philadelphia, Baltimore and Boston, American life in general and all life in particular? What did she want? Not social position, for she herself was an eminently respectable Philadelphian by birth; her father a famous clergyman; and her husband had been equally irreproachable, a descendant of one branch of the Virginia Lees, which had drifted to New York in search of fortune, and had found it, or enough of it to keep the young man there. His widow had her own place in society which no one disputed. Though not brighter than her neighbours, the world persisted in classing her among clever women; she had wealth, or at least enough of it to give her all that money can give by way of pleasure to a sensible woman in an American city; she had her house and her carriage; she dressed well; her table was good, and her furniture was never allowed to fall behind the latest standard of decorative art. She had travelled in Europe, and after several visits, covering some years of time, had returned home, carrying in one hand, as it were, a green-grey landscape, a remarkably pleasing specimen of Corot, and in the other some bales of Persian and Syrian rugs and embroideries, Japanese bronzes and porcelain. With this she declared Europe to be exhausted, and she frankly avowed that she was American to the tips of her fingers; she neither knew nor greatly cared whether America or Europe were best to live in; she had no violent love for either, and she had no objection to abusing both; but she meant to get all that American life had to offer, good or bad, and to drink it down to the dregs, fully determined that whatever there was in it she would have, and that whatever could be made out of it she would manufacture. "I know," said she, "that America produces petroleum and pigs; I have seen both on the steamers; and I am told it produces silver and gold. There is choice enough for any woman."

Yet, as has been already said, Mrs. Lee's first experience was not a success. She soon declared that New York might represent the petroleum or the pigs, but the gold of life was not to be discovered there by her eyes. Not but that there was variety enough; a variety of people, occupations, aims, and thoughts; but that all these, after growing to a certain height, stopped short. They found nothing to hold them up. She knew, more or less intimately, a dozen men whose fortunes ranged between one million and forty millions. What did they do with their money? What could they do with it that was different from what other men did? After all, it is absurd to spend more money than is enough to satisfy all one's wants; it is vulgar to live in two houses in the same street, and to drive six horses abreast. Yet, after setting aside a certain income sufficient for all one's wants, what was to be done with the rest? To let it accumulate was to own one's failure; Mrs. Lee's great grievance was that it did accumulate, without changing or improving the quality of its owners. To spend it in charity and public works was doubtless praiseworthy, but was it wise? Mrs. Lee had read enough political economy and pauper reports to be nearly convinced that public work should be public duty, and that great benefactions do harm as well as good. And even supposing it spent on these objects, how could it do more than increase and perpetuate that same kind of human nature which was her great grievance? Her New York friends could not meet this question except by falling back upon their native commonplaces, which she recklessly trampled upon, averring that, much as she admired the genius of the famous traveller, Mr. Gulliver, she never had been able, since she became a widow, to accept the Brobdingnagian doctrine that he who made two blades of grass grow where only one grew before deserved better of mankind than the whole race of politicians. She would not find fault with the philosopher had he required that the grass should be of an improved quality; "but," said she, "I cannot honestly pretend that I should be pleased to see two New York men where I now see one; the idea is too ridiculous; more than one and a half would be fatal to me."

Then came her Boston friends, who suggested that higher education was precisely what she wanted; she should throw herself into a crusade for universities and art-schools. Mrs. Lee turned upon them with a sweet smile; "Do you know," said she, "that we have in New York already the richest university in America, and that its only trouble has always been that it can get no scholars even by paying for them? Do you want me to go out into the streets and waylay boys? If the heathen refuse to be converted, can you give me power over the stake and the sword to compel them to come in? And suppose you can? Suppose I march all the boys in Fifth Avenue down to the university and have them all properly taught Greek and Latin, English literature, ethics, and German philosophy. What then? You do it in Boston. Now tell me honestly what comes of it. I suppose you have there a brilliant society; numbers of poets, scholars, philosophers, statesmen, all up and down Beacon Street. Your evenings must be sparkling. Your press must scintillate. How is it that we New Yorkers never hear of it? We don't go much into your society; but when we do, it doesn't seem so very much better than our own. You are just like the rest of us. You grow six inches high, and then you stop. Why will not somebody grow to be a tree and cast a shadow?"

The average member of New York society, although not unused to this contemptuous kind of treatment from his leaders, retaliated in his blind, common-sense way. "What does the woman want?" he said. "Is her head turned with the Tuileries and Marlborough House? Does she think herself made for a throne? Why does she not lecture for women's rights? Why not go on the stage? If she cannot be contented like other people, what need is there for abusing us just because she feels herself no taller than we are? What does she expect to get from her sharp tongue? What does she know, any way?"

Mrs. Lee certainly knew very little. She had read voraciously and promiscuously one subject after another. Ruskin and Taine had danced merrily through her mind, hand in hand with Darwin and Stuart Mill, Gustave Droz and Algernon Swinburne. She had even laboured over the literature of her own country. She was, perhaps, the only woman in New York who knew something of American history. Certainly she could not have repeated the list of Presidents in their order, but she knew that the Constitution divided the government into Executive, Legislative, and Judiciary; she was aware that the President, the Speaker, and the Chief Justice were important personages, and instinctively she wondered whether they might not solve her problem; whether they were the shade trees which she saw in her dreams.

Here, then, was the explanation of her restlessness, discontent, ambition, —call it what you will. It was the feeling of a passenger on an ocean steamer whose mind will not give him rest until he has been in the engine-room and talked with the engineer. She wanted to see with her own eyes the action of primary forces; to touch with her own hand the massive machinery of society; to measure with her own mind the capacity of the motive power. She was bent upon getting to the heart of the great American mystery of democracy and government. She cared little where her pursuit might lead her, for she put no extravagant value upon life, having already, as she said, exhausted at least two lives, and being fairly hardened to insensibility in the process. "To lose a husband and a baby," said she, "and keep one's courage and reason, one must become very hard or very soft. I am now pure steel. You may beat my heart with a trip-hammer and it will beat the trip-hammer back again."

Perhaps after exhausting the political world she might try again elsewhere; she did not pretend to say where she might then go, or what she should do; but at present she meant to see what amusement there might be in politics. Her friends asked what kind of amusement she expected to find among the illiterate swarm of ordinary people who in Washington represented constituencies so dreary that in comparison New York was a New Jerusalem, and Broad Street a grove of Academe. She replied that if Washington society were so bad as this, she should have gained all she wanted, for it would be a pleasure to return,—precisely the feeling she longed for. In her own mind, however, she frowned on the idea of seeking for men. What she wished to see, she thought, was the clash of interests, the interests of forty millions of people and a whole continent, centering at Washington; guided, restrained, controlled, or unrestrained and uncontrollable, by men of ordinary mould; the tremendous forces of government, and the machinery of society, at work. What she wanted, was POWER.

Perhaps the force of the engine was a little confused in her mind with that of the engineer, the power with the men who wielded it. Perhaps the human interest of politics was after all what really attracted her, and, however strongly she might deny it, the passion for exercising power, for its own sake, might dazzle and mislead a woman who had exhausted all the ordinary feminine resources. But why speculate about her motives? The stage was before her, the curtain was rising, the actors were ready to enter; she had only to go quietly on among the supernumeraries and see how the play was acted and the stage effects were produced; how the great tragedians mouthed, and the stage-manager swore.

Ambrose Bierce (1842–?1914)

For Ambrose Bierce the United States was "a great, broad blackness with two or three small points of light struggling and flickering in the universal blank of ignorance, crudity, conceit, tobacco-chewing, ill-dressing, unmannerly manners and general barbarity." One of these lights was Bierce himself, writing with a contempt based upon Puritanism inherited from Massachusetts and Connecticut ancestors, youthful years in Indiana, Civil War military experience, and journalistic activity on the amoral California frontier centered around San Francisco. Men, institutions, and the universe—Bierce found them all corrupt and suffocating. He expressed his sardonic views in prose and verse drawing upon the grim qualities of American humor which can be traced back from Bierce through Melville, Hawthorne, and Poe to the Puritans. Unlike Mark Twain, Bierce never flirted with hope or compassion. Persistently satiric and ironic, he expounded a savage Nietzschean individualism which admitted of no virtue in the alleged cant of piety and democracy. The irony of "Oil of Dog," the witty paradoxes of *The Devil's Dictionary* (1906), the bland mockeries of *Fantastic Fables* (1899), and the tall-tale trickery of Reverend Berosus Huggins in "Curried Cow" did not win Bierce a wide audience. His grotesque, macabre amalgamation of understatement, exaggeration, and psychological insight too brutally scratched the self-doubt which underlay an outwardly complacent American spirit. Perhaps Bierce might have attained a more complex humor, one more imbued with joyousness, if he had not wasted his best years in febrile, slashing journalism. The journalist who most resembles Bierce—H. L. Mencken (see pp. 483–88)—is virtually a laughing jester by comparison.

TEXT: *The Collected Writings of Ambrose Bierce*, ed. Clifton Fadiman, New York, 1946. COMMENTARY: Carey McWilliams, *Ambrose Bierce*, New York, 1929. Paul Fatout, *Ambrose Bierce: The Devil's Lexicographer*, Norman, Okla., 1951.

OIL OF DOG

My name is Boffer Bings. I was born of honest parents in one of the humbler walks of life, my father being a manufacturer of dog-oil and my mother having a small studio in the shadow of the village church, where she disposed of unwelcome babes. In my boyhood I was trained to habits of industry; I not only assisted my father in procuring dogs for his vats, but was frequently employed by my mother to carry away the debris of her work in the studio. In performance of this duty I sometimes had need of all my natural intelligence for all the law officers of the vicinity were opposed to my mother's business. They were not elected on an opposition ticket, and the matter had never been made a political issue; it just happened so. My father's business of making dog-oil was, naturally, less unpopular, though the owners of missing dogs sometimes regarded him with suspicion, which was reflected, to some extent, upon me. My father had, as silent partners, all the physicians of the town, who seldom wrote a prescription which did not contain what they were pleased to designate as *Ol. can.* It is really the most valuable medicine ever discovered. But most persons are unwilling to make personal sacrifices for the afflicted, and it was evident that many of the fattest dogs in town had been forbidden to play with me—a fact which pained my young sensibilities, and at one time came near driving me to become a pirate.

Looking back upon those days, I cannot but regret, at times, that by indirectly bringing my beloved parents to their death I was the author of misfortunes profoundly affecting my future.

One evening while passing my father's oil factory with the body of a foundling from my mother's studio I saw a constable who seemed to be closely watching my movements. Young as I was, I had learned that a constable's acts, of whatever apparent character, are prompted by the most reprehensible motives, and I avoided him by dodging into the oilery by a side door which happened to stand ajar. I locked it at once and was alone with my dead. My father had retired for the night. The only light in the place came from the furnace, which glowed a deep, rich crimson under one of the vats, casting ruddy reflections on the walls. Within the cauldron the oil still rolled in indolent ebullition, occasionally pushing to the surface a piece of dog. Seating myself to wait for the constable to go away, I held the naked body of the foundling in my lap and tenderly stroked its short, silken hair. Ah, how beautiful it was! Even at that early age I was passionately fond of children, and as I looked upon this cherub I could almost find it in my heart to wish that the small, red wound upon its breast—the work of my dear mother—had not been mortal.

It had been my custom to throw the babes into the river which nature had thoughtfully provided for the purpose, but that night I did not dare to leave the oilery for fear of the constable. "After all," I said to myself, "it cannot greatly matter if I put it into this cauldron. My father will never know the bones from those of a puppy, and the few deaths which may result from administering another kind of oil for the incomparable *ol. can.* are not important in a population which increases so rapidly." In short, I took the first step in crime and brought myself untold sorrow by casting the babe into the cauldron.

The next day, somewhat to my surprise, my father, rubbing his hands with satisfaction, informed me and my mother that he had obtained the finest quality of oil that was ever seen; that the physicians to whom he had shown samples had so pronounced it. He added that he had no knowledge as to how the result was obtained; the dogs had been treated in all respects as usual, and were of an ordinary breed. I deemed it my duty to explain—which I did, though palsied would have been my tongue if I could have foreseen the consequences. Bewailing their previous ignorance of the advantages of combining their industries, my parents at once took measures to repair the error. My mother removed her studio to a wing of the factory building and my duties in connection with the business ceased; I was no longer required to dispose of the bodies of the small superfluous, and there was no need of alluring dogs to their doom, for my father discarded them altogether, though they still had an honorable place in the name of the oil. So suddenly thrown into idleness, I might naturally have been expected to become vicious and dissolute, but I did not. The holy influence of my dear mother was ever about me to protect me from the temptations which beset youth, and my father was a deacon in a church. Alas, that through my fault these estimable persons should have come to so bad an end!

Finding a double profit in her business, my mother now devoted herself to it with a new assiduity. She removed not only superfluous and unwelcome babes to order, but went out into the highways and byways, gathering in children of a larger growth, and even such adults as she could entice to the oilery. My father, too, enamored of the superior quality of oil produced, purveyed for his vats with diligence and zeal. The conversion of their neighbors into dog-oil became, in short, the one passion of their lives—an absorbing and overwhelming greed took possession of their souls and served them in place of a hope in Heaven—by which, also, they were inspired.

So enterprising had they now become that a public meeting was held and resolutions passed severely censuring them. It was intimated by the chairman that any further raids upon the population would be met in a spirit of hostility. My poor parents left the meeting broken-hearted, desperate and, I believe, not altogether sane. Anyhow, I deemed it prudent not to enter the oilery with them that night, but slept outside in a stable.

At about midnight some mysterious impulse caused me to rise and peer through a window into the furnace-room, where I knew my father now slept. The fires were burning as brightly as if the following day's harvest had been expected to be abundant. One of the large cauldrons was slowly "walloping" with a mysterious appearance of self-restraint, as if it bided its time to put forth its full energy. My father was not in bed; he had risen in his nightclothes and was preparing a noose in a strong cord. From the looks which he cast at the door of my mother's bedroom I knew too well the purpose that he had in mind. Speechless and motionless with terror, I could do nothing in prevention or warning. Suddenly the door of my mother's apartment was opened, noiselessly, and the two confronted each other, both apparently surprised. The lady, also, was in her night clothes, and she held in her right hand the tool of her trade, a long, narrow-bladed dagger.

She, too, had been unable to deny herself the last profit which the unfriendly action of the citizens and my absence had left her. For one instant they looked into each other's blazing eyes and then sprang together with indescribable fury. Round and round the room they struggled, the man cursing, the woman shrieking, both fighting like demons—she to strike him with the dagger, he to strangle her with his great bare hands. I know not how long I had the unhappiness to observe this disagreeable instance of domestic infelicity, but at last, after a more than usually vigorous struggle, the combatants suddenly moved apart.

My father's breast and my mother's weapon showed evidences of contact. For another instant they glared at each other in the most unamiable way; then my poor, wounded father, feeling the hand of death upon him, leaped forward, unmindful of resistance, grasped my dear mother in his arms, dragged her to the side of the boiling cauldron, collected all his failing energies, and sprang in with her! In a moment, both had disappeared and were adding their oil to that of the committee of citizens who had called the day before with an invitation to the public meeting.

Convinced that these unhappy events closed to me every avenue to an honorable career in that town, I removed to the famous city of Otumwee, where these memoirs are written with a heart full of remorse for a heedless act entailing so dismal a commercial disaster.

Henry James (1843–1916)

The irony, the comic names, the stock comic characters, the misunderstandings, the confusions, the wit, and the plots of Henry James leave little doubt that his stories and novels comprise one of the largest bodies of humorous writing produced by an American author. If there is any hesitation about making this admission, it will probably stem from the fact that as James's style became increasingly complicated his humor became correspondingly more subtle. It was unmistakably present at the beginning of his career, however, when James deliberately and obviously undertook to treat humorously his favorite subject: the interplay of persons, manners, and values in society. This may be seen in such stories as "A Passionate Pilgrim" (1871), "A Bundle of Letters" (1879), and "The Point of View" (1882), and in such novels as *The American* (1877) and *The Bostonians* (1886), the latter a social and psychological satire which reveals James as content to use the staples of broad comedy in order to enliven and underline his moral and social judgments. Although James insisted in his early literary criticism that reality could only be plumbed by a writer with a sense of humor, he became increasingly impatient with post-Civil War American humor that was merely national in detail, broad in effect, and little else. But if "American humor" began to take on an invidious character for James, "humor" did not. James' humor became progressively international and complex enough to unite both the broadly "comic" and the deeply "tragic." The line of march from "A Passionate Pilgrim" through "A Bundle of Letters," *The Bostonians*, and "The Real Thing" (1890), to such late humorous stories as "Mrs. Medwin" (1902) and "The Birthplace" (1903), is remarkably straight and consistently entertaining.

TEXT: *A Bundle of Letters*, Boston, Mass., 1880; "Miss Birdseye's Friends," *The Bostonians*, New York, 1886. COMMENTARY: Richard Poirier, *The Comic Sense of Henry James*, New York, 1960.

A BUNDLE OF LETTERS

From Miss Miranda Hope, in Paris, to Mrs. Abraham C. Hope, at Bangor, Maine

September 5, 1879

My Dear Mother:—

I have kept you posted as far as Tuesday week last, and, although my letter will not have reached you yet, I will begin another, before my news accumulates too much. I am glad you show my letters round in the family, for I like them all to know what I am doing, and I can't write to every one, though I try to answer all reasonable expectations. But there are a great many unreasonable ones, as I suppose you know,—not yours, dear mother, for I am bound to say that you never required of me more than was natural. You see you are reaping your reward: I write to you before I write to any one else.

There is one thing, I hope—that you don't show any of my letters to William Platt. If he wants to see any of my letters, he knows the right way to go to work. I wouldn't have him see one of these letters, written for circulation in the family, for anything in the world. If he wants one for himself, he has got to write to me first. Let him write to me first, and then I will see about answering him. You can show him this if you like; but if you show him anything more, I will never write to you again. . . .

I told you in my last about my farewell to England, my crossing the channel, and my first impressions of Paris. I have thought a great deal about that lovely England since I left it, and all the famous historic scenes I visited; but I have come to the conclusion that it is not a country in which I should care to reside. The position of woman does not seem to me at all satisfactory, and that is a point, you know, on which I feel very strongly. It seems to me that in England they play a very faded-out part, and those with whom I conversed had a kind of depressed and humiliated tone; a little dull, tame look, as if they were used to being snubbed and bullied, which made me want to give them a good shaking. There are a great many people—and a great many things, too—over here that I should like to perform that operation upon. I should like to shake the starch out of some of them, and the dust out of the others. I know fifty girls in Bangor that come much more up to my notion of the stand a truly noble woman should take, than those young ladies in England. But they had a most lovely way of speaking (in England), and the men are *remarkably handsome.* (You can show this to William Platt, if you like.)

I gave you my first impressions of Paris, which quite came up to my expectations, much as I had heard and read about it. The objects of interest are extremely numerous, and the climate is remarkably cheerful and sunny. I should say the position of woman here was considerably higher, though by no means coming up to the American standard. The manners of the people are in some respects extremely peculiar, and I feel at last that I am indeed in *foreign parts.* It is, however, a truly elegant city (very superior to New York), and I have spent a great deal of time in visiting the various monuments and palaces. I won't give you an account of all my wanderings, though I have been most indefatigable; for I am keeping, as I told you before, a most *exhaustive* journal, which I will allow you the *privilege* of reading on my return to Bangor. I am getting on remarkably well, and I must say I am sometimes surprised at my universal good fortune. It only shows what a little energy and common-sense will accomplish. I have discovered none of these objections to a young lady travelling in Europe by herself, of which we heard so much before I left, and I don't expect I ever shall, for I certainly don't mean to look for them. I know what I want, and I always manage to get it.

I have received a great deal of politeness—some of it really most pressing, and I have experienced no drawbacks whatever. I have made a great many pleasant acquaintances in travelling round (both ladies and gentlemen), and had a great many most interesting talks. I have collected a great deal of information, for which I refer you to my journal. I assure you my journal is going to be a splendid thing. I do just exactly as I do in Bangor, and I find I do perfectly right; and, at any rate, I don't care if I don't. I didn't come to Europe to lead a merely conventional life; I could do that at Bangor. You know I never *would* do it at Bangor; so it isn't likely I am going to make myself miserable over here. So long as I accomplish what I desire, and make my money hold out, I shall regard the thing as a success. Sometimes I feel rather lonely, especially in the evening; but I generally manage to interest myself in something or some one. In the evening I usually read up about the objects of interest I have seen during the day, or I post up my journal. Sometimes I go to the theatre; or else I play the piano in the public parlour. The public parlour at the hotel isn't much; but the piano is better than that fearful old thing at the Sebago House.

Sometimes I go downstairs and talk to the lady who keeps the books,—a French lady, who is remarkably polite. She is very pretty, and always wears a black dress, with the most beautiful fit; she speaks a little English; she tells me she had to learn it, in order to converse with the Americans who come in such numbers to this hotel. She has given me a great deal of information about the position of woman in France, and much of it is very encouraging. But she has told me at the same time some things that I should not like to write to you (I am hesitating even about putting them into my journal), especially if my letters are to be handed round in the family. I assure you they appear to talk about things here that we never think of mentioning at Bangor, or even of thinking about. She seems to think she can tell me everything, because I told her I was travelling for general culture. Well, I *do* want to know so much that it seems sometimes as if I wanted to know everything; and yet there are some things that I think I don't want to know. But, as a general thing, everything is intensely interesting; I don't mean only everything that this French lady tells me, but everything I see and hear for myself. I feel really as if I should gain all I desire.

I meet a great many Americans, who, as a general thing, I must say, are not as polite to me as the people over here. The people over here—

especially the gentlemen—are much more what I should call *attentive*. I don't know whether Americans are more *sincere*; I haven't yet made up my mind about that. The only drawback I experience is when Americans sometimes express surprise that I should be travelling round alone; so you see it doesn't come from Europeans. I always have my answer ready: 'For general culture, to acquire the languages, and to see Europe for myself'; and that generally seems to satisfy them. Dear mother, my money holds out very well, and it *is* real interesting.

II

From the Same to the Same

September 16

Since I last wrote to you I have left that hotel, and come to live in a French family. It's a kind of boarding-house, combined with a kind of school; only it's not like an American boarding-house, or like an American school either. There are four or five people here that have come to learn the language,—not to take lessons, but to have an opportunity for conversation. I was very glad to come to such a place, for I had begun to realize that I was not making much progress with the French. It seemed to me that I should feel ashamed to have spent two months in Paris, and not to have acquired more insight into the language. I had always heard so much of French conversation, and I found I was having no more opportunity to practise it than if I had remained at Bangor. In fact, I used to hear a great deal more at Bangor, from those French Canadians that came down to cut the ice, then I saw I should ever hear at the hotel. The lady that kept the books seemed to want so much to talk to me in English (for the sake of practice, too, I suppose), that I couldn't bear to let her know I didn't like it. The chambermaid was Irish, and all the waiters were German, so that I never heard a word of French spoken. I suppose you might hear a great deal in the shops; only, as I don't buy anything—I prefer to spend my money for purposes of culture—I don't have that advantage.

I have been thinking some of taking a teacher, but I am well acquainted with the grammar already, and teachers always keep you bothering over the verbs. I was a good deal troubled, for I felt as if I didn't want to go away without having, at least, got a general idea of French conversation. The theatre gives you a good deal of insight, and, as I told you in my last, I go a good deal to places of amusement. I find no difficulty whatever in going to such places alone, and am always treated with the politeness which, as I told you before, I encounter everywhere. I see plenty of other ladies alone (mostly French), and they generally seem to be enjoying themselves as much as I. But, at the theatre, every one talks so fast that I can scarcely make out what they say; and, besides, there are a great many vulgar expressions which it is unnecessary to learn. But it was the theatre, nevertheless, that put me on the track. The very next day after I wrote to you last, I went to the Palais Royal, which is one of the principal theatres in Paris. It is very small, but it is very celebrated, and in my guidebook it is marked with *two stars*, which is a sign of importance attached only to *first-class* objects of interest. But after I had been there half an hour I found I couldn't understand a single word of the play, they gabbled it off so fast, and they made use of such peculiar expressions. I felt a good deal disappointed and troubled—I was afraid I shouldn't gain all I had come for. But while I was thinking it over—thinking what I *should* do —I heard two gentlemen talking behind me. It was between the acts, and I couldn't help listening to what they said. They were talking English, but I guess they were Americans.

'Well,' said one of them, 'it all depends on what you are after. I'm after French; that's what I'm after.'

'Well,' said the other, 'I'm after Art.'

'Well,' said the first, 'I'm after Art too; but I'm after French most.'

Then, dear mother, I am sorry to say the second swore a little. He said, 'Oh, damn French!'

'No, I won't damn French,' said his friend. 'I'll acquire it—that's what I'll do with it. I'll go right into a family."

'What family'll you go into?'

'Into some French family. That's the only way to do,—to go to some place where you can talk. If you're after Art, you want to stick to the galleries; you want to go right through the Louvre, room by room; you want to take a room a day, or something of that sort. But, if you want to acquire French, the thing to do is to look out for a family. There are lots of French families here that take you to board and teach you. My second cousin—that young lady I told you about—she got in with a crowd like that, and they booked her right up in three months. They just took her right in, and they talked to her. That's what they do to you; they set you right down, and they talk *at* you. You've got to understand them; you can't help yourself. That family my cousin was with has moved away somewhere, or I should try and get in with them. They were very smart people, that family; after she left, my cousin corresponded with them in French. But I mean to find some other crowd, if it takes a lot of trouble.'

I listened to all this with great interest, and when he spoke about his cousin I was on the point of turning around to ask him the address of the family that she was with; but the next moment he said they had moved away; so I sat still. The other gentleman, however, didn't seem to be affected in the same way as I was.

'Well,' he said, 'you may follow up that if you like; I mean to follow up the pictures. I don't believe there is ever going to be any considerable demand in the United States for French; but I can promise you that in about ten years there'll be a big demand for Art! And it won't be temporary, either.'

That remark may be very true, but I don't care anything about the demand; I want to know French for its own sake. I don't want to think I have been all this while without having gained an insight. . . . The very next day, I asked the lady who kept the books at the hotel whether she knew of any family that could take me to board and give me the benefit of their conversation. She instantly threw up her hands, with several little shrill cries (in their French way, you know) and told me that her dearest friend kept a regular place of that kind. If she had known I was looking out for such a place she would have told me before; she had not spoken of it herself, because she didn't wish to injure the hotel by being the cause of my going away. She told me this was a charming family, who had often received American ladies (and others as well) who wished to follow up the language, and she was sure I would be delighted with them. So she gave me their address, and offered to go with me to introduce me. But I was in such a hurry that I went off by myself, and I had no trouble in finding these good people. They were delighted to receive me, and I was very much pleased with what I saw of them. They seemed to have plenty of conversation, and there will be no trouble about that.

I came here to stay three days ago, and by this time I have seen a great deal of them. The price of board struck me as rather high; but I must remember that a quantity of conversation is thrown in. I have a very pretty little room—without any carpet, but with seven mirrors, two clocks, and five curtains. I was rather disappointed after I arrived to find that there are several other Americans here for the same purpose as myself. At least there are three Americans and two English people; and also a German gentleman. I am afraid, therefore, our conversation will be rather mixed, but I have not yet time to judge. I try to talk with Madame de Maisonrouge all I can (she is the lady of the house, and the *real* family consists only of herself and her two daughters). They are all most elegant, interesting women, and I am sure we shall become intimate friends. I will write you more about them in my next. Tell William Platt I don't care what he does.

III

From Miss Violet Ray, in Paris, to Miss Agnes Rich, in New York

September 21

We had hardly got here when father received a telegram saying he would have to come right back to New York. It was something about his business—I don't know exactly what; you know I never understand these things, and, what's more, I don't want to. We had just got settled at the hotel, in some charming rooms, and mother and I, as you may imagine, were greatly annoyed. Father is extremely fussy, as you know, and his first idea, as soon as he found he should have to go back, was that we should go back with him. He declared he would never leave us in Paris alone, and that we must return and come out again. I don't know what he thought would happen to us; I suppose he thought we would be too extravagant. It's father's theory that we are always running up bills, whereas a little observation would show him that we wear the same old *rags* FOR MONTHS. But father has no observation; he has nothing but theories. Mother and I, however, have, fortunately, a great deal of *practice*, and we succeeded in making him understand that we wouldn't budge from Paris, and that we would rather be chopped into small pieces than cross that dreadful ocean again. So, at last, he decided to go back alone, and to leave us here for three months. But, to show you how fussy he is, he refused to let us stay at the hotel, and insisted that we should go into a *family*. I don't know what put such an idea into his head, unless it was some advertisement he saw in one of the American papers that are published here.

There are families here who receive American and English people to live with them, under the pretence of teaching them French. You may imagine what people they are—I mean the families themselves. But the Americans who choose this peculiar manner of seeing Paris must be actually just as bad. Mother and I were horrified, and declared that *main force* should not remove us from the hotel. But father has a way of arriving at his ends which is more efficient than violence. He worries and fusses; he 'nags,' as we used to say at school; and, when mother and I are quite worn out, his triumph is assured. Mother is usually worn out more easily than I, and she ends with siding with father; so that, at last, when they combine their forces against poor little me, I have to succumb. You should have heard the way father went on and on about this 'family' plan; he talked to every one he saw about it; he used to go round to the banker's and talk to the people there,—the people in the post-office; he used to try and exchange ideas about it with the waiters at the hotel. He said it would be more safe, more respectable, more economical; that I should perfect my French; that mother would learn how a French household is conducted; that he should feel more easy, and five hundred reasons more. They were none of them good, but that made no difference. It's all humbug, his talking about economy, when every one knows that business in America has completely recovered, that the prostration is all over, and that *immense fortunes* are being made. We have been economizing for the last five years, and I supposed we came abroad to reap the benefits of it.

As for my French, it is quite as perfect as I want it to be. (I assure you I am often surprised at my own fluency, and, when I get a little more practice in the genders and the idioms, I shall do very well in this respect.) To make a long story short, however, father carried his point, as usual; mother basely deserted me at the last moment, and, after holding out alone for three days, I told them to do with me what they pleased! Father lost three steamers in succession by remaining in Paris to argue with me. You know he is like the parson in Goldsmith's *Deserted Village*—'e'en though vanquished, he would argue still.' He and mother went to look at some seventeen families (they had got the addresses somewhere), while I retired to my sofa, and would have nothing to do with it. At last they made arrangements, and I was transported to the establishment from which I now write you. I write you from the bosom of a Parisian ménage—from the depths of a second-rate boarding-house.

Father only left Paris after he had seen us what he calls comfortably settled here, and had informed Madame de Maisonrouge (the mistress of the establishment—the head of the 'family') that he wished my French pronunciation especially attended to. The pronunciation, as it happens, is just what I am most at home in; if he had said my genders or my idioms there would have been some sense. But poor father has no tact, and this defect is especially marked since he has been in Europe. He will be absent, however, for three months, and mother and I shall breathe a little more freely; the situation will be less intense. I must confess that we breathe more freely than I expected, in this place, where we have been for about a week. I was sure, before we came, that it would prove to be an establishment of the *lowest description*; but I must say that, in this respect, I am agreeably disappointed. The French are so clever that they know even how to manage a place of this kind. Of course it is very disagreeable to live with strangers, but as, after all, if I were not staying with Madame de Maisonrouge I should not be living in the Faubourg St.-Germain, I don't know that from the point of view of exclusiveness it is any great loss to be here.

Our rooms are very prettily arranged, and the table is remarkably good. Mamma thinks the whole thing—the place and the people, the manners and customs—very amusing; but mamma is very easily amused. As for me, you know, all that I ask is to be alone, and not to have people's society *forced upon me*. I have never wanted for society of my own choosing, and, so long as I retain possession of my faculties, I don't suppose I ever shall. As I said, however, the place is very well managed, and I succeed in doing as I please, which, you know, is my most cherished pursuit. Madame de Maisonrouge has a great deal of tact—much more than poor father. She is what they call here a *belle femme*, which means that she is a tall, ugly woman, with style. She dresses very well, and has a great deal of talk; but, though she is a very good imitation of a lady, I never see her behind her dinner table, in the evening, smiling and bowing, as the people come in, and looking all the while at the dishes and

the servants, without thinking of a *dame de comptoir* blooming in a
corner of a shop or restaurant. I am sure that, in spite of her fine name,
she was once a *dame de comptoir*. I am also sure that, in spite of her
smiles and the pretty things she says to every one, she hates us all, and
would like to murder us. She is a hard, clever Frenchwoman, who would
like to amuse herself and enjoy her Paris, and she must be bored to death
at passing all her time in the midst of stupid English people who mumble broken French at her. Some day she will poison the soup or the *vin
rouge*; but I hope that will not be until after mother and I shall have
left her. She has two daughters, who, except that one is decidedly pretty,
are meagre imitations of herself.

The 'family,' for the rest, consists altogether of our beloved compatriots,
and of still more beloved Englanders. There is an Englishman here,
with his sister, and they seem to be rather nice people. He is remarkably
handsome, but excessively affected and patronizing, especially to us Americans; and I hope to have a chance of biting his head off before very long.
The sister is very pretty, and, apparently, very nice; but, in costume, she is
Brittania incarnate. There is a very pleasant little Frenchman—when they
are nice they are charming—and a German doctor, a big, blond man,
who looks like a great, white bull; and two Americans, besides mother
and me. One of them is a young man from Boston,—an aesthetic young
man, who talks about its being 'a real Corot day,' etc., and a young
woman,—a girl, a female, I don't know what to call her,—from Vermont,
or Minnesota, or some such place. This young woman is the most
extraordinary specimen of artless Yankeeism that I ever encountered;
she is really too horrible. I have been three times to Clémentine about
your underskirt, etc.

IV

From Louis Leverett, in Paris, to Harvard Tremont, in Boston

September 25

My Dear Harvard:—

I have carried out my plan, of which I gave you a hint in my last,
and I only regret that I should not have done it before. It is human
nature, after all, that is the most interesting thing in the world, and it
only reveals itself to the truly earnest seeker. There is a want of earnestness in that life of hotels and railroad trains, which so many of our
countrymen are content to lead in this strange Old World, and I was
distressed to find how far I, myself, had been led along the dusty, beaten
track. I had, however, constantly wanted to turn aside into more un-
frequented ways; to plunge beneath the surface and see what I should
discover. But the opportunity had always been missing; somehow, I
never meet those opportunities that we hear about and read about,—

the things that happen to people in novels and biographies. And yet I am always on the watch to take advantage of any opening that may present itself; I am always looking out for experiences, for sensations,—I might almost say, for adventures.

The great thing is to *live*, you know,—to feel, to be conscious of one's possibilities; not to pass through life mechanically and insensibly, like a letter through the post-office. There are times, my dear Harvard, when I feel as if I were really capable of everything,—*capable de tout*, as they say here,—of the greatest excesses as well as the greatest heroism. Oh, to be able to say that one has lived—*qu'on a vécu*, as they say here,— that idea exercises an indefinable attraction for me. You will perhaps reply, it is easy to say it; but the thing is to make people believe you! And, then, I don't want any second-hand, spurious sensations; I want the knowledge that leaves a trace,—that leaves strange scars and stains and reveries behind it! But I am afraid I shock you, perhaps even frighten you.

If you repeat my remarks to any of the West Cedar St. circle, be sure you tone them down as your discretion will suggest. For yourself, you will know that I have always had an intense desire to see something of *real French life*. You are acquainted with my great sympathy with the French; with my natural tendency to enter into the French way of looking at life. I sympathize with the artistic temperament; I remember you used sometimes to hint to me that you thought my own temperament too artistic. I don't think that in Boston there is any real sympathy with the artistic temperament; we tend to make everything a matter of right and wrong. And in Boston one can't *live—on ne peut pas vivre*, as they say here. I don't mean one can't reside—for a great many people manage that; but one can't live aesthetically, I may almost venture to say sensuously. This is why I have always been so much drawn to the French, who are so aesthetic, so sensuous. I am so sorry that Théophile Gautier has passed away; I should have liked so much to go and see him and tell him all that I owe him. He was living when I was here before; but, you know, at that time I was travelling with the Johnsons, who are not aesthetic and who used to make me feel rather ashamed of my artistic temperament. If I had gone to see the great apostle of beauty, I should have had to go clandestinely,—*en cachette*, as they say here; and that is not my nature; I like to do everything frankly, freely, *naïvement, au grand jour*. That is the great thing,—to be free, to be frank, to be *naïf*. Doesn't Matthew Arnold say that somewhere—or is it Swinburne, or Pater?

When I was with the Johnsons everything was superficial; and, as regards life, everything was brought down to the question of right and wrong. They were too didactic; art should never be didactic; and what is life but an art? Pater has said that so well, somewhere. With the Johnsons I am afraid I lost many opportunities; the whole tone was grey and cottony; I might almost say woolly. But now, as I tell you, I have determined to take right hold for myself; to look right into European life, and judge it without Johnsonian prejudices. I have taken up my residence in a French family, in a real Parisian house. You see I have the courage of my opinions; I don't shrink from carrying out my theory that the great thing is to *live*.

You know I have always been intensely interested in Balzac, who never shrank from the reality, and whose almost *lurid* pictures of Parisian life have often haunted me in my wanderings through the old wicked-looking streets on the other side of the river. I am only sorry that my new friends—the French family—do not live in the old city,—*au coeur du vieux Paris*, as they say here. They live only in the Boulevard Hauss-man, which is less picturesque; but in spite of this they have a great deal of the Balzac tone. Madame de Maisonrouge belongs to one of the old-est and proudest families in France; but she has had reverses, which have compelled her to open an establishment in which a limited number of travellers, who are weary of the beaten track, who have the sense of local colour—she explains it herself, she expresses it so well—in short, to open a sort of boarding-house. I don't see why I should not, after all, use that expression, for it is the correlative of the term *pension bourgeoise*, em-ployed by Balzac in the *Père Goriot*. Do you remember the *pension bourgeoise* of Madame Vauquer, *née* de Conflans? But this establishment is not at all like that; and indeed it is not at all *bourgeoise*; there is some-thing distinguished, something aristocratic about it. The Pension Vauquer was dark, brown, sordid, *graisseux*; but this is in quite a different tone, with high, clear, lightly-draped windows, tender, subtle, almost morbid colours, and furniture in elegant, studied, reed-like lines. Madame de Maison-rouge reminds me of Madame Hulot—do you remember 'la belle Madame Hulot'?—in *Les Parents Pauvres*? She has a great charm; a little artificial, a little fatigued, with a little suggestion of hidden things in her life; but I have always been sensitive to the charm of fatigue, of duplicity. . . .

I am rather disappointed, I confess, in the society I find here; it is not so local, so characteristic, as I could have desired. Indeed, to tell the truth, it is not local at all; but, on the other hand, it is cosmopolitan, and there is a great advantage in that. We are French, we are English, we are American, we are German; and I believe there are some Russians and Hungarians expected.

I am much interested in the study of national types; in comparing, con-trasting, seizing the strong points, the weak points, the point of view of each. It is interesting to shift one's point of view—to enter into strange, exotic ways of looking at life.

The American types here are not, I am sorry to say, so interesting as they might be, and, excepting myself, are exclusively feminine. We are *thin*, my dear Harvard; we are pale, we are sharp. There is something meagre about us; our line is wanting in roundness, our composition in richness. We lack temperament; we don't know how to live: *nous ne savons pas vivre,* as they say here. The American temperament is represented (putting myself aside, and I often think my temperament is not at all American) by a young girl and her mother, and another young girl without her mother,—without her mother or any attendant or appendage whatever. These young girls are rather curious types; they have a certain interest, they have a certain grace; but they are disappointing, too; they don't go far; they don't keep all they promise; they don't satisfy the imagination. They are cold, slim, sexless; the physique is not generous, not abundant; it is only the drapery, the skirts and furbelows (that is, I mean, in the young lady who has her mother), that are abundant. They are very different: one of them all elegance, all expensiveness, with an air of high fashion, from New York; the other a plain, pure, clear-eyed, straight-waisted, straight-stepping maiden from the heart of New England. And yet they are very much alike too—more alike than they would care to think themselves; for they eye each other with cold, mistrustful, depreciating looks. They are both specimens of the emancipated young American girl,—practical, positive, passionless, subtle, and. knowing, as you please, either too much or too little. And yet, as I say, they have a certain stamp, a certain grace; I like to talk with them, to study them.

The fair New Yorker is, sometimes, very amusing; she asks me if every one in Boston talks like me—if every one is as 'intellectual' as your poor correspondent. She is forever throwing Boston up at me; I can't get rid of Boston. The other one rubs it into me too; but in a different way; she seems to feel about it as a good Mohammedan feels toward Mecca, and regards it as a kind of focus of light for the whole human race. Poor little Boston, what nonsense is talked in thy name! But this New England maiden is, in her way, a strange type; she is travelling all over Europe alone,—'to see it,' she says, 'for herself.' For herself! What can that stiff, slim self of hers do with such sights, such visions! She looks at everything, goes everywhere, passes her way, with her clear quiet eyes wide open, skirting the edge of obscene abysses without suspecting them, pushing through brambles without tearing her robe, exciting, without knowing it, the most injurious suspicions, and always holding her course, passionless, stainless, fearless, charmless! It is a little figure in which, after all, if you can get the right point of view, there is something rather striking.

By way of contrast, there is a lovely English girl, with eyes as shy as violets, and a voice as sweet! She has a sweet Gainsborough head, and a great Gainsborough hat, with a mighty plume in front of it, which makes a shadow over her quiet English eyes. Then she has a sage-green robe, 'mystic, wonderful,' all embroidered with subtle devices and flowers, and birds of tender tint; very straight and tight in front, and adorned behind, along the spine, with large, strange, iridescent buttons. The revival of taste, of the sense of beauty, in England, interests me deeply; what is

there in a simple row of spinal buttons to make one dream,—to *donner
à rêver*, as they say here? I think that a great aesthetic renascence is at
hand, and that a great light will be kindled in England, for all the world
to see. There are spirits there that I should like to commune with; I
think they would understand me.

This gracious English maiden, with her clinging robes, her amulets
and girdles, with something quaint and angular in her step, her carriage
something medieval and Gothic, in the details of her person and dress,
this lovely Evelyn Vane (isn't it a beautiful name?) is deeply, delight-
fully picturesque. She is much a woman,—*elle est bien femme*, as they
say here; simpler, softer, rounder, richer than the young girls I spoke of
just now. Not much talk—a great, sweet silence. Then the violet eye—
the very eye itself seems to blush; the great shadowy hat, making the brow
so quiet; the strange, clinging, clutching, pictured raiment! As I say, it is
a very gracious, tender type. She has her brother with her, who is a beautiful, fair-haired, grey-eyed young Englishman. He is purely objective; and
he, too, is very plastic.

V

From Miranda Hope to Her Mother

September 26

You must not be frightened at not hearing from me oftener; it is not
because I am in any trouble but because I am getting on so well. If I
were in any trouble I don't think I should write to you; I should just keep
quiet and see it through myself. But that is not the case at present; and,
if I don't write to you, it is because I am so deeply interested over here
that I don't seem to find time. It was a real providence that brought me
to this house, where, in spite of all obstacles, I am able to do much good
work. I wonder how I find the time for all I do; but when I think that
I have only got a year in Europe, I feel as if I wouldn't sacrifice a single
hour.

The obstacles I refer to are the disadvantages I have in learning French,
there being so many persons around me speaking English, and that, as
you may say, in the very bosom of a French family. It seems as if you
heard English everywhere; but I certainly didn't expect to find it in a
place like this. I am not discouraged, however, and I talk French all I
can, even with the other English boarders. Then I have a lesson every day
from Miss Maisonrouge (the elder daughter of the lady of the house),
and French conversation every evening in the *salon*, from eight to eleven,
with Madame herself and some friends of hers that often come in. Her
cousin, Mr. Verdier, a young French gentleman, is fortunately staying
with her, and I make a point of talking with him as much as possible.
I have *extra-private lessons* from him, and I often go out to walk with

him. Some night, soon, he is to accompany me to the opera. We have also a most interesting plan of visiting all the galleries in Paris together. Like most of the French, he converses with great fluency, and I feel as if I should really gain from him. He is remarkably handsome and extremely polite—paying a great many compliments which, I am afraid, are not always *sincere*. When I return to Bangor I will tell you some of the things he has said to me. I think you will consider them extremely curious, and very beautiful *in their way*.

The conversation in the parlour (from eight to eleven) is often remarkably brilliant, and I often wish that you, or some of the Bangor folks, could be there to enjoy it. Even though you couldn't understand it I think you would like to hear the way they go on; they seem to express so much. I sometimes think at Bangor they don't express enough (but it seems as if over there there was less to express). It seems as if, at Bangor, there were things that folks never *tried* to say; but here, I have learned from studying French, you have no idea what you *can* say before you try. At Bangor they seem to give it up beforehand; they don't make any effort. (I don't say this in the least for William Platt, *in particular*.)

I am sure I don't know what they will think of me when I get back. It seems as if, over here, I had learned to come out with everything. I suppose they will think I am not sincere; but isn't it more sincere to come out with things than to conceal them? I have become very good friends with every one in the house—that is (you see, I *am* sincere), with *almost* everyone. It is the most interesting circle I ever was in. There's a girl here, an American, that I don't like so much as the rest; but that is only because she won't let me. I should like to like her, ever so much, because she is most lovely and most attractive; but she doesn't seem to want to know me or to like me. She comes from New York, and she is remarkably pretty, with beautiful eyes and the most delicate features; she is also remarkably elegant,—in this respect would bear comparison with any one I have seen over here. But it seems as if she did not want to recognize me or associate with me; as if she wanted to make a difference between us. It is like people they call 'haughty' in books. I have never seen any one like that before—any one that wanted to make a difference; and at first I was right down interested, she seemed to me like a proud young lady in a novel. I kept saying to myself all day, 'haughty, haughty,' and I wished she would keep on so. But she did keep on; she kept on too long; and then I began to feel hurt. I couldn't think what I have done, and I can't think yet. It's as if she had got some idea about me, or had heard some one say something. If some girls should behave like that I shouldn't make any account of it; but this one is so refined, and looks as if she might be interesting if I once got to know her, that I think about it a good deal. I am bound to find out what her reason is,—for of course she has got some reason; I am right down curious to know.

I went up to her to ask her the day before yesterday; I thought that was the best way. I told her I wanted to know her better, and would like to come and see her in her room—they tell me she has got a lovely room— and that if she had heard anything against me, perhaps she would tell me when I came. But she was more distant than ever, and she just turned it off; said she had never heard me mentioned, and that her room was much too small to receive visitors. I suppose she spoke the truth, but I am sure she has got some reason, all the same. She has got some idea, and I am bound to find out before I go, if I have to ask everybody in the house. I am right down curious. I wonder if she doesn't think me refined—or if she had ever heard anything against Bangor? I can't think it is that. Don't you remember when Clara Barnard went to visit in New York, three years ago, how much attention she received? And you know Clara *is* Bangor to the soles of her shoes. Ask William Platt—so long as he isn't a native—if he doesn't consider Clara Barnard refined.

Apropos, as they say here, of refinement, there is another American in the house—a gentleman from Boston—who is just crowded with it. His name is Mr. Louis Leverett (such a beautiful name, I think) and he is about thirty years old. He is rather small, and he looks pretty sick; he suffers from some affection of the liver. But his conversation is remarkably interesting, and I delight to listen to him—he has such beautiful ideas. I feel as if it were hardly right, not being in French; but, fortunately, he uses a great many French expressions. It's in a different style from the conversation of Mr. Verdier,—not so complimentary but more intellectual. He is intensely fond of pictures, and has given me a great many ideas about them which I should never have gained without him; I shouldn't have known where to look for such ideas. He thinks everything of pictures; he thinks we don't make near enough of them. They seem to make a good deal of them here; but I couldn't help telling him the other day that in Bangor I really don't think we do.

If I had any money to spend I would buy some and take them back, to hang up. Mr. Leverett says it would do them good,—not the pictures but the Bangor folks. He thinks everything of the French, too, and says we don't make nearly enough of *them.* I couldn't help telling him the other day that at any rate they make enough of themselves. But it is very interesting to hear him go on about the French, and it is so much gain to me, so long as that is what I came for. I talk to him as much as I dare about Boston, but I do feel as if this were right down wrong—a stolen pleasure.

I can get all the Boston culture I want when I go back, if I carry out my plan, my happy vision, of going there to reside. I ought to direct all my efforts to European culture now, and keep Boston to finish off. But it seems as if I couldn't help taking a peep now and then, in advance—

with a Bostonian. I don't know when I may meet one again; but if there are many others like Mr. Leverett there, I shall be certain not to want when I carry out my dream. He is just as full of culture as he can live. But it seems strange how many different sorts there are.

There are two of the English here who I suppose are very cultivated, too; but it doesn't seem as if I could enter into theirs so easily, though I try all I can. I do love their way of speaking, and sometimes I feel almost as if it would be right to give up trying to learn French, and just try to learn to speak our own tongue as these English speak it. It isn't the things they say so much, though these are often rather curious; but it is in the way they pronounce and the sweetness of their voice. It seems as if they must *try* a good deal to talk like that; but these English that are here don't seem to try at all, either to speak or do anything else. They are a young lady and her brother. I believe they belong to some noble family. I have had a good deal of intercourse with them, because I have felt more free to talk to them than to the Americans—on account of the language. It seems as if in talking with them I was almost learning a new language.

I never supposed, when I left Bangor, that I was coming to Europe to learn *English!* If I do learn it, I don't think you will understand me when I get back, and I don't think you'll like it very much. I should be a good deal criticised if I spoke like that at Bangor. However, I verily believe Bangor is the most critical place on earth; I have seen nothing like it over here. Tell them all that I have come to the conclusion that they are *a great deal too fastidious.* But I was speaking about this English young lady and her brother. I wish I could put them before you. She is lovely to look at, she seems so modest and retiring. In spite of this, however, she dresses in a way that attracts great attention, as I couldn't help noticing when one day I went out to walk with her. She was ever so much looked at; but she didn't seem to notice it, until at last I couldn't help calling attention to it. Mr. Leverett thinks everything of it; he calls it the 'costume of the future.' I should call it rather the costume of the past—you know the English have such an attachment to the past. I said this the other day to Madame de Maisonrouge,—that Miss Vane dressed in the costume of the past. *De l'an passé, vous voulez dire?* said Madame, with her little French laugh (you can get William Platt to translate this, he used to tell me he knew so much French).

You know I told you in writing some time ago that I had tried to get some insight into the position of woman in England, and, being here with Miss Vane, it has seemed to me to be a good opportunity to get a little more. I have asked her a great deal about it; but she doesn't seem able to give me much information. The first time I asked her she told me the position of a lady depended upon the rank of her father, her eldest brother, her husband, etc. She told me her own position was very good, because her father was some relation—I forget what—to a lord. She thinks everything of this; and that proves to me that the position of woman in her country cannot be satisfactory; because, if it were, it wouldn't depend upon that of your relations, even your nearest. I don't know much about lords, and it does try my patience (though she is just as sweet as she can live) to hear her talk as if it were a matter of course that I should.

I feel as if it were right to ask her as often as I can if she doesn't consider every one equal; but she always says she doesn't, and she confesses that she doesn't think she is equal to Lady Something-or-other, who is the wife of that relation of her father. I try and persuade her all I can that she is; but it seems as if she didn't want to be persuaded; and when I ask her if Lady So-and-so is of the same opinion (that Miss Vane isn't her equal), she looks so soft and pretty with her eyes, and says, 'Of course she is!' When I tell her that this is right down bad for Lady So-and-so, it seems as if she wouldn't believe me, and the only answer she will make is that Lady So-and-so is 'extremely nice.' I don't believe she is nice at all; if she were nice she wouldn't have such ideas as that.

I tell Miss Vane that at Bangor we think such ideas vulgar; but then she looks as though she had never heard of Bangor. I often want to shake her, though she *is* so sweet. If she isn't angry with the people who make her feel that way, I am angry for her. I am angry with her brother, too, for she is evidently very much afraid of him, and this gives me some further insight into the subject. She thinks everything of her brother, and thinks it natural that she should be afraid of him, not only physically (for this *is* natural, as he is enormously tall and strong and has very big fists), but morally and intellectually. She seems unable, however, to take in any argument, and she makes me realize what I have often heard,—that if you are timid nothing will reason you out of it.

Mr. Vane also, the brother, seems to have the same prejudices, and when I tell him, as I often think it right to do, that his sister is not his subordinate, even if she does think so, but his equal and perhaps in some respects his superior, and that if my brother, in Bangor, were to treat me as he treats this poor young girl, who has not spirit enough to see the question in its true light, there would be an indignation meeting of the citizens, to protest against such an outrage to the sanctity of woman-hood,—when I tell him all this, at breakfast or dinner, he bursts out laughing so loud that all the plates clatter on the table.

But at such a time as this there is always one person who seems interested in what I say,—a German gentleman, a professor, who sits next to me at dinner, and whom I must tell you more about another time. He is very learned, and has a great desire for information; he appreciates a great many of my remarks, and, after dinner, in the salon, he often comes to me to ask me questions about them. I have to think a little, sometimes, to know what I did say or what I do think. He takes you right up where you left off, and he is almost as fond of discussing things as William Platt is. He is splendidly educated, in the German style, and he told me the other day that he was an 'intellectual broom.' Well, if he is, he sweeps clean; I told him that. After he has been talking to me I feel as if I hadn't got a speck of dust left in my mind anywhere. It's a most delightful feeling. He says he's an observer; and I am sure there is plenty over here to observe. But I have told you enough for today. I don't know how much longer I shall stay here; I am getting on so fast that it sometimes seems as if I shouldn't need all the time I have laid out. I suppose your cold weather has promptly begun, as usual; it sometimes makes me envy you. The fall weather here is very dull and damp and I feel very much as if I should like to be braced up.

VI

From Miss Evelyn Vane, in Paris, to the Lady Augusta Fleming, at Brighton

September 30, Paris

Dear Lady Augusta:—

I am afraid I shall not be able to come to you on January 7th, as you kindly proposed at Homburg. I am so very, very sorry; it is a great disappointment to me. But I have just heard that it has been settled that mamma and the children are coming abroad for a part of winter, and mamma wishes me to go with them to Hyères, where Georgina has been ordered for her lungs. She has not been at all well these three months, and now that the damp weather has begun, she is very poorly indeed; so that last week papa decided to have a consultation, and he and mamma went with her up to town and saw some three or four doctors. They all of them ordered the South of France, but they didn't agree about the place; so that mamma herself decided for Hyères, because it is the most economical. I believe it is very dull, but I hope it will do Georgina good. I am afraid, however, that nothing will do her good until she consents to take more care of herself; I am afraid she is very wild and wilful, and mamma tells me that all this month it has taken papa's positive orders to make her stop indoors.

She is very cross (mamma writes me) about coming abroad, and doesn't seem at all to mind the expense that papa has been put to,—talks very ill-naturedly about losing the hunting, etc. She expected to begin to hunt in December, and wants to know whether anybody keeps any hounds at Hyères. Fancy a girl wanting to follow the hounds when her lungs are so bad! But I dare say that when she gets there she will be glad enough to keep quiet, as they say that the heat is intense. It may cure Georgina, but I am sure it will make the rest of us very ill.

Mamma, however, is only going to bring Mary and Gus and Fred and Adelaide abroad with her; the others will remain at Kingscote until February, when they will go to Eastbourne for a month with Miss Philpotts, the new governess, who turned out such a very nice person. She is going to take Miss Travers, who has been with us so long, but who is only qualified for the younger children, to Hyères, and I believe some of the Kingscote servants. She has perfect confidence in Miss P.; it is only a pity she has such an odd name. Mamma thought of asking if she would mind taking another when she came; but papa thought she might object. Lady Battledown makes all her governesses take the same name; she gives five pounds more a year for the purpose. I forget what it is she calls them; I think it's Thompson (which to me always suggests a lady's maid). Governesses shouldn't have too pretty a name; they shouldn't have a nicer name than the family.

I suppose you heard from the Desmonds that I did not go back to England with them. When it began to be talked about that Georgina should be taken abroad, mamma wrote to me that I had better stop in Paris for a month with Harold, so that she could pick me up on their way to Hyères. It saves the expense of my journey to Kingscote and back, and gives me the opportunity to 'finish' a little, in French.

You know Harold came over here six weeks ago, to get up his French for those dreadful examinations that he has to pass so soon. He came to live with some French people that take in young men (and others) for this purpose; it's a kind of coaching place, only kept by women. Mamma had heard it was very nice; so she wrote me that I was to come and stop here with Harold. The Desmonds brought me and made the arrangement, or the bargain, or whatever you call it. Poor Harold was naturally not at all pleased; but he has been very kind and has treated me like an angel. He is getting on beautifully with his French; for though I don't think the place is so good as papa supposed, yet Harold is so immensely clever that he can scarcely help learning. I am afraid I learn much less; but, fortunately, I have not to pass an examination—except if mamma takes it into her head to examine me. But she will have so much to think of with Georgina that I hope this won't occur to her. If it does, I shall be as Harold says, in a beautiful funk.

This is not such a nice place for a girl as for a young man, and the Desmonds thought it exceedingly odd that mamma should wish me to come here. As Mrs. Desmond said, it is because she is so very unconventional. But you know Paris is so very amusing, and if only Harold remains good-natured about it, I shall be content to wait for the caravan (that's what he calls mamma and the children). The person who keeps the establishment, or whatever they call it, is rather odd and *exceedingly foreign*; but she is wonderfully civil and is perpetually sending to my door to see if I want anything. The servants are not at all like English servants, and come bursting in, the footman (they have only one) and the maids alike, at all sorts of hours, in the *most sudden way*. Then when one rings, it is half an hour before they come. All this is very uncomfortable, and I dare say it will be worse at Hyères. There, however, fortunately, we shall have our own people.

There are some very odd Americans here, who keep throwing Harold into fits of laughter. One is a dreadful little man, who is always sitting over the fire and talking about the colour of the sky. I don't believe he ever saw the sky except through the windowpane. The other day he took hold of my frock (the green one you thought so nice at Homburg) and told me that it reminded him of the texture of the Devonshire turf. And then he talked for half an hour about the Devonshire turf, which I thought such a very extraordinary subject. Harold says he is mad. It is very strange to be living in this way, with people one doesn't know,— I mean that one doesn't know as one knows them in England.

The other Americans (besides the mad gentleman) are two girls, about my own age, one of whom is rather nice. She has a mother; but the mother is always sitting in her bedroom, which seems so very odd. I should like mamma to ask them to Kingscote, but I am afraid mamma wouldn't like the mother, who is rather vulgar. The other girl is rather vulgar, too, and is travelling about quite alone. I think she is a kind of school mistress; but the other girl (I mean the nicer one, with the mother) tells me she is more respectable than she seems. She has, however, the most extraordinary opinions,—wishes to do away with the aristocracy, thinks it wrong that Arthur should have Kingscote when papa dies, etc. I don't see what it signifies to her that poor Arthur should come into the property, which will be so delightful—except for papa dying. But Harold says she is mad. He chaffs her tremendously about her radicalism, and he is so immensely clever that she can't answer him, though she is rather clever, too.

There is also a Frenchman, a nephew, or cousin, or something, of the person of the house, who is extremely nasty; and a German professor, or doctor, who eats with his knife and is a great bore. I am so very sorry about giving up my visit; I am afraid you will never ask me again.

VII

From Léon Verdier, in Paris, to Prosper Gobain, at Lille

September 28

My Dear Prosper:—

It is a long time since I have given you my news, and I don't know what puts it into my head tonight to recall myself to your affectionate memory. I suppose it is that when we are happy the mind reverts instinctively to those with whom formerly we shared our exultations and depressions, and *je t'en ai trop dit, dans le bons temps, mon gros Prosper,* and you always listened to me too imperturbably, with your pipe in your mouth, your waistcoat unbuttoned, for me not to feel that I can count upon your sympathy today. *Nous en sommes-nous flanquées des confidences?*—in those happy days when my first thought in seeing an adventure *poindre à l'horizon* was of the pleasure I should have in relating it to the great Prosper. As I tell thee, I am happy; decidedly, I am happy; and from this affirmation I fancy you can construct the rest. Shall I help thee a little? Take three adorable girls—three, my good Prosper,—the mystic number, neither more nor less. Take them and place thy insatiable little Léon in the midst of them! Is the situation sufficiently indicated and do you apprehend the motives of my felicity?

You expected, perhaps, I was going to tell you that I had made my fortune, or that Uncle Blondeau had at last decided to return into the breast of nature, after having constituted me his universal legatee. But I needn't remind you that women are always for something in the happiness of him who writes to thee—for something in his happiness and for a good deal more in his misery. But don't let me talk of misery now; time enough when it comes; *ces demoiselles* have gone to join the serried ranks of their amiable predecessors. Excuse me—I comprehend your impatience. I will tell you of whom *ces demoiselles* consist.

You have heard me speak of my *cousine* de Maisonrouge, that *grande belle femme,* who, after having married, *en secondes noces*—there had been, to tell the truth, some irregularity about her first union,—a venerable relic of the old noblesse of Poitou, was left, by the death of her husband, complicated by the indulgence of expensive tastes on an income of 17,000 francs, on the pavement of Paris, with two little demons of daughters to bring up in the path of virtue. She managed to bring them up; my little cousins are rigidly virtuous. If you ask me how she managed it, I can't tell you: it's no business of mine, and, *à fortiori,* none of yours. She is now fifty years old (she confesses to thirty-seven), and her daughters, whom she has never been able to marry, are respectively twenty-seven and twenty-three (they confess to twenty-two and eighteen). Three years ago she had the thrice-blessed idea of opening a sort of *pension* for the entertainment and instruction of the blundering barbarians who come to Paris in the hope of picking up a few stray particles of the language of Voltaire—or of Zola. The idea *lui a porté bonheur;* the shop does a very good business. Until within a few months ago it was carried on by my cousins alone; but lately the need of a few extensions and embellishments has caused itself to be felt. My cousin has undertaken them, regardless of expense; she has asked me to come and stay with her—board and lodging gratis—and keep an eye on the grammatical irregularities of her *pensionnaires.* I am the extension, my good Prosper; I am the embellishment! I live for nothing and I straighten out the accent of the prettiest

English lips. The English lips are not all pretty, Heaven knows, but enough of them are so to make it a gaining bargain for me.

Just now, as I told you, I am in daily conversation with three separate pairs. The owner of one of them has private lessons; she pays extra. My cousin doesn't give me a sou of the money; but I make bold, nevertheless, to say that my trouble is remunerated. But I am well, very well, with the proprietors of the two other pairs. One of them is a little Anglaise, of about twenty,—a little *figure de keepsake*; the most adorable miss that you ever, or at least that I ever, beheld. She is decorated all over with beads and bracelets and embroidered dandelions; but her principal decoration consists of the softest little grey eyes in the world, which rest upon you with a profundity of confidence,—a confidence that I really felt some compunction in betraying. She has a tint as white as this sheet of paper, except just in the middle of each cheek, where it passes into the purest and most transparent, most liquid, carmine. Occasionally this rosy fluid overflows into the rest of her face—by which I mean that she blushes—as softly as the mark of your breath on the windowpane.

Like every Anglaise, she is rather pinched and prim in public; but it is very easy to see that when no one is looking *elle ne demande qu'à se laisser aller!* Whenever she wants it I am always there, and I have given her to understand that she can count upon me. I have every reason to believe that she appreciates the assurance, though I am bound in honesty to confess that with her the situation is a little advanced than with the others. *Que voulez-vous?* The English are heavy, and the Anglaises move slowly, that's all. The movement, however, is perceptible, and once this fact is established I can let the pottage simmer. I can give her time to arrive, for I am over-well occupied with her *concurrentes. Celles-ci* don't keep me waiting, *par exemple!*

These young ladies are Americans, and you know that it is their national character to move fast. 'All right—go ahead!' (I am learning a great deal of English, or, rather, a great deal of American.) They go ahead at a rate that sometimes makes it difficult for me to keep up.

One of them is prettier than the other; but this latter (the one that takes the private lessons) is really *une fille prodigieuse. Ah, par exemple, elle brûle ses vaisseaux, celle-là!* She threw herself into my arms the very first day, and I almost owed her a grudge for having deprived me of that pleasure of gradation, of carrying the defences, one by one, which is almost as great as that of entering the place.

Would you believe that at the end of exactly twelve minutes she gave me a rendezvous? It is true it was in the Galerie d'Apollon, at the Louvre; but that was respectable for a beginning, and since then we have had them by the dozen. I have ceased to keep the account. *Non, c'est une fille qui me dépasse.*

The little one (she has a mother somewhere, out of sight, shut up in a closet or a trunk) is a good deal prettier, and, perhaps, on that account *elle y met plus de façons.* She doesn't knock about Paris with me by the hour; she contents herself with long interviews in the *petit salon*, with the curtains half-drawn, beginning at about three o'clock, when every one is *à la promenade*. She is admirable, this little one; a little too thin, the bones rather accentuated, but the detail, on the whole, most satisfactory. *Non, elle est bien gentille.* And you can say anything to her. She takes the trouble to appear not to understand, but her conduct, half an hour afterwards, reassures you completely—oh, completely!

However, it is the tall one, the one of the private lessons, that is the most remarkable. These private lessons, my dear Prosper, are the most brilliant inventions of the age, and a real stroke of genius on the part of Miss Miranda. They also take place in the *petit salon*, but with the doors tightly closed, and with explicit directions to every one in the house that we are not to be disturbed. And we are not, my dear Prosper; we are not! Not a sound, not a shadow, interrupts our felicity. My *cousine* is really admirable; the shop deserves to succeed.

Miss Miranda is tall and rather flat; she is too pale; she hasn't the adorable *rougeurs* of the little Anglaise. But she has bright, keen, inquisitive eyes, superb teeth, a nose modelled by a sculptor, and a way of holding up her head and looking every one in the face, which is the most finished piece of impertinence I ever beheld. She is making the *tour du monde*, entirely alone, without even a soubrette to carry the ensign, for the purpose of seeing for herself *à quoi s'en tenir sur les hommes et les choses*— on *les hommes* particularly. *Dis donc*, Prosper, it must be a *drôle de pays* over there, where young persons animated by this ardent curiosity are manufactured! If we should turn the tables, some day, thou and I, and go over there and see it for ourselves. It is as well that we should go and find them *chez elles*, as that they should come out here after us. *Dis donc, mon gros Prosper.* . . .

VIII

From Dr. Rudolf Staub, in Paris, to Dr. Julius Hirsch, at Göttingen

My Dear Brother in Science:—

I resume my hasty notes, of which I sent you the first instalment some weeks ago. I mentioned then that I intended to leave my hotel, not finding it sufficiently local and national. It was kept by a Pomeranian, and the waiters, without exception, were from the Fatherland. I fancied myself at Berlin, Unter den Linden, and I reflected that, having taken the serious step of visiting the headquarters of the Gaellic genius, I should try and project myself, as much as possible, into the circumstances, which are in part the consequence and in part the cause of its irrepressible activity. It seemed to me that there could be no well-grounded knowledge without this preliminary operation of placing myself in relations, as slightly as possible modified by elements proceeding from a different combination of causes, with the spontaneous home-life of the country.

I accordingly engaged a room in the house of a lady of pure French extraction and education, who supplements the shortcomings of an income insufficient to the ever-growing demands of the Parisian system of sense-gratification, by providing food and lodging for a limited number of distinguished strangers. I should have preferred to have my room alone in the house, and to take my meals in a brewery, of very good appearance, which I speedily discovered in the same street; but this arrangement, though very lucidly proposed by myself, was not acceptable to the mistress of the establishment (a woman with a mathematical head), and I have consoled myself for the extra expense by fixing my thoughts upon the opportunity that conformity to the customs of the house gives me of studying the table manners of my companions, and of observing the French nature at a peculiarly physiological moment, when the satisfaction of the *taste*, which is the governing quality in its composition, produces a kind of exhalation, an intellectual transpiration, which, though light, and perhaps invisible to a superficial spectator, is nevertheless appreciable by a properly adjusted instrument.

I have adjusted my instrument very satisfactorily (I mean the one I carry in my good, square German head), and I am not afraid of losing a single drop of this valuable fluid, as it condenses itself upon the plate of my observation. A prepared surface is what I need, and I have prepared my surface.

Unfortunately here, also, I find the individual native in the minority. There are only four French persons in the house,—the individuals concerned in its management, three of whom are women, and one a man. The preponderance of the feminine element is, however, in itself characteristic, as I need not remind you what an abnormally developed part this sex has played in French history. The remaining figure is apparently that of a man, but I hesitate to classify him so superficially. He appears to me less human than simian, and whenever I hear him talk I seem to myself to have paused in the street to listen to the shrill clatter of a hand-organ, to which the gambols of an hairy *homunculus* form an accompaniment.

I mentioned to you before that my expectation of rough usage, in consequence of my German nationality, has proved completely unfounded. No one seems to know or care what my nationality is, and I am treated, on the contrary, with the civility which is the portion of every traveller who pays the bill without scanning the items too narrowly. This, I confess, has been something of a surprise to me, and I have not yet made up my mind as to the fundamental cause of the anomaly.

My determination to take up my abode in a French interior was largely dictated by the supposition that I should be substantially disagreeable to its inmates. I wished to observe the different forms taken by the irritation that I should naturally produce; for it is under the influence of irritation that the French character most completely expresses itself. My presence, however, does not appear to operate as a stimulus, and in this respect I am materially disappointed. They treat me as they treat every one else; whereas, in order to be treated differently, I was resigned in advance to being treated worse.

I have not, as I say, fully explained to myself this logical contradiction; but this is the explanation to which I tend. The French are so exclusively occupied with the idea of themselves, that in spite of the very definite image the German personality presented to them by the war of 1870, they have at present no distinct apprehension of its existence. They are not very sure that there are any Germans; they have already forgotten the convincing proofs of the fact that were presented to them nine years ago. A German was something disagreeable, which they determined to keep out of their conception of things. I therefore think that we are wrong to govern ourselves upon the hypothesis of the *revanche*; the French nature is too shallow for that large and powerful plant to bloom in it.

The English-speaking specimens, too, I have not been willing to neglect the opportunity to examine; among these I have paid special attention to the American varieties, of which I find here several singular examples. The two most remarkable are a young man who presents all the characteristics of a period of national decadence; reminding me strongly of some diminutive Hellenized Roman of the third century. He is an illustration of the period of culture in which the faculty of appreciation has obtained such a preponderance over that of production that the latter sinks into a kind of rank sterility, and the mental condition becomes analogous to that of a malarious bog.

I learn from him that there is an immense number of Americans exactly resembling him, and that the city of Boston, indeed, is almost exclusively composed of them. (He communicated this fact very proudly, as if it were greatly to the credit of his native country; little perceiving the truly sinister impression it made upon me.)

What strikes one in it is that it is a phenomenon, to the best of my knowledge—and you know what my knowledge is—unprecedented and unique in the history of mankind; the arrival of a nation at an ultimate stage of evolution without having passed through the mediate one; the passage of the fruit, in other words, from crudity to rottenness, without the interposition of a period of useful (and ornamental) ripeness. With the Americans, indeed, the crudity and the rottenness are identical and simultaneous; it is impossible to say, as in the conversation of this deplorable young man, which is one and which is the other; they are inextricably mingled. I prefer the talk of the French *homunculus*; it is at least more amusing.

It is interesting in this manner to perceive, so largely developed, the germs of extinction in the so-called powerful Anglo-Saxon family. I find them in almost as recognizable a form in a young woman from the State of Maine, in the province of New England, with whom I have had a good deal of conversation. She differs somewhat from the young man I just mentioned, in that the faculty of production, of action, is, in her, less inanimate; she has more of the freshness and vigour that we suppose to belong to a young civilization. But unfortunately she produces nothing but evil, and her tastes and habits are similarly those of a Roman lady of the lower Empire. She makes no secret of them, and has, in fact, elaborated a complete system of licentious behaviour. As the opportunities she finds in her own country do not satisfy her, she has come to Europe 'to try,' as she says, 'for herself.'

It is the doctrine of universal experience professed with a cynicism that is really most extraordinary, and which, presenting itself in a young woman of considerable education, appears to me to be the judgment of a society.

Another observation which pushes me to the same induction—that of the premature vitiation of the American population—is the attitude of the Americans whom I have before me with regard to each other. There is another young lady here, who is less abnormally developed than the one I have just described, but who yet bears the stamp of this peculiar combination of incompleteness and effeteness.

These three persons look with the greatest mistrust and aversion upon each other; and each has repeatedly taken me aside and assured me, secretly, that he or she only is the real, the genuine, the typical American. A type that has lost itself before it has been fixed,—what can you look for from this?

Add to this that there are two young Englanders in the house, who hate all the Americans in a lump, making between them none of the distinctions and favourable comparisons which they insist upon, and you will, I think, hold me warranted in believing that, between precipitate decay and internecine enmities, the English-speaking family is destined to consume itself, and that with its decline the prospect of general pervasiveness, to which I alluded above, will brighten for the deep-lunged children of the Fatherland!

IX

Miranda Hope to Her Mother

October 22

Dear Mother:—

I am off in a day or two to visit some new country; I haven't decided which. I have satisfied myself with regard to France, and obtained a good knowledge of the language. I have enjoyed my visit to Madame de Maison-rouge deeply, and feel as if I were leaving a circle of real friends. Every-thing has gone on beautifully up to the end, and every one has been as kind and attentive as if I were their own sister, especially Mr. Verdier, the French gentleman, from whom I have gained more than I ever ex-pected (in six weeks) and with whom I have promised to *correspond*. So you can imagine me dashing off the most correct French letters; and, if you don't believe it, I will keep the rough draft to show you when I go back.

The German gentleman is also more interesting the more you know him; it seems sometimes as if I could fairly drink in his ideas. I have found out why the young lady from New York doesn't like me! It is because I said one day at dinner that I *admired* to go to the Louvre. Well, when I first came it seemed as if I *did* admire everything!

Tell William Platt his letter has come. I knew he would have to write, and I was bound I would make him! I haven't decided what country I will visit yet; it seems as if there were so many to choose from. But I shall take care to pick out a good one, and to meet plenty of fresh experiences.

Dearest mother, my money holds out, and it *is* most interesting!

MISS BIRDSEYE'S FRIENDS

IV

She had told him before they started that they should be early; she wished to see Miss Birdseye alone, before the arrival of any one else. This was just for the pleasure of seeing her—it was an opportunity; she was always so taken up with others. She received Miss Chancellor in the hall of the mansion, which had a salient front, an enormous and very high number—756—painted in gilt on the glass light above the door, a tin sign bearing the name of a doctress (Mary J. Prance) suspended from one of the windows of the basement, and a peculiar look of being both new and faded—a kind of modern fatigue—like certain articles of com-merce which are sold at a reduction as shop-worn. The hall was very narrow; a considerable part of it was occupied by a large hat-tree, from which several coats and shawls already depended; the rest offered space for certain lateral demonstrations on Miss Birdseye's part. She sidled about her visitors, and at last went round to open for them a door of further admission, which happened to be locked inside. She was a little old lady, with an enormous head; that was the first thing Ransom no-ticed—the vast, fair, protuberant, candid, ungarnished brow, surmount-ing a pair of weak, kind, tired-looking eyes, and ineffectually balanced in the rear by a cap which had the air of falling backward, and which Miss Birdseye suddenly felt for while she talked, with unsuccessful irrelevant movements. She had a sad, soft, pale face, which (and it was the effect of her whole head) looked as if it had been soaked, blurred, and made vague by exposure to some slow dissolvent. The long practice of philanthrophy had not given accent to her features; it had rubbed out their transitions, their meanings. The waves of sympathy, of enthusiasm, had wrought upon them in the same way in which the waves of time finally modify the surface of old marble busts, gradually washing away their sharpness, their details. In her large countenance her dim little smile scarcely showed. It was a mere sketch of a smile, a kind of instalment, or payment on account; it seemed to say that she would smile more if she had time, but that you could see, without this, that she was gentle and easy to beguile.

She always dressed in the same way: she wore a loose black jacket, with deep pockets, which were stuffed with papers, memoranda of a voluminous correspondence; and from beneath her jacket depended a short stuff dress. The brevity of this simple garment was the one device by which Miss Birdseye managed to suggest that she was a woman of business, that she wished to be free for action. She belonged to the Short-Skirts League, as a matter of course; for she belonged to any and every league that had been founded for almost any purpose whatever. This did not prevent her being a confused, entangled, inconsequent, discursive old woman, whose charity began at home and ended nowhere, whose credulity kept pace with it, and who knew less about her fellow-creatures, if possible, after fifty years of humanitary zeal, than on the day she had gone into the field to testify against the iniquity of most arrangements. Basil Ransom knew very little about such a life as hers, but she seemed to him a revelation of a class, and a multitude of socialistic figures, of names and episodes that he had heard of, grouped themselves behind her. She looked as if she had spent her life on platforms, in audiences, in conventions, in phalansteries, in *séances*; in her faded face there was a kind of reflection of ugly lecture-lamps; with its habit of an upward angle, it seemed turned toward a public speaker, with an effort of respiration in the thick air in which social reforms are usually discussed. She talked continually, in a voice of which the spring seemed broken, like that of an over-worked bell-wire; and when Miss Chancellor explained that she had brought Mr. Ransom because he was so anxious to meet Mrs. Farrinder, she gave the young man a delicate, dirty, democratic little hand, looking at him kindly, as she could not help doing, but without the smallest discrimination as against others who might not have the good fortune (which involved, possibly, an injustice) to be present on such an interesting occasion. She struck him as very poor, but it was only afterward that he learned she had never had a penny in her life. No one had an idea how she lived; whenever money was given her she gave it away to a negro or a refugee.

No woman could be less invidious, but on the whole she preferred these two classes of the human race. Since the Civil War much of her occupation was gone; for before that her best hours had been spent in fancying that she was helping some Southern slave to escape. It would have been a nice question whether, in her heart of hearts, for the sake of this excitement, she did not sometimes wish the blacks back in bondage. She had suffered in the same way by the relaxation of many European despotisms, for in former years much of the romance of her life had been in smoothing the pillow of exile for banished conspirators. Her refugees had been very precious to her; she was always trying to raise money for some cadaverous Pole, to obtain lessons for some shirtless Italian. There was a legend that an Hungarian had once possessed himself of her affections, and had disappeared after robbing her of everything she possessed. This, however, was very apocryphal, for she had never possessed anything, and it was open to grave doubt that she could have entertained a sentiment so personal. She was in love, even in those days, only with causes, and she languished only for emancipations. But they had been the happiest days, for when causes were embodied in foreigners (what else were the Africans?), they were certainly more appealing.

She had just come down to see Doctor Prance—to see whether she wouldn't like to come up. But she wasn't in her room, and Miss Birdseye guessed she had gone out to her supper; she got her supper at a boarding-table about two blocks off. Miss Birdseye expressed the hope that Miss Chancellor had had hers; she would have had plenty of time to take it, for no one had come in yet; she didn't know what made them all so late. Ransom perceived that the garments suspended to the hat-rack were not a sign that Miss Birdseye's friends had assembled; if he had gone a little further still he would have recognised the house as one of those in which mysterious articles of clothing are always hooked to something in the hall. Miss Birdseye's visitors, those of Doctor Prance, and of other tenants—for Number 756 was the common residence of several persons, among whom there prevailed much vagueness of boundary—used to leave things to be called for; many of them went about with satchels and reticules, for which they were always looking for places of deposit. What completed the character of this interior was Miss Birdseye's own apartment, into which her guests presently made their way, and where they were joined by various other members of the good lady's circle. Indeed, it completed Miss Birdseye herself, if anything could be said to render that office to this essentially formless old woman, who had no more outline than a bundle of hay. But the bareness of her long, loose, empty parlour (it was shaped exactly like Miss Chancellor's) told that she had never had any needs but moral needs, and that all her history had been that of her sympathies. The place was lighted by a small hot glare of gas, which made it look white and featureless. It struck even Basil Ransom with its flatness, and he said to himself that his cousin must have a very big bee in her bonnet to make her like such a house. He did not know then, and he never knew, that she mortally disliked it, and that in a career in which she was constantly exposing herself to offence and laceration, her most poignant suffering came from the injury of her taste. She had tried to kill that nerve, to persuade herself that taste was only frivolity in the disguise of knowledge; but her susceptibility was constantly blooming afresh and making her wonder whether an absence of nice arrangements were a necessary part of the enthusiasm of humanity. Miss Birdseye was always trying to obtain employment, lessons in drawing, orders for portraits, for poor foreign artists, as to the greatness of whose talent she pledged herself without reserve; but in point of fact she had not the faintest sense of the scenic or plastic side of life.

Toward nine o'clock the light of her hissing burners smote the majestic person of Mrs. Farrinder, who might have contributed to answer that question of Miss Chancellor's in the negative. She was a copious, handsome woman, in whom angularity had been corrected by the air of success; she had a rustling dress (it was evident what *she* thought about taste), abundant hair of a glossy blackness, a pair of folded arms, the expression of which seemed to say that rest, in such a career as hers, was as sweet as it was brief, and a terrible regularity of feature. I apply that adjective to her fine placid mask because she seemed to face you with a question of which the answer was preordained, to ask you how a countenance could fail to be noble of which the measurements were so correct. You could contest neither the measurements nor the nobleness, and had to feel that Mrs. Farrinder imposed herself. There was a lithographic smoothness about her, and a mixture of the American matron and the public character. There was something public in her eye, which was large, cold, and quiet; it had acquired a sort of exposed reticence from the habit of looking down from a lecture-desk, over a sea of heads, while its distinguished owner was eulogised by a leading citizen. Mrs. Farrinder, at almost any time, had the air of being introduced by a few remarks. She talked with great slowness and distinctness, and evidently a high sense of responsibility; she pronounced every syllable of every word and insisted on being explicit. If, in conversation with her, you attempted to take anything for granted, or to jump two or three steps at a time, she paused, looking at you with a cold patience, as if she knew that trick, and then went on at her own measured pace. She lectured on temperance and the rights of women; the ends she laboured for were to give the ballot to every woman in the country and to take the flowing bowl from every man. She was held to have a very fine manner, and to embody the domestic virtues and the graces of the drawing-room; to be a shining proof, in short, that the forum, for ladies, is not necessarily hostile to the fireside. She had a husband, and his name was Amariah.

Doctor Prance had come back from supper and made her appearance in response to an invitation that Miss Birdseye's relaxed voice had tinkled down to her from the hall over the banisters, with much repetition, to secure attention. She was a plain, spare young woman, with short hair and an eye-glass; she looked about her with a kind of near-sighted deprecation, and seemed to hope that she should not be expected to generalise in any way, or supposed to have come up for any purpose more social than to see what Miss Birdseye wanted this time. By nine o'clock twenty other persons had arrived, and had placed themselves in the chairs that were ranged along the sides of the long, bald room, in which they ended by producing the similitude of an enormous street-car. The apartment contained little else but these chairs, many of which had a borrowed aspect, an implication of bare bedrooms in the upper regions; a table or two with a discoloured marble top, a few books, and a collection of newspapers piled up in corners. Ransom could see for himself that the occasion was not crudely festive; there was a want of convivial movement, and, among most of the visitors, even of mutual recognition. They sat there as if they were waiting for something; they looked obliquely and silently at Mrs. Farrinder, and were plainly under the impression that, fortunately, they were not there to amuse themselves. The ladies, who were much the more numerous, wore their bonnets, like Miss Chancellor; the men were in the garb of toil, many of them in weary-looking overcoats. Two or three had retained their overshoes, and as you approached them the odour of the india-rubber was perceptible. It was not, however, that Miss Birdseye ever noticed anything of that sort; she neither knew what she smelled nor tasted what she ate. Most of her friends had an anxious, haggard look, though there were sundry exceptions—half a dozen placid, florid faces. Basil Ransom wondered who they all were; he had a general idea they were mediums, communists, vegetarians. It was not, either, that Miss Birdseye failed to wander about among them with repetitions of inquiry and friendly absences of attention; she sat down near most of them in turn, saying 'Yes, yes,' vaguely and kindly, to remarks they made to her, feeling for the papers in the pockets of her loosened bodice, recovering her cap and sacrificing her spectacles, wondering most of all what had been her idea in convoking these people. Then she remembered that it had been connected in some way with Mrs. Farrinder; that this eloquent woman had promised to favour the company with a few reminiscences of her last campaign; to sketch even, perhaps, the lines on which she intended to operate during the coming winter. This was what Olive Chancellor had come to hear; this would be the attraction for the dark-eyed young man (he looked like a genius) she had brought with her. Miss Birdseye made her way back to the great lecturess, who was bending an indulgent attention on Miss Chancellor; the latter compressed into a small space, to be near her, and sitting with clasped hands and a concentration of inquiry which by contrast made Mrs. Farrinder's manner seem large and free. In her transit, however, the hostess was checked by the arrival of fresh pilgrims; she had no idea she had mentioned the occasion to so many people—she only remembered, as it were, those she had forgotten—and it was certainly a proof of the interest felt in Mrs. Farrinder's work. The people who had just come in were Doctor and Mrs. Tarrant and their daughter Verena; he was a mesmeric healer and she was of old Abolitionist stock. Miss Birdseye rested her dim, dry smile upon the daughter, who was new to her, and it floated before her that she would probably be remarkable as a genius; her parentage was an implication of that. There was a genius for Miss Birdseye in every bush. Selah Tarrant had effected wonderful cures; she knew so many people—if they would only try him. His wife was a daughter of Abraham Greenstreet; she had kept a runaway slave in her house for thirty days. That was years before, when this girl must have been a child; but hadn't it thrown a kind of rainbow over her cradle, and wouldn't she naturally have some gift? The girl was very pretty, though she had red hair.

v

Mrs. Farrinder, meanwhile, was not eager to address the assembly. She confessed as much to Olive Chancellor, with a smile which asked that a temporary lapse of promptness might not be too harshly judged. She had addressed so many assemblies, and she wanted to hear what other people had to say. Miss Chancellor herself had thought so much on the vital subject; would not she make a few remarks and give them some of her experiences? How did the ladies on Beacon Street feel about the ballot? Perhaps she could speak for *them* more than for some others. That was a branch of the question on which, it might be, the leaders had not information enough; but they wanted to take in everything, and why shouldn't Miss Chancellor just make that field her own? Mrs. Farrinder spoke in the tone of one who took views so wide that they might easily, at first, before you could see how she worked round, look almost meretricious; she was conscious of a scope that exceeded the first flight of your imagination. She urged upon her companion the idea of labouring in the world of fashion, appeared to attribute to her familiar relations with that mysterious realm, and wanted to know why she shouldn't stir up some of her friends down there on the Mill-dam?

Olive Chancellor received this appeal with peculiar feelings. With her immense sympathy for reform, she found herself so often wishing that reformers were a little different. There was something grand about Mrs. Farrinder; it lifted one up to be with her: but there was a false note when she spoke to her young friend about the ladies in Beacon Street. Olive hated to hear that fine avenue talked about as if it were such a remarkable place, and to live there were a proof of worldly glory. All sorts of inferior people lived there, and so brilliant a woman as Mrs. Farrinder, who lived at Roxbury, ought not to mix things up. It was, of course, very wretched to be irritated by such mistakes; but this was not the first time Miss Chancellor had observed that the possession of nerves was not by itself a reason for embracing the new truths. She knew her place in the Boston hierarchy, and it was not what Mrs. Farrinder supposed; so that there was a want of perspective in talking to her as if she had been a representative of the aristocracy. Nothing could be weaker, she knew very well, than (in the United States) to apply that term too literally; nevertheless, it would represent a reality if one were to say that, by distinction, the Chancellors belonged to the *bourgeoisie*—the oldest and best. They might care for such a position or not (as it happened, they were very proud of it), but there they were, and it made Mrs. Farrinder seem provincial (there was something provincial, after all, in the way she did her hair too) not to understand. When Miss Birdseye spoke as if one were a 'leader of society,' Olive could forgive her even that odious expression, because, of course, one never pretended that she, poor dear, had the smallest sense of the real. She was heroic, she was sublime, the whole moral history of Boston was reflected in her displaced spectacles; but it was a part of her originality, as it were, that she was deliciously provincial. Olive Chancellor seemed to herself to have privileges enough without being affiliated to the exclusive set and having invitations to the smaller parties, which were the real test; it was a mercy for her that she had not that added immorality on her conscience. The ladies Mrs. Farrinder meant (it was to be supposed she meant some particular ones) might speak for themselves. She wished to work in another field; she had long been preoccupied with the romance of the people. She had an immense desire to know intimately some *very* poor girl. This might seem one of the most accessible of pleasures; but, in point of fact, she had not found it so. There were two or three pale shop-maidens whose acquaintance she had sought; but they had seemed afraid of her, and the attempt had come to nothing. She took them more tragically than they took themselves; they couldn't make out what she wanted them to do, and they always ended by being odiously mixed up with Charlie. Charlie was a young man in a white overcoat and a paper collar; it was for him, in the last analysis, that they cared much the most. They cared far more about Charlie than about the ballot. Olive Chancellor wondered how Mrs. Farrinder would treat that branch of the question. In her researches among her young townswomen she had always found this obtrusive swain planted in her path, and she grew at last to dislike him extremely. It filled her with exasperation to think that he should be necessary to the happiness of his victims (she had learned that whatever they might talk about with her, it was of him and him only that they discoursed among themselves), and one of the main recommendations of the evening club for her fatigued, underpaid sisters, which it had long been her dream to establish, was that it would in some degree undermine his position—distinct as her prevision might be that he would be in waiting at the door. She hardly knew what to say to Mrs. Farrinder when this momentarily misdirected woman, still preoccupied with the Mill-dam, returned to the charge.

'We want labourers in that field, though I know two or three lovely women—sweet *home-women*—moving in circles that are for the most part closed to every new voice, who are doing their best to help on the fight. I have several names that might surprise you, names well known on State Street. But we can't have too many recruits, especially among those whose refinement is generally acknowledged. If it be necessary, we are prepared to take certain steps to conciliate the shrinking. Our movement is for all—it appeals to the most delicate ladies. Raise the standard among them, and bring me a thousand names. I know several that I should like to have. I look after the details as well as the big currents,' Mrs. Farrinder added, in a tone as explanatory as could be expected of such a woman, and with a smile of which the sweetness was thrilling to her listener.

'I can't talk to those people, I can't!' said Olive Chancellor, with a face which seemed to plead for a remission of responsibility. 'I want to give myself up to others; I want to know everything that lies beneath and out of sight, don't you know? I want to enter into the lives of women who are lonely, who are piteous. I want to be near to them—to help them. I want to do something—oh, I should like so to speak!'

'We should be glad to have you make a few remarks at present,' Mrs. Farrinder declared, with a punctuality which revealed the faculty of presiding.

'Oh dear, no, I can't speak; I have none of that sort of talent. I have no self-possession, no eloquence; I can't put three words together. But I do want to contribute.'

'What *have* you got?' Mrs. Farrinder inquired, looking at her interlocutress, up and down, with the eye of business, in which there was a certain chill. 'Have you got money?'

Olive was so agitated for the moment with the hope that this great woman would approve of her on the financial side that she took no time to reflect that some other quality might, in courtesy, have been suggested. But she confessed to possessing a certain capital, and the tone seemed rich and deep in which Mrs. Farrinder said to her, 'Then contribute that!' She was so good as to develop this idea, and her picture of the part Miss Chancellor might play by making liberal donations to a fund for the diffusion among the women of America of a more adequate conception of their public and private rights—a fund her adviser had herself lately inaugurated—this bold, rapid sketch had the vividness which characterised the speaker's most successful public efforts. It placed Olive under the spell; it made her feel almost inspired. If her life struck others in that way—especially a woman like Mrs. Farrinder, whose horizon was so full—then there must be something for her to do. It was one thing to choose for herself, but now the great representative of the enfranchisement of their sex (from every form of bondage) had chosen for her.

The barren, gas-lighted room grew richer and richer to her earnest eyes; it seemed to expand, to open itself to the great life of humanity. The serious, tired people, in their bonnets and overcoats, began to glow like a company of heroes. Yes, she would do something, Olive Chancellor said to herself; she would do something to brighten the darkness of that dreadful image that was always before her, and against which it seemed to her at times that she had been born to lead a crusade—the image of the unhappiness of women. The unhappiness of women! The voice of their silent sufferings was always in her ears, the ocean of tears that they had shed from the beginning of time seemed to pour through her own eyes. Ages of oppression had rolled over them; uncounted millions had lived only to be tortured, to be crucified. They were her sisters, they were her own, and the day of their delivery had dawned. This was the only sacred cause; this was the great, the just revolution. It must triumph, it must sweep everything before it; it must exact from the other, the brutal, blood-stained, ravening race, the last particle of expiation! It would be the greatest change the world had seen; it would be a new era for the human family, and the names of those who had helped to show the way and lead the squadrons would be the brightest in the tables of fame. They would be names of women weak, insulted, persecuted, but devoted in every pulse of their being to the cause, and asking no better fate than to die for it. It was not clear to this interesting girl in what manner such a sacrifice (as this last) would be required of her, but she saw the matter through a kind of sunrise-mist of emotion which made danger as rosy as success. When Miss Birdseye approached, it transfigured her familiar, her comical shape, and made the poor little humanitary hack seem already a martyr. Olive Chancellor looked at her with love, remembered that she had never, in her long, unrewarded, weary life, had a thought or an impulse for herself. She had been consumed by the passion of sympathy; it had crumpled her into as many creases as an old glazed, distended glove. She had been laughed at, but she never knew it; she was treated as a bore, but she never cared. She had nothing in the world but the clothes on her back, and when she should go down into the grave she would leave nothing behind her but her grotesque, undistinguished, pathetic little name. And yet people said that women were vain, that they were personal, that they were interested! While Miss Birdseye stood there, asking Mrs. Farrinder if she wouldn't say something, Olive Chancellor tenderly fastened a small battered brooch which confined her collar and which had half detached itself.

Joel Chandler Harris (1848–1908)

Literary interest in American sectional and local characteristics assumed the proportions of a movement after the Civil War. The idea of Union had triumphed over the idea of independent sections. However, the nation was still expanding into regions whose unique novelties roused interest in sectional differences. In addition, nostalgic concern arose for those sections whose individualities had been subsumed under an image of national unity. Writers who specialized in the phenomena of local color, in the people, customs, and landscapes of localities as diverse as the farms of Vermont or the streets and homes of antebellum New Orleans, tended to interfuse their works with humor. Temperamental affinities provide a partial explanation. Equally important is the fact that the lower-class characters and scenes of local color literature had traditionally been dealt with almost entirely by writers of humor. Furthermore, earlier humorists also had pioneered with a literary realism which facilitated the local colorists' delineation of speech, objects, topography, and personalities as particular and unique. The most humorous and artistically satisfactory local-color fiction was written by those who, like Georgia newspaperman Joel Chandler Harris, did not vitiate their authentic local-color details with excessive sentimentality or condescension. The fantasy world of Harris's beast fables is only superficially more peaceful than the one which generated Ambrose Bierce's *Fantastic Fables*. Harris portrays Brer Rabbit, the alter ego of Uncle Remus, as engaged in an unmistakable if amusing contest for survival with fox, bear, and wolf. The irony, wisdom, and imagination of Uncle Remus, much of which was Harris's and much of which derived from American Negro folklore, triumphed over the stereotype of the happy plantation slave in which one part of Harris's mind apparently believed. Harris's accurate rendition of Negro dialect earned Mark Twain's praise. The Uncle Remus stories began to appear in the Atlanta *Constitution* in 1879 and were collected in *Uncle Remus: His Songs and Sayings* (1881) and many succeeding volumes.

TEXT: *Uncle Remus: His Songs and Sayings*, New York, 1895. COMMENTARY: Julia C. Harris, *The Life and Letters of Joel Chandler Harris*, Boston, Mass., 1918.

HOW MR. RABBIT SUCCEEDED IN RAISING A DUST

"In dem times," said Uncle Remus, gazing admiringly at himself in a fragment of looking-glass, "Brer Rabbit, en Brer Fox, en Brer Coon, en dem yuther creeturs go co'tin' en sparklin' 'roun' de naberhood mo' samer dan folks. 'Twan't no 'Lemme a hoss,' ner 'Fetch me my buggy,' but dey des up'n lit out en tote deyse'f. Dar's ole Brer Fox, he des wheel 'roun' en fetch his flank one swipe wid 'is tongue en he'd be koam up; en Brer Rabbit, he des spit on his han' en twis' it 'roun' 'mongst de roots er his years en his ha'r'd be roach. Dey wuz dat flirtashus," continued the old man, closing one eye at his image in the glass, "dat Miss Meadows en de gals don't se no peace fum one week een' ter de udder. Chuseday wuz same as Sunday, en Friday wuz same as Chuseday, en hit come down ter dat pass dat w'en Miss Meadows 'ud have chicken-fixins fer dinner, in 'ud drap Brer Fox en Brer Possum, en w'en she'd have fried greens in 'ud pop ole Brer Rabbit, twel 'las' Miss Meadows, she tuck'n tell de gals dat she be dad-blame ef she gwineter keep no tavvum. So dey fix it up 'mong deyse'f, Miss Meadows en de gals did, dat de nex' time de gents call dey'd gin um a game. De gents, dey wuz a co'tin, but Miss Meadows, she don't wanter marry none un um, en needer duz de gals, en likewise dey don't wanter have um pester'n 'roun'. Las', one Chuseday, Miss Meadows, she tole um dat ef dey come down ter her house de nex' Sat'day evenin', de whole caboodle un um 'ud go down de road a piece, whar der wuz a big flint rock, en de man w'at could take a sluge-hammer en knock de dus' out'n dat rock, he wuz de man w'at 'ud git de pick er de gals. Dey all say dey gwine do it, but ole Brer Rabbit, he crope off whar der wuz a cool place under some jimson weeds, en dar he sot wukkin his mind how he gwineter git dus' out'n dat rock. Bimeby, w'ile he wuz a settin' dar, up he jump en crack his heels tergedder en sing out:

> " 'Make a bow ter de Buzzard en
> den ter de Crow,
> Takes a limber-toe gemmun fer
> ter jump Jim Crow,'

en wid dat he put out for Brer Coon house en borrer his slippers. W'en Sat'day evenin' come, dey wuz all dere. Miss Meadows en de gals, dey wuz dere; en Brer Coon, en Brer Fox, en Brer Possum, en Brer Tarrypin, dey wuz dere."

"Where was the Rabbit?" the little boy asked.

"Youk'n put yo' 'pennunce in ole Brer Rabbit," the old man replied, with a chuckle. "He wuz dere, but he shuffle up kinder late, kaze w'en Miss Meadows en de ballunce un um done gone down ter de place, Brer Rabbit, he crope 'roun' ter de ash-hopper, en fill Brer Coon slippers full er ashes, en den he tuck'n put um on en march off. He got dar atter 'w'ile, en soon's Miss Meadows en de gals seed 'im, dey up'n giggle, en make a great 'miration kaze Brer Rabbit got on slippers. Brer Fox, he so smart, he holler out, he did, en say he lay Brer Rabbit got de groun' eatch, but Brer Rabbit, he sorter shet one eye, he did, en say, sezee:

" 'I bin so useter ridin' hoss-back, ez deze ladies knows, dat I'm gittin' sorter tender-footed;' en dey don't hear much mo' fum Brer Fox dat day, kaze he 'member how Brer Rabbit done bin en rid him; en hit 'uz des 'bout much ez Miss Meadows en de gals could do fer ter keep der snickers fum gittin' up a 'sturbance 'mong de congregashun. But, never mine dat, old Brer Rabbit, he wuz dar, en he so brash dat lettle mo' en he'd er grab up de sludge-hammer en er open up de racket 'fo' ennybody gun de word; but Brer Fox, he shove Brer Rabbit out'n de way en pick up de sludge hisse'f. Now den," continued the old man, with pretty much the air of one who had been the master of similar ceremonies, "de progance wuz dish yer: Eve'y gent wer ter have th'ee licks at de rock, en de gent w'at fetch de dus' he wer de one w'at gwineter take de pick er de gals. Ole Brer Fox, he grab de sludge-hammer, he did, en he come down on de rock—*blim!* No dus' ain't come. Den he draw back en down he come ag'in —*blam!* No dus' ain't come. Den he spit in his han's, en give 'er a big swing en down she come—*ker-blap!* En yit no dus' ain't flew'd. Den Brer Possum he make triul, en Brer Coon, en all de ballunce un um 'cep' Brer Tarrypin, en he 'low dat he got a crick in his neck. Den Brer Rabbit, he grab holt er de sludge, en he lipt up in de a'r en come down on de rock all at de same time—*pow!*—en de ashes, dey flew'd up so, dey did, dat Brer Fox, he tuck'n had a sneezin' spell, en Miss Meadows en de gals dey up'n koff. Th'ee times Brer Rabbit jump up en crack his heels tergedder en come down wid de sludge-hammer—*ker-blam!*—en eve'y time he jump up, he holler out:

" 'Stan' fudder, ladies! Yer come de dus'!' en sho nuff, de dus' come.

"Leas'ways," continued Uncle Remus, "Brer Rabbit got one er de gals, en dey had a weddin' en a big infa'r."

"Which of the girls did the Rabbit marry?" asked the little boy, dubiously.

"I did year tell un 'er name," replied the old man, with a great affectation of interest, "but look like I done gone en fergit it off'n my mine. Ef I don't disremember," he continued, "hit wuz Miss Molly Cottontail, en I speck we better let it go at dat."

THE WONDERFUL TAR-BABY STORY

"Didn't the fox *never* catch the rabbit, Uncle Remus?" asked the little boy the next evening.

"He come mighty nigh it, honey, sho's you born—Brer Fox did. One day atter Brer Rabbit fool 'im wid dat calamus root, Brer Fox went ter wuk en got 'im some tar, en mix it wid some turkentime, en fix up a contrapshun wat he call a Tar-Baby, en he tuck dish yer Tar-Baby en he sot 'er in de big road, en den he lay off in de bushes fer to see wat de news wuz gwineter be. En he didn't hatter wait long, nudder, kaze bimeby here come Brer Rabbit pacin' down de road—lippity-clippity, clippity-lippity—dez ez sassy ez a jay-bird. Brer Fox, he lay low. Brer Rabbit come prancin' 'long twel he spy de Tar-Baby, en den he fotch up on his behime legs like he wuz 'stonished. De Tar-Baby, she sot dar, she did, en Brer Fox, he lay low.

" 'Mawnin'!' sez Brer Rabbit, sezee—'nice wedder dis mawnin',' sezee.

"Tar-Baby ain't sayin' nothin', en Brer Fox, he lay low.

" 'How duz yo' sym'tums seem ter segashuate?' sez Brer Rabbit, sezee.

"Brer Fox, he wink his eye slow, en lay low, en de Tar-Baby, she ain't sayin' nothin'.

" 'How you come on, den? Is you deaf?' sez Brer Rabbit, sezee. 'Kaze if you is, I kin holler louder,' sezee.

"Tar-Baby stay still, en Brer Fox, he lay low.

" 'Youer stuck up, dat's w'at you is,' says Brer Rabbit, sezee, 'en I'm gwineter kyore you, dat's w'at I'm a gwineter do,' sezee.

"Brer Fox, he sorter chuckle in his stummuck, he did, but Tar-Baby ain't sayin' nothin'.

" 'I'm gwineter larn you howter talk ter 'specttubble fokes ef hit's de las' ack,' sez Brer Rabbit, sezee. 'Ef you don't take off dat hat en tell me howdy, I'm gwineter bus' you wide open,' sezee.

"Tar-Baby stay still, en Brer Fox, he lay low.

"Brer Rabbit keep on axin' 'im, en de Tar-Baby, she keep on sayin' nothin', twel present'y Brer Rabbit draw back wid his fis', he did, en blip he tuck 'er side er de head. Right dar's whar he broke his merlasses jug. His fis' stuck, en he can't pull loose. De tar hilt 'im. But Tar-Baby, she stay still, en Brer Fox, he lay low.

" 'Ef you don't lemme loose, I'll knock you agin,' sez Brer Rabbit, sezee, en wid dat he fotch 'er a wipe wid de udder han', en dat stuck. Tar-Baby, she ain't sayin' nothin', en Brer Fox, he lay low.

" 'Tu'n me loose, fo' I kick de natal stuffin' outen you,' sez Brer Rabbit, sezee, but de Tar-Baby, she ain't sayin' nothin'. She des hilt on, en den Brer Rabbit lose de use er his feet in de same way. Brer Fox, he lay low. Den Brer Rabbit squall out dat ef de Tar-Baby don't tu'n 'im loose he butt 'er cranksided. En den he butted, en his head got stuck. Den Brer Fox, he sa'ntered fort', lookin' des ez innercent ez one er yo' mammy's mockin'-birds.

" 'Howdy, Brer Rabbit,' sez Brer Fox, sezee. 'You look sorter stuck up dis mawnin',' sezee, en den he rolled on de groun', en laughed en laughed twel he couldn't laugh no mo'. 'I speck you'll take dinner wid me dis time, Brer Rabbit. I done laid in some calamus root, en I ain't gwineter take no skuse,' sez Brer Fox, sezee."

Here Uncle Remus paused, and drew a two-pound yam out of the ashes.

"Did the fox eat the rabbit?" asked the little boy to whom the story had been told.

"Dat's all de fur de tale goes," replied the old man. "He mout, en den agin he moutent. Some say Jedge B'ar come 'long en loosed 'im—some say he didn't. I hear Miss Sally callin'. You better run 'long."

Sarah Orne Jewett (1849–1909)

Sarah Orne Jewett of Maine wrote local color stories with a delicate irony akin to that of one of her favorite writers, Jane Austen. Miss Jewett also resembled a fellow New-Englander, Nathaniel Hawthorne, in the extent of her moral sensitivity and in the delicate nuances of her prose style. The sad and often tragic lives of the inhabitants of Maine's old fishing villages and rural areas roused her compassion. She was moved to indignation by materialistic values, social injustice, and the hypocrisy and selfishness of individuals. In some of her stories Miss Jewett's restrained irony often takes on overtones of direct satire, though she never loses her good manners. Irony and satire combine to render "The Dulham Ladies" (1886) amusing as well as touching. The ludicrous names, the punning confusion between "Dobin" and "Dobbin," the mocking portrayal of the sisters' hollow gentility, and the behavior of Dulham's inhabitants carry Miss Jewett's story beyond pathos to fine humor.

TEXT: *A White Heron and Other Stories*, Boston, Mass., 1886. COMMENTARY: F. O. Matthiessen, *Sarah Orne Jewett*, Boston, Mass., 1929.

THE DULHAM LADIES

To be leaders of society in the town of Dulham was as satisfactory to Miss Dobin and Miss Lucinda Dobin as if Dulham were London itself. Of late years, though they would not allow themselves to suspect such treason, the most ill-bred of the younger people in the village made fun of them behind their backs, and laughed at their treasured summer mantillas, their mincing steps, and the shape of their parasols.

They were always conscious of the fact that they were the daughters of a once eminent Dulham minister; but beside this unanswerable claim to the respect of the First Parish, they were aware that their mother's social position was one of superior altitude. Madam Dobin's grandmother was a Greenaple, of Boston. In her younger days she had often visited her relatives, the Greenaples and Hightrees, and in seasons of festivity she could relate to a select and properly excited audience her delightful experiences of town life. Nothing could be finer than her account of having taken tea at Governor Clovenfoot's on Beacon Street in company with an English lord, who was indulging himself in a brief vacation from his arduous duties at the Court of St. James.

"He exclaimed that he had seldom seen in England so beautiful and intelligent a company of ladies," Madam Dobin would always say in conclusion. "He was decorated with the blue ribbon of the Knights of the Garter." Miss Dobin and Miss Lucinda thought for many years that this famous blue ribbon was tied about the noble gentleman's leg. One day they even discussed the question openly; Miss Dobin placing the decoration at his knee, and Miss Lucinda locating it much lower down, according to the length of the short gray socks with which she was familiar.

"You have no imagination, Lucinda," the elder sister replied impatiently. "Of course, those were the days of small-clothes and long silk stockings!"—whereat Miss Lucinda was rebuked, but not persuaded.

"I wish that my dear girls could have the outlook upon society which fell to my portion," Madam Dobin sighed, after she had set these ignorant minds to rights, and enriched them by communicating the final truth about the blue ribbon. "I must not chide you for the absence of opportunities, but if our cousin Harriet Greenaple were only living you would not lack enjoyment or social education."

Madam Dobin had now been dead a great many years. She seemed an elderly woman to her daughters some time before she left them; later they thought that she had really died comparatively young, since their own years had come to equal the record of hers. When they visited her tall white tombstone in the orderly Dulham burying-ground, it was a strange thought to both the daughters that they were older women than their mother had been when she died. To be sure, it was the fashion to appear older in her day,—they could remember the sober effect of really youthful married persons in cap and frisette; but, whether they owed it to the changed times or to their own qualities, they felt no older themselves than ever they had. Beside upholding the ministerial dignity of their father, they were obliged to give a lenient sanction to the ways of the world for their mother's sake; and they combined the two duties with reverence and impartiality.

Madam Dobin was, in her prime, a walking example of refinements and courtesies. If she erred in any way, it was by keeping too strict watch and rule over her small kingdom. She acted with great dignity in all matters of social administration and etiquette, but, while it must be owned that the parishioners felt a sense of freedom for a time after her death, in their later years they praised and valued her more and more, and often lamented her generously and sincerely.

Several of her distinguished relatives attended Madam Dobin's funeral, which was long considered the most dignified and elegant pageant of that sort which had ever taken place in Dulham. It seemed to mark the close of a famous epoch in Dulham history, and it was increasingly difficult forever afterward to keep the tone of society up to the old standard. Somehow, the distinguished relatives had one by one disappeared, though they all had excellent reasons for the discontinuance of their visits. A few

412 *Sarah Orne Jewett*

had left this world altogether, and the family circle of the Greenaples and Hightrees was greatly reduced in circumference. Sometimes, in summer, a stray connection drifted Dulham-ward, and was displayed to the townspeople (not to say paraded) by the gratified hostesses. It was a disappointment if the guest could not be persuaded to remain over Sunday and appear at church. When household antiquities became fashionable, the ladies remarked a surprising interest in their corner cupboard and best chairs, and some distant relatives revived their almost forgotten custom of paying a summer visit to Dulham. They were not long in finding out with what desperate affection Miss Dobin and Miss Lucinda clung to their mother's wedding china and other inheritances, and were allowed to depart without a single teacup. One graceless descendant of the Hightrees prowled from garret to cellar, and admired the household belongings diligently, but she was not asked to accept even the dislocated cherry-wood footstool that she had discovered in the far corner of the parsonage pew.

Some of the Dulham friends had long suspected that Madam Dobin made a social misstep when she chose the Reverend Edward Dobin for her husband. She was no longer young when she married, and though she had gone through the wood and picked up a crooked stick at last, it made a great difference that her stick possessed an ecclesiastical bark. The Reverend Edward was, moreover, a respectable graduate of Harvard College, and to a woman of her standards a clergyman was by no means insignificant. It was impossible not to respect his office, at any rate, and she must have treated him with proper veneration for the sake of that, if for no other reason, though his early advantages had been insufficient, and he was quite insensible to the claims of the Greenaple pedigree, and preferred an Indian pudding to pie crust that was, without exaggeration, half a quarter high. The delicacy of Madam Dobin's touch and preference in everything, from hymns to cookery, was quite lost upon this respected preacher, yet he was not without pride or complete confidence in his own decisions.

The Reverend Mr. Dobin was never very enlightening in his discourses, and was providentially stopped short by a stroke of paralysis in the middle of his clerical career. He lived on and on through many dreary years, but his children never accepted the fact that he was a tyrant, and served him humbly and patiently. He fell at last into a condition of great incapacity and chronic trembling, but was able for nearly a quarter of a century to be carried to the meeting-house from time to time to pronounce farewell discourses. On high days of the church he was always placed in the pulpit, and held up his shaking hands when the benediction was pronounced, as if the divine gift were exclusively his own, and the other minister did but say empty words. Afterward, he was usually tired and displeased and hard to cope with, but there was always a proper notice taken of these too often recurring events. For old times' and for pity's sake and from natural goodness of heart, the elder parishioners rallied manfully about the Reverend Mr. Dobin; and whoever his successor or colleague might be, the Dobins were always called the minister's folks, while the active laborer in the vineyard was only Mr. Smith or Mr. Jones, as the case might be. At last the poor old man died, to everybody's relief and astonishment; and after he was properly preached about and lamented, his daughters, Miss Dobin and Miss Lucinda, took a good look at life from a new standpoint, and decided that now they were no longer constrained by home duties they must make themselves a great deal more used to the town.

Sometimes there is such a household as this (which has been perhaps too minutely described), where the parents linger until their children are far past middle age, and always keep them in a too childish and unworthy state of subjection. The Misses Dobin's characters were much influenced by such an unnatural prolongation of the filial relationship, and they were amazingly slow to suspect that they were not so young as they used to be. There was nothing to measure themselves by but Dulham people and things. The elm-trees were growing yet, and many of the ladies of the First Parish were older than they, and called them, with pleasant familiarity, the Dobin girls. These elderly persons seemed really to be growing old, and Miss Lucinda frequently lamented the change in society; she thought it a freak of nature and too sudden blighting of earthly hopes that several charming old friends of her mother's were no longer living. They were advanced in age when Miss Lucinda was a young girl, though time and space are but relative, after all.

Their influence upon society would have made a great difference in many ways. Certainly, the new parishioners, who had often enough been instructed to pronounce their pastor's name as if it were spelled with one "b," would not have boldly returned again and again to their obnoxious habit of saying Dobbin. Miss Lucinda might carefully speak to the neighbor and new-comers of "my sister, Miss Do-bin;" only the select company of intimates followed her lead, and at last there was something humiliating about it, even though many persons spoke of them only as "the ladies."

"The name was originally *D'Aubigne*, we think," Miss Lucinda would say coldly and patiently, as if she had already explained this foolish mistake a thousand times too often. It was like the sorrows in many a provincial château in the Reign of Terror. The ladies looked on with increasing dismay at the retrogression in society. They felt as if they were a feeble garrison, to whose lot it had fallen to repulse a noisy, irreverent mob, an increasing band of marauders who would overthrow all land-marks of the past, all etiquette and social rank. The new minister himself was a round-faced, unspiritual-looking young man, whom they would have instinctively ignored if he had not been a minister. The new people who came to

Dulham were not like the older residents, and they had no desire to be taught better. Little they cared about the Greenaples or the Hightrees; and once, when Miss Dobin essayed to speak of some detail of her mother's brilliant opportunities in Boston high life, she was interrupted, and the new-comer who sat next her at the parish sewing society began to talk about something else. We cannot believe it could have been the tea-party at Governor Clovenfoot's which the rude creature so disrespectfully ignored, but some persons are capable of showing any lack of good taste.

The ladies had an unusual and most painful sense of failure, as they went home together that evening. "I have always made it my object to improve and interest the people at such times; it would seem so possible to elevate their thoughts and direct them into higher channels," said Miss Dobin sadly. "But as for that Woolden woman, there is no use in casting pearls before swine!"

Miss Lucinda murmured an indignant assent. She had a secret suspicion that the Woolden woman had heard the story in question oftener than had pleased her. She was but an ignorant creature; though she had lived in Dulham twelve or thirteen years, she was no better than when she came. The mistake was in treating sister Harriet as if she were on a level with the rest of the company. Miss Lucinda had observed more than once, lately, that her sister sometimes repeated herself, unconsciously, a little oftener than was agreeable. Perhaps they were getting a trifle dull; toward spring it might be well to pass a few days with some of their friends, and have a change.

"If I have tried to do anything," said Miss Dobin in an icy tone, "it has been to stand firm in my lot and place, and to hold the standard of cultivated mind and elegant manners as high as possible. You would think it had been a hundred years since our mother's death, so completely has the effect of her good breeding and exquisite hospitality been lost sight of, here in Dulham. I could wish that our father had chosen to settle in a larger and more appreciative place. They would like to put us on the shelf, too. I can see that plainly."

"I am sure we have our friends," said Miss Lucinda anxiously, but with a choking voice. "We must not let them think we do not mean to keep up with the times, as we always have. I do feel as if perhaps—our hair"—

And the sad secret was out at last. Each of the sisters drew a long breath of relief at this beginning of a confession.

It was certain that they must take some steps to retrieve their lost ascendency. Public attention had that evening been called to their fast-disappearing locks, poor ladies; and Miss Lucinda felt the discomfort most, for she had been the inheritor of the Hightree hair, long and curly, and chestnut in color. There used to be a waviness about it, and sometimes pretty escaping curls, but these were gone long ago. Miss Dobin resembled her father, and her hair had not been luxuriant, so that she was less changed by its absence than one might suppose. The straightness and thinness had increased so gradually that neither sister had quite accepted the thought that other persons would particularly notice their altered appearance.

They had shrunk, with the reticence born of close family association, from speaking of the cause even to each other, when they made themselves pretty little lace and dotted muslin caps. Breakfast caps, they called them, and explained that these were universally worn in town; the young Princess of Wales originated them, or at any rate adopted them. The ladies offered no apology for keeping the breakfast caps on until bedtime, and in spite of them a forward child had just spoken, loud and shrill, an untimely question in the ears of the for once silent sewing society. "Do Miss Dobbinses wear them great caps because their bare heads is cold?" the little beast had said; and everybody was startled and dismayed.

Miss Dobin had never shown better her good breeding and valor, the younger sister thought.

"No, little girl," replied the stately Harriet, with a chilly smile. "I believe that our head-dresses are quite in the fashion for ladies of all ages. And you must remember that it is never polite to make such personal remarks." It was after this that Miss Dobin had been reminded of Madam Somebody's unusual head-gear at the evening entertainment in Boston. Nobody but the Woolden woman could have interrupted her under such trying circumstances.

Miss Lucinda, however, was certain that the time had come for making some effort to replace her lost adornment. The child had told an unwelcome truth, but had paved the way for further action, and now was the time to suggest something that had slowly been taking shape in Miss Lucinda's mind. A young grand-nephew of their mother and his bride had passed a few days with them, two or three summers before, and the sisters had been quite shocked to find that the pretty young woman wore a row of frizzes, not originally her own, over her smooth forehead. At the time, Miss Dobin and Miss Lucinda had spoken severely with each other of such bad taste, but now it made a great difference that the wearer of the frizzes was not only a relative by marriage and used to good society, but also that she came from town, and might be supposed to know what was proper in the way of toilet.

"I really think, sister, that we had better see about having some—arrangements, next time we go anywhere," Miss Dobin said unexpectedly, with a slight tremble in her voice, just as they reached their own door. "There seems to be quite a fashion for them nowadays. For the parish's sake we ought to recognize"—and Miss Lucinda responded with instant satisfaction. She did not like to complain, but she had been troubled with neuralgic pains in her forehead on suddenly meeting the cold air.

The sisters felt a new bond of sympathy in keeping this secret with and for each other; they took pains to say to several acquaintances that they were thinking of going to the next large town to do a few errands for Christmas.

A bright, sunny morning seemed to wish the ladies good-fortune. Old Hetty Downs, their faithful maid-servant and protector, looked after them in affectionate foreboding. "Dear sakes, what devil's wiles may be played on them blessed innocents afore they're safe home again!" she murmured, as they vanished round the corner of the street that led to the railway station.

Miss Dobin and Miss Lucinda paced discreetly side by side down the main street of Westbury. It was nothing like Boston, of course, but the noise was slightly confusing, and the passers-by sometimes roughly pushed against them. Westbury was a consequential manufacturing town, but a great convenience at times like this. The trifling Christmas gifts for their old neighbors and Sunday-school scholars were purchased and stowed away in their neat Fayal basket before the serious commission of the day was attended to. Here and there, in the shops, disreputable frizzes were displayed in unblushing effrontery, but no such vulgar shopkeeper merited the patronage of the Misses Dobin. They pretended not to observe the unattractive goods, and went their way to a low, one-storied building on a side street, where an old tradesman lived. He had been useful to the minister while he still remained upon the earth and had need of a wig, sandy in hue and increasingly sprinkled with gray, as if it kept pace with other changes of existence. But old Paley's shutters were up, and a bar of rough wood was nailed firmly across the one that had lost its fastening and would rack its feeble hinges in the wind. Old Paley had always been polite and bland; they really had looked forward to a little chat with him; they had heard a year or two before of his wife's death, and meant to offer sympathy. His business of hair-dressing had been carried on with that of parasol and umbrella mending, and the condemned umbrella which was his sign cracked and swung in the rising wind, a tattered skeleton before the closed door. The ladies sighed and turned away; they were beginning to feel tired; the day was long, and they had not met with any pleasures yet. "We might walk up the street a little farther," suggested Miss Lucinda; "that is, if you are not tired," as they stood hesitating on the corner after they had finished a short discussion of Mr. Paley's disappearance. Happily it was only a few minutes before they came to a stop together in front of a new, shining shop, where smirking waxen heads all in a row were decked with the latest fashions of wigs and frizzes. One smiling fragment of a gentleman stared so straight at Miss Lucinda with his black eyes that she felt quite coy and embarrassed, and was obliged to feign not to be conscious of his admiration. But Miss

Dobin, after a brief delay, boldly opened the door and entered; it was better to be sheltered in the shop than exposed to public remark as they gazed in at the windows. Miss Lucinda felt her heart beat and her courage give out; she, coward like, left the transaction of their business to her sister, and turned to contemplate the back of the handsome model. It was a slight shock to find that he was not so attractive from this point of view. The wig he wore was well made all round, but his shoulders were roughly finished in a substance that looked like plain plaster of Paris.

"What can I have ze pleasure of showing you, young ladees?" asked a person who advanced; and Miss Lucinda faced about to discover a smiling, middle-aged Frenchman, who rubbed his hands together and looked at his customers, first one and then the other, with delightful deference. He seemed a very civil, nice person, the young ladies thought.

"My sister and I were thinking of buying some little arrangements to wear above the forehead," Miss Dobin explained, with pathetic dignity; but the Frenchman spared her any further words. He looked with eager interest at the bonnets, as if no lack had attracted his notice before. "Ah, yes. *Je comprends*; ze high foreheads are not now ze mode. Je prefer them, moi, yes, yes, but ze ladies must accept ze fashion; zay must now cover ze forehead with ze frizzes, ze bangs, you say. As you wis', as you wis'!" and the tactful little man, with many shrugs and merry gestures at such girlish fancies, pulled down one box after another.

It was a great relief to find that this was no worse, to say the least, than any other shopping, though the solemnity and secrecy of the occasion were infringed upon by the great supply of "arrangements" and the loud discussion of the color of some crimps a noisy girl was buying from a young saleswoman the other side of the shop.

Miss Dobin waved aside the wares which were being displayed for her approval. "Something—more simple, if you please,"—she did not like to say "older."

"But these are *très simple*," protested the Frenchman. "We have nothing younger;" and Miss Dobin and Miss Lucinda blushed, and said no more. The Frenchman had his own way; he persuaded them that nothing was so suitable as some conspicuous forelocks that matched their hair as it used to be. They would have given anything rather than leave their breakfast caps at home, if they had known that their proper winter bonnets must come off. They hardly listened to the wig merchant's glib voice as Miss Dobin stood revealed before the merciless mirror at the back of the shop.

He made everything as easy as possible, the friendly creature, and the ladies were grateful to him. Beside, now that the bonnet was on again there was a great improvement in Miss Dobin's appearance. She turned to Miss Lucinda, and saw a gleam of delight in her eager countenance. "It really is very becoming. I like the way it parts over your forehead," said the younger sister, "but if it were long enough to go behind the ears"—"*Non, non,*" entreated the Frenchman. "To make her the old woman at once would be cruelty!" And Lucinda, who was wondering how well she would look in her turn, succumbed promptly to such protestations. Yes, there was no use in being old before their time. Dulham was not quite keeping pace with the rest of the world in these days, but they need not drag behind everybody else, just because they lived there.

The price of the little arrangements was much less than the sisters expected, and the uncomfortable expense of their reverend father's wigs had been, it was proved, a thing of the past. Miss Dobin treated her polite Frenchman with great courtesy; indeed, Miss Lucinda had more than once whispered to her to talk French, and as they were bowed out of the shop the gracious *Bong-sure* of the elder lady seemed to act like the string of a shower-bath, and bring down an awesome torrent of foreign words upon the two guileless heads. It was impossible to reply; the ladies bowed again, however, and Miss Lucinda caught a last smile from the handsome wax countenance in the window. He appeared to regard her with fresh approval, and she departed down the street with mincing steps.

"I feel as if anybody might look at me now, sister," said gentle Miss Lucinda. "I confess, I have really suffered sometimes, since I knew I looked so distressed."

"Yours is lighter than I thought it was in the shop," remarked Miss Dobin, doubtfully, but she quickly added that perhaps it would change a little. She was so perfectly satisfied with her own appearance that she could not bear to dim the pleasure of any one else. The truth remained that she never would have let Lucinda choose that particular arrangement if she had seen it first in a good light. And Lucinda was thinking exactly the same of her companion.

"I am sure we shall have no more neuralgia," said Miss Dobin. "I am sorry we waited so long, dear," and they tripped down the main street of Westbury, confident that nobody would suspect them of being over thirty. Indeed, they felt quite girlish, and unconsciously looked sideways as they went along, to see their satisfying reflections in the windows. The great panes made excellent mirrors, with not too clear or lasting pictures of these comforted passers-by.

The Frenchman in the shop was making merry with his assistants. The two great frisettes had long been out of fashion; he had been lying in wait with them for two unsuspecting country ladies, who could be cajoled into such a purchase.

"Sister," Miss Lucinda was saying, "you know there is still an hour to wait before our train goes. Suppose we take a little longer walk down the other side of the way;" and they strolled slowly back again. In fact, they nearly missed the train, naughty girls! Hetty would have been so worried, they assured each other, but they reached the station just in time.

"Lutie," said Miss Dobin, "put up your hand and part it from your forehead; it seems to be getting out of place a little;" and Miss Lucinda, who had just got breath enough to speak, returned the information that Miss Dobin's was almost covering her eyebrows. They might have to trim them a little shorter; of course it could be done. The darkness was falling; they had taken an early dinner before they started, and now they were tired and hungry after the exertion of the afternoon, but the spirit of youth flamed afresh in their hearts, and they were very happy. If one's heart remains young, it is a sore trial to have the outward appearance entirely at variance. It was the ladies' nature to be girlish, and they found it impossible not to be grateful to the flimsy, ineffectual disguise which seemed to set them right with the world. The old conductor, who had known them for many years, looked hard at them as he took their tickets, and, being a man of humor and compassion, affected not to notice anything remarkable in their appearance. "You ladies never mean to grow old, like the rest of us," he said gallantly, and the sisters fairly quaked with joy.

"Bless us!" the obnoxious Mrs. Woolden was saying, at the other end of the car. "There's the old maid Dobbinses, and they've bought 'em some bangs. I expect they wanted to get thatched in a little before real cold weather; but don't they look just like a pair o' poodle dogs."

The little ladies descended wearily from the train. Somehow they did not enjoy a day's shopping as much as they used. They were certainly much obliged to Hetty for sending her niece's boy to meet them, with a lantern; also for having a good warm supper ready when they came in. Hetty took a quick look at her mistresses, and returned to the kitchen. "I knew somebody would be foolin' of 'em," she assured herself angrily, but she had to laugh. Their dear, kind faces were wrinkled and pale, and the great frizzes had lost their pretty curliness, and were hanging down, almost straight and very ugly, into the ladies' eyes. They could not tuck them up under their caps, as they were sure might be done.

Then came a succession of rainy days, and nobody visited the rejuvenated household. The frisettes looked very bright chestnut by the light of day, and it must be confessed that Miss Dobin took the scissors and shortened Miss Lucinda's half an inch, and Miss Lucinda returned the compliment quite secretly, because each thought her sister's forehead lower than her own. Their dear gray eyebrows were honestly displayed, as if it were the fashion not to have them match with wigs. Hetty at last spoke out, and begged her mistresses, as they sat at breakfast, to let her take the frizzes back and change them. Her sister's daughter worked in that very shop, and, though in the work-room, would be able to oblige them, Hetty was sure.

But the ladies looked at each other in pleased assurance, and then turned together to look at Hetty, who stood already a little apprehensive near the table, where she had just put down a plateful of smoking drop-cakes. The good creature really began to look old.

"They are worn very much in town," said Miss Dobin. "We think it was quite fortunate that the fashion came in just as our hair was growing a trifle thin. I dare say we may choose those that are a shade duller in color when these are a little past. Oh, we shall not want tea this evening, you remember, Hetty. I am glad there is likely to be such a good night for the sewing circle." And Miss Dobin and Miss Lucinda nodded and smiled.

"Oh, my sakes alive!" the troubled handmaiden groaned. "Going to the circle, be they, to be snickered at! Well, the Dobbin girls they was born, and the Dobbin girls they will remain till they die; but if they ain't innocent Christian babes to those that knows 'em well, mark me down for an idjit myself! They believe them frontpieces has set the clock back forty year or more, but if they're pleased to think so, let 'em!"

Away paced the Dulham ladies, late in the afternoon, to grace the parish occasion, and face the amused scrutiny of their neighbors. "I think we owe it to society to observe the fashions of the day," said Miss Lucinda. "A lady cannot afford to be unattractive. I feel now as if we were prepared for anything!"

Mary E. Wilkins Freeman (1852–1930)

"The actual, the immediate, the whole sound and sense of the dry realities of rustic New England are what, for comedy and elegy, she has touched with the firmest hand." Thus Henry James wrote of the emotionally rich short stories in which Mary E. Wilkins Freeman charted the lives of people like those who lived in her native village of Randolph, Massachusetts. Mrs. Freeman's stories are probably the most brilliant of any written by the local colorists. Her understanding of psychological repression and social realities was great; her style was economical and vivid. Additional artistic power was provided by a dramatic sense which enabled her to manipulate character and situation in a grotesque swirl of ever-increasing tension. Mrs. Freeman's protagonists succumb to the force of unavoidable tragedy. Like Candace Whitcomb in "A Village Singer" (1891), however, they often react against fate with such startling idiosyncrasy that they are enveloped in a grim comedy like that which Poe, Hawthorne, and Faulkner have created. Many of Mrs. Freeman's stories end with humorous surprises similar to the one concluding "A Village Singer."

TEXT: *A New England Nun and Other Stories*, New York, 1891. COMMENTARY: Edward Foster, *Mary E. Wilkins Freeman*, New York, 1956.

A VILLAGE SINGER

The trees were in full leaf, a heavy south wind was blowing, and there was a loud murmur among the new leaves. The people noticed it, for it was the first time that year that the trees had so murmured in the wind. The spring had come with a rush during the last few days.

The murmur of the trees sounded loud in the village church, where the people sat waiting for the service to begin. The windows were open; it was a very warm Sunday for May.

The church was already filled with this soft sylvan music—the tender harmony of the leaves and the south wind, and the sweet, desultory whistles of birds—when the choir arose and began to sing.

In the centre of the row of women singers stood Alma Way. All the people stared at her, and turned their ears critically. She was the new leading soprano. Candace Whitcomb, the old one, who had sung in the choir for forty years, had lately been given her dismissal. The audience considered that her voice had grown too cracked and uncertain on the upper notes. There had been much complaint, and after long deliberation the church-officers had made known their decision as mildly as possible to the old singer. She had sung for the last time the Sunday before, and Alma Way had been engaged to take her place. With the exception of the organist, the leading soprano was the only paid musician in the large choir. The salary was very modest, still the village people considered it large for a young woman. Alma was from the adjoining village of East Derby; she had quite a local reputation as a singer.

Now she fixed her large solemn blue eyes; her long, delicate face, which had been pretty, turned paler; the blue flowers on her bonnet trembled; her little thin gloved hands, clutching the singing-book, shook perceptibly; but she sang out bravely. That most formidable mountain-height of the world, self-distrust and timidity, arose before her, but her nerves were braced for its ascent. In the midst of the hymn she had a solo; her voice rang out piercingly sweet; the people nodded admiringly at each other; but suddenly there was a stir; all the faces turned toward the windows on the south side of the church. Above the din of the wind and the birds, above Alma Way's sweetly straining tones, arose another female voice, singing another hymn to another tune.

"It's her," the women whispered to each other; they were half aghast, half smiling.

Candace Whitcomb's cottage stood close to the south side of the church. She was playing on her parlor organ, and singing, to drown out the voice of her rival.

Alma caught her breath; she almost stopped; the hymn-book waved like a fan; then she went on. But the long husky drone of the parlor organ and the shrill clamor of the other voice seemed louder than anything else.

When the hymn was finished, Alma sat down. She felt faint; the woman next her slipped a peppermint into her hand. "It ain't worth minding," she whispered, vigorously. Alma tried to smile; down in the audience a young man was watching her with a kind of fierce pity.

In the last hymn Alma had another solo. Again the parlor organ droned above the carefully delicate accompaniment of the church organ, and again Candace Whitcomb's voice clamored forth in another tune.

After the benediction, the other singers pressed around Alma. She did not say much in return for their expressions of indignation and sympathy. She wiped her eyes furtively once or twice, and tried to smile. William Emmons, the choir leader, elderly, stout, and smooth-faced, stood over her, and raised his voice. He was the old musical dignitary of the village, the leader of the choral club and the singing-schools. "A most outrageous proceeding," he said. People had coupled his name with Candace Whitcomb's. The old bachelor tenor and old maiden soprano had been wont to walk together to her home next door after the Saturday night rehearsals, and they had sung duets to the parlor organ. People had watched sharply her old face, on which the blushes of youth sat pitifully, when William Emmons entered the singing-seats. They wondered if he would ever ask her to marry him.

And now he said further to Alma Way that Candace Whitcomb's voice had failed utterly of late, that she sang shockingly, and ought to have had sense enough to know it.

When Alma went down into the audience-room, in the midst of the chattering singers, who seemed to have descended, like birds, from song flights to chirps, the minister approached her. He had been waiting to speak to her. He was a steady-faced, fleshy old man, who had preached from that one pulpit over forty years. He told Alma, in his slow way, how much he regretted the annoyance to which she had been subjected, and intimated that he would endeavor to prevent a recurrence of it. "Miss Whitcomb—must be—reasoned with," said he; he had a slight hesitation of speech, not an impediment. It was as if his thoughts did not slide readily into his words, although both were present. He walked down the aisle with Alma, and bade her good-morning when he saw Wilson Ford waiting for her in the doorway. Everybody knew that Wilson Ford and Alma were lovers; they had been for the last ten years.

Alma colored softly, and made a little imperceptible motion with her head; her silk dress and the lace on her mantle fluttered, but she did not speak. Neither did Wilson, although they had not met before that day. They did not look at each other's faces—they seemed to see each other without that—and they walked along side by side.

They reached the gate before Candace Whitcomb's little house. Wilson looked past the front yard, full of pink and white spikes on flowering bushes, at the lace-curtained windows; a thin white profile, stiffly inclined, apparently over a book, was visible at one of them. Wilson gave his head a shake. He was a stout man, with features so strong that they overcame his flesh. "I'm going up home with you, Alma," said he; "and then—I'm just coming back, to give Aunt Candace one blowing up."

"Oh, don't, Wilson."

"Yes, I shall. If you want to stand this kind of a thing you may; I sha'n't."

"There's no need of your talking to her. Mr. Pollard's going to."

"Did he say he was?"

"Yes. I think he's going in before the afternoon meeting, from what he said."

"Well, there's one thing about it, if she does that thing again this afternoon, I'll go in there and break that old organ up into kindling-wood." Wilson set his mouth hard, and shook his head again.

Alma gave little side glances up at him, her tone was deprecatory, but her face was full of soft smiles. "I suppose she does feel dreadfully about it," said she. "I can't help feeling kind of guilty, taking her place."

"I don't see how you're to blame. It's outrageous, her acting so."

"The choir gave her a photograph album last week, didn't they?"

"Yes. They went there last Thursday night, and gave her an album and a surprise-party. She ought to behave herself."

"Well, she's sung there so long, I suppose it must be dreadful hard for her to give it up."

Other people going home from church were very near Wilson and Alma. She spoke softly that they might not hear; he did not lower his voice in the least. Presently Alma stopped before a gate.

"What are you stopping here for?" asked Wilson.

"Minnie Lansing wanted me to come and stay with her this noon."

"You're going home with me."

"I'm afraid I'll put your mother out."

"Put mother out! I told her you were coming, this morning. She's got all ready for you. Come along; don't stand here."

He did not tell Alma of the pugnacious spirit with which his mother had received the announcement of her coming, and how she had stayed at home to prepare the dinner, and make a parade of her hard work and her injury.

Wilson's mother was the reason why he did not marry Alma. He would not take his wife home to live with her, and was unable to support separate establishments. Alma was willing enough to be married and put up with Wilson's mother, but she did not complain of his decision. Her delicate blond features grew sharper, and her blue eyes more hollow. She had had a certain fine prettiness, but now she was losing it, and beginning to look old, and there was a prim, angular, old maiden carriage about her narrow shoulders.

Wilson never noticed it, and never thought of Alma as not possessed of eternal youth, or capable of losing or regretting it.

"Come along, Alma," said he; and she followed meekly after him down the street.

Soon after they passed Candace Whitcomb's house, the minister went up the front walk and rang the bell. The pale profile at the window had never stirred as he opened the gate and came up the walk. However, the door was promptly opened, in response to his ring. "Good-morning, Miss Whitcomb," said the minister.

"*Good*-morning." Candace gave a sweeping toss of her head as she spoke. There was a fierce upward curl to her thin nostrils and her lips, as if she scented an adversary. Her black eyes had two tiny cold sparks of fury in them, like an enraged bird's. She did not ask the minister to enter, but he stepped lumberingly into the entry, and she retreated rather than led the way into her little parlor. He settled into the great rocking-chair and wiped his face. Candace sat down again in her old place by the window. She was a tall woman, but very slender and full of pliable motions, like a blade of grass.

"It's a—very pleasant day," said the minister.

Candace made no reply. She sat still, with her head drooping. The wind stirred the looped lace-curtains; a tall rose-tree outside the window waved; soft shadows floated through the room. Candace's parlor organ stood in front of an open window that faced the church; on the corner was a pitcher with a bunch of white lilacs. The whole room was scented with them. Presently the minister looked over at them and sniffed pleasantly.

"You have—some beautiful—lilacs there."

Candace did not speak. Every line of her slender figure looked flexible, but it was a flexibility more resistant than rigor.

The minister looked at her. He filled up the great rocking-chair; his arms in his shiny black coat-sleeves rested squarely and comfortably upon the hair-cloth arms of the chair.

"Well, Miss Whitcomb, I suppose I—may as well come to—the point. There was—a little—matter I wished to speak to you about. I don't suppose you were—at least I can't suppose you were—aware of it, but—this morning, during the singing by the choir, you played and—sung a little too—loud. That is, with—the windows open. It—disturbed us—a little. I hope you won't feel hurt—my dear Miss Candace, but I knew you would rather I would speak of it, for I knew—you would be more disturbed than anybody else at the idea of such a thing."

Candace did not raise her eyes; she looked as if his words might sway her through the window. "I ain't disturbed at it," said she. "I did it on purpose; I meant to."

The minister looked at her.

"You needn't look at me. I know jest what I'm about. I sung the way I did on purpose, an' I'm goin' to do it again, an' I'd like to see you stop me. I guess I've got a right to set down to my own organ, an' sing a psalm tune on a Sabbath day, 'f I want to; an' there ain't no amount of talkin' an' palaverin' a-goin' to stop me. See there!" Candace swung aside her skirts a little. "Look at that!"

The minister looked. Candace's feet were resting on a large red-plush photograph album.

"Makes a nice footstool, don't it?" said she.

The minister looked at the album, then at her; there was a slowly gathering alarm in his face; he began to think she was losing her reason.

Candace had her eyes full upon him now, and her head up. She laughed, and her laugh was almost a snarl. "Yes; I thought it would make a beautiful footstool," said she. "I've been wantin' one for some time." Her tone was full of vicious irony.

"Why, miss—" began the minister; but she interrupted him:

"I know what you're a-goin' to say, Mr. Pollard, an' now I'm goin' to have my say; I'm a-goin' to speak. I want to know what you think of folks that pretend to be Christians treatin' anybody the way they've treated me? Here I've sung in those singin'-seats forty year. I ain't never missed a Sunday, except when I've been sick, an' I've gone an' sung a good many times when I'd better been in bed, an' now I'm turned out without a word of warnin'. My voice is jest as good as ever 'twas; there can't anybody say it ain't. It wa'n't ever quite so high-pitched as that Way girl's, mebbe; but she flats the whole durin' time. My voice is as good an' high to-day as it was twenty year ago; an' if it wa'n't, I'd like to know where the Christianity comes in. I'd like to know if it wouldn't be more to the credit of folks in a church to keep an old singer an' an old minister, if they didn't sing an' hold forth quite so smart as they used to, ruther than turn 'em off an' hurt their feelin's. I guess it would be full as much to the glory of God. S'pose the singin' an' the preachin' wa'n't quite so good, what difference would it make? Salvation don't hang on anybody's hittin' a high note, that I ever heard of. Folks are gettin' as high-steppin' an' fussy in a meetin'-house as they are in a tavern, nowadays. S'pose they should turn you off, Mr. Pollard, come an' give you a photograph album, an' tell you to clear out, how'd you like it? I ain't findin' any fault with your preachin'; it was always good enough to suit me; but it don't stand to reason folks'll be as took up with your sermons as when you was a young man. You can't expect it. S'pose they should turn you out in your old age, an' call in some young bob squirt, how'd you feel? There's William Emmons, too; he's three years older'n I am, if he does lead the choir an' run all the singin' in town. If my voice has gi'en out, it stan's to reason his has. It ain't, though. William Emmons sings jest as well as he ever did. Why don't they turn him out the way they have me, an' give him a photograph album? I dun know but it would be a good idea to send everybody, as soon as they get a little old an' gone by, an' young folks begin to push, onto some desert island, an' give 'em each a photograph album. Then they can sit down an' look at pictures the rest of their days. Mebbe government'll take it up.

"There they come here last week Thursday, all the choir, jest about eight o'clock in the evenin', an' pretended they'd come to give me a nice little surprise. Surprise! h'm! Brought cake an' oranges, an' was jest as nice as they could be, an' I was real tickled. I never had a surprise-party before in my life. Jenny Carr she played, an' they wanted me to sing alone, an' I never suspected a thing. I've been mad ever since to think what a fool I was, an' how they must have laughed in their sleeves.

"When they'd gone I found this photograph album on the table, all done up as nice as you please, an' directed to Miss Candace Whitcomb from her many friends, an' I opened it, an' there was the letter inside givin' me notice to quit.

"If they'd gone about it any decent way, told me right out honest that they'd got tired of me, an' wanted Alma Way to sing instead of me, I wouldn't minded so much; I should have been hurt 'nough, for I'd felt as if some that had pretended to be my friends wa'n't; but it wouldn't have been as bad as this. They said in the letter that they'd always set great value on my services, an' it wa'n't from any lack of appreciation that they turned me off, but they thought the duty was gettin' a little too arduous for me. H'm! I hadn't complained. If they'd turned me right out fair an' square, showed me the door, an' said, 'Here, you get out,' but to go an' spill molasses, as it were, all over the threshold, tryin' to make me think it's all nice an' sweet—

"I'd sent that photograph album back quick's I could pack it, but I didn't know who started it, so I've used it for a footstool. It's all it's good for, 'cordin' to my way of thinkin'. An' I ain't been particular to get the dust off my shoes before I used it neither."

Mr. Pollard, the minister, sat staring. He did not look at Candace; his eyes were fastened upon a point straight ahead. He had a look of helpless solidity, like a block of granite. This country minister, with his steady, even temperament, treading with heavy precision his one track for over forty years, having nothing new in his life except the new sameness of the seasons, and desiring nothing new, was incapable of understanding a woman like this, who had lived as quietly as he, and all the time held within herself the elements of revolution. He could not account for such violence, such extremes, except in a loss of reason. He had a conviction that Candace was getting beyond herself. He himself was not a typical New-Englander; the national elements of character were not pronounced in him. He was aghast and bewildered at this outbreak, which was tropical, and more than tropical, for a New England nature has a floodgate, and the power which it releases is an accumulation. Candace Whitcomb had been a quiet woman, so delicately resolute that the quality had been scarcely noticed in her, and her ambition had been unsuspected. Now the resolution and the ambition appeared raging over her whole self.

She began to talk again. "I've made up my mind that I'm goin' to sing Sundays the way I did this mornin', an' I don't care what folks say," said she. "I've made up my mind that I'm goin' to take matters into my own hands. I'm goin' to let folks see that I ain't trod down quite flat, that there's a little rise left in me. I ain't goin' to give up beat yet a while; an' I'd like to see anybody stop me. If I ain't got a right to play a psalm tune on my organ an' sing, I'd like to know. If you don't like it, you can move the meetin'-house."

Candace had had an inborn reverence for clergymen. She had always treated Mr. Pollard with the utmost deference. Indeed, her manner toward all men had been marked by a certain delicate stiffness and dignity. Now she was talking to the old minister with the homely freedom with which she might have addressed a female gossip over the back fence. He could not say much in return. He did not feel competent to make headway against any such tide of passion; all he could do was to let it beat against him. He made a few expostulations, which increased Candace's vehemence; he expressed his regret over the whole affair, and suggested that they should kneel and ask the guidance of the Lord in the matter, that she might be led to see it all in a different light.

Candace refused flatly. "I don't see any use prayin' about it," said she. "I don't think the Lord's got much to do with it, anyhow."

It was almost time for the afternoon service when the minister left. He had missed his comfortable noontide rest, through this encounter with his revolutionary parishioner. After the minister had gone, Candace sat by the window and waited. The bell rang, and she watched the people file past. When her nephew Wilson Ford with Alma appeared, she grunted to herself. "She's thin as a rail," said she; "guess there won't be much left of her by the time Wilson gets her. Little soft-spoken nippin' thing, she wouldn't make him no kind of a wife, anyway. Guess it's jest as well."

When the bell had stopped tolling, and all the people entered the church, Candace went over to her organ and seated herself. She arranged a singing-book before her, and sat still, waiting. Her thin, colorless neck and temples were full of beating pulses; her black eyes were bright and eager; she leaned stiffly over toward the music-rack, to hear better. When the church organ sounded out she straightened herself; her long skinny fingers pressed her own organ-keys with nervous energy. She worked the pedals with all her strength; all her slender body was in motion. When the first notes of Alma's solo began, Candace sang. She had really possessed a fine voice, and it was wonderful how little she had lost it. Straining her throat with jealous fury, her notes were still for the main part true. Her voice filled the whole room; she sang with wonderful fire and expression. That, at least, mild little Alma Way could never emulate. She was full of steadfastness and unquestioning constancy, but there were in her no smouldering fires of ambition and resolution. Music was not to her what it had been to her older rival. To this obscure woman, kept relentlessly by circumstances in a narrow track, singing in the village choir had been as much as Italy was to Napoleon—and now on her island of exile she was still showing fight.

After the church service was done, Candace left the organ and went over to her old chair by the window. Her knees felt weak, and shook under her. She sat down, and leaned back her head. There were red spots on her cheeks. Pretty soon she heard a quick slam of her gate, and an impetuous tread on the gravel-walk. She looked up, and there was her nephew Wilson Ford hurrying up to the door. She cringed a little, then she settled herself more firmly in her chair.

Wilson came into the room with a rush. He left the door open, and the wind slammed it to after him.

"Aunt Candace, where are you?" he called out, in a loud voice.

She made no reply. He looked around fiercely, and his eyes seemed to pounce upon her.

"Look here, Aunt Candace," said he, "are you crazy?" Candace said nothing. "Aunt Candace!" She did not seem to see him. "If you don't answer me," said Wilson, "I'll just go over there and pitch that old organ out of the window!"

"Wilson Ford!" said Candace, in a voice that was almost a scream.

"Well, what say! What have you got to say for yourself, acting the way you have? I tell you what 'tis, Aunt Candace, I won't stand it."

"I'd like to see you help yourself."

"I will help myself. I'll pitch that old organ out of the window, and then I'll board up the window on that side of your house. Then we'll see."

"It ain't your house, and it won't never be."

"Who said it was my house? You're my aunt, and I've got a little lookout for the credit of the family. Aunt Candace, what are you doing this way for?"

"It don't make no odds what I'm doin' so for. I ain't bound to give my reasons to a young fellar like you, if you do act so mighty toppin'. But I'll tell you one thing, Wilson Ford, after the way you've spoke to-day, you sha'n't never have one cent of my money, an' you can't never marry that Way girl if you don't have it. You can't never take her home to live with your mother, an' this house would have been mighty nice an' convenient for you some day. Now you won't get it. I'm goin' to make another will. I'd made it, if you did but know it. Now you won't get a cent of my money, you nor your mother neither. An' I ain't goin' to live a dreadful while longer, neither. Now I wish you'd go home; I want to lay down. I'm 'bout sick."

Wilson could not get another word from his aunt. His indignation had not in the least cooled. Her threat of disinheriting him did not cow him at all; he had too much rough independence, and indeed his aunt Candace's house had always been too much of an air-castle for him to contemplate seriously. Wilson, with his burly frame and his headlong common-sense, could have little to do with air-castles, had he been hard enough to build them over graves. Still, he had not admitted that he never could marry Alma. All his hopes were based upon a rise in his own fortunes, not by some sudden convulsion, but by his own long and steady labor. Some time, he thought, he should have saved enough for the two homes.

He went out of his aunt's house still storming. She arose after the door had shut behind him, and got out into the kitchen. She thought that she would start a fire and make a cup of tea. She had not eaten anything all day. She put some kindling-wood into the stove and touched a match to it; then she went back to the sitting-room, and settled down again into the chair by the window. The fire in the kitchen-stove roared, and the light wood was soon burned out. She thought no more about it. She had not put on the teakettle. Her head ached, and once in a while she shivered. She sat at the window while the afternoon waned and the dusk came on. At seven o'clock the meeting bell rang again, and the people flocked by. This time she did not stir. She had shut her parlor organ. She did not need to out-sing her rival this evening; there was only congregational singing at the Sunday-night prayer-meeting.

She sat still until it was nearly time for meeting to be done; her head ached harder and harder, and she shivered more. Finally she arose. "Guess I'll go to bed," she muttered. She went about the house, bent over and shaking, to lock the doors. She stood a minute in the back door, looking over the fields to the woods. There was a red light over there. "The woods are on fire," said Candace. She watched with a dull interest the flames roll up, withering and destroying the tender green spring foliage. The air was full of smoke, although the fire was half a mile away.

Candace locked the door and went in. The trees with their delicate garlands of new leaves, with the new nests of song birds, might fall, she was in the roar of an intenser fire; the growths of all her springs and the delicate wontedness of her whole life were going down in it. Candace went to bed in her little room off the parlor, but she could not sleep. She lay awake all night. In the morning she crawled to the door and hailed a little boy who was passing. She bade him go for the doctor as quickly as he could, then to Mrs. Ford's, and ask her to come over. She held on to the door while she was talking. The boy stood staring wonderingly at her. The spring wind fanned her face. She had drawn on a dress skirt and put her shawl over her shoulders, and her gray hair was blowing over her red cheeks.

She shut the door and went back to her bed. She never arose from it again. The doctor and Mrs. Ford came and looked after her, and she lived a week. Nobody but herself thought until the very last that she would die; the doctor called her illness merely a light run of fever; she had her senses fully.

But Candace gave up at the first. "It's my last sickness," she said to Mrs. Ford that morning when she first entered; and Mrs. Ford had laughed at the notion; but the sick woman held to it. She did not seem to suffer much physical pain; she only grew weaker and weaker, but she was distressed mentally. She did not talk much, but her eyes followed everybody with an agonized expression.

On Wednesday William Emmons came to inquire for her. Candace heard him out in the parlor. She tried to raise herself on one elbow that she might listen better to his voice.

"William Emmons come in to ask how you was," Mrs. Ford said, after he was gone.

"I—heard him," replied Candace. Presently she spoke again. "Nancy," said she, "where's that photograph album?"

"On the table," replied her sister, hesitatingly.

"Mebbe—you'd better—brush it up a little."

"Well."

Sunday morning Candace wished that the minister should be asked to come in at the noon intermission. She had refused to see him before. He came and prayed with her, and she asked his forgiveness for the way she had spoken the Sunday before. "I—hadn't ought to—spoke so," said she. "I was—dreadful wrought up."

"Perhaps it was your sickness coming on," said the minister, soothingly.

Candace shook her head. "No—it wa'n't. I hope the Lord will—forgive me."

After the minister had gone, Candace still appeared unhappy. Her pitiful eyes followed her sister everywhere with the mechanical persistency of a portrait.

"What is it you want, Candace?" Mrs. Ford said at last. She had nursed her sister faithfully, but once in a while her impatience showed itself.

"Nancy!"

"What say?"

"I wish—you'd go out when—meetin's done, an'—head off Alma an' Wilson, an'—ask 'em to come in. I feel as if—I'd like to—hear her sing."

Mrs. Ford stared. "Well," said she.

The meeting was now in session. The windows were all open, for it was another warm Sunday. Candace lay listening to the music when it began, and a look of peace came over her face. Her sister had smoothed her hair back, and put on a clean cap. The white curtain in the bedroom window waved in the wind like a white sail. Candace almost felt as if she were better, but the thought of death seemed easy.

Mrs. Ford at the parlor window watched for the meeting to be out. When the people appeared, she ran down the walk and waited for Alma and Wilson. When they came she told them what Candace wanted, and they all went in together.

"Here's Alma an' Wilson, Candace," said Mrs. Ford, leading them to the bedroom door.

Candace smiled. "Come in," she said, feebly. And Alma and Wilson entered and stood beside the bed. Candace continued to look at them, the smile straining her lips.

"Wilson!"

"What is it, Aunt Candace?"

"I ain't altered that—will. You an' Alma can—come here an'—live—when I'm—gone. Your mother won't mind livin' alone. Alma can have—all—my things."

"Don't, Aunt Candace." Tears were running over Wilson's cheeks, and Alma's delicate face was all of a quiver.

"I thought—maybe—Alma'd be willin' to—sing for me," said Candace.

"What do you want me to sing?" Alma asked, in a trembling voice.

" 'Jesus, lover of my soul.' "

Alma, standing there beside Wilson, began to sing. At first she could hardly control her voice, then she sang sweetly and clearly.

Candace lay and listened. Her face had a holy and radiant expression. When Alma stopped singing it did not disappear, but she looked up and spoke, and it was like a secondary glimpse of the old shape of a forest tree through the smoke and flame of the transfiguring fire the instant before it falls. "You flatted a little on—soul," said Candace.

Stephen Crane (1871–1900)

The light comedy of "The Bride Comes to Yellow Sky" (1898) represents one element of Stephen Crane's varied humor. It appears also in his Sullivan County sketches of 1891–1892 and in his *Whilomville Stories* (1900). But there are sardonically grim touches in "The Bride Comes to Yellow Sky"—Scratchy Wilson's sadistic treatment of the dog and the town's abject fright at his bullying—which make the anticlimax brutally ironic as well as amusing. Crane was amused by man and the universe; he was also roused to anger. His early journalism was often satirical; many of the characterizations and images in his poetry and fiction are compressed bits of contemptuous irony; his major work, *The Red Badge of Courage*, is a compassionate ironic lament over man's self-destructiveness. The spirit which impelled Crane to cloak objects, characters, situations, and institutions with a grotesquerie reminiscent of Poe's is succinctly expressed in "The Blue Hotel" (1898), one of Crane's finest stories: "One viewed the existence of man then as a marvel, and conceded a glamor of wonder to these lice which were caused to cling to a whirling, fire-smitten, ice-locked, disease-stricken, space-lost bulb. The conceit of man was explained by this storm to be the very engine of life."

TEXT: *The Open Boat and Other Tales of Adventure*, New York, 1898. COMMENTARY: John Berryman, *Stephen Crane*, New York, 1950; Daniel G. Hoffman, *The Poetry of Stephen Crane*, New York, 1957.

THE BRIDE COMES TO YELLOW SKY

I

The great Pullman was whirling onward with such dignity of motion that a glance from the window seemed simply to prove that the plains of Texas were pouring eastward. Vast flats of green grass, dull-hued spaces of mesquit and cactus, little groups of frame houses, woods of light and tender trees, all were sweeping into the east, sweeping over the horizon, a precipice.

A newly married pair had boarded this coach at San Antonio. The man's face was reddened from many days in the wind and sun, and a direct result of his new black clothes was that his brick-colored hands were constantly performing in a most conscious fashion. From time to time he looked down respectfully at his attire. He sat with a hand on each knee, like a man waiting in a barber's shop. The glances he devoted to other passengers were furtive and shy.

The bride was not pretty, nor was she very young. She wore a dress of blue cashmere, with small reservations of velvet here and there, and with steel buttons abounding. She continually twisted her head to regard her puff sleeves, very stiff, straight, and high. They embarrassed her. It was quite apparent that she had cooked, and that she expected to cook, dutifully. The blushes caused by the careless scrutiny of some passengers as she had entered the car were strange to see upon this plain, underclass countenance, which was drawn in placid, almost emotionless lines.

They were evidently very happy. "Ever been in a parlor car before?" he asked, smiling with delight.

"No," she answered, "I never was. It's fine, ain't it?"

"Great! And then after a while we'll go forward to the diner, and get a big layout. Finest meal in the world. Charge a dollar."

"Oh, do they?" cried the bride. "Charge a dollar? Why, that's too much—for us—ain't it, Jack?"

"Not this trip, anyhow," he answered bravely. "We're going to go the whole thing."

Later he explained to her about the trains. "You see, it's a thousand miles from one end of Texas to the other; and this train runs right across it, and never stops but for four times." He had the pride of an owner. He pointed out to her the dazzling fittings of the coach; and in truth her eyes opened wider as she contemplated the sea-green figured velvet, the shining brass, silver, and glass, the wood that gleamed as darkly brilliant as the surface of a pool of oil. At one end a bronze figure sturdily held a support for a separated chamber, and at convenient places on the ceiling were frescos in olive and silver.

To the minds of the pair, their surroundings reflected the glory of their marriage that morning in San Antonio; this was the environment of their new estate; and the man's face in particular beamed with an elation that made him appear ridiculous to the negro porter. This individual at times surveyed them from afar with an amused and superior grin. On other occasions he bullied them with skill in ways that did not make it exactly plain to them that they were being bullied. He subtly used all the manners of the most unconquerable kind of snobbery. He oppressed them; but of this oppression they had small knowledge, and they speedily forgot that infrequently a number of travellers covered them with stares of derisive enjoyment. Historically there was supposed to be something infinitely humorous in their situation.

"We are due in Yellow Sky at 3:42," he said, looking tenderly into her eyes.

"Oh, are we?" she said, as if she had not been aware of it. To evince surprise at her husband's statement was part of her wifely amiability. She took from a pocket a little silver watch; and as she held it before her, and stared at it with a frown of attention, the new husband's face shone.

"I bought it in San Anton' from a friend of mine," he told her gleefully.

"It's seventeen minutes past twelve," she said, looking up at him with a kind of shy and clumsy coquetry. A passenger, noting this play, grew excessively sardonic, and winked at himself in one of the numerous mirrors.

At last they went to the dining-car. Two rows of negro waiters, in glowing white suits, surveyed their entrance with the interest, and also the equanimity, of men who had been forewarned. The pair fell to the lot of a waiter who happened to feel pleasure in steering them through their meal. He viewed them with the manner of a fatherly pilot, his countenance radiant with benevolence. The patronage, entwined with the ordinary deference, was not plain to them. And yet, as they returned to their coach, they showed in their faces a sense of escape.

To the left, miles down a long, purple slope, was a little ribbon of mist where moved the keening Rio Grande. The train was approaching it at an angle, and the apex was Yellow Sky. Presently it was apparent that, as the distance from Yellow Sky grew shorter, the husband became commensurately restless. His brick-red hands were more insistent in their prominence. Occasionally he was even rather absent-minded and faraway when the bride leaned forward and addressed him.

As a matter of truth, Jack Potter was beginning to find the shadow of a deed weigh upon him like a leaden slab. He, the town marshal of Yellow Sky, a man known, liked, and feared in his corner, a prominent person, had gone to San Antonio to meet a girl he believed he loved, and there, after the usual prayers, had actually induced her to marry him, without consulting Yellow Sky for any part of the transaction. He was now bringing his bride before an innocent and unsuspecting community.

Of course, people in Yellow Sky married as it pleased them, in accordance with a general custom; but such was Potter's thought of his duty to his friends, or of their idea of his duty, or of an unspoken form which does not control men in these matters, that he felt he was heinous. He had committed an extraordinary crime. Face to face with this girl in San Antonio, and spurred by his sharp impulse, he had gone headlong over all the social hedges. At San Antonio he was like a man hidden in the dark. A knife to sever any friendly duty, any form, was easy to his hand in that remote city. But the hour of Yellow Sky—the hour of daylight—was approaching.

He knew full well that his marriage was an important thing to his town. It could only be exceeded by the burning of the new hotel. His friends could not forgive him. Frequently he had reflected on the advisability of telling them by telegraph, but a new cowardice had been upon him. He feared to do it. And now the train was hurrying him toward a scene of amazement, glee, and reproach. He glanced out of the window at the line of haze swinging slowly in toward the train.

Yellow Sky had a kind of brass band, which played painfully, to the delight of the populace. He laughed without heart as he thought of it. If the citizens could dream of his prospective arrival with his bride, they would parade the band at the station and escort them, amid cheers and laughing congratulations, to his adobe home.

He resolved that he would use all the devices of speed and plains-craft in making the journey from the station to his house. Once within that safe citadel, he could issue some sort of vocal bulletin, and then not go among the citizens until they had time to wear off a little of their enthusiasm.

The bride looked anxiously at him. "What's worrying you, Jack?"

He laughed again. "I'm not worrying, girl; I'm only thinking of Yellow Sky."

She flushed in comprehension.

A sense of mutual guilt invaded their minds and developed a finer tenderness. They looked at each other with eyes softly aglow. But Potter often laughed the same nervous laugh; the flush upon the bride's face seemed quite permanent.

The traitor to the feelings of Yellow Sky narrowly watched the speeding landscape. "We're nearly there," he said.

Presently the porter came and announced the proximity of Potter's home. He held a brush in his hand, and, with all his airy superiority gone, he brushed Potter's new clothes as the latter slowly turned this way and that way. Potter fumbled out a coin and gave it to the porter, as he had seen others do. It was a heavy and muscle-bound business, as that of a man shoeing his first horse.

The porter took their bag, and as the train began to slow they moved forward to the hooded platform of the car. Presently the two engines and their long string of coaches rushed into the station of Yellow Sky.

"They have to take water here," said Potter, from a constricted throat and in mournful cadence, as one announcing death. Before the train stopped his eye had swept the length of the platform, and he was glad and astonished to see there was none upon it but the station agent, who, with a slightly hurried and anxious air, was walking toward the water tanks. When the train had halted, the porter alighted first, and placed in position a little temporary step.

"Come on, girl," said Potter hoarsely. As he helped her down they each laughed on a false note. He took the bag from the negro, and bade his wife cling to his arm. As they slunk rapidly away, his hangdog glance perceived that they were unloading the two trunks, and also that the station agent, far ahead near the baggage car, had turned and was running toward him, making gestures. He laughed, and groaned as he laughed, when he noted the first effect of his marital bliss upon Yellow Sky. He gripped his wife's arm firmly to his side, and they fled. Behind them the porter stood, chuckling fatuously.

II

The California express on the Southern Railway was due at Yellow Sky in twenty-one minutes. There were six men at the bar of the Weary Gentleman saloon. One was a drummer, who talked a great deal and rapidly; three were Texans, who did not care to talk at that time; and two were Mexican sheepherders, who did not talk as a general practice in the Weary Gentleman saloon. The barkeeper's dog lay on the board-walk that crossed in front of the door. His head was on his paws, and he glanced drowsily here and there with the constant vigilance of a dog that is kicked on occasion. Across the sandy street were some vivid green grass-plots, so wonderful in appearance, amid the sands that burned near them in a blazing sun, that they caused a doubt in the mind. They exactly resembled the grass mats used to represent lawns on the stage. At the cooler end of the railway station, a man without a coat sat in a tilted chair and smoked his pipe. The fresh-cut bank of the Rio Grande circled near the town, and there could be seen beyond it a great plum-colored plain of mesquit.

Save for the busy drummer and his companions in the saloon, Yellow Sky was dozing. The newcomer leaned gracefully upon the bar, and recited many tales with the confidence of a bard who has come upon a new field.

"—and at the moment that the old man fell downstairs with the bureau in his arms, the old woman was coming up with two scuttles of coal, and of course—"

The drummer's tale was interrupted by a young man who suddenly appeared in the open door. He cried: "Scratchy Wilson's drunk, and has turned loose with both hands." The two Mexicans at once set down their glasses and faded out of the rear entrance of the saloon.

The drummer, innocent and jocular, answered: "All right, old man. S'pose he has? Come in and have a drink, anyhow."

But the information had made such an obvious cleft in every skull in the room that the drummer was obliged to see its importance. All had become instantly solemn. "Say," said he, mystified, "what is this?" His three companions made the introductory gesture of eloquent speech; but the young man at the door forestalled them.

"It means, my friend," he answered, as he came into the saloon, "that for the next two hours this town won't be a health resort."

The barkeeper went to the door, and locked and barred it; reaching out of the window, he pulled in heavy wooden shutters, and barred them. Immediately a solemn, chapel-like gloom was upon the place. The drummer was looking from one to another.

"But say," he cried, "what is this, anyhow? You don't mean there is going to be a gun-fight?"

"Don't know whether there'll be a fight or not," answered one man, grimly; "but there'll be some shootin'—some good shootin'."

The young man who had warned them waved his hand. "Oh, there'll be a fight fast enough, if any one wants it. Anybody can get a fight out there in the street. There's a fight just waiting."

The drummer seemed to be swayed between the interest of a foreigner and a perception of personal danger.

"What did you say his name was?" he asked.

"Scratchy Wilson," they answered in chorus.

"And will he kill anybody? What are you going to do? Does this happen often? Does he rampage around like this once a week or so? Can he break in that door?"

"No; he can't break down that door," replied the barkeeper. "He's tried it three times. But when he comes you'd better lay down on the floor, stranger. He's dead sure to shoot at it, and a bullet may come through."

Thereafter the drummer kept a strict eye upon the door. The time had not yet been called for him to hug the floor, but as a minor precaution, he sidled near to the wall. "Will he kill anybody?" he said again.

The men laughed low and scornfully at the question.

"He's out to shoot, and he's out for trouble. Don't see any good in experimentin' with him."

"But what do you do in a case like this? What do you do?"

A man responded, "Why, he and Jack Potter—"

"But," in chorus the other men interrupted, "Jack Potter's in San Anton'."

"Well, who is he? What's he got to do with it?"

"Oh, he's the town marshal. He goes out and fights Scratchy when he gets on one of these tears."

"Wow!" said the drummer, mopping his brow. "Nice job he's got."

The voices had toned away to mere whisperings. The drummer wished to ask further questions, which were born of an increasing anxiety and bewilderment; but when he attempted them, the men merely looked at him in irritation and motioned him to remain silent. A tense, waiting hush was upon them. In the deep shadows of the room their eyes shone as they listened for sounds from the street. One man made three gestures at the barkeeper; and the latter, moving like a ghost, handed him a glass and a bottle. The man poured a full glass of whisky, and set down the bottle noiselessly. He gulped the whisky in a swallow, and turned again toward the door in immovable silence. The drummer saw that the bar-keeper, without a sound, had taken a Winchester from beneath the bar. Later he saw this individual beckoning to him, so he tiptoed across the room.

"You better come with me back of the bar."

"No, thanks," said the drummer, perspiring. "I'd rather be where I can make a break for the back door."

Whereupon the man of bottles made a kindly but peremptory gesture. The drummer obeyed it, and finding himself seated on a box with his head below the level of the bar, balm was laid upon his soul at sight of various zinc and copper fittings that bore a resemblance to armor plate. The barkeeper took a seat comfortably upon an adjacent box.

"You see," he whispered, "this here Scratchy Wilson is a wonder with a gun—a perfect wonder; and when he goes on the war-trail, we hunt our holes—naturally. He's about the last one of the old gang that used to hang out along the river here. He's a terror when he's drunk. When he's sober he's all right—kind of simple—wouldn't hurt a fly—nicest fellow in town. But when he's drunk—whoo!"

There were periods of stillness. "I wish Jack Potter was back from San Anton'," said the barkeeper. "He shot Wilson up once—in the leg—and he would sail in and pull out the kinks in this thing."

Presently they heard from a distance the sound of a shot, followed by three wild yowls. It instantly removed a bond from the men in the darkened saloon. There was a shuffling of feet. They looked at each other. "Here he comes," they said.

III

A man in a maroon-colored flannel shirt, which had been purchased for purposes of decoration, and made principally by some Jewish women on the East Side of New York, rounded a corner and walked into the mid-dle of the main street of Yellow Sky. In either hand the man held a long, heavy, blue-black revolver. Often he yelled, and these cries rang through a semblance of a deserted village, shrilly flying over the roofs in a volume that seemed to have no relation to the ordinary vocal strength of a man. It was as if the surrounding stillness formed the arch of a tomb over him. These cries of ferocious challenge rang against walls of silence. And his boots had red tops with gilded imprints, of the kind beloved in winter by little sledding boys on the hillsides of New England.

The man's face flamed in a rage begot of whisky. His eyes, rolling, and yet keen for ambush, hunted the still doorways and windows. He walked with the creeping movement of the midnight cat. As it occurred to him, he roared menacing information. The long revolvers in his hands were as easy as straws; they were moved with an electric swiftness. The little fingers of each hand played sometimes in a musician's way. Plain from the low collar of the shirt, the cords of his neck straightened and sank, straightened and sank, as passion moved him. The only sounds were his terrible invitations. The calm adobes preserved their demeanor at the passing of this small thing in the middle of the street.

There was no offer of fight—no offer of fight. The man called to the sky. There were no attractions. He bellowed and fumed and swayed his revolvers here and everywhere.

The dog of the barkeeper of the Weary Gentleman saloon had not appreciated the advance of events. He yet lay dozing in front of his master's door. At sight of the dog, the man paused and raised his revolver humorously. At sight of the man, the dog sprang up and walked diagonally away, with a sullen head, and growling. The man yelled, and the dog broke into a gallop. As it was about to enter an alley, there was a loud noise, a whistling, and something spat the ground directly before it. The dog screamed, and wheeling in terror, galloped headlong in a new direction. Again there was a noise, a whistling, and sand was kicked viciously before it. Fear-stricken, the dog turned and flurried like an animal in a pen. The man stood laughing, his weapons at his hips.

Ultimately the man was attracted by the closed door of the Weary Gentleman saloon. He went to it, and, hammering with a revolver, demanded drink.

The door remaining imperturbable, he picked a bit of paper from the walk, and nailed it to the framework with a knife. He then turned his back contemptuously upon this popular resort, and, walking to the opposite side of the street and spinning there on his heel quickly and lithely, fired at the bit of paper. He missed it by a half inch. He swore at himself, and went away. Later he comfortably fusilladed the windows of his most intimate friend. The man was playing with this town; it was a toy for him.

But still there was no offer of fight. The name of Jack Potter, his ancient antagonist, entered his mind, and he concluded that it would be a glad thing if he should go to Potter's house, and by bombardment induce him to come out and fight. He moved in the direction of his desire, chanting Apache scalp-music.

When he arrived at it, Potter's house presented the same still front as had the other adobes. Taking up a strategic position, the man howled a challenge. But this house regarded him as might a great stone god. It gave no sign. After a decent wait, the man howled further challenges, mingling with them wonderful epithets.

Presently there came the spectacle of a man churning himself into deepest rage over the immobility of a house. He fumed at it as the winter wind attacks a prairie cabin in the North. To the distance there should have gone the sound of a tumult like the fighting of two hundred Mexicans. As necessity bade him, he paused for breath or to reload his revolvers.

IV

Potter and his bride walked sheepishly and with speed. Sometimes they laughed together shamefacedly and low.

"Next corner, dear," he said finally.

They put forth the efforts of a pair walking bowed against a strong wind. Potter was about to raise a finger to point the first appearance of the new home when, as they circled the corner, they came face to face with a man in a maroon-colored shirt, who was feverishly pushing cartridges into a large revolver. Upon the instant the man dropped his revolver to the ground, and, like lightning, whipped another from its holster. The second weapon was aimed at the bridegroom's chest.

There was a silence. Potter's mouth seemed to be merely a grave for his tongue. He exhibited an instinct to at once loosen his arm from the woman's grip, and he dropped the bag to the sand. As for the bride, her face had gone as yellow as old cloth. She was a slave to hideous rites, gazing at the apparitional snake.

The two men faced each other at a distance of three paces. He of the revolver smiled with a new and quiet ferocity.

"Tried to sneak up on me," he said. "Tried to sneak up on me!" His eyes grew more baleful. As Potter made a slight movement, the man thrust his revolver venomously forward. "No; don't you do it, Jack Potter. Don't you move a finger toward a gun just yet. Don't you move an eyelash. The time has come for me to settle with you, and I'm goin' to do it my own way, and loaf along with no interferin'. So if you don't want a gun bent on you, just mind what I tell you."

Potter looked at his enemy. "I ain't got a gun on me, Scatchy," he said. "Honest, I ain't." He was stiffening and steadying, but yet somewhere at the back of his mind a vision of the Pullman floated: the sea-green figured velvet, the shining brass, silver, and glass, the wood that gleamed as darkly brilliant as the surface of a pool of oil—all the glory of the marriage, the environment of the new estate. "You know I fight when it comes to fighting, Scratchy Wilson; but I ain't got a gun on me. You'll have to do all the shootin' yourself."

His enemy's face went livid. He stepped forward, and lashed his weapon to and fro before Potter's chest. "Don't you tell me you ain't got no gun on you, you whelp. Don't tell me no lie like that. There ain't a man in Texas ever seen you without no gun. Don't take me for no kid." His eyes blazed with light, and his throat worked like a pump.

"I ain't takin' you for no kid," answered Potter. His heels had not moved an inch backward. "I'm takin' you for a——fool. I tell you I ain't got a gun, and I ain't. If you're goin' to shoot me up, you better begin now; you'll never get a chance like this again."

So much enforced reasoning had told on Wilson's rage; he was calmer.

"If you ain't got a gun, why ain't you got a gun?" he sneered. "Been to Sunday school?"

"I ain't got a gun because I've just come from San Anton' with my wife. I'm married," said Potter. "And if I'd thought there was going to be any galoots like you prowling around when I brought my wife home, I'd had a gun, and don't you forget it."

"Married!" said Scratchy, not at all comprehending.

"Yes, married. I'm married," said Potter, distinctly.

"Married?" said Scratchy. Seemingly for the first time, he saw the drooping, drowning woman at the other man's side. "No!" he said. He was like a creature allowed a glimpse of another world. He moved a pace backward, and his arm, with the revolver, dropped to his side. "Is this the lady?" he asked.

"Yes; this is the lady," answered Potter.

There was another period of silence.

"Well," said Wilson at last, slowly, "I s'pose it's all off now."

"It's all off if you say so, Scratchy. You know I didn't make the trouble." Potter lifted his valise.

"Well, I 'low it's off, Jack," said Wilson. He was looking at the ground. "Married!" He was not a student of chivalry; it was merely that in the presence of this foreign condition he was a simple child of the earlier plains. He picked up his starboard revolver, and, placing both weapons in their holsters, he went away. His feet made funnel-shaped tracks in the heavy sand.

George Ade (1866–1944)

Some of the best humor written at the end of the nineteenth century arose in the Middle West, where flush times like those of the pre-Civil War Southwest were made bitter by social and economic discontent. A free-wheeling Chicago journalism encouraged vigorous writing, just as the journalism of California had earlier encouraged Ambrose Bierce of Indiana and Mark Twain of Missouri. The two outstanding Midwestern humorists were newspapermen George Ade of Indiana and Finley Peter Dunne. Both were unhampered by many of the restrictive inhibitions of the Eastern genteel tradition. Their pervasive influence can be discerned in the style and critical humor of such later Midwestern writers as Sherwood Anderson, Ring Lardner, Sinclair Lewis, James Thurber, F. Scott Fitzgerald, and Ernest Hemingway. Ade used slang and colloquialisms so blandly in his popular "fables in slang" that many of his numerous readers were unaware that he was laughing at them; the joy of finding nonstandard words and phrases given mock-dignity by capital letters and a pompous tone reduced the shock of Ade's ironic deflation of middle-class values and customs. As Ade put it mockingly, "I never wanted to be a comic or tried to be one. Always I wrote for the 'family trade' and I used no word or phrase which might give offense to mother and the girls or to a professor of English." Ade was more revealing when he wrote that "My enthusiasms include golf, travel, horse-racing, and the spoken drama. My antipathies are social show-offs, bigots on religion, fanatics on total abstinence, and all persons who take themselves seriously."

TEXT: *More Fables*, Chicago, Ill., 1900. COMMENTARY: Fred C. Kelly, *George Ade: Warmhearted Satirist*, Indianapolis, Ind., 1947.

THE FABLE OF THE HONEST MONEY-MAKER AND THE PARTNER OF HIS JOYS, SUCH AS THEY WERE

The Prosperous Farmer lived in an Agricultural Section of the Middle West. He commanded the Respect of all his Neighbors. He owned a Section, and had a Raft of big Horses and white-faced Cows and Farm Machinery, and Money in the Bank besides. He still had the first Dollar he ever made, and it could not have been taken away from him with Pincers.

Henry was a ponderous, Clydesdale kind of Man, with Warts on his Hands. He did not have to travel on Appearances, because the whole County knew what he was Worth. Of course he was Married. Years be-

443

fore he had selected a willing Country Girl with Pink Cheeks, and put her into his Kitchen to serve the Remainder of her Natural Life. He let her have as high as Two Dollars a Year to spend for herself. Her Hours were from 6:00 A.M. to 6:00 A.M., and if she got any Sleep she had to take it out of her Time. The Eight-Hour Day was not recognized on Henry's Place.

After Ten Years of raising Children, Steaming over the Washtub, Milking the Cows, Carrying in Wood, Cooking for the Hands, and other Delsarte such as the Respected Farmer usually Frames Up for his Wife, she was as thin as a Rail and humped over in the Shoulders. She was Thirty, and looked Sixty. Her Complexion was like Parchment and her Voice had been worn to a Cackle. She was losing her Teeth, too, but Henry could not afford to pay Dentist Bills because he needed all his Money to buy more Poland Chinas and build other Cribs. If she wanted a Summer Kitchen or a new Wringer or a Sewing Machine, or Anything Else that would lighten her Labors, Henry would Moan and Grumble and say she was trying to land him in the Poorhouse.

They had a dandy big Barn, painted Red with White Trimmings, and a Patent Fork to lift the Hay into the Mow, and the Family lived in a Pine Box that had not been Painted in Years and had Dog-Fennel all around the Front of it.

The Wife of the Respected Farmer was the only Work Animal around the Place that was not kept Fat and Sleek. But, of course, Henry did not count on Selling her. Henry often would fix up his Blooded Stock for the County Fair and tie Blue Ribbons on the Percherons and Herefords, but it was never noticed that he tied any Blue Ribbons on the Wife.

And yet Henry was a Man to be Proud of. He never Drank and he was a Good Hand with Horses, and he used to go to Church on Sunday Morning and hold a Cud of Tobacco in his Face during Services and sing Hymns with Extreme Unction. He would sing that he was a Lamb and had put on the Snow-White Robes and that Peace attended him. People would see him there in his Store Suit, with the Emaciated Wife and the Scared Children sitting in the Shadow of his Greatness, and they said that she was Lucky to have a Man who was so Well Off and lived in the Fear of the Lord.

Henry was Patriotic as well as Pious. He had a Picture of Abraham Lincoln in the Front Room, which no one was permitted to Enter, and he was glad that Slavery had been abolished.

Henry robbed the Cradle in order to get Farm-Hands. As soon as the Children were able to Walk without holding on, he started them for the Corn-Field, and told them to Pay for the Board that they had been Sponging off of him up to that Time. He did not want them to get too much Schooling for fear that they would want to sit up at Night and Read instead of Turning In so as to get an Early Start along before Daylight next Morning. So they did not get any too much, rest easy. And he never Foundered them on Stick Candy or Raisins or any such Delicatessen for sale at a General Store. Henry was undoubtedly the Tightest Wad in the Township. Some of the Folks who had got into a Box through Poor Management, and had been Foreclosed out of House and Home by Henry and his Lawyer, used to say that Henry was a Skin, and was too Stingy to give his Family enough to Eat, but most People looked up to Henry, for there was no getting around it that he was Successful.

When the Respected Farmer had been Married for Twenty Years and the Children had developed into long Gawks who did not know Anything except to get out and Toil all Day for Pa and not be paid anything for it, and after Henry had scraped together more Money than you could load on a Hay-Rack, an Unfortunate Thing happened. His Wife began to Fail. She was now Forty, but the Fair and Fat did not go with it. At that Age some Women are Buxom and just blossoming into the Full Charm of Matronly Womanhood. But Henry's Wife was Gaunt and Homely and all Run Down. She had been Poorly for Years, but she had to keep up and do the Chores as well as the House-Work, because Henry could not afford to hire a Girl. At last her Back gave out, so that she had to sit down and Rest every Once in a While. Henry would come in for his Meals and to let her know how Hearty all the Calves seemed to be, and he began to Notice that she was not very Chipper. It Worried him more than a little, because he did not care to pay any Doctor Bills. He told her she had better go and get some Patent Medicine that he had seen advertised on the Fence coming out from Town. It was only Twenty-Five cents a Bottle, and was warranted to Cure Anything. So she tried it, but it did not seem to restore her Youth and she got Weaker, and at last Henry just had to have the Doctor, Expense or No Expense. The Doctor said that as nearly as he could Diagnose her Case, she seemed to be Worn Out. Henry was Surprised, and said she had not been Complaining any more than Usual.

Next Afternoon he was out Dickering for a Bull, and his Woman, lying on the cheap Bedstead, up under the hot Roof, folded her lean Hands and slipped away to the only Rest she had known since she tied up with a Prosperous and Respected Farmer.

Henry was all Broken Up. He Wailed and Sobbed and made an Awful Fuss at the Church. The Preacher tried to Comfort him by saying that the Ways of Providence were beyond all Finding Out. He said that probably there was some Reason why the Sister had been taken right in the Prime of her Usefulness, but it was not for Henry to know it. He said the only Consolation he could offer was the Hope that possibly she was Better Off. There did not seem to be much Doubt about that.

In about a Month the Respected Farmer was riding around the Country in his Buck-Board looking for Number Two. He had a business Head and he knew it was Cheaper to Marry than to Hire one. His Daughter was only Eleven and not quite Big Enough as yet to do all the Work for five Men.

Finally he found one who had the Reputation of being a Good Worker. When he took her over to his House to Break Her In, the Paper at the County Seat referred to them as the Happy Couple.

MORAL: *Be Honest and Respected and it Goes.*

Finley Peter Dunne (1867–1936)

"Traveller, archaeologist, historian, social observer, saloon-keeper, economist, and philosopher, who has not been out of the ward for twenty-five years 'but twict.'" Thus Finley Peter Dunne described "Martin Dooley," the profound Chicago Irishman whose dialect discourses with "Hennessey" the clod threw a sharply humorous light upon American life as the nineteenth century passed into the twentieth. A Chicago newspaperman eager to combat municipal political corruption in 1893, Dunne had found it personally expedient to assume an urban comic mask. Dunne's acute mind and unusually sagacious comprehension of domestic and foreign affairs then led him to convert "Mr. Dooley" into a full-scale pundit, whose witty, ironic, and satiric observations made him a national figure in his times and are still among the most valuable commentaries upon his age. Dunne skillfully handled Irish-American brogue, only occasionally descending to the misspellings which had marred "cracker-box philosopher" types in the past. "Mr. Dooley" is a consistent, plausible and complex folk-character, blessed with compassion yet not sentimental, disgusted with imperialism's inhumanity to "natives" yet not above manifesting a conservative folk antipathy toward the Negro and women's rights. Amusing though his dialect may be, it is "Mr. Dooley's" wisdom which turned him into the outstanding creation of his kind in American humorous literature.

TEXT: *Mr. Dooley in the Hearts of His Countrymen*, Boston, Mass., 1899. COMMENTARY: Elmer Ellis, *Mr. Dooley's America: A Life of Finley Peter Dunne*, New York, 1941.

EXPANSION

"Whin we plant what Hogan calls th' starry banner iv Freedom in th' Ph'lippeens," said Mr. Dooley, "an' give th' sacred blessin' iv liberty to the poor, downtrodden people iv thim unfortunate isles,—dam thim!— we'll larn thim a lesson."

"Sure," said Mr. Hennessy, sadly, "we have a thing or two to larn oursilves."

"But it isn't f'r thim to larn us," said Mr. Dooley. " 'Tis not f'r thim wretched an' degraded crathers, without a mind or a shirt iv their own, f'r to give lessons in politeness an' liberty to a nation that manny-facthers more dhressed beef than anny other imperyal nation in th' wurruld. We say to thim: 'Naygurs,' we say, 'poor, dissolute, uncovered wretches,' says

447

we, 'whin th' crool hand iv Spain forged man'cles f'r ye'er limbs, as Hogan says, who was it crossed th' say an' sthruck off th' comealongs? We did,— by dad, we did. An' now, ye mis'rable, childish-minded apes, we propose f'r to larn ye th' uses iv liberty. In ivry city in this unfair land we will erect school-houses an' packin' houses an' houses iv correction; an' we'll larn ye our language, because 'tis aisier to larn ye ours than to larn our-silves yours. An' we'll give ye clothes, if ye pay f'r thim; an', if ye don't, ye can go without. An', whin ye're hungry, ye can go to th' morgue—we mane th' resth'rant—an' ate a good square meal iv ar-rmy beef. An' we'll sind th' gr-reat Gin'ral Eagan over f'r to larn ye etiquette, an' Andhrew Carnegie to larn ye pathriteism with blow-holes into it, an' Gin'ral Alger to larn ye to hould onto a job; an', whin ye've become edycated an' have all th' blessin's iv civilization that we don't want, that'll count ye one. We can't give ye anny votes, because we haven't more thin enough to go round now; but we'll threat ye th' way a father shud threat his childher if we have to break ivry bone in ye'er bodies. So come to our ar-rms,' says we.

"But, glory be, 'tis more like a rasslin' match than a father's embrace. Up gets this little monkey iv an' Aggynaldoo, an' says he, 'Not for us,' he says. 'We thank ye kindly; but we believe,' he says, 'in pathronizin' home industhries,' he says. 'An',' he says, 'I have on hand,' he says, 'an' f'r sale,' he says, 'a very superyor brand iv home-made liberty, like ye'er mother used to make,' he says. ' 'Tis a long way fr'm ye'er plant to here,' he says, 'an' be th' time a cargo iv liberty,' he says, 'got out here an' was handled be th' middlemen,' he says, 'it might spoil,' he says. 'We don't want anny col' storage or embalmed liberty,'' he says. 'What we want an' what th' ol' reliable house iv Aggynaldoo,' he says, 'supplies to th' thrade,' he says, 'is fr-esh liberty r-right off th' far-rm,' he says. 'I can't do anny-thing with ye'er proposition,' he says. 'I can't give up,' he says, 'th' rights f'r which f'r five years I've fought an' bled ivry wan I cud reach,' he says. 'Onless,' he says, 'ye'd feel like buyin' out th' whole business,' he says. 'I'm a pathrite,' he says; 'but I'm no bigot,' he says.

"An' there it stands, Hinnissy, with th' indulgent parent kneelin' on th' stomach iv his adopted child, while a dillygation fr'm Boston bastes him with an umbrella. There it stands, an' how will it come out I dinnaw. I'm not much iv an expansionist mesilf. F'r th' las' tin years I've been thryin' to decide whether 'twud be good policy an' thrue to me thraditions to make this here bar two or three feet longer, an manny's th' night I've laid awake tryin' to puzzle it out. But I don't know what to do with th' Ph'lippeens anny more thin I did las' summer, befure I heerd tell iv thim. We can't give thim to anny wan without makin' th' wan that gets thim feel th' way Doherty felt to Clancy whin Clancy med a frindly call an' give Doherty's childher th' measles. We can't sell thim, we can't ate thim, an' we can't throw thim into th' alley whin no wan is lookin'. An' 'twud be a disgrace f'r to lave befure we've pounded these frindless an' ongrateful people into insinsibility. So I suppose, Hinnissy, we'll have to stay an' do th' best we can, an' lave Andhrew Carnegie secede fr'm th' Union. They'se wan consolation; an' that is, if th' American people can govern thimsilves, they can govern annything that walks."

"An' what 'd ye do with Aggy—what-d'ye-call-him?" asked Mr. Hennessy.

"Well," Mr. Dooley replied, with brightening eyes, "I know what they'd do with him in this ward. They'd give that pathrite what he asks, an' thin they'd throw him down an' take it away fr'm him."

THE UNION OF TWO GREAT FORTUNES

"They'se wan thing that always makes me feel sure iv what Hogan calls th' safety iv our dimmyrcratic institutions," said Mr. Dooley, "an' that's th' intherest th' good people iv New York takes in a weddin' iv th' millyionaires. Anny time a millyionaire condiscinds to enther th' martial state, as Hogan says, an', as Hogan says, make vows to Hyman, which is the Jew god iv marredge, he can fill th' house an' turn people away fr'm th' dure. An' he does. Th' sthreets is crowded. Th' cars can har'ly get through. Th' polis foorce is out, an' hammerin' th' heads iv th' delighted throng. Riprisintatives iv th' free an' inlightened press, th' pollutyem iv our liberties, as Hogan says, bright, intilligent young journalists, iver ready to probe fraud an' sham, disgeesed as waithers, is dashin' madly about, makin' notes on their cuffs. Business is suspinded. They'se no money in Wall Sthreet. It's all at th' sacred scene. Hour be hour, as th' prisints ar-re delivered, th' bank rates go up. Th' Threeasury Departmint has to go on a silver basis, there bein' no goold to mannyfacther into plunks.

"Inside th' house th' prisints cast a goolden gleam on th' beauchious scene. Th' happy father is seen seated at a table, dictattin' millyion-dollar checks to a stinographer. Th' goold chandeliers is draped with r-ropes iv dimon's an' pearls. Th' hired girl is passin' dhrinks in goolden goblets. Twinty firemen fr'm th' New York Cinthral Railroad is shovellin' di'mon'-studded pickle crutes into th' back yard, among th' yachts an' horses. Chansy Depoo enthers an' thrips over a box iv bonds. 'Ar-re these th' holy bonds iv mathrimony?' he says; f'r he is a wild divvle, an' ye can't stop his jokin', avin on solemn occasions.

"Th' soggarth comes in afther a while, carryin' a goold prayer-book, th' gift iv th' Rothscheelds, an' stands behind a small but valyable pree Doo. To th' soft, meelojous chune iv th' Wagner Palace Weddin' March fr'm 'Long Green,' th' groom enthers, simply but ixpinsively attired in governmint fours, an' fannin' himsilf with a bunch iv first morgedge bonds.

"Th' prayers f'r th' occasion, printed on negotyable paper, is disthributed among th' guests. Th' bride was delayed be th' crowd outside. Women screamed an' waved their handkerchefs, sthrong men cheered an' wept; an' 'twas not until th' polis had clubbed tin hardy pathrites to death that th' lady cud enther th' house where her fate was to be sealed. But fin'lly she med it; an' th' two happy, happy childher, whose sunshiny youth riprisinted five thousan' miles iv thrack, eight goold mines, wan hundherd millyion dollars' woth iv rollin' stock, an' a majority intherest in th' Chicago stock yards, was r-ready f'r th' nicissary thransfers that wud establish th' com-bination.

"Th' ceremony was brief, but intherestin'. Th' happy father foorced his way through dimon' stomachers; an' they was tears in his eyes as he handed th' clargyman, whose name was Murphy,—but he carried himsilf as well as if he was used to it,—handed him a check f'r tin millyion dollars. I don't blame him. Divvle th' bit! Me own hear-rt is har-rd an' me eyes ar-re dhry, but I'd break down if I had to hand anny wan that much. 'I suppose th' check is good,' says th' clargyman. ' 'Tis certified,' says th' weepin' father. 'Do ye take this check,' says th' clargyman, 'to have an' to hold, until some wan parts ye fr'm it?' he says. 'I do,' says th' young man. 'Thin,' says th' clargyman, 'I see no reason why ye shudden't be marrid an' live comfortable,' he says. An' marrid they were, in th' same ol' foolish way that people's been marrid in f'r cinchries. 'Tis a wondher to me th' ceremony ain't changed. Th' time is comin', Hinnissy, whin millyionaires 'll not be marrid be Father Murphy, but be th' gov'nors iv th' stock exchange. They'll be put through th' clearin' house, me faith, an' securities 'll be issued be th' combination. Twinty-year, goold-secured, four per cint. bonds iv mathrimony! Aha, 'tis a joke that Chansy Depoo might 've med!

"Th' crowd outside waited, cheerin' an' fightin' th' polis. In this here land iv liberty an' akequality, Hinnissy, ivry man is as good as ivry other man, except a polisman. An' it showed how thrue th' people in New York is to th' thraditions iv Jefferson that divvle a wan iv thim 'd move away till th' check 'd been passed fr'm father to son, an' th' important part iv th' sacred ceremony was over. Thin a few iv thim wint home to cook dinner f'r their husbands, who was previnted be their jooties at th' gas-house fr'm attindin' th' function. Th' rest raymained an' see th' two gr-reat fortunes get into their carredge, pursued be th' guests to th' amount iv five hundhred millyions, peltin' thim with seed pearls."

"Sure," said Mr. Hennessy, "mebbe 'twasn't as bad as th' pa-apers let on. Ye can't always thrust thim."

"P'rhaps not," said Mr. Dooley. "Th' pa-apers say, 'Two gr-reat fortunes united'; an', if that's it, they didn't need th' sarvices iv a priest, but a lawyer an' a thrust comp'ny. P'rhaps, with all th' certyfied checks, 'twas two rale people that was marrid; an', if that's so, it explains th' prisince iv Father Murphy."

Edith Wharton (1862–1937)

The fiction of Edith Wharton was a tonic phenomenon in early twentieth-century America, for meretricious emotion and humor generally dominated its "serious" fiction. *The Decoration of Houses* (1897), Mrs. Wharton's pioneer study of poor taste in interior decoration, had already revealed that she was unsentimental, fierce, and uncompromising in her judgment of human foibles. Her stories and novels continued her inquiries into individual and social behavior with ever-increasing satirical intensity and range. Mrs. Wharton's tone could be acidly malevolent in such stories as "The Pelican" (1899) and "After Holbein" (1928); it could emphasize light comedy in "The Descent of Man" (1904) and "Xingu" (1916). Probably the best expression of her values and artistry is to be found in the disciplined irony of such novels as *The House of Mirth* (1905) and *The Age of Innocence* (1920), and of such stories as "The Other Two" (1904) and "The Eyes" (1910). In those works her interest in psychological and social detail led her to blend ridicule and mirth harmoniously rather than to isolate them in excessively broad strokes. "The Other Two" reveals the beneficial influence of Henry James' sensitive comic spirit; the amusing irony is presented with some of the indirection characteristic of James' last phase. Like James, Mrs. Wharton uses situations, manners, and characters to evoke laughter at the ineptitude of the American middle-class aristocrat. What gives Waythorn a shred of dignity and preserves him from collapse is his final resilient ability to view himself and his predicament in a humorous light.

TEXT: *The Descent of Man and Other Stories*, New York, 1904. COMMENTARY: Blake Nevius, *Edith Wharton: A Study of Her Fiction*, Berkeley, Calif., 1953.

THE OTHER TWO

I

Waythorn, on the drawing-room hearth, waited for his wife to come down to dinner.

It was their first night under his own roof, and he was surprised at his thrill of boyish agitation. He was not so old, to be sure—his glass gave him little more than the five-and-thirty years to which his wife confessed —but he had fancied himself already in the temperate zone; yet here he was listening for her step with a tender sense of all it symbolised, with some old trail of verse about the garlanded nuptial door-posts floating through his enjoyment of the pleasant room and the good dinner just beyond it.

They had been hastily recalled from their honeymoon by the illness of Lily Haskett, the child of Mrs. Waythorn's first marriage. The little girl, at Waythorn's desire, had been transferred to his house on the day of her mother's wedding, and the doctor, on their arrival, broke the news that she was ill with typhoid, but declared that all the symptoms were favourable. Lily could show twelve years of unblemished health, and the case promised to be a light one. The nurse spoke as reassuringly, and after a moment of alarm Mrs. Waythorn had adjusted herself to the situation. She was very fond of Lily—her affection for the child had perhaps been her decisive charm in Waythorn's eyes—but she had the perfectly balanced nerves which her little girl had inherited, and no woman ever wasted less tissue in unproductive worry. Waythorn was therefore quite prepared to see her come in presently, a little late because of a last look at Lily, but as serene and well-appointed as if her good-night kiss had been laid on the brow of health. Her composure was restful to him; it acted as ballast to his somewhat unstable sensibilities. As he pictured her bending over the child's bed he thought how soothing her presence must be in illness: her very step would prognosticate recovery.

His own life had been a gray one, from temperament rather than circumstance, and he had been drawn to her by the unperturbed gaiety which kept her fresh and elastic at an age when most women's activities are growing either slack or febrile. He knew what was said about her; for, popular as she was, there had always been a faint undercurrent of detraction. When she had appeared in New York, nine or ten years earlier, as the pretty Mrs. Haskett whom Gus Varick had unearthed somewhere—was it in Pittsburgh or Utica?—society, while promptly accepting her, had reserved the right to cast a doubt on its own indiscrimination. Enquiry, however, established her undoubted connection with a socially reigning family, and explained her recent divorce as the natural result of a runaway match at seventeen; and as nothing was known of Mr. Haskett it was easy to believe the worst of him.

Alice Haskett's remarriage with Gus Varick was a passport to the set whose recognition she coveted, and for a few years the Varicks were the most popular couple in town. Unfortunately, the alliance was brief and stormy, and this time the husband had his champions. Still, even Varick's stanchest supporters admitted that he was not meant for matrimony, and Mrs. Varick's grievances were of a nature to bear the inspection of the New York courts. A New York divorce is in itself a diploma of virtue, and in the semi-widowhood of this second separation Mrs. Varick took on an air of sanctity, and was allowed to confide her wrongs to some of the most scrupulous ears in town. But when it was known that she was to marry Waythorn there was a momentary reaction. Her best friends would have preferred to see her remain in the rôle of the injured wife, which was as becoming to her as crape to a rosy complexion. True, a decent time had elapsed, and it was not even suggested that Waythorn had supplanted his predecessor. People shook their heads over him, however, and one grudging friend, to whom he affirmed that he took the step with his eyes open, replied oracularly: "Yes—and with your ears shut."

Waythorn could afford to smile at these innuendoes. In the Wall Street phrase, he had "discounted" them. He knew that society has not yet adapted itself to the consequences of divorce, and that till the adaptation takes place every woman who uses the freedom the law accords her must be her own social justification. Waythorn had an amused confidence in his wife's ability to justify herself. His expectations were fulfilled, and before the wedding took place Alice Varick's group had rallied openly to her support. She took it all imperturbably: she had a way of surmounting obstacles without seeming to be aware of them, and Waythorn looked back with wonder at the trivialities over which he had worn his nerves thin. He had the sense of having found refuge in a richer, warmer nature than his own, and his satisfaction, at the moment, was humourously summed up in the thought that his wife, when she had done all she could for Lily, would not be ashamed to come down and enjoy a good dinner.

The anticipation of such enjoyment was not, however, the sentiment expressed by Mrs. Waythorn's charming face when she presently joined him. Though she had put on her most engaging teagown she had neglected to assume the smile that went with it, and Waythorn thought he had never seen her look so nearly worried.

"What is it?" he asked. "Is anything wrong with Lily?"

"No; I've just been in and she's still sleeping." Mrs. Waythorn hesitated. "But something tiresome has happened."

He had taken her two hands, and now perceived that she was crushing a paper between them.

"This letter?"

"Yes—Mr. Haskett has written—I mean his lawyer has written."

Waythorn felt himself flush uncomfortably. He dropped his wife's hands.

"What about?"

"About seeing Lily. You know the courts—"

"Yes, yes," he interrupted nervously.

Nothing was known about Haskett in New York. He was vaguely supposed to have remained in the outer darkness from which his wife had been rescued, and Waythorn was one of the few who were aware that he had given up his business in Utica and followed her to New York in order to be near his little girl. In the days of his wooing, Waythorn had often met Lily on the doorstep, rosy and smiling, on her way "to see papa."

"I am so sorry," Mrs. Waythorn murmured.

He roused himself. "What does he want?"

"He wants to see her. You know she goes to him once a week."

"Well—he doesn't expect her to go to him now, does he?"

"No—he has heard of her illness; but he expects to come here."

"*Here?*"

Mrs. Waythorn reddened under his gaze. They looked away from each other.

"I'm afraid he has the right. . . . You'll see. . . ." She made a proffer of the letter.

Waythorn moved away with a gesture of refusal. He stood staring about the softly lighted room, which a moment before had seemed so full of bridal intimacy.

"I'm so sorry," she repeated. "If Lily could have been moved—"

"That's out of the question," he returned impatiently.

"I suppose so."

Her lip was beginning to tremble, and he felt himself a brute.

"He must come, of course," he said. "When is—his day?"

"I'm afraid—to-morrow."

"Very well. Send a note in the morning."

The butler entered to announce dinner.

Waythorn turned to his wife. "Come—you must be tired. It's beastly, but try to forget about it," he said, drawing her hand through his arm.

"You're so good, dear. I'll try," she whispered back.

Her face cleared at once, and as she looked at him across the flowers, between the rosy candle-shades, he saw her lips waver back into a smile.

"How pretty everything is!" she sighed luxuriously.

He turned to the butler. "The champagne at once, please. Mrs. Waythorn is tired."

In a moment or two their eyes met above the sparkling glasses. Her own were quite clear and untroubled: he saw that she had obeyed his injunction and forgotten.

II

Waythorn, the next morning, went down town earlier than usual. Haskett was not likely to come till the afternoon, but the instinct of flight drove him forth. He meant to stay away all day—he had thoughts of dining at his club. As his door closed behind him he reflected that before he opened it again it would have admitted another man who had as much right to enter it as himself, and the thought filled him with a physical repugnance.

He caught the "elevated" at the employés' hour, and found himself crushed between two layers of pendulous humanity. At Eighth Street the man facing him wriggled out, and another took his place. Waythorn glanced up and saw that it was Gus Varick. The men were so close together that it was impossible to ignore the smile of recognition on Varick's handsome overblown face. And after all—why not? They had always been on good terms, and Varick had been divorced before Waythorn's attentions to his wife began. The two exchanged a word on the perennial grievance of the congested trains, and when a seat at their side was miraculously left empty the instinct of self-preservation made Waythorn slip into it after Varick.

The latter drew the stout man's breath of relief. "Lord—I was beginning to feel like a pressed flower." He leaned back, looking unconcernedly at Waythorn. "Sorry to hear that Sellers is knocked out again."

"Sellers?" echoed Waythorn, starting at his partner's name.

Varick looked surprised. "You didn't know he was laid up with the gout?"

"No. I've been away—I only got back last night." Waythorn felt himself reddening in anticipation of the other's smile.

"Ah—yes; to be sure. And Sellers's attack came on two days ago. I'm afraid he's pretty bad. Very awkward for me, as it happens, because he was just putting through a rather important thing for me."

"Ah?" Waythorn wondered vaguely since when Varick had been dealing in "important things." Hitherto he had dabbled only in the shallow pools of speculation, with which Waythorn's office did not usually concern itself.

It occurred to him that Varick might be talking at random, to relieve the strain of their propinquity. That strain was becoming momentarily more apparent to Waythorn, and when, at Cortlandt Street, he caught sight of an acquaintance and had a sudden vision of the picture he and Varick must present to an initiated eye, he jumped up with a muttered excuse.

"I hope you'll find Sellers better," said Varick civilly, and he stammered back: "If I can be of any use to you—" and let the departing crowd sweep him to the platform.

At his office he heard that Sellers was in fact ill with the gout, and would probably not be able to leave the house for some weeks.

"I'm sorry it should have happened so, Mr. Waythorn," the senior clerk said with affable significance. "Mr. Sellers was very much upset at the idea of giving you such a lot of extra work just now."

"Oh, that's no matter," said Waythorn hastily. He secretly welcomed the pressure of additional business, and was glad to think that, when the day's work was over, he would have to call at his partner's on the way home.

He was late for luncheon, and turned in at the nearest restaurant instead of going to his club. The place was full, and the waiter hurried him to the back of the room to capture the only vacant table. In the cloud of cigar-smoke Waythorn did not at once distinguish his neighbours; but presently, looking about him, he saw Varick seated a few feet off. This time, luckily, they were too far apart for conversation, and Varick, who faced another way, had probably not even seen him; but there was an irony in their renewed nearness.

Varick was said to be fond of good living, and as Waythorn sat despatching his hurried luncheon he looked across half enviously at the other's leisurely degustation of his meal. When Waythorn first saw him he had been helping himself with critical deliberation to a bit of Camembert at the ideal point of liquefaction, and now, the cheese removed, he was just pouring his *café double* from its little two-storied earthen pot. He poured slowly, his ruddy profile bent above the task, and one beringed white hand steadying the lid of the coffee-pot; then he stretched his other hand to the decanter of cognac at his elbow, filled a liqueur-glass, took a tentative sip, and poured the brandy into his coffee-cup.

Waythorn watched him in a kind of fascination. What was he thinking of—only of the flavour of the coffee and the liqueur? Had the morning's meeting left no more trace in his thoughts than on his face? Had his wife so completely passed out of his life that even this odd encounter with her present husband, within a week after her remarriage, was no more than an incident in his day? And as Waythorn mused, another idea struck him: had Haskett ever met Varick as Varick and he had just met? The recollection of Haskett perturbed him, and he rose and left the restaurant, taking a circuitous way out to escape the placid irony of Varick's nod.

It was after seven when Waythorn reached home. He thought the footman who opened the door looked at him oddly.

"How is Miss Lily?" he asked in haste.

"Doing very well, sir. A gentleman—"

"Tell Barlow to put off dinner for half an hour," Waythorn cut him off, hurrying upstairs.

He went straight to his room and dressed without seeing his wife. When he reached the drawing-room she was there, fresh and radiant. Lily's day had been good; the doctor was not coming back that evening.

At dinner Waythorn told her of Sellers's illness and of the resulting complications. She listened sympathetically, adjuring him not to let himself be overworked, and asking vague feminine questions about the routine of the office. Then she gave him the chronicle of Lily's day; quoted the nurse and doctor, and told him who had called to inquire. He had never seen her more serene and unruffled. It struck him, with a curious pang, that she was very happy in being with him, so happy that she found a childish pleasure in rehearsing the trivial incidents of her day.

After dinner they went to the library, and the servant put the coffee and liqueurs on a low table before her and left the room. She looked singularly soft and girlish in her rosy pale dress, against the dark leather of one of his bachelor armchairs. A day earlier the contrast would have charmed him.

He turned away now, choosing a cigar with affected deliberation.

"Did Haskett come?" he asked, with his back to her.

"Oh, yes—he came."

"You didn't see him, of course?"

She hesitated a moment. "I let the nurse see him."

That was all. There was nothing more to ask. He swung round toward her, applying a match to his cigar. Well, the thing was over for a week, at any rate. He would try not to think of it. She looked up at him, a trifle rosier than usual, with a smile in her eyes.

"Ready for your coffee, dear?"

He leaned against the mantelpiece, watching her as she lifted the coffee-pot. The lamplight struck a gleam from her bracelets and tipped her soft hair with brightness. How light and slender she was, and how each gesture flowed into the next! She seemed a creature all compact of harmonies. As the thought of Haskett receded, Waythorn felt himself yielding again to the joy of possessorship. They were his, those white hands with their flitting motions, his the light haze of hair, the lips and eyes. . . .

She set down the coffee-pot, and reaching for the decanter of cognac, measured off a liqueur-glass and poured it into his cup.

Waythorn uttered a sudden exclamation.

"What is the matter?" she said, startled.

"Nothing; only—I don't take cognac in my coffee."

"Oh, how stupid of me," she cried.

Their eyes met, and she blushed a sudden agonised red.

III

Ten days later, Mr. Sellers, still house-bound, asked Waythorn to call on his way down town.

The senior partner, with his swaddled foot propped up by the fire, greeted his associate with an air of embarrassment.

"I'm sorry, my dear fellow; I've got to ask you to do an awkward thing for me."

Waythorn waited, and the other went on, after a pause apparently given to the arrangement of his phrases: "The fact is, when I was knocked out I had just gone into a rather complicated piece of business for—Gus Varick."

"Well?" said Waythorn, with an attempt to put him at his ease.

"Well—it's this way: Varick came to me the day before my attack. He had evidently had an inside tip from somebody, and had made about a hundred thousand. He came to me for advice, and I suggested his going in with Vanderlyn."

"Oh, the deuce!" Waythorn exclaimed. He saw in a flash what had happened. The investment was an alluring one, but required negotiation. He listened quietly while Sellers put the case before him, and, the statement ended, he said: "You think I ought to see Varick?"

"I'm afraid I can't as yet. The doctor is obdurate. And this thing can't wait. I hate to ask you, but no one else in the office knows the ins and outs of it."

Waythorn stood silent. He did not care a farthing for the success of Varick's venture, but the honour of the office was to be considered, and he could hardly refuse to oblige his partner.

"Very well," he said, "I'll do it."

That afternoon, apprised by telephone, Varick called at the office. Waythorn, waiting in his private room, wondered what the others thought of it. The newspapers, at the time of Mrs. Waythorn's marriage, had acquainted their readers with every detail of her previous matrimonial ventures, and Waythorn could fancy the clerks smiling behind Varick's back as he was ushered in.

Varick bore himself admirably. He was easy without being undignified, and Waythorn was conscious of cutting a much less impressive figure. Varick had no experience of business, and the talk prolonged itself for nearly an hour while Waythorn set forth with scrupulous precision the details of the proposed transaction.

"I'm awfully obliged to you," Varick said as he rose. "The fact is I'm not used to having much money to look after, and I don't want to make an ass of myself—" He smiled, and Waythorn could not help noticing that there was something pleasant about his smile. "It feels uncommonly queer to have enough cash to pay one's bills. I'd have sold my soul for it a few years ago!"

Waythorn winced at the allusion. He had heard it rumoured that a lack of funds had been one of the determining causes of the Varick separation, but it did not occur to him that Varick's words were intentional. It seemed more likely that the desire to keep clear of embarrassing topics had fatally drawn him into one. Waythorn did not wish to be outdone in civility.

"We'll do the best we can for you," he said. "I think this is a good thing you're in."

"Oh, I'm sure it's immense. It's awfully good of you—" Varick broke off, embarrassed. "I suppose the things settled now—but if—"

"If anything happens before Sellers is about, I'll see you again," said Waythorn quietly. He was glad, in the end, to appear the more self-possessed of the two.

The course of Lily's illness ran smooth, and as the days passed Waythorn grew used to the idea of Haskett's weekly visit. The first time the day came round, he stayed out late, and questioned his wife as to the visit on his return. She replied at once that Haskett had merely seen the nurse downstairs, as the doctor did not wish any one in the child's sick-room till after the crisis.

The following week Waythorn was again conscious of the recurrence of the day, but had forgotten it by the time he came home to dinner. The crisis of the disease came a few days later, with a rapid decline of fever, and the little girl was pronounced out of danger. In the rejoicing which ensued the thought of Haskett passed out of Waythorn's mind, and one afternoon, letting himself into the house with a latchkey, he went straight to his library without noticing a shabby hat and umbrella in the hall.

In the library he found a small effaced-looking man with a thinnish gray beard sitting on the edge of a chair. The stranger might have been a piano-tuner, or one of those mysteriously efficient persons who are summoned in emergencies to adjust some detail of the domestic machinery. He blinked at Waythorn through a pair of gold-rimmed spectacles and said mildly: "Mr. Waythorn, I presume? I am Lily's father."

Waythorn flushed. "Oh—" he stammered uncomfortably. He broke off, disliking to appear rude. Inwardly he was trying to adjust the actual Haskett to the image of him projected by his wife's reminiscences. Waythorn had been allowed to infer that Alice's first husband was a brute.

"I am sorry to intrude," said Haskett, with his over-the-counter politeness.

"Don't mention it," returned Waythorn, collecting himself. "I suppose the nurse has been told?"

"I presume so. I can wait," said Haskett. He had a resigned way of speaking, as though life had worn down his natural powers of resistance.

Waythorn stood on the threshold, nervously pulling off his gloves.

"I'm sorry you've been detained. I will send for the nurse," he said; and as he opened the door he added with an effort: "I'm glad we can give you a good report of Lily." He winced as the *we* slipped out, but Haskett seemed not to notice it.

"Thank you, Mr. Waythorn. It's been an anxious time for me."

"Ah, well, that's past. Soon she'll be able to go to you." Waythorn nodded and passed out.

In his own room he flung himself down with a groan. He hated the womanish sensibility which made him suffer so acutely from the grotesque chances of life. He had known when he married that his wife's former husbands were both living, and that amid the multiplied contacts of modern existence there were a thousand chances to one that he would run against one or the other, yet he found himself as much disturbed by his brief encounter with Haskett as though the law had not obligingly removed all difficulties in the way of their meeting.

Waythorn sprang up and began to pace the room nervously. He had not suffered half as much from his two meetings with Varick. It was Haskett's presence in his own house that made the situation so intolerable. He stood still, hearing steps in the passage.

"This way, please," he heard the nurse say. Haskett was being taken upstairs, then: not a corner of the house but was open to him. Waythorn dropped into another chair, staring vaguely ahead of him. On his dressing-table stood a photograph of Alice, taken when he had first known her. She was Alice Varick then—how fine and exquisite he had thought her! Those were Varick's pearls about her neck. At Waythorn's instance they had been returned before her marriage. Had Haskett ever given her any trinkets—and what had become of them, Waythorn wondered? He realised suddenly that he knew very little of Haskett's past or present situation; but from the man's appearance and manner of speech he could reconstruct with curious precision the surroundings of Alice's first marriage. And it startled him to think that she had, in the background of her life, a phase of existence so different from anything with which he had connected her. Varick, whatever his faults, was a gentleman, in the conventional, traditional sense of the term: the sense which at that moment seemed, oddly enough, to have most meaning to Waythorn. He and Varick had the same social habits, spoke the same language, understood the same allusions. But this other man . . . it was grotesquely uppermost in Waythorn's mind that Haskett had worn a made-up tie attached with an elastic. Why should that ridiculous detail symbolise the whole man? Waythorn was exasperated by his own paltriness, but the fact of the tie expanded, forced itself on him, became as it were the key to Alice's past. He could see her, as Mrs. Haskett, sitting in a "front parlour" furnished in plush, with a pianola, and a copy of "Ben Hur" on the centre-table. He could see her going to the theatre with Haskett—or perhaps even to a "Church Sociable"—she in a "picture hat" and Haskett in a black frock-coat, a little creased, with the made-up tie on an elastic. On the way home they would stop and look at the illuminated shop-windows, lingering over the photographs of New York actresses. On Sunday afternoons Haskett would take her for a walk, pushing Lily ahead of them in a white enamelled perambulator, and Waythorn had a vision of the people they would stop and talk to. He could fancy how pretty Alice must have looked, in a dress adroitly constructed from the hints of a New York fashion-paper, and how she must have looked down on the other women, chafing at her life, and secretly feeling that she belonged in a bigger place.

For the moment his foremost thought was one of wonder at the way in which she had shed the phase of existence which her marriage with Haskett implied. It was as if her whole aspect, every gesture, every inflection, every allusion, were a studied negation of that period of her life. If she had denied being married to Haskett she could hardly have stood more convicted of duplicity than in this obliteration of the self which had been his wife.

Waythorn started up, checking himself in the analysis of her motives. What right had he to create a fantastic effigy of her and then pass judgment on it? She had spoken vaguely of her first marriage as unhappy, had hinted, with becoming reticence, that Haskett had wrought havoc among her young illusions. . . . It was a pity for Waythorn's peace of mind that Haskett's very inoffensiveness shed a new light on the nature of those illusions. A man would rather think that his wife has been brutalised by her first husband than that the process has been reversed.

IV

"Mr. Waythorn, I don't like that French governess of Lily's."

Haskett, subdued and apologetic, stood before Waythorn in the library, revolving his shabby hat in his hand.

Waythorn, surprised in his armchair over the evening paper, stared back perplexedly at his visitor.

"You'll excuse my asking to see you," Haskett continued. "But this is my last visit, and I thought if I could have a word with you it would be a better way than writing to Mrs. Waythorn's lawyer."

Waythorn rose uneasily. He did not like the French governess either; but that was irrelevant.

"I am not so sure of that," he returned stiffly; "but since you wish it I will give your message to—my wife." He always hesitated over the possessive pronoun in addressing Haskett.

The latter sighed. "I don't know as that will help much. She didn't like it when I spoke to her."

Waythorn turned red. "When did you see her?" he asked.

"Not since the first day I came to see Lily—right after she was taken sick. I remarked to her then that I didn't like the governess."

Waythorn made no answer. He remembered distinctly that, after that first visit, he had asked his wife if she had seen Haskett. She had lied to him then, but she had respected his wishes since; and the incident cast a curious light on her character. He was sure she would not have seen Haskett that first day if she had divined that Waythorn would object, and the fact that she did not divine it was almost as disagreeable to the latter as the discovery that she had lied to him.

"I don't like the woman," Haskett was repeating with mild persistency. "She ain't straight, Mr. Waythorn—she'll teach the child to be underhand. I've noticed a change in Lily—she's too anxious to please—and she don't always tell the truth. She used to be the straightest child, Mr. Waythorn—" He broke off, his voice a little thick. "Not but what I want her to have a stylish education," he ended.

Waythorn was touched. "I'm sorry, Mr. Haskett; but frankly, I don't quite see what I can do."

Haskett hesitated. Then he laid his hat on the table, and advanced to the hearth-rug, on which Waythorn was standing. There was nothing aggressive in his manner, but he had the solemnity of a timid man resolved on a decisive measure.

"There's just one thing you can do, Mr. Waythorn," he said. "You can remind Mrs. Waythorn that, by the decree of the courts, I am entitled to have a voice in Lily's bringing up." He paused, and went on more deprecatingly: "I'm not the kind to talk about enforcing my rights, Mr. Waythorn. I don't know as I think a man is entitled to rights he hasn't known how to hold on to; but this business of the child is different. I've never let go there—and I never mean to."

The scene left Waythorn deeply shaken. Shamefacedly, in indirect ways, he had been finding out about Haskett; and all that he had learned was favourable. The little man, in order to be near his daughter, had sold out his share in a profitable business in Utica, and accepted a modest clerkship in a New York manufacturing house. He boarded in a shabby street and had few acquaintances. His passion for Lily filled his life. Waythorn felt that this exploration of Haskett was like groping about with a dark-lantern in his wife's past; but he saw now that there were recesses his lantern had not explored. He had never enquired into the exact circumstances of his wife's first matrimonial rupture. On the surface all had been fair. It was she who had obtained the divorce, and the court had given her the child. But Waythorn knew how many ambiguities such a verdict might cover. The mere fact that Haskett retained a right over his daughter implied an unsuspected compromise. Waythorn was an idealist. He always refused to recognise unpleasant contingencies till he found himself confronted with them, and then he saw them followed by a spectral train of consequences. His next days were thus haunted, and he determined to try to lay the ghosts by conjuring them up in his wife's presence.

When he repeated Haskett's request a flame of anger passed over her face; but she subdued it instantly and spoke with a slight quiver of outraged motherhood.

"It is very ungentlemanly of him," she said.

The word grated on Waythorn. "That is neither here nor there. It's a bare question of rights."

She murmured: "It's not as if he could ever be a help to Lily—"

Waythorn flushed. This was even less to his taste. "The question is," he repeated, "what authority has he over her?"

She looked downward, twisting herself a little in her seat. "I am willing to see him—I thought you objected," she faltered.

In a flash he understood that she knew the extent of Haskett's claims. Perhaps it was not the first time she had resisted them.

"My objecting has nothing to do with it," he said coldly; "if Haskett has a right to be consulted you must consult him."

She burst into tears, and he saw that she expected him to regard her as a victim.

Haskett did not abuse his rights. Waythorn had felt miserably sure that he would not. But the governess was dismissed, and from time to time the little man demanded an interview with Alice. After the first outburst she accepted the situation with her usual adaptability. Haskett had once reminded Waythorn of the piano-tuner, and Mrs. Waythorn, after a month or two, appeared to class him with that domestic familiar. Waythorn could not but respect the father's tenacity. At first he had tried to cultivate the suspicion that Haskett might be "up to" something, that he had an object in securing a foothold in the house. But in his heart Waythorn was sure of Haskett's single-mindedness; he even guessed in the latter a mild contempt for such advantages as his relation with the Waythorns might offer. Haskett's sincerity of purpose made him invulnerable, and his successor had to accept him as a lien on the property.

Mr. Sellers was sent to Europe to recover from his gout, and Varick's affairs hung on Waythorn's hands. The negotiations were prolonged and complicated; they necessitated frequent conferences between the two men, and the interests of the firm forbade Waythorn's suggesting that his client should transfer his business to another office.

Varick appeared well in the transaction. In moments of relaxation his coarse streak appeared, and Waythorn dreaded his geniality; but in the office he was concise and clear-headed, with a flattering deference to Waythorn's judgment. Their business relations being so affably established, it would have been absurd for the two men to ignore each other in society. The first time they met in a drawing-room, Varick took up their intercourse in the same easy key, and his hostess's grateful glance obliged Waythorn to respond to it. After that they ran across each other frequently, and one evening at a ball Waythorn, wandering through the remoter rooms, came upon Varick seated beside his wife. She coloured a little, and faltered in what she was saying; but Varick nodded to Waythorn without rising, and the latter strolled on.

In the carriage, on the way home, he broke out nervously: "I didn't know you spoke to Varick."

Her voice trembled a little. "It's the first time—he happened to be standing near me; I didn't know what to do. It's so awkward, meeting everywhere—and he said you had been very kind about some business."

"That's different," said Waythorn.

She paused a moment. "I'll do just as you wish," she returned pliantly. "I thought it would be less awkward to speak to him when we meet."

Her pliancy was beginning to sicken him. Had she really no will of her own—no theory about her relation to these men? She had accepted Haskett—did she mean to accept Varick? It was "less awkward," as she had said, and her instinct was to evade difficulties or to circumvent them. With sudden vividness Waythorn saw how the instinct had developed. She was "as easy as an old shoe"—a shoe that too many feet had worn. Her elasticity was the result of tension in too many different directions. Alice Haskett—Alice Varick—Alice Waythorn—she had been each in turn, and had left hanging to each name a little of her privacy, a little of her personality, a little of the inmost self where the unknown god abides.

"Yes—it's better to speak to Varick," said Waythorn wearily.

v

The winter wore on, and society took advantage of the Waythorns' acceptance of Varick. Harassed hostesses were grateful to them for bridging over a social difficulty, and Mrs. Waythorn was held up as a miracle of good taste. Some experimental spirits could not resist the diversion of throwing Varick and his former wife together, and there were those who thought he found a zest in the propinquity. But Mrs. Waythorn's conduct remained irreproachable. She neither avoided Varick nor sought him out. Even Waythorn could not but admit that she had discovered the solution of the newest social problem.

He had married her without giving much thought to that problem. He had fancied that a woman can shed her past like a man. But now he saw that Alice was bound to hers both by the circumstances which forced her into continued relation with it, and by the traces it had left on her nature. With grim irony Waythorn compared himself to a member of the syndicate. He held so many shares in his wife's personality and his predecessors were his partners in the business. If there had been any element of passion in the transaction he would have felt less deteriorated by it. The fact that Alice took her change of husbands like a change of weather reduced the situation to mediocrity. He could have forgiven her for blunders, for excesses; for resisting Haskett, for yielding to Varick; for anything but her acquiescence and her tact. She reminded him of a juggler tossing knives; but the knives were blunt and she knew they would never cut her.

And then, gradually, habit formed a protecting surface for his sensibilities. If he paid for each day's comfort with the small change of his illusions, he grew daily to value the comfort more and set less store upon the coin. He had drifted into a dulling propinquity with Haskett and Varick and he took refuge in the cheap revenge of satirising the situation. He even began to reckon up the advantages which accrued from it, to ask himself if it were not better to own a third of a wife who knew how to make a man happy than a whole one who had lacked opportunity to acquire the art. For it *was* an art, and made up, like all others, of concessions, eliminations and embellishments; of lights judiciously thrown and shadows skilfully softened. His wife knew exactly how to manage the lights, and he knew exactly to what training she owed her skill. He even tried to trace the source of his obligations, to discriminate between the influences which had combined to produce his domestic happiness: he perceived that Haskett's commonness had made Alice worship good breeding, while Varick's liberal construction of the marriage bond had taught her to value the conjugal virtues; so that he was directly indebted to his predecessors for the devotion which made his life easy if not inspiring.

From this phase he passed into that of complete acceptance. He ceased to satirise himself because time dulled the irony of the situation and the joke lost its humour with its sting. Even the sight of Haskett's hat on the hall table had ceased to touch the springs of epigram. The hat was often seen there now, for it had been decided that it was better for Lily's father to visit her than for the little girl to go to his boarding-house. Waythorn, having acquiesced in this arrangement, had been surprised to find how little difference it made. Haskett was never obtrusive, and the few visitors who met him on the stairs were unaware of his identity. Waythorn did not know how often he saw Alice, but with himself Haskett was seldom in contact.

One afternoon, however, he learned on entering that Lily's father was waiting to see him. In the library he found Haskett occupying a chair in his usual provisional way. Waythorn always felt grateful to him for not leaning back.

"I hope you'll excuse me, Mr. Waythorn," he said rising. "I wanted to see Mrs. Waythorn about Lily, and your man asked me to wait here till she came in."

"Of course," said Waythorn, remembering that a sudden leak had that morning given over the drawing-room to the plumbers.

He opened his cigar-case and held it out to his visitor, and Haskett's acceptance seemed to mark a fresh stage in their intercourse. The spring evening was chilly, and Waythorn invited his guest to draw up his chair to the fire. He meant to find an excuse to leave Haskett in a moment; but he was tired and cold, and after all the little man no longer jarred on him.

The two were enclosed in the intimacy of their blended cigar-smoke when the door opened and Varick walked into the room. Waythorn rose abruptly. It was the first time that Varick had come to the house, and the surprise of seeing him, combined with the singular inopportuneness of his arrival, gave a new edge to Waythorn's blunted sensibilities. He stared at his visitor without speaking.

Varick seemed too preoccupied to notice his host's embarrassment.

"My dear fellow," he exclaimed in his most expansive tone, "I must apologise for tumbling in on you in this way, but I was too late to catch you down town, and so I thought—"

He stopped short, catching sight of Haskett, and his sanguine colour deepened to a flush which spread vividly under his scant blond hair. But in a moment he recovered himself and nodded slightly. Haskett returned the bow in silence, and Waythorn was still groping for speech when the footman came in carrying a tea-table.

The intrusion offered a welcome vent to Waythorn's nerves. "What the deuce are you bringing this here for?" he said sharply.

"I beg your pardon, sir, but the plumbers are still in the drawing-room, and Mrs. Waythorn said she would have tea in the library." The footman's perfectly respectful tone implied a reflection on Waythorn's reasonableness.

"Oh, very well," said the latter resignedly, and the footman proceeded to open the folding tea-table and set out its complicated appointments. While this interminable process continued the three men stood motionless, watching it with a fascinated stare, till Waythorn, to break the silence, said to Varick: "Won't you have a cigar?"

He held out the case he had just tendered to Haskett, and Varick helped himself with a smile. Waythorn looked about for a match, and finding none, proffered a light from his own cigar. Haskett, in the background, held his ground mildly, examining his cigar-tip now and then, and stepping forward at the right moment to knock its ashes into the fire.

The footman at last withdrew, and Varick immediately began: "If I could just say half a word to you about this business—"

"Certainly," stammered Waythorn; "in the dining-room—"

But as he placed his hand on the door it opened from without, and his wife appeared on the threshold.

She came in fresh and smiling, in her street dress and hat, shedding a fragrance from the boa which she loosened in advancing.

"Shall we have tea in here, dear?" she began; and then she caught sight of Varick. Her smile deepened, veiling a slight tremor of surprise.

"Why, how do you do?" she said with a distinct note of pleasure.

As she shook hands with Varick she saw Haskett standing behind him. Her smile faded for a moment, but she recalled it quickly, with a scarcely perceptible side-glance at Waythorn.

"How do you do, Mr. Haskett?" she said, and shook hands with him a shade less cordially.

The three men stood awkwardly before her, till Varick, always the most self-possessed, dashed into an explanatory phrase.

"We—I had to see Waythorn a moment on business," he stammered, brick-red from chin to nape.

Haskett stepped forward with his air of mild obstinacy. "I am sorry to intrude; but you appointed five o'clock—" he directed his resigned glance to the time-piece on the mantel.

She swept aside their embarrassment with a charming gesture of hospitality.

"I'm so sorry—I'm always late; but the afternoon was so lovely." She stood drawing off her gloves, propitiatory and graceful, diffusing about her a sense of ease and familiarity in which the situation lost its grotesqueness. "But before talking business," she added brightly, "I'm sure every one wants a cup of tea."

She dropped into her low chair by the tea-table, and the two visitors, as if drawn by her smile, advanced to receive the cups she held out.

She glanced about for Waythorn, and he took the third cup with a laugh.

Edwin Arlington Robinson (1869–1935)

Shortly after Edwin Arlington Robinson died, Robert Frost praised his fellow New England poet for having so persistently blended "outer seriousness" with "inner humor," "inner seriousness" with "outer humor." This, so Frost emphasized, explained Robinson's ability to cope artistically with the unhappiness which was one of his major themes. Robinson's expression of mingled thought and laughter was great, not only in quality but in quantity and variety as well. Even if his mother had not been a collateral descendant of Anne Bradstreet, the Puritan poet, thus linking him with an early moment in American culture, there are so many elements of earlier American humorous literature in Robinson's work that he may on that score alone be said to reach back through time from the twentieth century to the seventeenth, and to be a culminating figure in his own right. In "Thomas Hood," a poem in Robinson's first book (*The Torrent and the Night Before*, 1896), he set forth his wish to achieve the kind of synthesis later acclaimed by Frost. "Dear Friends" and other poems in the 1896 volume scornfully rejected the materialistic values which seemed in Robinson's judgment to be blocking his progress. The belief that American culture repressed the artist and the iconoclast was never abandoned by Robinson, fostering a bitterness visible in the mordant irony and satire of "Richard Cory" (1897), "Karma" (1925), and "Dionysus in Doubt" (1925). In general, however, Robinson's "grim humor" was balanced but not offset by his equally natural flair for the light, ironic humor visible in the innocent pastoral tone of "Isaac and Archibald" (1902), the burlesque farce of "Miniver Cheevy" (1910), and the social comedy of *Talifer* (1933). "New England," which became controversial in the 1920's, admirably illustrates the exquisitely balanced irony which in Robinson's deft hands became so all-embracing that even he was caught up in its net. First published in 1923 in the *New Republic* and the *Literary Digest*, the poem's unmistakable satire of Puritanism led to the printing of a letter attacking the poet in the *Journal* of Gardiner, Maine, the "Tilbury Town" prominent in Robinson's poems. Robinson replied that his irony had been misunderstood, for he had satirized not New England but rather the "patronizing pagans" who themselves attack New England. As if to eliminate any future misunderstandings, Robinson made some minor changes in the poem, the only significant one being the substitution of "Wonder begets" for "Intolerance tells" in line 3, and printed the revised version in *Dionysus in Doubt* (1925). But clearly Robinson had written the poem with an unconscious double-edged irony, for while it is true that he satirized the "pagans" of the 1920's in lines 4 through 8, a glance at Thoreau's "Conscience" (see pp. 281–82) will confirm the fact that Robinson had intended to satirize New England Puritanism but had forgotten that he was a New England Puritan until reminded of it by the attack upon him.

TEXT: "Dear Friends," *The Torrent and the Night Before*, Cambridge, Mass., 1896; "Richard Cory" and "Cliff Klingenhagen," *The Children of the Night*, Boston, Mass., 1897; "Isaac and Archibald," *Captain Craig: A Book of Poems*, Boston, Mass., 1902; "New England," *Collected Poems of Edwin Arlington Robinson*, New York, 1937. COMMENTARY: Ellsworth Barnard, *Edwin Arlington Robinson: A Critical Study*, New York, 1952; Charles Cestre, *An Introduction to Edwin Arlington Robinson*, New York, 1930; Estelle Kaplan, *Philosophy in the Poetry of Edwin Arlington Robinson*, New York, 1940.

DEAR FRIENDS

Dear friends, reproach me not for what I do,
Nor counsel me, nor pity me; nor say
That I am wearing half my life away
For bubble-work that only fools pursue.
And if my bubbles be too small for you,
Blow bigger then your own: the games we play
To fill the frittered minutes of a day,
Good glasses are to read the spirit through.
And whoso reads may get him some shrewd skill;
And some unprofitable scorn resign,
To praise the very thing that he deplores;
So, friends (dear friends), remember, if you will,
The shame I win for singing is all mine,
The gold I miss for dreaming is all yours.

RICHARD CORY

Whenever Richard Cory went down town,
We people on the pavement looked at him:
He was a gentleman from sole to crown,
Clean favored, and imperially slim.

And he was always quietly arrayed,
And he was always human when he talked;
But still he fluttered pulses when he said,
"Good-morning," and he glittered when he walked.

And he was rich—yes, richer than a king—
And admirably schooled in every grace:
In fine, we thought that he was everything
To make us wish that we were in his place.

So on we worked, and waited for the light,
And went without the meat, and cursed the bread;
And Richard Cory, one calm summer night,
Went home and put a bullet through his head.

CLIFF KLINGENHAGEN

Cliff Klingenhagen had me in to dine
With him one day; and after soup and meat,
And all the other things there were to eat,
Cliff took two glasses and filled one with wine
And one with wormwood. Then, without a sign
For me to choose at all, he took the draught
Of bitterness himself, and lightly quaffed
It off, and said the other one was mine.

And when I asked him what the deuce he meant
By doing that, he only looked at me
And grinned, and said it was a way of his.
And though I know the fellow, I have spent
Long time a-wondering when I shall be
As happy as Cliff Klingenhagen is.

ISAAC AND ARCHIBALD

Isaac and Archibald were two old men.
I knew them, and I may have laughed at them
A little; but I must have honored them
For they were old, and they were geniuses.

I do not think of either of them now,
Without remembering, infallibly,
A journey that I made one afternoon
With Isaac to find out what Archibald
Was doing with his oats. It was high time
Those oats were cut, said Isaac; and he feared

That Archibald—well, he could never feel
Quite sure of Archibald. Accordingly
The good old man invited me—that is,
Permitted me—to go along with him;
And I, with a small boy's adhesiveness
To competent old age, got up and went.
I do not know that I cared overmuch
For Archibald's or anybody's oats,
But Archibald was quite another thing,
And Isaac yet another; and the world
Was wide, and there was gladness everywhere.
We walked together down the River Road
With all the warmth and wonder of the land
Around us, and the wayside flash of leaves,—
And Isaac said the day was glorious;
But somewhere at the end of the first mile
I found that I was figuring to find
How long those ancient legs of his would keep
The pace that he had set for them. The sun
Was hot, and I was ready to sweat blood;
But Isaac, for aught I could make of him,
Was cool to his hat-band. So I said then
With a dry gasp of affable despair,
Something about the scorching days we have
In August without knowing it sometimes;
But Isaac said the day was like a dream,
And praised the Lord, and talked about the breeze.
I made a fair confession of the breeze,
And crowded casually on his thought
The nearness of a profitable nook
That I could see. First I was half inclined
To caution him that he was growing old,
But something that was not compassion soon
Made plain the folly of all subterfuge.
Isaac was old, but not so old as that.

So I proposed, without an overture,
That we be seated in the shade a while,
And Isaac made no murmur. Soon the talk
Was turned on Archibald, and I began
To feel some premonitions of a kind
That only childhood knows; for the old man
Had looked at me and clutched me with his eye,
And asked if I had ever noticed things.

I told him that I could not think of them,
And I knew then, by the frown that left his face
Unsatisfied, that I had injured him.
"My good young friend," he said, "you cannot feel
What I have seen so long. You have the eyes—
Oh, yes—but you have not the other things:
The sight within that never will deceive,
You do not know—you have no right to know;
The twilight warning of experience,
The singular idea of loneliness,—
These are not yours. But they have long been mine,
And they have shown me now for seven years
That Archibald is changing. It is not
So much that he should come to his last hand,
And leave the game, and go the old way down;
But I have known him in and out so long,
And I have seen so much of good in him
That other men have shared and have not seen,
And I have gone so far through thick and thin,
Through cold and fire with him, that now it brings
To this old heart of mine an ache that you
Have not yet lived enough to know about.
But even unto you, with your boy's faith,
Your freedom, and your untried confidence,
A time will come to find out what it means
To know that you are losing what was yours,
To know that you are being left behind;
And then the long contempt of innocence—
God bless you, boy!—don't think the worse of it
Because an old man chatters in the shade—
Will all be like a story you have read
In childhood and remembered for the pictures.
And when the best friend of your life goes down,
When first you know in him the slackening
That comes, and coming always tells the end,—
Now in a common word that would have passed
Uncaught from any other lips than his,
Now in some trivial act of every day,
Done as he might have done it all along
But for a twinging little difference
That bites you like a squirrel's teeth—oh, yes,
Then you will understand it well enough.
But oftener it comes in other ways;
It comes without your knowing when it comes;

You know that he is changing, and you know
That he is going—just as I know now
That Archibald is going, and that I
Am staying. . . . Look at me, my boy,
And when the time shall come for you to see
That I must follow after him, try then
To think of me, to bring me back again,
Just as I was to-day. Think of the place
Where we are sitting now, and think of me—
Think of old Isaac as you knew him then,
When you set out with him in August once
To see old Archibald."—The words come back
Almost as Isaac must have uttered them,
And there comes with them a dry memory
Of something in my throat that would not move.

If you had asked me then to tell just why
I made so much of Isaac and the things
He said, I should have reached far for an answer;
For I knew it was not sorrow that I felt,
Whatever I may have wished it, or tried then
To make myself believe. My mouth was full
Of words, and they would have been comforting
To Isaac, spite of my twelve years, I think;
But there was not in me the willingness
To speak them out. Therefore I watched the ground;
And I was wondering what made the Lord
Create a thing so nervous as an ant,
When Isaac, with commendable unrest,
Ordained that we should take the road again—
For it was yet three miles to Archibald's,
And one to the first pump. I felt relieved
All over when the old man told me that;
I felt that he had stilled a fear of mine
That those extremities of heat and cold
Which he had long gone through with Archibald
Had made the man impervious to both;
But Isaac had a desert somewhere in him,
And at the pump he thanked God for all things
That He had put on earth for men to drink,
And he drank well,—so well that I proposed
That we go slowly lest I learn too soon
The bitterness of being left behind,
And all those other things. That was a joke

To Isaac, and it pleased him very much;
And that pleased me—for I was twelve years old.

At the end of an hour's walking after that
The cottage of old Archibald appeared.
Little and white and high on a smooth round hill
It stood, with hackmatacks and apple-trees
Before it, and a big barn-roof beyond;
And over the place—trees, houses, fields and all—
Hovered an air of still simplicity
And a fragrance of old summers—the old style
That lives the while it passes. I dare say
That I was lightly conscious of all this
When Isaac, of a sudden, stopped himself,
And for the long first quarter of a minute
Gazed with incredulous eyes, forgetful quite
Of breezes and of me and of all else
Under the scorching sun but a smooth-cut field,
Faint yellow in the distance. I was young,
But there were a few things that I could see,
And this was one of them.—"Well, well!" said he;
And "Archibald will be surprised, I think,"
Said I. But all my childhood subtlety
Was lost on Isaac, for he strode along
Like something out of Homer—powerful
And awful on the wayside, so I thought.
Also I thought how good it was to be
So near the end of my short-legged endeavor
To keep the pace with Isaac for five miles.

Hardly had we turned in from the main road
When Archibald, with one hand on his back
And the other clutching his huge-headed cane,
Came limping down to meet us.—"Well! well! well!"
Said he; and then he looked at my red face,
All streaked with dust and sweat, and shook my hand
And said it must have been a right smart walk
That we had had that day from Tilbury Town.—
"Magnificent," said Isaac; and he told
About the beautiful west wind there was
Which cooled and clarified the atmosphere.
"You must have made it with your legs, I guess,"
Said Archibald; and Isaac humored him
With one of those infrequent smiles of his
Which he kept in reserve, apparently,

For Archibald alone. "But why," said he,
"Should Providence have cider in the world
If not for such an afternoon as this?"
And Archibald, with a soft light in his eyes,
Replied that if he chose to go down cellar,
There he would find eight barrels—one of which
Was newly tapped, he said, and to his taste
An honor to the fruit. Isaac approved
Most heartily of that, and guided us
Forthwith, as if his venerable feet
Were measuring the turf in his own door-yard,
Straight to the open rollway. Down we went,
Out of the fiery sunshine to the gloom,
Grateful and half sepulchral, where we found
The barrels, like eight potent sentinels,
Close ranged along the wall. From one of them
A bright pine spile stuck out convincingly,
And on the black flat stone, just under it,
Glimmered a late-spilled proof that Archibald
Had spoken from unfeigned experience.
There was a fluted antique water-glass
Close by, and in it, prisoned, or at rest,
There was a cricket, of the brown soft sort
That feeds on darkness. Isaac turned him out,
And touched him with his thumb to make him jump,
And then composedly pulled out the plug
With such a practised hand that scarce a drop
Did even touch his fingers. Then he drank
And smacked his lips with a slow patronage
And looked along the line of barrels there
With a pride that may have been forgetfulness
That they were Archibald's and not his own.
"I never twist a spigot nowadays,"
He said, and raised the glass up to the light,
"But I thank God for orchards." And that glass
Was filled repeatedly for the same hand
Before I thought it worth while to discern
Again that I was young, and that old age,
With all his woes, had some advantages.

"Now, Archibald," said Isaac, when we stood
Outside again, "I have it in my mind
That I shall take a sort of little walk—
To stretch my legs and see what you are doing."

You stay and rest your back and tell the boy
A story: Tell him all about the time
In Stafford's cabin forty years ago,
When four of us were snowed up for ten days
With only one dried haddock. Tell him all
About it, and be wary of your back.
Now I will go along."—I looked up then
At Archibald, and as I looked I saw
Just how his nostrils widened once or twice
And then grew narrow. I can hear to-day
The way the old man chuckled to himself—
Not wholesomely, not wholly to convince
Another of his mirth,—as I can hear
The lonely sigh that followed.—But at length
He said: "The orchard now's the place for us;
We may find something like an apple there,
And we shall have the shade, at any rate."
So there we went and there we laid ourselves
Where the sunlight could not reach us; and I champed
A dozen of worm-blighted astrakhans
While Archibald said nothing—merely told
The tale of Stafford's cabin, which was good,
Though "master chilly"—after his own phrase—
Even for a day like that. But other thoughts
Were moving in his mind, imperative,
And writhing to be spoken: I could see
The glimmer of them in a glance or two,
Cautious, or else unconscious, that he gave
Over his shoulder: . . . "Stafford and the rest
Would have had no story of their own to tell;
They would have left it all for others—yes—
But that's an old song now, and Archibald
And Isaac are old men. Remember, boy,
That we are old. Whatever we have gained,
Or lost, or thrown away, we are old men.
You look before you and we look behind,
And we are playing life out in the shadow—
But that's not all of it. The sunshine lights
A good road yet before us if we look,
And we are doing that when least we know it;
For both of us are children of the sun,
Like you, and like the weed there at your feet.
The shadow calls us, and it frightens us—
We think; but there's a light behind the stars

And we old fellows who have dared to live,
We see it—and we see the other things,
The other things . . . Yes, I have seen it come
These eight years, and these ten years, and I know
Now that it cannot be for very long
That Isaac will be Isaac. You have seen—
Young as you are, you must have seen the strange
Uncomfortable habit of the man?
He'll take my nerves and tie them in a knot
Sometimes, and that's not Isaac. I know that—
And I know what it is: I get it here
A little, in my knees, and Isaac—here."
The old man shook his head regretfully
And laid his knuckles three times on his forehead.
"That's what it is: Isaac is not quite right.
You see it, but you don't know what it means:
The thousand little differences—no,
You do not know them, and it's well you don't;
You'll know them soon enough—God bless you, boy!—
You'll know them, but not all of them—not all.
So think of them as little as you can:
There's nothing in them for you, or for me—
But I am old and I must think of them;
I'm in the shadow, but I don't forget
The light, my boy,—the light behind the stars.
Remember that: remember that I said it;
And when the time that you think far away
Shall come for you to say it—say it, boy;
Let there be no confusion or distrust
In you, no snarling of a life half lived,
Nor any cursing over broken things
That your complaint has been the ruin of.
Live to see clearly and the light will come
To you, and as you need it. But there, there,
I'm going it again, as Isaac says,
And I'll stop now before you go to sleep.—
Only be sure that you growl cautiously,
And always where the shadow may not reach you."

Never shall I forget, long as I live,
The quaint thin crack in Archibald's voice,
The lonely twinkle in his little eyes,
Or the way it made me feel to be with him.
I know I lay and looked for a long time

Down through the orchard and across the road,
Across the river and the sun-scorched hills
That ceased in a blue forest, where the world
Ceased with it. Now and then my fancy caught
A flying glimpse of a good life beyond—
Something of ships and sunlight, streets and singing,
Troy falling, and the ages coming back,
And ages coming forward: Archibald
And Isaac were good fellows in old clothes
And Agamemnon was a friend of mine;
Ulysses coming home again to shoot
With bows and feathered arrows made another,
And all was as it should be. I was young.

So I lay dreaming of what things I would,
Calm and incorrigibly satisfied
With apples and romance and ignorance,
And the floating smoke from Archibald's clay pipe.
There was a stillness over everything,
As if the spirit of heat had laid its hand
Upon the world and hushed it; and I felt
Within the mightiness of the white sun
That smote the land around us and wrought out
A fragrance from the trees, a vital warmth
And fullness for the time that was to come,
And a glory for the world beyond the forest.
The present and the future and the past,
Isaac and Archibald, the burning bush,
The Trojans and the walls of Jericho,
Were beautifully fused; and all went well
Till Archibald began to fret for Isaac
And said it was a master day for sunstroke.
That was enough to make a mummy smile,
I thought; and I remained hilarious,
In face of all precedence and respect,
Till Isaac (who had come to us unheard)
Found he had no tobacco, looked at me
Peculiarly, and asked of Archibald
What ailed the boy to make him chirrup so.
From that he told us what a blessed world
The Lord had given us.—"But, Archibald,"
He added, with a sweet severity
That made me think of peach-skins and goose-flesh,
"I'm half afraid you cut those oats of yours

A day or two before they were well set."
"They were set well enough," said Archibald,—
And I remarked the process of his nose
Before the words came out; "but never mind
Your neighbor's oats: you stay here in the shade
And rest yourself while I go find the cards.
We'll have a little game of seven-up
And let the boy keep count."—"We'll have the game,
Assuredly," said Isaac; "and I think
That I will have a draught of cider, also."
They marched away together towards the house
And left me to my childish ruminations
Upon the ways of men. I followed them
Down cellar with my fancy, and then left them
For a fairer vision of all things at once
That was anon to be destroyed again
By the sound of voices and of heavy feet—
One of the sounds of life that I remember,
Though I forget so many that rang first
As if they were thrown down to me from Sinai.

So I remember, even to this day,
Just how they sounded, how they placed themselves,
And how the game went on while I made marks
And crossed them out, and meanwhile made some Trojans.
Likewise I made Ulysses, after Isaac,
And a little after Flaxman. Archibald
Was wounded when he found himself left out,
But he had no heroics, and I said so:
I told him that his white beard was too long
And too straight down to be like things in Homer.
"Quite so," said Isaac.—"Low," said Archibald;
And he threw down a deuce with a deep grin
That showed his yellow teeth and made me happy.
So they played on till a bell rang from the door,
And Archibald said, "Supper."—After that
The old men smoked while I sat watching them
And wondered with all comfort what might come
To me, and what might never come to me;
And when the time came for the long walk home
With Isaac in the twilight, I could see
The forest and the sunset and the sky-line,
No matter where it was that I was looking:
The flame beyond the boundary, the music,

The foam and the white ships, and two old men
Were things that would not leave me.—And that night
There came to me a dream—a shining one,
With two old angels in it. They had wings,
And they were sitting where a silver light
Suffused them, face to face. The wings of one
Began to palpitate as I approached,
But I was yet unseen when a dry voice
Cried thinly, with unpatronizing triumph,
"I've got you, Isaac: high, low, jack, and the game."

Isaac and Archibald have gone their way
To the silence of the loved and well-forgotten.
I knew them, and I may have laughed at them;
But there's a laughing that has honor in it,
And I have no regret for light words now.
Rather I think sometimes they may have made
Their sport of me;—but they would not do that,
They were too old for that. They were old men,
And I may laugh at them because I knew them.

NEW ENGLAND

Here where the wind is always north-north-east
And children learn to walk on frozen toes,
Wonder begets an envy of all those
Who boil elsewhere with such a lyric yeast
Of love that you will hear them at a feast
Where demons would appeal for some repose,
Still clamoring where the chalice overflows
And crying wildest who have drunk the least.

Passion is here a soilure of the wits,
We're told, and Love a cross for them to bear;
Joy shivers in the corner where she knits
And Conscience always has the rocking-chair,
Cheerful as when she tortured into fits
The first cat that was ever killed by Care.

Robert Frost (1874–   )

The poetic genius and Yankee sensibility of Robert Frost have made him the twentieth century's outstanding example of that traditional American humorous character, the crackerbox philosopher. Like earlier rustic sages, Frost is also sophisticated and urbane; his homespun mask frequently slips to one side and reveals a mind as metropolitan as that of any city slicker. This occurs often, for example, in the rural hilarity of *New Hampshire* (1923). Many of Frost's more recent satires of modern cultural values, institutions, and practices would be accepted as readily from a Bostonian or a New Yorker as from a New England villager or farmer. Indeed Frost's increasing tendency to be satirical and the more caustic tone of his irony suggest that the bucolic peace of the countryside may no longer exist in modern America. In almost all of his best works Frost displays the qualities which make him a humorous poet regardless of setting: verbal wit, mirthful observation, colloquial idiom, boastfulness understated as well as overstated, amusing anecdote, jocular quipping, and an unsentimental merger of what are ordinarily regarded as incompatible opposites. Frost's high praise of Edwin Arlington Robinson for the latter's blending of seriousness and humor is equally applicable to Frost himself.

TEXT: *Complete Poems of Robert Frost*, New York, 1949. Lawrance Thompson, *Fire and Ice: The Art and Thought of Robert Frost*, New York, 1942.

THE BEAR

The bear puts both arms around the tree above her
And draws it down as if it were a lover
And its choke cherries lips to kiss good-bye,
And lets it snap back upright in the sky.
Her next step rocks a boulder on the wall
(She's making her cross-country in the fall).
Her great weight creaks the barbed-wire in its staples
As she flings over and off down through the maples,
Leaving on one wire tooth a lock of hair.
Such is the uncaged progress of the bear.
The world has room to make a bear feel free;
The universe seems cramped to you and me.
Man acts more like the poor bear in a cage

That all day fights a nervous inward rage,
His mood rejecting all his mind suggests.
He paces back and forth and never rests
The toe-nail click and shuffle of his feet,
The telescope at one end of his beat,
And at the other end the microscope,
Two instruments of nearly equal hope,
And in conjunction giving quite a spread.
Or if he rests from scientific tread
'Tis only to sit back and sway his head
Through ninety odd degrees of arc, it seems,
Between two metaphysical extremes.
He sits back on his fundamental butt
With lifted snout and eyes (if any) shut,
(He almost looks religious but he's not),
And back and forth he sways from cheek to cheek,
At one extreme agreeing with one Greek,
At the other agreeing with another Greek
Which may be thought, but only so to speak.
A baggy figure, equally pathetic
When sedentary and when peripatetic.

H. L. Mencken (1880–1956)

For over thirty years, from the early 1900's to the early 1930's, H. L. Mencken boisterously castigated what he believed to be American culture's stupid complacency and provincial ignorance. He was the twentieth century's reincarnation of two earlier satirists, Poe and Bierce. As the crusading editor of *Smart Set* and *American Mercury*, iconoclastic essayist of pieces boldly published as *Prejudices*, and gadfly-at-large to the American republic, Mencken exhorted, excoriated, enraged, and entertained. Taking advantage of the freedom of American journalism, Mencken spared no institution, no social class, no person, and no idea from his raillery and derision. As "In Memoriam: W. J. B." (1925) indicates, Mencken's style was calculated to devastate and amuse. It was a scathing combination of erudition and colloquial idiom, bold to the point of slander, laden with jokes, invective, and judgments. His criticism was frankly personal, based on what he himself detested or upheld; he could as easily scoff at unrealistic professors as at the vulgar mob. Mencken's forcefulness did much to create the liberating atmosphere of the 1920's and encouraged the development of critical humor by Anderson, Cummings, Fitzgerald, Hemingway, and Faulkner.

TEXT: *Prejudices: Fifth Series*, New York, 1926. COMMENTARY: Edgar Kemler, *The Irreverent Mr. Mencken*, Boston, Mass., 1950; William Manchester, *Disturber of the Peace*, New York, 1951.

IN MEMORIAM: W. J. B.

Has it been duly marked by historians that the late William Jennings Bryan's last secular act on this globe of sin was to catch flies? A curious detail, and not without its sardonic overtones. He was the most sedulous flycatcher in American history, and in many ways the most successful. His quarry, of course, was not *Musca domestica* but *Homo neandertalensis*. For forty years he tracked it with coo and bellow, up and down the rustic backways of the Republic. Wherever the flambeaux of Chautauqua smoked and guttered, and the bilge of Idealism ran in the veins, and Baptist pastors dammed the brooks with the sanctified, and men gathered who were weary and heavy laden, and their wives who were full of Peruna and as fecund as the shad (*Alosa sapidissima*)—there the indefatigable Jennings set up his traps and spread his bait. He knew every country town in the South and West, and he could crowd the most remote of them to suffocation by simply winding his horn. The city prole-

tariat, transiently flustered by him in 1896, quickly penetrated his bun-
combe and would have no more of him; the cockney gallery jeered him
at every Democratic national convention for twenty-five years. But out
where the grass grows high, and the horned cattle dream away the lazy
afternoons, and men still fear the powers and principalities of the air—
out there between the corn-rows he held his old puissance to the end.
There was no need of beaters to drive in his game. The news that he
was coming was enough. For miles the flivver dust would choke the roads.
And when he rose at the end of the day to discharge his Message there
would be such breathless attention, such a rapt and enchanted ecstasy,
such a sweet rustle of amens as the world had not known since Johann
fell to Herod's ax.

There was something peculiarly fitting in the fact that his last days
were spent in a one-horse Tennessee village, and that death found him
there. The man felt at home in such simple and Christian scenes. He
liked people who sweated freely, and were not debauched by the refinements of the toilet. Making his progress up and down the Main street
of little Dayton, surrounded by gaping primates from the upland valleys
of the Cumberland Range, his coat laid aside, his bare arms and hairy
chest shining damply, his bald head sprinkled with dust—so accoutred
and on display he was obviously happy. He liked getting up early in the
morning, to the tune of cocks crowing on the dunghill. He liked the
heavy, greasy victuals of the farmhouse kitchen. He liked country lawyers,
country pastors, all country people. He liked the country sounds and
country smells. I believe that this liking was sincere—perhaps the only
sincere thing in the man. His nose showed no uneasiness when a hillman
in faded overalls and hickory shirt accosted him on the street, and besought him for light upon some mystery of Holy Writ. The simian gabble of the cross-roads was not gabble to him, but wisdom of an occult
and superior sort. In the presence of city folks he was palpably uneasy.
Their clothes, I suspect, annoyed him, and he was suspicious of their too
delicate manners. He knew all the while that they were laughing at him—
if not at his baroque theology, then at least at his alpaca pantaloons.
But the yokels never laughed at him. To them he was not the huntsman
but the prophet, and toward the end, as he gradually forsook mundane
politics for more ghostly concerns, they began to elevate him in their
hierarchy. When he died he was the peer of Abraham. His old enemy,
Wilson, aspiring to the same white and shining robe, came down with
a thump. But Bryan made the grade. His place in Tennessee hagiography
is secure. If the village barber saved any of his hair, then it is curing
gall-stones down there to-day.

But what label will he bear in more urbane regions? One, I fear, of
a far less flattering kind. Bryan lived too long, and descended too deeply
into the mud, to be taken seriously hereafter by fully literate men, even

of the kind who write school-books. There was a scattering of sweet words in his funeral notices, but it was no more than a response to conventional sentimentality. The best verdict the most romantic editorial writer could dredge up, save in the humorless South, was to the general effect that his imbecilities were excused by his earnestness—that under his clowning, as under that of the juggler of Notre Dame, there was the zeal of a steadfast soul. But this was apology, not praise; precisely the same thing might be said of Mary Baker G. Eddy, the late Czar Nicholas, or Czolgosz. The truth is that even Bryan's sincerity will probably yield to what is called, in other fields, definitive criticism. Was he sincere when he opposed imperialism in the Philippines, or when he fed it with deserving Democrats in Santo Domingo? Was he sincere when he tried to shove the Prohibitionists under the table, or when he seized their banner and began to lead them with loud whoops? Was he sincere when he bellowed against war, or when he dreamed of himself as a tin-soldier in uniform, with a grave reserved among the generals? Was he sincere when he denounced the late John W. Davis, or when he swallowed Davis? Was he sincere when he fawned over Champ Clark, or when he betrayed Clark? Was he sincere when he pleaded for tolerance in New York, or when he bawled for the faggot and the stake in Tennessee?

This talk of sincerity, I confess, fatigues me. If the fellow was sincere, then so was P. T. Barnum. The word is disgraced and degraded by such uses. He was, in fact, a charlatan, a mountebank, a zany without shame or dignity. His career brought him into contact with the first men of his time; he preferred the company of rustic ignoramuses. It was hard to believe, watching him at Dayton, that he had traveled, that he had been received in civilized societies, that he had been a high officer of state. He seemed only a poor clod like those around him, deluded by a childish theology, full of an almost pathological hatred of all learning, all human dignity, all beauty, all fine and noble things. He was a peasant come home to the barnyard. Imagine a gentleman, and you have imagined everything that he was not. What animated him from end to end of his grotesque career was simply ambition—the ambition of a common man to get his hand upon the collar of his superiors, or, failing that, to get his thumb into their eyes. He was born with a roaring voice, and it had the trick of inflaming half-wits. His whole career was devoted to raising those half-wits against their betters, that he himself might shine. His last battle will be grossly misunderstood if it is thought of as a mere exercise in fanaticism—that is, if Bryan the Fundamentalist Pope is mistaken for one of the bucolic Fundamentalists. There was much more in it than that, as everyone knows who saw him on the field. What moved him, at bottom, was simply hatred of the city men who had laughed at him so long, and brought him at last to so tatterdemalion an estate. He lusted for revenge upon them. He yearned to lead the anthropoid rabble against them, to punish them for their execution upon him by attacking the very vitals of their civilization. He went far beyond the bounds of any merely religious frenzy, however inordinate. When he began denouncing the notion that man is a mammal even some of the hinds at Dayton were agape. And when, brought upon Darrow's cruel hook, he writhed and tossed in a very fury of malignancy, bawling against the baldest elements of sense and decency like a man frantic—when he came to that tragic climax of his striving there were snickers among the hinds as well as hosannas.

Upon that hook, in truth, Bryan committed suicide, as a legend as well as in the body. He staggered from the rustic court ready to die, and he staggered from it ready to be forgotten, save as a character in a third-rate farce, witless and in poor taste. It was plain to everyone who knew him, when he came to Dayton, that his great days were behind him—that, for all the fury of his hatred, he was now definitely an old man, and headed at last for silence. There was a vague, unpleasant manginess about his appearance; he somehow seemed dirty, though a close glance showed him as carefully shaven as an actor, and clad in immaculate linen. All the hair was gone from the dome of his head, and it had begun to fall out, too, behind his ears, in the obscene manner of the late Samuel Gompers. The resonance had departed from his voice; what was once a bugle blast had become reedy and quavering. Who knows that, like Demosthenes, he had a lisp? In the old days, under the magic of his eloquence, no one noticed it. But when he spoke at Dayton it was always audible.

When I first encountered him, on the sidewalk in front of the office of the rustic lawyers who were his associates in the Scopes case, the trial was yet to begin, and so he was still expansive and amiable. I had printed in the *Nation*, a week or so before, an article arguing that the Tennessee anti-evolution law, whatever its wisdom, was at least constitutional— that the rustics of the State had a clear right to have their progeny taught whatever they chose, and kept secure from whatever knowledge violated their superstitions. The old boy professed to be delighted with the argument, and gave the gaping bystanders to understand that I was a publicist of parts. Not to be outdone, I admired the preposterous country shirt that he wore—sleeveless and with the neck cut very low. We parted in the manner of two ambassadors. But that was the last touch of amiability that I was destined to see in Bryan. The next day the battle joined and his face became hard. By the end of the week he was simply a walking fever. Hour by hour he grew more bitter. What the Christian Scientists call malicious animal magnetism seemed to radiate from him like heat from a stove. From my place in the courtroom, standing upon a table, I looked directly down upon him, sweating horribly and pumping his palm-leaf fan. His eyes fascinated me; I watched them all day long. They were blazing points of hatred. They glittered like occult and sinister gems.

Now and then they wandered to me, and I got my share, for my reports of the trial had come back to Dayton, and he had read them. It was like coming under fire.

Thus he fought his last fight, thirsting savagely for blood. All sense departed from him. He bit right and left, like a dog with rabies. He descended to demagogy so dreadful that his very associates at the trial table blushed. His one yearning was to keep his yokels heated up—to lead his forlorn mob of imbeciles against the foe. That foe, alas, refused to be alarmed. It insisted upon seeing the whole battle as a comedy. Even Darrow, who knew better, occasionally yielded to the prevailing spirit. One day he lured poor Bryan into the folly I have mentioned: his astounding argument against the notion that man is a mammal. I am glad I heard it, for otherwise I'd never believe in it. There stood the man who had been thrice a candidate for the Presidency of the Republic— there he stood in the glare of the world, uttering stuff that a boy of eight would laugh at! The artful Darrow led him on: he repeated it, ranted for it, bellowed it in his cracked voice. So he was prepared for the final slaughter. He came into life a hero, a Galahad, in bright and shining armor. He was passing out a poor mountebank.

The chances are that history will put the peak of democracy in America in his time; it has been on the downward curve among us since the campaign of 1896. He will be remembered perhaps, as its supreme impostor, the *reductio ad absurdum* of its pretension. Bryan came very near being President. In 1896, it is possible, he was actually elected. He lived long enough to make patriots thank the inscrutable gods for Harding, even for Coolidge. Dullness has got into the White House, and the smell of cabbage boiling, but there is at least nothing to compare to the intolerable buffoonery that went on in Tennessee. The President of the United States may be an ass, but he at least doesn't believe that the earth is square, and that witches should be put to death, and that Jonah swallowed the whale. The Golden Text is not painted weekly on the White House wall, and there is no need to keep ambassadors waiting while Pastor Simpson, of Smithville, prays for rain in the Blue Room. We have escaped something —by a narrow margin, but still we have escaped.

That is, so far. The Fundamentalists, once apparently sweeping all before them, now face minorities prepared for battle even in the South —here and there with some assurance of success. But it is too early, it seems to me, to send the firemen home; the fire is still burning on many a far-flung hill, and it may begin to roar again at any moment. The evil that men do lives after them. Bryan, in his malice, started something that it will not be easy to stop. In ten thousand country towns his old heelers, the evangelical pastors, are propagating his gospel, and everywhere the yokels are ready for it. When he disappeared from the big cities, the big cities made the capital error of assuming that he was done for.

If they heard of him at all, it was only as a crimp for real-estate speculators —the heroic foe of the unearned increment hauling it in with both hands. He seemed preposterous, and hence harmless. But all the while he was busy among his old lieges, preparing for a *jacquerie* that should floor all his enemies at one blow. He did his job competently. He had vast skill at such enterprises. Heave an egg out of a Pullman window, and you will hit a Fundamentalist almost everywhere in the United States to-day. They swarm in the country towns, inflamed by their *shamans*, and with a saint, now, to venerate. They are thick in the mean streets behind the gas-works. They are everywhere where learning is too heavy a burden for mortal minds to carry, even the vague, pathetic learning on tap in little red schoolhouses. They march with the Klan, with the Christian Endeavor Society, with the Junior Order of United American Mechanics, with the Epworth League, with all the rococo bands that poor and unhappy folk organize to bring some light of purpose into their lives. They have had a thrill, and they are ready for more.

Such is Bryan's legacy to his country. He couldn't be President, but he could at least help magnificently in the solemn business of shutting off the Presidency from every intelligent and self-respecting man. The storm, perhaps, won't last long, as time goes in history. It may help, indeed, to break up the democratic delusion, now already showing weakness, and so hasten its own end. But while it lasts it will blow off some roofs.

Sherwood Anderson (1876–1941)

It seemed to Sherwood Anderson in the early 1920's that the traditional "American laugh" had disappeared, that American humor had
become superficial. In *Winesburg, Ohio* (1919) and in such stories as
"The Egg" (1921), however, Anderson already had done much to ensure
a profound strain of humor in Hemingway, Fitzgerald, Faulkner, and
other writers who came to maturity in the 1920's. Anderson recalled that
he had freed himself from an unpleasant business career for a life of art
"by a kind of mocking laughter" applied to himself and his values. A
"mocking laughter," that of the Negro, pervaded Anderson's only best-
seller, *Dark Laughter* (1925). It was not accidental that Anderson's term
for the materials he presented in *Winesburg, Ohio* and "The Egg" was
"grotesque," for Poe, an earlier master of sharp laughter, had also used
the term to describe his individual brand of absurd incongruity. The vein
of critical humor which Anderson exploited in "The Egg" will not be
found in all his works. He tended to be more compassionate than either
Poe, Fitzgerald, Hemingway, or Faulkner. The gentle irony of "I'm a
Fool" came more easily to Anderson, and that also has left its mark
upon many writers.

TEXT: *The Triumph of the Egg*, New York, 1921. COMMENTARY: Irving
Howe, *Sherwood Anderson*, New York, 1951; James Schevill, *Sherwood
Anderson: His Life and Work*, Denver, Col., 1951.

THE EGG

My father was, I am sure, intended by nature to be a cheerful, kindly
man. Until he was thirty-four years old he worked as a farm-hand for a
man named Thomas Butterworth whose place lay near the town of
Bidwell, Ohio. He had then a horse of his own and on Saturday evenings
drove into town to spend a few hours in social intercourse with other
farm-hands. In town he drank several glasses of beer and stood about in
Ben Head's saloon—crowded on Saturday evenings with visiting farm-
hands. Songs were sung and glasses thumped on the bar. At ten o'clock
father drove home along a lonely country road, made his horse comfortable
for the night and himself went to bed, quite happy in his position in life.
He had at that time no notion of trying to rise in the world.

It was in the spring of his thirty-fifth year that father married my
mother, then a country school-teacher, and in the following spring I came
wriggling and crying into the world. Something happened to the two

489

people. They became ambitious. The American passion for getting up in the world took possession of them.

It may have been that mother was responsible. Being a school-teacher she had no doubt read books and magazines. She had, I presume, read of how Garfield, Lincoln, and other Americans rose from poverty to fame and greatness and as I lay beside her—in the days of her lying-in—she may have dreamed that I would some day rule men and cities. At any rate she induced father to give up his place as a farm-hand, sell his horse and embark on an independent enterprise of his own. She was a tall silent woman with a long nose and troubled grey eyes. For herself she wanted nothing. For father and myself she was incurably ambitious.

The first venture into which the two people went turned out badly. They rented ten acres of poor stony land on Griggs's Road, eight miles from Bidwell, and launched into chicken raising. I grew into boyhood on the place and got my first impressions of life there. From the beginning they were impressions of disaster and if, in my turn, I am a gloomy man inclined to see the darker side of life, I attribute it to the fact that what should have been for me the happy joyous days of childhood were spent on a chicken farm.

One unversed in such matters can have no notion of the many and tragic things that can happen to a chicken. It is born out of an egg, lives for a few weeks as a tiny fluffy thing such as you will see pictured on Easter cards, then becomes hideously naked, eats quantities of corn and meal bought by the sweat of your father's brow, gets diseases called pip, cholera, and other names, stands looking with stupid eyes at the sun, becomes sick and dies. A few hens and now and then a rooster, intended to serve God's mysterious ends, struggle through to maturity. The hens lay eggs out of which come other chickens and the dreadful cycle is thus made complete. It is all unbelievably complex. Most philosophers must have been raised on chicken farms. One hopes for so much from a chicken and is so dreadfully disillusioned. Small chickens, just setting out on the journey of life, look so bright and alert and they are in fact so dreadfully stupid. They are so much like people they mix one up in one's judgments of life. If disease does not kill them they wait until your expectations are thoroughly aroused and then walk under the wheels of a wagon—to go squashed and dead back to their maker. Vermin infest their youth, and fortunes must be spent for curative powders. In later life I have seen how a literature has been built up on the subject of fortunes to be made out of the raising of chickens. It is intended to be read by the gods who have just eaten of the tree of the knowledge of good and evil. It is a hopeful literature and declares that much may be done by simple ambitious people who own a few hens. Do not be led astray by it. It was not written for you. Go hunt for gold on the frozen hills of Alaska, put your faith in the honesty of a politician, believe if you will that the world is daily growing better and that good will triumph over evil, but do not read and believe the literature that is written concerning the hen. It was not written for you.

I, however, digress. My tale does not primarily concern itself with the hen. If correctly told it will centre on the egg. For ten years my father and mother struggled to make our chicken farm pay and then they gave up that struggle and began another. They moved into the town of Bidwell, Ohio and embarked in the restaurant business. After ten years of worry with incubators that did not hatch, and with tiny—and in their own way lovely—balls of fluff that passed on into semi-naked pullethood and from that into dead henhood, we threw all aside and packing our belongings on a wagon drove down Griggs's Road toward Bidwell, a tiny caravan of hope looking for a new place from which to start on our upward journey through life.

We must have been a sad looking lot, not, I fancy, unlike refugees fleeing from a battlefield. Mother and I walked in the road. The wagon that contained our goods had been borrowed for the day from Mr. Albert Griggs, a neighbor. Out of its sides stuck the legs of cheap chairs and at the back of the pile of beds, tables, and boxes filled with kitchen utensils was a crate of live chickens, and on top of that the baby carriage in which I had been wheeled about in my infancy. Why we stuck to the baby carriage I don't know. It was unlikely other children would be born and the wheels were broken. People who have few possessions cling tightly to those they have. That is one of the facts that make life so discouraging.

Father rode on top of the wagon. He was then a bald-headed man of forty-five, a little fat and from long association with mother and the chickens he had become habitually silent and discouraged. All during our ten years on the chicken farm he had worked as a laborer on neighboring farms and most of the money he had earned had been spent for remedies to cure chicken diseases, on Wilmer's White Wonder Cholera Cure or Professor Bidlow's Egg Producer or some other preparations that mother found advertised in the poultry papers. There were two little patches of hair on father's head just above his ears. I remember that as a child I used to sit looking at him when he had gone to sleep in a chair before the stove on Sunday afternoons in the winter. I had at that time already begun to read books and have notions of my own and the bald path that led over the top of his head was, I fancied, something like a broad road, such a road as Caesar might have made on which to lead his legions out of Rome and into the wonders of an unknown world. The tufts of hair that grew above father's ears were, I thought, like forests. I fell into a half-sleeping, half-waking state and dreamed I was a tiny thing going along the road into a far beautiful place where there were no chicken farms and where life was a happy eggless affair.

One might write a book concerning our flight from the chicken farm into town. Mother and I walked the entire eight miles—she to be sure that nothing fell from the wagon and I to see the wonders of the world. On the seat of the wagon beside father was his greatest treasure. I will tell you of that.

On a chicken farm where hundreds and even thousands of chickens come out of eggs surprising things sometimes happen. Grotesques are born out of eggs as out of people. The accident does not often occur—perhaps once in a thousand births. A chicken is, you see, born that has four legs, two pairs of wings, two heads or what not. The things do not live. They go quickly back to the hand of their maker that has for a moment trembled. The fact that the poor little things could not live was one of the tragedies of life to father. He had some sort of notion that if he could but bring into henhood or roosterhood a five-legged hen or a two-headed rooster his fortune would be made. He dreamed of taking the wonder about to county fairs and of growing rich by exhibiting it to other farm-hands.

At any rate he saved all the little monstrous things that had been born on our chicken farm. They were preserved in alcohol and put each in its own glass bottle. These he had carefully put into a box and on our journey into town it was carried on the wagon seat beside him. He drove the horses with one hand and with the other clung to the box. When we got to our destination the box was taken down at once and the bottles removed. All during our days as keepers of a restaurant in the town of Bidwell, Ohio, the grotesques in their little glass bottles sat on a shelf back of the counter. Mother sometimes protested but father was a rock on the subject of his treasure. The grotesques were, he declared, valuable. People, he said, liked to look at strange and wonderful things.

Did I say that we embarked in the restaurant business in the town of Bidwell, Ohio? I exaggerated a little. The town itself lay at the foot of a low hill and on the shore of a small river. The railroad did not run through the town and the station was a mile away to the north at a place called Pickleville. There had been a cider mill and pickle factory at the station, but before the time of our coming they had both gone out of business. In the morning and in the evening busses came down to the station along a road called Turner's Pike from the hotel on the main street of Bidwell. Our going to the out of the way place to embark in the restaurant business was mother's idea. She talked of it for a year and then one day went off and rented an empty store building opposite the railroad station. It was her idea that the restaurant would be profitable. Travelling men, she said, would be always waiting around to take trains out of town and town people would come to the station to await incoming trains. They would come to the restaurant to buy pieces of pie and drink coffee. Now that I am older I know that she had another motive in going. She was ambitious for me. She wanted me to rise in the world, to get into a town school and become a man of the towns.

At Pickleville father and mother worked hard as they always had done. At first there was the necessity of putting our place into shape to be a restaurant. That took a month. Father built a shelf on which he put tins of vegetables. He painted a sign on which he put his name in large red letters. Below his name was the sharp command—"EAT HERE"—that was so seldom obeyed. A show case was bought and filled with cigars and tobacco. Mother scrubbed the floor and the walls of the room. I went to school in the town and was glad to be away from the farm and from the presence of the discouraged, sad-looking chickens. Still I was not very joyous. In the evening I walked home from school along Turner's Pike and remembered the children I had seen playing in the town school yard. A troop of little girls had gone hopping about and singing. I tried that. Down along the frozen road I went hopping solemnly on one leg. "Hippity Hop To The Barber Shop," I sang shrilly. Then I stopped and looked doubtfully about. I was afraid of being seen in my gay mood. It must have seemed to me that I was doing a thing that should not be done by one who, like myself, had been raised on a chicken farm where death was a daily visitor.

Mother decided that our restaurant should remain open at night. At ten in the evening a passenger train went north past our door followed by a local freight. The freight crew had switching to do in Pickleville and when the work was done they came to our restaurant for hot coffee and food. Sometimes one of them ordered a fried egg. In the morning at four they returned north-bound and again visited us. A little trade began to grow up. Mother slept at night and during the day tended the restaurant and fed our boarders while father slept. He slept in the same bed mother had occupied during the night and I went off to the town of Bidwell and to school. During the long nights, while mother and I slept, father cooked meats that were to go into sandwiches for the lunch baskets of our boarders. Then an idea in regard to getting up in the world came into his head. The American spirit took hold of him. He also became ambitious.

In the long nights when there was little to do father had time to think. That was his undoing. He decided that he had in the past been an unsuccessful man because he had not been cheerful enough and that in the future he would adopt a cheerful outlook on life. In the early morning he came upstairs and got into bed with mother. She woke and the two talked. From my bed in the corner I listened.

It was my father's idea that both he and mother should try to entertain the people who came to eat at our restaurant. I cannot now remember his words, but he gave the impression of one about to become in some obscure way a kind of public entertainer. When people, particularly young people from the town of Bidwell, came into our place, as on very rare occasions they did, bright entertaining conversation was to be made. From father's words I gathered that something of the jolly inn-keeper effect was to be sought. Mother must have been doubtful from the first, but she said nothing discouraging. It was father's notion that a passion for the company of himself and mother would spring up in the breasts of the younger people of the town of Bidwell. In the evening bright happy groups would come singing down Turner's Pike. They would troop shouting with joy and laughter into our place. There would be song and festivity. I do not mean to give the impression that father spoke so elaborately of the matter. He was as I have said an uncommunicative man. "They want some place to go. I tell you they want some place to go," he said over and over. That was as far as he got. My own imagination has filled in the blanks.

For two or three weeks this notion of father's invaded our house. We did not talk much, but in our daily lives tried earnestly to make smiles take the place of glum looks. Mother smiled at the boarders and I, catching the infection, smiled at our cat. Father became a little feverish in his anxiety to please. There was no doubt, lurking somewhere in him, a touch of the spirit of the showman. He did not waste much of his ammunition on the railroad men he served at night but seemed to be waiting for a young man or woman from Bidwell to come in to show what he could do. On the counter in the restaurant there was a wire basket kept always filled with eggs, and it must have been before his eyes when the idea of being entertaining was born in his brain. There was something pre-natal about the way eggs kept themselves connected with the development of his idea. At any rate an egg ruined his new impulse in life. Late one night I was awakened by a roar of anger coming from father's throat. Both mother and I sat upright in our beds. With trembling hands she lighted a lamp that stood on a table by her head. Downstairs the front door of our restaurant went shut with a bang and in a few minutes father tramped up the stairs. He held an egg in his hand and his hand trembled as though he were having a chill. There was a half insane light in his eyes. As he stood glaring at us I was sure he intended throwing the egg at either mother or me. Then he laid it gently on the table beside the lamp and dropped on his knees beside mother's bed. He began to cry like a boy and I, carried away by his grief, cried with him. The two of us filled the little upstairs room with our wailing voices. It is ridiculous, but of the picture we made I can remember only the fact that mother's hand continually stroked the bald path that ran across the top of his head. I have forgotten what mother said to him and how she induced him to tell her of what had happened downstairs. His explanation also has gone out of my mind. I remember only my own grief and fright and the shiny path over father's head glowing in the lamp light as he knelt by the bed.

As to what happened downstairs. For some unexplainable reason I know the story as well as though I had been a witness to my father's discomfiture. One in time gets to know many unexplainable things. On that evening young Joe Kane, son of a merchant of Bidwell, came to Pickleville to meet his father, who was expected on the ten o'clock evening train from the South. The train was three hours late and Joe came into our place to loaf about and to wait for its arrival. The local freight train came in and the freight crew were fed. Joe was left alone in the restaurant with father.

From the moment he came into our place the Bidwell young man must have been puzzled by my father's actions. It was his notion that father was angry at him for hanging around. He noticed that the restaurant keeper was apparently disturbed by his presence and he thought of going out. However, it began to rain and he did not fancy the long walk to town and back. He bought a five-cent cigar and ordered a cup of coffee. He had a newspaper in his pocket and took it out and began to read. "I'm waiting for the evening train. It's late," he said apologetically.

For a long time father, whom Joe Kane had never seen before, remained silently gazing at his visitor. He was no doubt suffering from an attack of stage fright. As so often happens in life he had thought so much and so often of the situation that now confronted him that he was somewhat nervous in its presence.

For one thing, he did not know what to do with his hands. He thrust one of them nervously over the counter and shook hands with Joe Kane. "How-de-do," he said. Joe Kane put his newspaper down and stared at him. Father's eye lighted on the basket of eggs that sat on the counter and he began to talk. "Well," he began hesitatingly, "well, you have heard of Christopher Columbus, eh?" He seemed to be angry. "That Christopher Columbus was a cheat," he declared emphatically. "He talked of making an egg stand on its end. He talked, he did, and then he went and broke the end of the egg."

My father seemed to his visitor to be beside himself at the duplicity of Christopher Columbus. He muttered and swore. He declared it was wrong to teach children that Christopher Columbus was a great man when, after all, he cheated at the critical moment. He had declared he would make an egg stand on end and then when his bluff had been called he had done a trick. Still grumbling at Columbus, father took an egg from the basket on the counter and began to walk up and down. He rolled the egg between the palms of his hands. He smiled genially. He began to mumble words regarding the effect to be produced on an egg by the electricity that comes out of the human body. He declared that without breaking its shell and by virtue of rolling it back and forth in his hands he could stand the egg on its end. He explained that the warmth of his hands and the gentle rolling movement he gave the egg created a new centre of gravity, and Joe Kane was mildly interested. "I have handled thousands of eggs," father said. "No one knows more about eggs than I do."

He stood the egg on the counter and it fell on its side. He tried the trick again and again, each time rolling the egg between the palms of his hands and saying the words regarding the wonders of electricity and the laws of gravity. When after a half hour's effort he did succeed in making the egg stand for a moment he looked up to find that his visitor was no longer watching. By the time he had succeeded in calling Joe Kane's attention to the success of his effort the egg had again rolled over and lay on its side.

Afire with the showman's passion and at the same time a good deal disconcerted by the failure of his first effort, father now took the bottles containing the poultry monstrosities down from their place on the shelf and began to show them to his visitor. "How would you like to have seven legs and two heads like this fellow?" he asked, exhibiting the most remarkable of his treasures. A cheerful smile played over his face. He reached over the counter and tried to slap Joe Kane on the shoulder as he had seen men do in Ben Head's saloon when he was a young farmhand and drove to town on Saturday evenings. His visitor was made a little ill by the sight of the body of the terribly deformed bird floating in the alcohol in the bottle and got up to go. Coming from behind the counter father took hold of the young man's arm and led him back to his seat. He grew a little angry and for a moment had to turn his face away and force himself to smile. Then he put the bottles back on the shelf. In an outburst of generosity he fairly compelled Joe Kane to have a fresh cup of coffee and another cigar at his expense. Then he took a pan and filling it with vinegar, taken from a jug that sat beneath the counter, he declared himself about to do a new trick. "I will heat this egg in this pan of vinegar," he said. "Then I will put it through the neck of a bottle without breaking the shell. When the egg is inside the bottle it will resume its normal shape and the shell will become hard again. Then I will give the bottle with the egg in it to you. You can take it about with you wherever you go. People will want to know how you got the egg in the bottle. Don't tell them. Keep them guessing. That is the way to have fun with this trick."

Father grinned and winked at his visitor. Joe Kane decided that the man who confronted him was mildly insane but harmless. He drank the cup of coffee that had been given him and began to read his paper again. When the egg had been heated in vinegar father carried it on a spoon to the counter and going into a back room got an empty bottle. He was angry because his visitor did not watch him as he began to do his trick, but nevertheless went cheerfully to work. For a long time he struggled, trying to get the egg to go through the neck of the bottle. He put the pan of vinegar back on the stove, intending to reheat the egg, then picked it up and burned his fingers. After a second bath in the hot vinegar the shell of the egg had been softened a little but not enough for his purpose. He worked and worked and a spirit of desperate determination took possession of him. When he thought that at last the trick was about to be consummated the delayed train came in at the station and Joe Kane started to go nonchalantly out at the door. Father made a last desperate effort to conquer the egg and make it do the thing that would establish his reputation as one who knew how to entertain guests who came into his restaurant. He worried the egg. He attempted to be somewhat rough with it. He swore and the sweat stood out on his forehead. The egg broke under his hand. When the contents spurted over his clothes, Joe Kane, who had stopped at the door, turned and laughed.

A roar of anger rose from my father's throat. He danced and shouted a string of inarticulate words. Grabbing another egg from the basket on the counter, he threw it, just missing the head of the young man as he dodged through the door and escaped.

Father came upstairs to mother and me with an egg in his hand. I do not know what he intended to do. I imagine he had some idea of destroying it, of destroying all eggs, and that he intended to let mother and me see him begin. When, however, he got into the presence of mother something happened to him. He laid the egg gently on the table and dropped on his knees by the bed as I have already explained. He later decided to close the restaurant for the night and to come upstairs and get into bed. When he did so he blew out the light and after much muttered conversation both he and mother went to sleep. I suppose I went to sleep also, but my sleep was troubled. I awoke at dawn and for a long time looked at the egg that lay on the table. I wondered why eggs had to be and why from the egg came the hen who again laid the egg. The question got into my blood. It has stayed there, I imagine, because I am the son of my father. At any rate, the problem remains unsolved in my mind. And that, I conclude, is but another evidence of the complete and final triumph of the egg—at least as far as my family is concerned.

Wallace Stevens (1879–1955)

Wallace Stevens will long be remembered for his brilliant wit and satire. Whether he described fanciful characters, exotic objects and landscapes, or his own feelings, Stevens always managed to play entrancingly with the elements of his poetic medium: colors, sounds, metaphors, images, and words. He was most successful when elegantly ironic as in "A High-Toned Old Christian Woman" (1923) or elegantly comic as in "Disillusionment of Ten O'clock" (1923). The first of these poems also contains the mocking bite and the sophisticated jocularity which are so frequently encountered in his lines.

TEXT: *The Collected Poems of Wallace Stevens*, New York, 1954.
COMMENTARY: William Van O'Connor, *The Shaping Spirit: A Study of Wallace Stevens*, Chicago, Ill., 1950; Robert Pack, *Wallace Stevens: An Approach to His Poetry and Thought*, New Brunswick, N.J., 1958.

A HIGH-TONED OLD CHRISTIAN WOMAN

Poetry is the supreme fiction, madame.
Take the moral law and make a nave of it
And from the nave build haunted heaven. Thus,
The conscience is converted into palms,
Like windy citherns hankering for hymns.
We agree in principle. That's clear. But take
The opposing law and make a peristyle,
And from the peristyle project a masque
Beyond the planets. Thus, our bawdiness,
Unpurged by epitaph, indulged at last,
Is equally converted into palms,
Squiggling like saxophones. And palm for palm,
Madame, we are where we began. Allow,
Therefore, that in the planetary scene
Your disaffected flagellants, well-stuffed,
Smacking their muzzy bellies in parade,
Proud of such novelties of the sublime,
Such tink and tank and tunk-a-tunk-tunk,
May, merely may, madame, whip from themselves
A jovial hullabaloo among the spheres.
This will make widows wince. But fictive things
Wink as they will. Wink most when widows wince.

DISILLUSIONMENT OF TEN O'CLOCK

The houses are haunted
By white night-gowns.
None are green,
Or purple with green rings,
Or green with yellow rings,
Or yellow with blue rings.
None of them are strange,
With socks of lace
And beaded ceintures.
People are not going
To dream of baboons and periwinkles.
Only, here and there, an old sailor,
Drunk and asleep in his boots,
Catches tigers
In red weather.

Ring Lardner (1885–1933)

American humorists brought the vernacular into literature during the nineteenth century and Mark Twain developed it into a complex expressive medium in *Adventures of Huckleberry Finn*. In doing so he rescued the vernacular from the "literary comedians," who exploited its superficial novelties, neglected to listen to the language as it was really spoken, and turned it into a fraud composed of misspellings and malapropisms. The vernacular sorely needed rescuing again in the twentieth century, for it had degenerated into a routine device for conveying the quaintness and sentimentality of immigrants, urban proletariat, villagers, and farmers. The Chicago newspapermen Dunne and Ade had begun the task of refurbishing the vernacular and their work was completed by Ring Lardner, also a Chicago newspaperman. The world of professional sports in which Lardner spent his formative years as a reporter provided him with fresh characters, idiom, and situations. Lardner happily permitted an average baseball player to tell his own story in his own words. Though the letters in *You Know Me, Al* (1916) ironically revealed the petty meanness of Lardner's character, Lardner's irony was obscured by comic misspellings and mirth-provoking predicaments. But Lardner had little patience with mere amusement even though he became a well-paid professional humorist. In such sardonically humorous stories as "Some Like Them Cold" (1921), "The Golden Honeymoon" (1922), and "Haircut" (1925) he went on to reproduce ordinary American speech with brilliant fidelity. There was no longer any possibility of mistaking Lardner's intention. The brutally ironic contrast between the self-understanding of his characters and the significance of their behavior was designed to shatter the myth of American innocence with the same force that Lardner's friend F. Scott Fitzgerald displayed on his identical mission in *The Great Gatsby*.

TEXT: *The Love Nest and Other Stories*, New York, 1926. COMMENTARY: Donald Elder, *Ring Lardner*, New York, 1956.

HAIRCUT

I got another barber that comes over from Carterville and helps me out Saturdays, but the rest of the time I can get along all right alone. You can see for yourself that this ain't no New York City and besides that, the most of the boys works all day and don't have no leisure to drop in here and get themselves prettied up.

You're a newcomer, ain't you? I thought I hadn't seen you round before. I hope you like it good enough to stay. As I say, we ain't no New York City or Chicago, but we have pretty good times. Not as good, though, since Jim Kendall got killed. When he was alive, him and Hod Meyers used to keep this town in an uproar. I bet they was more laughin' done here than any town its size in America.

Jim was comical, and Hod was pretty near a match for him. Since Jim's gone, Hod tries to hold his end up just the same as ever, but it's tough goin' when you ain't got nobody to kind of work with.

They used to be plenty fun in here Saturdays. This place is jam-packed Saturdays, from four o'clock on. Jim and Hod would show up right after their supper, round six o'clock. Jim would set himself down in that big chair, nearest the blue spittoon. Whoever had been settin' in that chair, why they'd get up when Jim come in and give it to him.

You'd of thought it was a reserved seat like they have sometimes in a theayter. Hod would generally always stand or walk up and down, or some Saturdays, of course, he'd be settin' in this chair part of the time, gettin' a haircut.

Well, Jim would set there a w'ile without openin' his mouth only to spit, and then finally he'd say to me, "Whitey,"—my right name, that is, my right first name, is Dick, but everybody round here calls me Whitey— Jim would say, "Whitey, your nose looks like a rosebud tonight. You must of been drinkin' some of your aw de cologne."

So I'd say, "No, Jim, but you look like you'd been drinkin' somethin' of that kind or somethin' worse."

Jim would have to laugh at that, but then he'd speak up and say, "No, I ain't had nothin' to drink, but that ain't sayin' I wouldn't like somethin'. I wouldn't even mind if it was wood alcohol."

Then Hod Meyers would say, "Neither would your wife." That would set everybody to laughin' because Jim and his wife wasn't on very good terms. She'd of divorced him only they wasn't no chance to get alimony and she didn't have no way to take care of herself and the kids. She couldn't never understand Jim. He *was* kind of rough, but a good fella at heart.

Him and Hod had all kinds of sport with Milt Sheppard. I don't suppose you've seen Milt. Well, he's got an Adam's apple that looks more like a mushmelon. So I'd be shavin' Milt and when I'd start to shave down here on his neck, Hod would holler, "Hey, Whitey, wait a minute! Before you cut into it, let's make up a pool and see who can guess closest to the number of seeds."

And Jim would say, "If Milt hadn't of been so hoggish, he'd of ordered a half a cantaloupe instead of a whole one and it might not of stuck in his throat."

All the boys would roar at this and Milt himself would force a smile, though the joke was on him. Jim certainly was a card!

There's his shavin' mug, settin' on the shelf, right next to Charley Vail's. "Charles M. Vail." That's the druggist. He comes in regular for his shave, three times a week. And Jim's is the cup next to Charley's. "James H. Kendall." Jim won't need no shavin' mug no more, but I'll leave it there just the same for old time's sake. Jim certainly was a character!

Years ago, Jim used to travel for a canned goods concern over in Carterville. They sold canned goods. Jim had the whole northern half of the State and was on the road five days out of every week. He'd drop in here Saturdays and tell his experiences for that week. It was rich.

I guess he paid more attention to playin' jokes than makin' sales. Finally the concern let him out and he come right home here and told everybody he'd been fired instead of sayin' he'd resigned like most fellas would of.

It was a Saturday and the shop was full and Jim got up out of that chair and says, "Gentlemen, I got an important announcement to make. I been fired from my job."

Well, they asked him if he was in earnest and he said he was and nobody could think of nothin' to say till Jim finally broke the ice himself. He says, "I been sellin' canned goods and now I'm canned goods myself."

You see, the concern he'd been workin' for was a factory that made canned goods. Over in Carterville. And now Jim said he was canned himself. He was certainly a card!

Jim had a great trick that he used to play w'ile he was travelin'. For instance, he'd be ridin' on a train and they'd come to some little town like, well, like, we'll say, like Benton. Jim would look out the train window and read the signs on the stores.

For instance, they'd be a sign, "Henry Smith, Dry Goods." Well, Jim would write down the name and the name of the town and when he got to wherever he was goin' he'd mail back a postal card to Henry Smith at Benton and not sign no name to it, but he'd write on the card, well, somethin' like "Ask your wife about that book agent that spent the afternoon last week," or "Ask your Missus who kept her from gettin' lonesome the last time you was in Carterville." And he'd sign the card, "A Friend."

Of course, he never knew what really come of none of these jokes, but he could picture what *probably* happened and that was enough.

Jim didn't work very steady after he lost his position with the Carterville people. What he did earn, doin' odd jobs round town, why he spent pretty near all of it on gin and his family might of starved if the stores hadn't of carried them along. Jim's wife tried her hand at dressmakin', but they ain't nobody goin' to get rich makin' dresses in this town.

As I say, she'd of divorced Jim, only she seen that she couldn't support herself and the kids and she was always hopin' that some day Jim would cut out his habits and give her more than two or three dollars a week.

They was a time when she would go to whoever he was workin' for and ask them to give her his wages, but after she done this once or twice, he beat her to it by borrowin' most of his pay in advance. He told it all round town, how he had outfoxed his Missus. He certainly was a caution!

But he wasn't satisfied with just outwittin' her. He was sore the way she had acted, tryin' to grab off his pay. And he made up his mind he'd get even. Well, he waited till Evans's Circus was advertised to come to town. Then he told his wife and two kiddies that he was goin' to take them to the circus. The day of the circus, he told them he would get the tickets and meet them outside the entrance to the tent.

Well, he didn't have no intentions of bein' there or buyin' tickets or nothin'. He got full of gin and laid round Wright's poolroom all day. His wife and the kids waited and waited and of course he didn't show up. His wife didn't have a dime with her, or nowhere else, I guess. So she finally had to tell the kids it was all off and they cried like they wasn't never goin' to stop.

Well, it seems, w'ile they was cryin', Doc Stair came along and he asked what was the matter, but Mrs. Kendall was stubborn and wouldn't tell him, but the kids told him and he insisted on takin' them and their mother in the show. Jim found this out afterwards and it was one reason why he had it in for Doc Stair.

Doc Stair come here about a year and a half ago. He's a mighty handsome young fella and his clothes always look like he has them made to order. He goes to Detroit two or three times a year and w'ile he's there he must have a tailor take his measure and then make him a suit to order. They cost pretty near twice as much, but they fit a whole lot better than if you just bought them in a store.

For a w'ile everybody was wonderin' why a young doctor like Doc Stair should come to a town like this where we already got old Doc Gamble and Doc Foote that's both been here for years and all the practice in town was always divided between the two of them.

Then they was a story got round that Doc Stair's gal had throwed him over, a gal up in the Northern Peninsula somewheres, and the reason he come here was to hide himself away and forget it. He said himself that he thought they wasn't nothin' like general practice in a place like ours to fit a man to be a good all round doctor. And that's why he'd came.

Anyways, it wasn't long before he was makin' enough to live on, though they tell me that he never dubbed nobody for what they owed him, and the folks here certainly has got the owin' habit, even in my business. If I had all that was comin' to me for just shaves alone, I could go to Carterville and put up at the Mercer for a week and see a different picture every night. For instance, they's old George Purdy—but I guess I shouldn't ought to be gossipin'.

Well, last year, our coroner died, died of the flu. Ken Beatty, that was his name. He was the coroner. So they had to choose another man to be coroner in his place and they picked Doc Stair. He laughed at first and said he didn't want it, but they made him take it. It ain't no job that anybody would fight for and what a man makes out of it a year would just about buy seeds for their garden. Doc's the kind, though, that can't say no to nothin' if you keep at him long enough.

But I was goin' to tell you about a poor boy we got here in town—Paul Dickson. He fell out of a tree when he was about ten years old. Lit on his head and it done somethin' to him and he ain't never been right. No harm in him, but just silly. Jim Kendall used to call him cuckoo; that's a name Jim had for anybody that was off their head, only he called people's head their bean. That was another of his gags, callin' head bean and callin' crazy people cuckoo. Only poor Paul ain't crazy, but just silly.

You can imagine that Jim used to have all kinds of fun with Paul. He'd send him to the White Front Garage for a left-handed monkey wrench. Of course they ain't no such a thing as a left-handed monkey wrench.

And once we had a kind of a fair here and they was a baseball game between the fats and the leans and before the game started Jim called Paul over and sent him way down to Schrader's hardware store to get a key for the pitcher's box.

They wasn't nothin' in the way of gags that Jim couldn't think up, when he put his mind to it.

Poor Paul was always kind of suspicious of people, maybe on account of how Jim had kept foolin' him. Paul wouldn't have much to do with anybody only his own mother and Doc Stair and a girl here in town named Julie Gregg. That is, she ain't a girl no more, but pretty near thirty or over.

When Doc first come to town, Paul seemed to feel like here was a real friend and he hung round Doc's office most of the w'ile; the only time he wasn't there was when he'd go home to eat or sleep or when he seen Julie Gregg doin' her shoppin'.

When he looked out Doc's window and seen her, he'd run downstairs and join her and tag along with her to the different stores. The poor boy was crazy about Julie and she always treated him mighty nice and made him feel like he was welcome, though of course it wasn't nothin' but pity on her side.

Doc done all he could to improve Paul's mind and he told me once that he really thought the boy was gettin' better, that they was times when he was as bright and sensible as anybody else.

But I was goin' to tell you about Julie Gregg. Old Man Gregg was in the lumber business, but he got to drinkin' and lost the most of his money and when he died, he didn't leave nothin' but the house and just enough insurance for the girl to skimp along on.

Her mother was a kind of a half invalid and didn't hardly ever leave the house. Julie wanted to sell the place and move somewheres else after the old man died, but the mother said she was born here and would die here. It was tough on Julie, as the young people round this town—well, she's too good for them.

She's been away to school and Chicago and New York and different places and they ain't no subject she can't talk on, where you take the rest of the young folks here and you mention anything to them outside of Gloria Swanson or Tommy Meighan and they think you're delirious. Did you see Gloria in Wages of Virtue? You missed somethin'!

Well, Doc Stair hadn't been here more than a week when he come in one day to get shaved and I recognized who he was as he had been pointed out to me, so I told him about my old lady. She's been ailin' for a couple years and either Doc Gamble or Doc Foote, neither one, seemed to be helpin' her. So he said he would come out and see her, but if she was able to get out herself, it would be better to bring her to his office where he could make a completer examination.

So I took her to his office and w'ile I was waitin' for her in the reception room, in come Julie Gregg. When somebody comes in Doc Stair's office, they's a bell that rings in his inside office so as he can tell they's somebody to see him.

So he left my old lady inside and come out to the front office and that's the first time him and Julie met and I guess it was what they call love at first sight. But it wasn't fifty-fifty. This young fella was the slickest lookin' fella she'd ever seen in this town and she went wild over him. To him she was just a young lady that wanted to see the doctor.

She'd came on about the same business I had. Her mother had been doctorin' for years with Doc Gamble and Doc Foote and without no results. So she'd heard they was a new doc in town and decided to give him a try. He promised to call and see her mother that same day.

I said a minute ago that it was love at first sight on her part. I'm not only judgin' by how she acted afterwards but how she looked at him that first day in his office. I ain't no mind reader, but it was wrote all over her face that she was gone.

Now Jim Kendall, besides bein' a jokesmith and a pretty good drinker, well, Jim was quite a lady-killer. I guess he run pretty wild durin' the time he was on the road for them Carterville people, and besides that, he'd had a couple little affairs of the heart right here in town. As I say, his wife could of divorced him, only she couldn't.

But Jim was like the majority of men, and women, too, I guess. He wanted what he couldn't get. He wanted Julie Gregg and worked his head off tryin' to land her. Only he'd of said bean instead of head.

Well, Jim's habits and his jokes didn't appeal to Julie and of course he was a married man, so he didn't have no more chance than, well, than a rabbit. That's an expression of Jim's himself. When somebody didn't have no chance to get elected or somethin', Jim would always say they didn't have no more chance than a rabbit.

He didn't make no bones about how he felt. Right in here, more than once, in front of the whole crowd, he said he was stuck on Julie and anybody that could get her for him was welcome to his house and his wife and kids included. But she wouldn't have nothin' to do with him; wouldn't even speak to him on the street. He finally seen he wasn't gettin' nowheres with his usual line so he decided to try the rough stuff. He went right up to her house one evenin' and when she opened the door he forced his way in and grabbed her. But she broke loose and before he could stop her, she run in the next room and locked the door and phoned to Joe Barnes. Joe's the marshal. Jim could hear who she was phonin' to and he beat it before Joe got there.

Joe was an old friend of Julie's pa. Joe went to Jim the next day and told him what would happen if he ever done it again.

I don't know how the news of this little affair leaked out. Chances is that Joe Barnes told his wife and she told somebody else's wife and they told their husband. Anyways, it did leak out and Hod Meyers had the nerve to kid Jim about it, right here in this shop. Jim didn't deny nothin' and kind of laughed it off and said for us all to wait; that lots of people had tried to make a monkey out of him, but he always got even.

Meanw'ile everybody in town was wise to Julie's bein' wild mad over the Doc. I don't suppose she had any idear how her face changed when him and her was together; of course she couldn't of, or she'd of kept away from him. And she didn't know that we was all noticin' how many times she made excuses to go up to his office or pass it on the other side of the street and look up in his window to see if he was there. I felt sorry for her and so did most other people.

Hod Meyers kept rubbin' it into Jim about how the Doc had cut him out. Jim didn't pay no attention to the kiddin' and you could see he was plannin' one of his jokes.

One trick Jim had was the knack of changin' his voice. He could make you think he was a girl talkin' and he could mimic any man's voice. To show you how good he was along this line, I'll tell you the joke he played on me once.

You know, in most towns of any size, when a man is dead and needs a shave, why the barber that shaves him soaks him five dollars for the job; that is, he don't soak *him*, but whoever ordered the shave. I just charge three dollars because personally I don't mind much shavin' a dead person. They lay a whole lot stiller than live customers. The only thing is that you don't feel like talkin' to them and you get kind of lonesome.

Well, about the coldest day we ever had here, two years ago last winter, the phone rung at the house w'ile I was home to dinner and I answered the phone and it was a woman's voice and she said she was Mrs. John Scott and her husband was dead and would I come out and shave him.

Old John had always been a good customer of mine. But they live seven miles out in the country, on the Streeter road. Still I didn't see how I could say no.

So I said I would be there, but would have to come in a jitney and it might cost three or four dollars besides the price of the shave. So she, or the voice, it said that was all right, so I got Frank Abbott to drive me out to the place and when I got there, who should open the door but old John himself! He wasn't no more dead than, well, than a rabbit.

It didn't take no private detective to figure out who had played me this little joke. Nobody could of thought it up but Jim Kendall. He certainly was a card!

I tell you this incident just to show you how he could disguise his voice and make you believe it was somebody else talkin'. I'd of swore it was Mrs. Scott had called me. Anyways, some woman.

Well, Jim waited till he had Doc Stair's voice down pat; then he went after revenge.

He called Julie up on a night when he knew Doc was over in Carterville. She never questioned but what it was Doc's voice. Jim said he must see her that night; he couldn't wait no longer to tell her somethin'. She was all excited and told him to come to the house. But he said he was expectin' an important long distance call and wouldn't she please forget her manners for once and come to his office. He said they couldn't nothin' hurt her and nobody would see her and he just *must* talk to her a little w'ile. Well, poor Julie fell for it.

Doc always keeps a night light in his office, so it looked to Julie like they was somebody there.

Meanw'ile Jim Kendall had went to Wright's poolroom, where they was a whole gang amusin' themselves. The most of them had drank plenty of gin, and they was a rough bunch even when sober. They was always strong for Jim's jokes and when he told them to come with him and see some fun they give up their card games and pool games and followed along.

Doc's office is on the second floor. Right outside his door they's a flight of stairs leadin' to the floor above. Jim and his gang hid in the dark behind these stairs.

Well, Julie come up to Doc's door and rung the bell and they was nothin' doin'. She rung it again and she rung it seven or eight times. Then she tried the door and found it locked. Then Jim made some kind of a noise and she heard it and waited a minute, and then she says, "Is that you, Ralph?" Ralph is Doc's first name.

They was no answer and it must of came to her all of a sudden that she'd been bunked. She pretty near fell downstairs and the whole gang after her. They chased her all the way home, hollerin', "Is that you, Ralph?" and "Oh, Ralphie, dear, is that you?" Jim says he couldn't holler it himself, as he was laughin' too hard.

Poor Julie! She didn't show up here on Main Street for a long, long time afterward.

And of course Jim and his gang told everybody in town, everybody but Doc Stair. They was scared to tell him, and he might of never knowed only for Paul Dickson. The poor cuckoo, as Jim called him, he was here in the shop one night when Jim was still gloatin' yet over what he'd done to Julie. And Paul took in as much of it as he could understand and he run to Doc with the story.

It's a cinch Doc went up in the air and swore he'd make Jim suffer. But it was a kind of a delicate thing, because if it got out that he had beat Jim up, Julie was bound to hear of it and then she'd know that Doc knew and of course knowin' that he knew would make it worse for her than ever. He was goin' to do somethin', but it took a lot of figurin'.

Well, it was a couple days later when Jim was here in the shop again, and so was the cuckoo. Jim was goin' duck-shootin' the next day and had came in lookin' for Hod Meyers to go with him. I happened to know that Hod had went over to Carterville and wouldn't be home till the end of the week. So Jim said he hated to go alone and he guessed he would call it off. Then poor Paul spoke up and said if Jim would take him he would go along. Jim thought a w'ile and then he said, well, he guessed a half-wit was better than nothin'.

I suppose he was plottin' to get Paul out in the boat and play some joke on him, like pushin' him in the water. Anyways, he said Paul could go. He asked him had he ever shot a duck and Paul said no, he'd never even had a gun in his hands. So Jim said he could set in the boat and watch him and if he behaved himself, he might lend him his gun for a couple of shots. They made a date to meet in the mornin' and that's the last I seen of Jim alive.

Next mornin', I hadn't been open more than ten minutes when Doc Stair come in. He looked kind of nervous. He asked me had I seen Paul Dickson. I said no, but I knew where he was, out duck-shootin' with Jim Kendall. So Doc says that's what he had heard, and he couldn't understand it because Paul had told him he wouldn't never have no more to do with Jim as long as he lived.

He said Paul had told him about the joke Jim had played on Julie. He said Paul had asked him what he thought of the joke and the Doc had told him that anybody that would do a thing like that ought not to be let live.

I said it had been a kind of a raw thing, but Jim just couldn't resist no kind of a joke, no matter how raw. I said I thought he was all right at heart, but just bubblin' over with mischief. Doc turned and walked out.

At noon he got a phone call from old John Scott. The lake where Jim and Paul had went shootin' is on John's place. Paul had came runnin' up to the house a few minutes before and said they'd been an accident. Jim had shot a few ducks and then give the gun to Paul and told him to try his luck. Paul hadn't never handled a gun and he was nervous. He was shakin' so hard that he couldn't control the gun. He let fire and Jim sunk back in the boat, dead.

Doc Stair, bein' the coroner, jumped in Frank Abbott's flivver and rushed out to Scott's farm. Paul and old John was down on the shore of the lake. Paul had rowed the boat to shore, but they'd left the body in it, waitin' for Doc to come.

Doc examined the body and said they might as well fetch it back to town. They was no use leavin' it there or callin' a jury, as it was a plain case of accidental shootin'.

Personally I wouldn't never leave a person shoot a gun in the same boat I was in unless I was sure they knew somethin' about guns. Jim was a sucker to leave a new beginner have his gun, let alone a half-wit. It probably served Jim right, what he got. But still we miss him round here. He certainly was a card!

Comb it wet or dry?

T. S. Eliot (1888–   )

One of the major contributions of T. S. Eliot has been his demonstration that levity and sobriety are inseparable in profound works of literature. In making this clear Eliot accomplished for modern poetry what James Joyce had done for the modern novel. Most earlier American writers who had not been professional humorists were hesitant and defensive when attempting to link humor with "serious" themes, painfully aware that their culture would suspect them of latent triviality, of being "low," of being entertainers for the moment, of lacking the capacity to deal with the meaningful and the lofty. No such qualms troubled Eliot. His sense of his own high seriousness was buttressed by his learning in philosophy, literature, anthropology, and religion; influenced by Hawthorne and James, Eliot also found models for emulation in cultures other than the American and in centuries other than the nineteenth. Furthermore, Eliot was familiar with the theory of modern classical scholars and cultural anthropologists that elements which are found separately in Greek tragedy and Greek comedy respectively had earlier functioned together harmoniously in the ritual drama of Greek religion. The triumphant reunion of the diverged elements by Elizabethan poets and playwrights, particularly by Shakespeare and Donne, suggested to Eliot that their feat might be repeated in modern times with the identical means they had employed. Eliot's leap back into the seventeenth century thus made him in a sense a contemporary of the New England Puritans; his poems, as it happens, reveal an identical religious and moral intensity, elegiac sensibility, verbal playfulness (puns, words, coined paradoxes, and the like), penchant for the concrete detail, and intellectual depth. His capacity to deal with the phenomena of his own world was enhanced by his affinity for the ironic manner of the late nineteenth-century French poets Tristan Corbière and Jules Laforgue.

Eliot's earliest poems—those in *Prufrock and Other Observations* (1917) and *Poems* (1919)—subjected the ugly vulgarity and sterile gentility of Western civilization to laughter and derision. But poems such as "Mr. Apollinax" (1916) impressed many as being in the genial tradition of Oliver Wendell Holmes, and Eliot was mistakenly regarded as a skilled light versifier. The later publication of poems such as "The Waste Land" (1922) and *Sweeney Agonistes* (1932) brought about a re-evaluation of Eliot's poetic role. Now the humor was ignored and Eliot became solely a gloomy prophet of Western decline. There is humor as well as understandable impatience in the self-description of "Lines for Cuscuscaraway and Mirza Murad Ali Beg" (1933). Indeed Eliot was neither a light versifier nor a serious poet in the conventional meaning of either term.

His mind and sensibility had found expression in a poetry which was neither comic nor tragic, but both at once in a manner for which no term other than high humor seems adequate. The parody, burlesque, slang, musical comedy lyrics, bawdy allusions, satire, word play, and ludicrous shifts of time and scene in Eliot's poetry are some of the essential devices he has used to convey his profound view of man and his world.

TEXT: *Collected Poems, 1909–1935*, New York, 1936. COMMENTARY: Hugh Kenner, *The Invisible Poet: T. S. Eliot*, New York, 1959; F. O. Matthiessen, *The Achievement of T. S. Eliot*, 3d ed., New York, 1958; Leonard Unger, ed., *T. S. Eliot: A Selected Critique*, New York, 1948.

MR. APOLLINAX

Ω τῆς καινότητος. Ἡράκλεις, τῆς παραδοξολογίας. εὐμήχανος ἄνθρωπος.
LUCIAN

When Mr. Apollinax visited the United States
His laughter tinkled among the teacups.
I thought of Fragilion, that shy figure among the birch-trees,
And of Priapus in the shrubbery
Gaping at the lady in the swing.
In the palace of Mrs. Phlaccus, at Professor Channing-Cheetah's
He laughed like an irresponsible foetus.
His laughter was submarine and profound
Like the old man of the sea's
Hidden under coral islands
Where worried bodies of drowned men drift down in the green silence,
Dropping from fingers of surf.
I looked for the head of Mr. Apollinax rolling under a chair

Or grinning over a screen
With seaweed in its hair.
I heard the beat of centaur's hoofs over the hard turf
As his dry and passionate talk devoured the afternoon.
"He is a charming man"—"But after all what did he mean?"—
"His pointed ears. . . . He must be unbalanced,"—
"There was something he said that I might have challenged."
Of dowager Mrs. Phlaccus, and Professor and Mrs. Cheetah
I remember a slice of lemon, and a bitten macaroon.

LINES FOR CUSCUSCARAWAY AND MIRZA MURAD ALI BEG

How unpleasant to meet Mr. Eliot!
With his features of clerical cut,
And his brow so grim
And his mouth so prim
And his conversation, so nicely
Restricted to What Precisely
And If and Perhaps and But.
How unpleasant to meet Mr. Eliot!
With a bobtail cur
In a coat of fur
And a porpentine cat
And a wopsical hat:
How unpleasant to meet Mr. Eliot!
      (Whether his mouth be open or shut).

James Thurber (1894–1961)

One of the most distinguished professional humorists contributing to the reputation of the *New Yorker* magazine was James Thurber. Together with E. B. White, Ogden Nash, and S. J. Perelman, Thurber demonstrated that intelligence and knowledge can be assets rather than liabilities in the field of literary entertainment. He raptly contemplated myriad incongruities and frustrations of twentieth-century urban life, then recreated them with the bewildered amusement that is his hallmark. Thurber, to quote an admirer, T. S. Eliot, constructed "a form of humor which is also a way of saying something serious." Furthermore, Thurber was gifted with a keen ear for nuance and phrasing and a command of language which served him well in his parodies of writers such as Henry James and in his renditions of urban idioms. He could be forcefully ironic when unmasking sophisticated pretension and delicate when composing humorous fantasies for children. Thurber's range of humor and form—stories, plays, sketches, drawings, fables, parodies, and bemused studies of radio serials —brought him extensive popularity. Long interested in the stage, he collaborated with Elliott Nugent on the *Male Animal* (1940) and appeared on Broadway as an actor in the *Thurber Carnival* (1960). The universality of Thurber's genial humor was demonstrated when "The Catbird Seat" was filmed in England as *The Battle of the Sexes* and the scene of its comedy laid in Scotland.

TEXT: *The Thurber Carnival*, New York, 1945.

THE CATBIRD SEAT

Mr. Martin bought the pack of Camels on Monday night in the most crowded cigar store on Broadway. It was theater time and seven or eight men were buying cigarettes. The clerk didn't even glance at Mr. Martin, who put the pack in his overcoat pocket and went out. If any of the staff at F & S had seen him buy the cigarettes, they would have been astonished, for it was generally known that Mr. Martin did not smoke, and never had. No one saw him.

It was just a week to the day since Mr. Martin had decided to rub out Mrs. Ulgine Barrows. The term "rub out" pleased him because it suggested nothing more than the correction of an error—in this case an error of Mr. Fitweiler. Mr. Martin had spent each night of the past week working out his plan and examining it. As he walked home now he went over it again. For the hundredth time he resented the element of imprecision, the margin of guesswork that entered into the business. The project as he had worked it out was casual and bold, the risks were considerable. Something might go wrong anywhere along the line. And therein lay the cunning of his scheme. No one would ever see in it the cautious, painstaking hand of Erwin Martin, head of the filing department at F & S, of whom Mr. Fitweiler had once said, "Man is fallible but Martin isn't." No one would see his hand, that is, unless it were caught in the act.

Sitting in his apartment, drinking a glass of milk, Mr. Martin reviewed his case against Mrs. Ulgine Barrows, as he had every night for seven nights. He began at the beginning. Her quacking voice and braying laugh had first profaned the halls of F & S on March 7, 1941 (Mr. Martin had a head for dates). Old Roberts, the personnel chief, had introduced her as the newly appointed special adviser to the president of the firm, Mr. Fitweiler. The woman had appalled Mr. Martin instantly, but he hadn't shown it. He had given her his dry hand, a look of studious concentration, and a faint smile. "Well," she had said, looking at the papers on his desk, "are you lifting the oxcart out of the ditch?" As Mr. Martin recalled that moment, over his milk, he squirmed slightly. He must keep his mind on her crimes as a special adviser, not on her peccadillos as a personality. This he found difficult to do, in spite of entering an objection and sustaining it. The faults of the woman as a woman kept chattering on in his mind like an unruly witness. She had, for almost two years now, baited him. In the halls, in the elevator, even in his own office, into which she romped now and then like a circus horse, she was constantly shouting these silly questions at him. "Are you lifting the oxcart out of the ditch? Are you tearing up the pea patch? Are you hollering down the rain barrel? Are you scraping around the bottom of the pickle barrel? Are you sitting in the catbird seat?"

It was Joey Hart, one of Mr. Martin's two assistants, who had explained what the gibberish meant. "She must be a Dodger fan," he had said. "Red Barber announces the Dodger games over the radio and he uses those expressions—picked 'em up down South." Joey had gone on to explain one or two. "Tearing up the pea patch" meant going on a rampage; "sitting in the catbird seat" meant sitting pretty, like a batter with three balls and no strikes on him. Mr. Martin dismissed all this with an effort. It had been annoying, it had driven him near to distraction, but he was too solid a man to be moved to murder by anything so childish. It was fortunate, he reflected as he passed on to the important charges against Mrs. Barrows, that he had stood up under it so well. He had maintained always an outward appearance of polite tolerance. "Why, I even believe you like the woman," Miss Paird, his other assistant, had once said to him. He had simply smiled.

A gavel rapped in Mr. Martin's mind and the case proper was resumed.

Mrs. Ulgine Barrows stood charged with willful, blatant, and persistent attempts to destroy the efficiency and system of F & S. It was competent, material, and relevant to review her advent and rise to power. Mr. Martin had got the story from Miss Paird, who seemed always able to find things out. According to her, Mrs. Barrows had met Mr. Fitweiler at a party, where she had rescued him from the embraces of a powerfully built drunken man who had mistaken the president of F & S for a famous retired Middle Western football coach. She had led him to a sofa and somehow worked upon him a monstrous magic. The aging gentleman had jumped to the conclusion there and then that this was a woman of singular attainments, equipped to bring out the best in him and in the firm. A week later he had introduced her into F & S as his special adviser. On that day confusion got its foot in the door. After Miss Tyson, Mr. Brundage, and Mr. Bartlett had been fired and Mr. Munson had taken his hat and stalked out, mailing in his resignation later, old Roberts had been emboldened to speak to Mr. Fitweiler. He mentioned that Mr. Munson's department had been "a little disrupted" and hadn't they perhaps better resume the old system there? Mr. Fitweiler had said certainly not. He had the greatest faith in Mrs. Barrows' ideas. "They require a little seasoning, a little seasoning, is all," he had added. Mr. Roberts had given it up. Mr. Martin reviewed in detail all the changes wrought by Mrs. Barrows. She had begun chipping at the cornices of the firm's edifice and now she was swinging at the foundation stones with a pickaxe.

Mr. Martin came now, in his summing up, to the afternoon of Monday, November 2, 1942—just one week ago. On that day, at 3 P.M., Mrs. Barrows had bounced into his office. "Boo!" she had yelled. "Are you scraping around the bottom of the pickle barrel?" Mr. Martin had looked at her from under his green eyeshade, saying nothing. She had begun to wander about the office, taking it in with her great, popping eyes. "Do you really need *all* these filing cabinets?" she had demanded suddenly. Mr. Martin's heart had jumped. "Each of these files," he had said, keeping his voice even, "plays an indispensable part in the system of F & S." She brayed at him, "Well, don't tear up the pea patch!" and gone to the door. From there she had bawled, "But you sure have got a lot of fine scrap in here!" Mr. Martin could no longer doubt that the finger was on his beloved department. Her pickaxe was on the upswing, poised for the first blow. It had not come yet; he had received no blue memo from the enchanted Mr. Fitweiler bearing nonsensical instructions deriving from the obscene woman. But there was no doubt in Mr. Martin's mind that one would be forthcoming. He must act quickly. Already a precious week had gone by. Mr. Martin stood up in his living room, still holding his milk glass. "Gentlemen of the jury," he said to himself. "I demand the death penalty for this horrible person."

The next day Mr. Martin followed his routine, as usual. He polished his glasses more often and once sharpened an already sharp pencil, but not even Miss Paird noticed. Only once did he catch sight of his victim; she swept past him in the hall with a patronizing "Hi!" At five-thirty he walked home, as usual, and had a glass of milk, as usual. He had never drunk anything stronger in his life—unless you could count ginger ale. The late Sam Schlosser, the S of F & S, had praised Mr. Martin at a staff meeting several years before for his temperate habits. "Our most efficient worker neither drinks nor smokes," he had said. "The results speak for themselves." Mr. Fitweiler had sat by, nodding approval.

Mr. Martin was still thinking about that red-letter day as he walked over to the Schrafft's on Fifth Avenue near Forty-sixth Street. He got there, as he always did, at eight o'clock. He finished his dinner and the financial page of the *Sun* at a quarter to nine, as he always did. It was his custom after dinner to take a walk. This time he walked down Fifth Avenue at a casual pace. His gloved hands felt moist and warm, his forehead cold. He transferred the Camels from his overcoat to a jacket pocket. He wondered, as he did so, if they did not represent an unnecessary note of strain. Mrs. Barrows smoked only Luckies. It was his idea to puff a few puffs on a Camel (after the rubbing-out), stub it out in the ashtray holding her lipstick-stained Luckies, and thus drag a small red herring across the trail. Perhaps it was not a good idea. It would take time. He might even choke, too loudly.

Mr. Martin had never seen the house on West Twelfth Street where Mrs. Barrows lived, but he had a clear enough picture of it. Fortunately, she had bragged to everybody about her ducky first-floor apartment in the perfectly darling three-story red-brick. There would be no doorman or other attendants; just the tenants of the second and third floors. As he walked along, Mr. Martin realized that he would get there before nine-thirty. He had considered walking north on Fifth Avenue from Schrafft's to a point from which it would take him until ten o'clock to reach the house. At that hour people were less likely to be coming in or going out. But the procedure would have made an awkward loop in the straight thread of his casualness, and he had abandoned it. It was impossible to figure when people would be entering or leaving the house, anyway. There was a great risk at any hour. If he ran into anybody, he would simply have to place the rubbing-out of Ulgine Barrows in the inactive file forever. The same thing would hold true if there were someone in her apartment. In that case he would just say that he had been passing by, recognized her charming house and thought to drop in.

It was eighteen minutes after nine when Mr. Martin turned into Twelfth Street. A man passed him, and a man and a woman talking. There was no one within fifty paces when he came to the house, halfway down the block. He was up the steps and in the small vestibule in no time, pressing the bell under the card that said "Mrs. Ulgine Barrows." When the clicking in the lock started, he jumped forward against the door. He got inside fast, closing the door behind him. A bulb in a lantern hung from the hall ceiling on a chain seemed to give monstrously bright light. There was nobody on the stair, which went up ahead of him along the left wall. A door opened down the hall in the wall on the right. He went toward it swiftly, on tiptoe.

"Well, for God's sake, look who's here!" bawled Mrs. Barrows, and her braying laugh rang out like the report of a shotgun. He rushed past her like a football tackle, bumping her. "Hey, quit shoving!" she said, closing the door behind them. They were in her living room, which seemed to Mr. Martin to be lighted by a hundred lamps. "What's after you?" she said. "You're as jumpy as a goat." He found he was unable to speak. His heart was wheezing in his throat. "I—yes," he finally brought out. She was jabbering and laughing as she started to help him off with his coat. "No, no," he said. "I'll put it here." He took it off and put it on a chair near the door. "Your hat and gloves, too," she said. "You're in a lady's house." He put his hat on top of the coat. Mrs. Barrows seemed larger than he had thought. He kept his gloves on. "I was passing by," he said. "I recognized—is there anyone here?" She laughed louder than ever. "No," she said, "we're all alone. You're as white as a sheet, you funny man. Whatever *has* come over you? I'll mix you a toddy." She started toward a door across the room. "Scotch-and-soda be all right? But say, you don't drink, do you?" She turned and gave him her amused look. Mr. Martin pulled himself together. "Scotch-and-soda will be all right," he heard himself say. He could hear her laughing in the kitchen.

Mr. Martin looked quickly around the living room for the weapon. He had counted on finding one there. There were andirons and a poker and something in a corner that looked like an Indian club. None of them would do. It couldn't be that way. He began to pace around. He came to a desk. On it lay a metal paper knife with an ornate handle. Would it be sharp enough? He reached for it and knocked over a small brass jar. Stamps spilled out of it and it fell to the floor with a clatter. "Hey," Mrs. Barrows yelled from the kitchen, "are you tearing up the pea patch?" Mr. Martin gave a strange laugh. Picking up the knife, he tried its point against his left wrist. It was blunt. It wouldn't do.

When Mrs. Barrows reappeared, carrying two highballs, Mr. Martin, standing there with his gloves on, became acutely conscious of the fantasy he had wrought. Cigarettes in his pocket, a drink prepared for him—it was all too grossly improbable. It was more than that; it was impossible. Somewhere in the back of his mind a vague idea stirred, sprouted. "For heaven's sake, take off those gloves," said Mrs. Barrows. "I always wear them in the house," said Mr. Martin. The idea began to bloom, strange and wonderful. She put the glasses on a coffee table in front of a sofa and sat on the sofa. "Come over here, you odd little man," she said. Mr. Martin went over and sat beside her. It was difficult getting a cigarette out of the pack of Camels, but he managed it. She held a match for him, laughing. "Well," she said, handing him his drink, "this is perfectly marvelous. You with a drink and cigarette."

Mr. Martin puffed, not too awkwardly, and took a gulp of the highball. "I drink and smoke all the time," he said. He clinked his glass against hers. "Here's nuts to that old windbag, Fitweiler," he said, and gulped again. The stuff tasted awful, but he made no grimace. "Really, Mr. Martin," she said, her voice and posture changing, "you are insulting our employer." Mrs. Barrows was now all special adviser to the president. "I am preparing a bomb," said Mr. Martin, "which will blow the old goat higher than hell." He had only had a little of the drink, which was not strong. It couldn't be that. "Do you take dope or something?" Mrs. Barrows asked coldly. "Heroin," said Mr. Martin. "I'll be coked to the gills when I bump that old buzzard off." "Mr. Martin!" she shouted, getting to her feet. "That will be all of that. You must go at once." Mr. Martin took another swallow of his drink. He tapped his cigarette out in the ashtray and put the pack of Camels on the coffee table. Then he got up. She stood glaring at him. He walked over and put on his hat and coat. "Not a word about this," he said, and laid an index finger against his lips. All Mrs. Barrows could bring out was "Really!" Mr. Martin put his hand on the doorknob. "I'm sitting in the catbird seat," he said. He stuck his tongue out at her and left. Nobody saw him go.

Mr. Martin got to his apartment, walking, well before eleven. No one saw him go in. He had two glasses of milk after brushing his teeth, and he felt elated. It wasn't tipsiness, because he hadn't been tipsy. Anyway, the walk had worn off all effects of the whisky. He got in bed and read a magazine for a while. He was asleep before midnight.

Mr. Martin got to the office at eight-thirty the next morning, as usual. At a quarter to nine, Ulgine Barrows, who had never before arrived at work before ten, swept into his office. "I'm reporting to Mr. Fitweiler now!" she shouted. "If he turns you over to the police, it's no more than you deserve!" Mr. Martin gave her a look of shocked surprise. "I beg your pardon?" he said. Mrs. Barrows snorted and bounced out of the room, leaving Miss Paird and Joey Hart staring after her. "What's the matter with that old devil now?" asked Miss Paird. "I have no idea," said Mr. Martin, resuming his work. The other two looked at him and then at each other. Miss Paird got up and went out. She walked slowly past the closed door of Mr. Fitweiler's office. Mrs. Barrows was yelling inside, but she was not braying. Miss Paird could not hear what the woman was saying. She went back to her desk.

Forty-five minutes later, Mrs. Barrows left the president's office and went into her own, shutting the door. It wasn't until half an hour later that Mr. Fitweiler sent for Mr. Martin. The head of the filing department, neat, quiet, attentive, stood in front of the old man's desk. Mr. Fitweiler was pale and nervous. He took his glasses off and twiddled them. He made a small, bruffing sound in his throat. "Martin," he said, "you have been with us more than twenty years." "Twenty-two, sir," said Mr. Martin. "In that time," pursued the president, "your work and your—uh—manner have been exemplary." "I trust so, sir," said Mr. Martin. "I have understood, Martin," said Mr. Fitweiler, "that you have never taken a drink or smoked." "That is correct, sir," said Mr. Martin. "Ah, yes." Mr. Fitweiler polished his glasses. "You may describe what you did after leaving the office yesterday, Martin," he said. Mr. Martin allowed less than a second for his bewildered pause. "Certainly, sir," he said. "I walked home. Then I went to Schrafft's for dinner. Afterward I walked home again. I went to bed early, sir, and read a magazine for a while. I was asleep before eleven." "Ah, yes," said Mr. Fitweiler again. He was silent for a moment, searching for the proper words to say to the head of the filing department. "Mrs. Barrows," he said finally, "Mrs. Barrows has worked hard, Martin, very hard. It grieves me to report that she has suffered a severe breakdown. It has taken the form of a persecution complex accompanied by distressing hallucinations." "I am very sorry, sir," said Mr. Martin. "Mrs. Barrows is under the delusion," continued Mr. Fitweiler, "that you visited her last evening and behaved yourself in an—uh—unseemly manner." He raised his hand to silence Mr. Martin's little pained outcry. "It is the nature of these psychological diseases," Mr. Fitweiler said, "to fix upon the least likely and most innocent party as the —uh—source of persecution. These matters are not for the lay mind to grasp, Martin. I've just had my psychiatrist, Dr. Fitch, on the phone. He would not, of course, commit himself, but he made enough generalizations to substantiate my suspicions. I suggested to Mrs. Barrows when she had completed her—uh—story to me this morning, that she visit Dr. Fitch, for I suspected a condition at once. She flew, I regret to say, into a rage, and demanded—uh—requested that I call you on the carpet. You may not know, Martin, but Mrs. Barrows had planned a reorganization of your department—subject to my approval, of course, subject to my approval. This brought you, rather than anyone else, to her mind—but again that is a phenomenon for Dr. Fitch and not for us. So, Martin, I am afraid Mrs. Barrows' usefulness here is at an end." "I am dreadfully sorry, sir," said Mr. Martin.

It was at this point that the door to the office blew open with the suddenness of a gas-main explosion and Mrs. Barrows catapulted through it. "Is the little rat denying it?" she screamed. "He can't get away with that!" Mr. Martin got up and moved discreetly to a point beside Mr. Fitweiler's chair. "You drank and smoked at my apartment," she bawled at Mr. Martin, "and you know it! You called Mr. Fitweiler an old windbag and said you were going to blow him up when you got coked to the gills on your heroin!" She stopped yelling to catch her breath and a new glint came into her popping eyes. "If you weren't such a drab, ordinary little man," she said, "I'd think you'd planned it all. Sticking your tongue out, saying you were sitting in the catbird seat, because you thought no one would believe me when I told it! My God, it's really too perfect!" She brayed loudly and hysterically, and the fury was on her again. She glared at Mr. Fitweiler. "Can't you see how he has tricked us, you old fool? Can't you see his little game?" But Mr. Fitweiler had been surreptitiously pressing all the buttons under the top of his desk and employees of F & S began pouring into the room. "Stockton," said Mr. Fitweiler, "you and Fishbein will take Mrs. Barrows to her home. Mrs. Powell, you will go with them." Stockton, who had played a little football in high school, blocked Mrs. Barrows as she made for Mr. Martin. It took him and Fishbein together to force her out of the door into the hall, crowded with stenographers and office boys. She was still screaming imprecations at Mr. Martin, tangled and contradictory imprecations. The hubbub finally died out down the corridor.

"I regret that this has happened," said Mr. Fitweiler. "I shall ask you to dismiss it from your mind, Martin." "Yes, sir," said Mr. Martin, anticipating his chief's "That will be all" by moving to the door. "I will dismiss it." He went out and shut the door, and his step was light and quick in the hall. When he entered his department he had slowed down to his customary gait, and he walked quietly across the room to the W20 file, wearing a look of studious concentration.

E. E. Cummings (1894–   )

The most exciting humorous poet in twentieth-century America has been E. E. Cummings. Others have also written parodies and satires, mocked the corruption of men and institutions and the fallacies of ideological stereotypes, played with words and with typographical conventions. None have been as gayly earnest, as vividly lyrical, as determined as Cummings to exemplify the joyousness of life when living is a happy adventure of fresh emotional and intellectual discovery. What in other writers often seems to be mere cynicism is in Cummings deeply responsible feeling and thought. He is unwilling to wear anybody else's blinkers; for example, he will not meekly accept conventional grammar and punctuation, preferring to examine them analytically in his poems in order to test their capacity to hinder or advance the development of individual awareness. A profoundly meaningful humor is to be found in his prose and plays as well.

TEXT: *Collected Poems*, New York, 1938. COMMENTARY: Charles Norman, *The Magic Maker: E. E. Cummings*, New York, 1958.

58

here is little Effie's head
whose brains are made of gingerbread
when the judgment day comes
God will find six crumbs

stooping by the coffinlid
waiting for something to rise
as the other somethings did—
you imagine His surprise

bellowing through the general noise
Where is Effie who was dead?
—to God in a tiny voice,
i am may the first crumb said

whereupon its fellow five
crumbs chuckled as if they were alive
and number two took up the song,
might i'm called and did no wrong

cried the third crumb, i am should
and this is my little sister could
with our big brother who is would
don't punish us for we were good;

and the last crumb with some shame
whispered unto God, my name
is must and with the others i've
been Effie who isn't alive

just imagine it I say
God amid a monstrous din
watch your step and follow me
stooping by Effie's little, in

(want a match or can you see?)
which the six subjunctive crumbs
twitch like mutilated thumbs:
picture His peering biggest whey

coloured face on which a frown
puzzles, but I know the way—
(nervously Whose eyes approve
the blessed while His ears are crammed

with the strenuous music of
the innumerable capering damned)
—staring wildly up and down
the here we are now judgment day

cross the threshold have no dread
lift the sheet back in this way.
here is little Effie's head
whose brains are made of gingerbread

F. Scott Fitzgerald (1896–1940)

The talent of F. Scott Fitzgerald at its best is found in *The Great Gatsby* (1925). There, brought together in one rich and carefully polished whole, are the effects which separately dominated many of the fine stories he wrote before and after *The Great Gatsby:* the grotesque fantasy of "The Curious Case of Benjamin Button" (1922), the science-fiction satire of "The Diamond as Big as the Ritz" (1922), the tragic irony of "Absolution" (1924), the light comedy of "The Baby Party" (1925), the poignancy of "Babylon Revisited" (1931), and the amusing, ironic mis-understanding of "Three Hours Between Planes" (1941). For a variety of reasons Fitzgerald never managed to continue his best qualities again in a novel after *The Great Gatsby*, neither in the "serious" *Tender Is the Night* (1934) nor in the unfinished *Last Tycoon*. That the profound and almost ruthless humor of *The Great Gatsby* nevertheless remained an in-trinsic possession of Fitzgerald's, even if it never reappeared again so fully, may be seen in the articles, notebooks, and letters published posthumously in *The Crack-Up* (1945). After Fitzgerald's close friend Ring Lardner had finished reading the page proofs of *The Great Gatsby*, he singled out the second chapter as one of the two sections which had impressed him most. The grotesquely fantastic eyes, the wasteland of ashes, the brutal, barbaric, and rich Buchanan, the vulgarity and ineptitude of the lower classes, and the uncomfortably comic party in Buchanan's love nest are a savagely ironic commentary upon post-World War I America. Not even the acquiescent narrator, Nick Carraway, is spared Fitzgerald's lash, for Carraway's failure to judge events and persons is a tacit ironic declaration that none of those in the novel have been spared from moral bankruptcy.

TEXT: *The Great Gatsby*, New York, 1958. COMMENTARY: Arthur Mizener, *The Far Side of Paradise: A Biography of F. Scott Fitzgerald*, Boston, Mass., 1951; *F. Scott Fitzgerald: The Man and His Work*, ed. Alfred Kazin, Cleveland, O., 1951; James E. Miller, *The Fictional Technique of Scott Fitzgerald*, The Hague, 1957.

A PARTY AT THE LOVE NEST

CHAPTER II

About half way between West Egg and New York the motor road hastily joins the railroad and runs beside it for a quarter of a mile, so as to shrink away from a certain desolate area of land. This is a valley of ashes—a fantastic farm where ashes grow like wheat into ridges and hills and grotesque gardens; where ashes take the forms of houses and chimneys and rising smoke and, finally, with a transcendent effort, of men who move dimly and already crumbling through the powdery air. Occasionally a line of gray cars crawls along an invisible track, gives out a ghastly creak, and comes to rest, and immediately the ash-gray men swarm up with leaden spades and stir up an impenetrable cloud, which screens their obscure operations from your sight.

But above the gray land and the spasms of bleak dust which drift endlessly over it, you perceive, after a moment, the eyes of Doctor T. J. Eckleburg. The eyes of Doctor T. J. Eckleburg are blue and gigantic— their retinas are one yard high. They look out of no face, but, instead, from a pair of enormous yellow spectacles which pass over a non-existent nose. Evidently some wild wag of an oculist set them there to fatten his practice in the borough of Queens, and then sank down himself into eternal blindness, or forgot them and moved away. But his eyes, dimmed a little by many paintless days under sun and rain, brood on over the solemn dumping ground.

The valley of ashes is bounded on one side by a small foul river, and, when the drawbridge is up to let barges through, the passengers on waiting trains can stare at the dismal scene for as long as half an hour. There is always a halt there of at least a minute, and it was because of this that I first met Tom Buchanan's mistress.

The fact that he had one was insisted upon wherever he was known. His acquaintances resented the fact that he turned up in popular restaurants with her and, leaving her at a table, sauntered about, chatting with whomsoever he knew. Though I was curious to see her, I had no desire to meet her—but I did. I went up to New York with Tom on the train one afternoon and when we stopped by the ashheaps he jumped to his feet and, taking hold of my elbow, literally forced me from the car.

"We're getting off," he insisted. "I want you to meet my girl."

I think he'd tanked up a good deal at luncheon, and his determination to have my company bordered on violence. The supercilious assumption was that on Sunday afternoon I had nothing better to do.

I followed him over a low whitewashed railroad fence, and we walked back a hundred yards along the road under Doctor Eckleburg's persistent stare. The only building in sight was a small block of yellow brick sitting on the edge of the waste land, a sort of compact Main Street ministering to it, and contiguous to absolutely nothing. One of the three shops it contained was for rent and another was an all-night restaurant, approached by a trail of ashes; the third was a garage—*Repairs.* GEORGE B. WILSON. *Cars bought and sold.*—and I followed Tom inside.

The interior was unprosperous and bare; the only car visible was the dust-covered wreck of a Ford which crouched in a dim corner. It had occurred to me that this shadow of a garage must be a blind, and that sumptuous and romantic apartments were concealed overhead, when the proprietor himself appeared in the door of an office, wiping his hands on a piece of waste. He was a blond, spiritless man, anæmic, and faintly handsome. When he saw us a damp gleam of hope sprang into his light blue eyes.

"Hello, Wilson, old man," said Tom, slapping him jovially on the shoulder. "How's business?"

"I can't complain," answered Wilson unconvincingly. "When are you going to sell me that car?"

"Next week; I've got my man working on it now."

"Works pretty slow, don't he?"

"No, he doesn't," said Tom coldly. "And if you feel that way about it, maybe I'd better sell it somewhere else after all."

"I don't mean that," explained Wilson quickly. "I just meant——"

His voice faded off and Tom glanced impatiently around the garage. Then I heard footsteps on a stairs, and in a moment the thickish figure of a woman blocked out the light from the office door. She was in the middle thirties, and faintly stout, but she carried her surplus flesh sensuously as some women can. Her face, above a spotted dress of dark blue crêpe-de-chine, contained no facet or gleam of beauty, but there was an immediately perceptible vitality about her as if the nerves of her body were continually smouldering. She smiled slowly and, walking through her husband as if he were a ghost, shook hands with Tom, looking him flush in the eye. Then she wet her lips, and without turning around spoke to her husband in a soft, coarse voice:

"Get some chairs, why don't you, so somebody can sit down."

"Oh, sure," agreed Wilson hurriedly, and went toward the little office mingling immediately with the cement color of the walls. A white ashen dust veiled his dark suit and his pale hair as it veiled everything in the vicinity—except his wife, who moved close to Tom.

"I want to see you," said Tom intently. "Get on the next train."

"All right."

"I'll meet you by the news-stand on the lower level."

She nodded and moved away from him just as George Wilson emerged with two chairs from his office door.

We waited for her down the road and out of sight. It was a few days before the Fourth of July, and a gray, scrawny Italian child was setting torpedoes in a row along the railroad track.

"Terrible place, isn't it," said Tom, exchanging a frown with Doctor Eckleburg.

"Awful."

"It does her good to get away."

"Doesn't her husband object?"

"Wilson? He thinks she goes to see her sister in New York. He's so dumb he doesn't know he's alive."

So Tom Buchanan and his girl and I went up together to New York—

or not quite together, for Mrs. Wilson sat discreetly in another car. Tom deferred that much to the sensibilities of those East Eggers who might be on the train.

She had changed her dress to a brown figured muslin, which stretched tight over her rather wide hips as Tom helped her to the platform in New York. At the newsstand she bought a copy of *Town Tattle* and a moving-picture magazine, and in the station drug-store some cold cream and a small flask of perfume. Up-stairs, in the solemn echoing drive she let four taxicabs drive away before she selected a new one, lavender-colored with gray upholstery, and in this we slid out from the mass of the station into the glowing sunshine. But immediately she turned sharply from the window and, leaning forward, tapped on the front glass.

"I want to get one of those dogs," she said earnestly. "I want to get one for the apartment. They're nice to have—a dog."

We backed up to a gray old man who bore an absurd resemblance to John D. Rockefeller. In a basket swung from his neck cowered a dozen very recent puppies of an indeterminate breed.

"What kind are they?" asked Mrs. Wilson eagerly, as he came to the taxi-window.

"All kinds. What kind do you want, lady?"

"I'd like to get one of those police dogs; I don't suppose you got that kind?"

The man peered doubtfully into the basket, plunged in his hand and drew one up, wriggling, by the back of the neck.

"That's no police dog," said Tom.

"No, it's not exactly a *police* dog," said the man with disappointment in his voice. "It's more of an Airedale." He passed his hand over the brown washrag of a back. "Look at that coat. Some coat. That's a dog that'll never bother you with catching cold."

"I think it's cute," said Mrs. Wilson enthusiastically. "How much is it?"

"That dog?" He looked at it admiringly. "That dog will cost you ten dollars."

The Airedale—undoubtedly there was an Airedale concerned in it somewhere, though its feet were startlingly white—changed hands and settled down into Mrs. Wilson's lap, where she fondled the weather-proof coat with rapture.

"Is it a boy or a girl?" she asked delicately.

"That dog? That dog's a boy."

"It's a bitch," said Tom decisively. "Here's your money. Go and buy ten more dogs with it."

We drove over to Fifth Avenue, so warm and soft, almost pastoral, on the summer Sunday afternoon that I wouldn't have been surprised to see a great flock of white sheep turn the corner.

"Hold on," I said, "I have to leave you here."

"No, you don't," interposed Tom quickly. "Myrtle'll be hurt if you don't come up to the apartment. Won't you, Myrtle?"

"Come on," she urged. "I'll telephone my sister Catherine. She's said to be very beautiful by people who ought to know."

"Well, I'd like to, but——"

We went on, cutting back again over the Park toward the West Hundreds. At 158th Street the cab stopped at one slice in a long white cake of apartment-houses. Throwing a regal homecoming glance around the neighborhood, Mrs. Wilson gathered up her dog and her other purchases, and went haughtily in.

"I'm going to have the McKees come up," she announced as we rose in the elevator. "And, of course, I got to call up my sister, too."

The apartment was on the top floor—a small living-room, a small dining-room, a small bedroom, and a bath. The living-room was crowded to the doors with a set of tapestried furniture entirely too large for it, so that to move about was to stumble continually over scenes of ladies swinging in the gardens of Versailles. The only picture was an over-enlarged photograph, apparently a hen sitting on a blurred rock. Looked at from a distance, however, the hen resolved itself into a bonnet, and the countenance of a stout old lady beamed down into the room. Several old copies of *Town Tattle* lay on the table together with a copy of *Simon Called Peter*, and some of the small scandal magazines of Broadway. Mrs. Wilson was first concerned with the dog. A reluctant elevator-boy went for a box full of straw and some milk, to which he added on his own initiative a tin of large, hard dog-biscuits—one of which decomposed alphabetically in the saucer of milk all afternoon. Meanwhile Tom brought out a bottle of whiskey from a locked bureau door.

I have been drunk just twice in my life, and the second time was that afternoon; so everything that happened has a dim, hazy cast over it, although until after eight o'clock the apartment was full of cheerful sun. Sitting on Tom's lap Mrs. Wilson called up several people on the telephone; then there were no cigarettes, and I went out to buy some at the drugstore on the corner. When I came back they had disappeared, so I sat down discreetly in the living-room and read a chapter of *Simon Called Peter*—either it was terrible stuff or the whiskey distorted things, because it didn't make any sense to me.

Just as Tom and Myrtle (after the first drink Mrs. Wilson and I called each other by our first names) reappeared, company commenced to arrive at the apartment-door.

The sister, Catherine, was a slender, worldly girl of about thirty, with a solid, sticky bob of red hair, and a complexion powdered milky white. Her eyebrows had been plucked and then drawn on again at a more rakish angle but the efforts of nature toward the restoration of the old alignment gave a blurred air to her face. When she moved about there was an incessant clicking as innumerable pottery bracelets jingled up and down upon her arms. She came in with such a proprietary haste, and looked around so possessively at the furniture that I wondered if she lived here. But when I asked her she laughed immoderately, repeated my question aloud, and told me she lived with a girl friend at a hotel.

Mr. McKee was a pale, feminine man from the flat below. He had just shaved, for there was a white spot of lather on his cheekbone, and he was most respectful in his greeting to every one in the room. He informed me that he was in the "artistic game," and I gathered later that he was a photographer and had made the dim enlargement of Mrs. Wilson's mother which hovered like an ectoplasm on the wall. His wife was shrill, languid, handsome, and horrible. She told me with pride that her husband had photographed her a hundred and twenty-seven times since they had been married.

Mrs. Wilson had changed her costume some time before, and was now attired in an elaborate afternoon dress of cream-colored chiffon, which gave out a continual rustle as she swept about the room. With the influence of the dress her personality had also undergone a change. The intense vitality that had been so remarkable in the garage was converted into impressive hauteur. Her laughter, her gestures, her assertions became more violently affected moment by moment, and as she expanded the room grew smaller around her, until she seemed to be revolving on a noisy, creaking pivot through the smoky air.

"My dear," she told her sister in a high, mincing shout, "most of these fellas will cheat you every time. All they think of is money. I had a woman up here last week to look at my feet, and when she gave me the bill you'd of thought she had my appendicitis out."

"What was the name of the woman?" asked Mrs. McKee.

"Mrs. Eberhardt. She goes around looking at people's feet in their own homes."

"I like your dress," remarked Mrs. McKee, "I think it's adorable."

Mrs. Wilson rejected the compliment by raising her eyebrow in disdain.

"It's just a crazy old thing," she said. "I just slip it on sometimes when I don't care what I look like."

"But it looks wonderful on you, if you know what I mean," pursued Mrs. McKee. "If Chester could only get you in that pose I think he could make something of it."

We all looked in silence at Mrs. Wilson, who removed a strand of hair from over her eyes and looked back at us with a brilliant smile. Mr. McKee regarded her intently with his head on one side, and then moved his hand back and forth slowly in front of his face.

"I should change the light," he said after a moment. "I'd like to bring out the modelling of the features. And I'd try to get hold of all the back hair."

"I wouldn't think of changing the light," cried Mrs. McKee. "I think it's—"

Her husband said "*Sh!*" and we all looked at the subject again, whereupon Tom Blanchard yawned audibly and got to his feet.

"You McKees have something to drink," he said. "Get some more ice and mineral water, Myrtle, before everybody goes to sleep."

"I told that boy about the ice." Myrtle raised her eyebrows in despair at the shiftlessness of the lower orders. "These people! You have to keep after them all the time."

She looked at me and laughed pointlessly. Then she flounced over to the dog, kissed it with ecstasy, and swept into the kitchen, implying that a dozen chefs awaited her orders there.

"I've done some nice things out on Long Island," asserted Mr. McKee. Tom looked at him blankly.

"Two of them we have framed down-stairs."

"Two what?" demanded Tom.

"Two studies. One of them I call *Montauk Point—The Gulls*, and the other I call *Montauk Point—The Sea*."

The sister Catherine sat down beside me on the couch.

"Do you live down on Long Island, too?" she inquired.

"I live at West Egg."

"Really? I was down there at a party about a month ago. At a man named Gatsby's. Do you know him?"

"I live next door to him."

"Well, they say he's a nephew or a cousin of Kaiser Wilhelm's. That's where all his money comes from."

"Really?"

She nodded.

"I'm scared of him. I'd hate to have him get anything on me."

This absorbing information about my neighbor was interrupted by Mrs. McKee's pointing suddenly at Catherine:

"Chester, I think you could do something with *her*," she broke out, but Mr. McKee only nodded in a bored way, and turned his attention to Tom.

"I'd like to do more work on Long Island, if I could get the entry. All I ask is that they should give me a start."

"Ask Myrtle," said Tom, breaking into a short shout of laughter as Mrs. Wilson entered with a tray. "She'll give you a letter of introduction, won't you, Myrtle?"

"Do what?" she asked, startled.

"You'll give McKee a letter of introduction to your husband, so he can do some studies of him." His lips moved silently for a moment as he invented. "*George B. Wilson at the Gasoline Pump*, or something like that."

Catherine leaned close to me and whispered in my ear:

"Neither of them can stand the person they're married to."

"Can't they?"

"Can't *stand* them." She looked at Myrtle and then at Tom. "What I say is, why go on living with them if they can't stand them? If I was them I'd get a divorce and get married to each other right away."

"Doesn't she like Wilson either?"

The answer to this was unexpected. It came from Myrtle, who had overheard the question, and it was violent and obscene.

"You see," cried Catherine triumphantly. She lowered her voice again. "It's really his wife that's keeping them apart. She's a Catholic, and they don't believe in divorce."

Daisy was not a Catholic, and I was a little shocked at the elaborateness of the lie.

"When they do get married," continued Catherine, "they're going West to live for a while until it blows over."

"It'd be more discreet to go to Europe."

"Oh, do you like Europe?" she exclaimed surprisingly. "I just got back from Monte Carlo."

"Really."

"Just last year. I went over there with another girl."

"Stay long?"

"No, we just went to Monte Carlo and back. We went by way of Marseilles. We had over twelve hundred dollars when we started, but we got gypped out of it all in two days in the private rooms. We had an awful time getting back, I can tell you. God, how I hated that town!"

The late afternoon sky bloomed in the window for a moment like the blue honey of the Mediterranean—then the shrill voice of Mrs. McKee called me back into the room.

"I almost made a mistake, too," she declared vigorously. "I almost married a little kike who'd been after me for years. I knew he was below me. Everybody kept saying to me: 'Lucille, that man's 'way below you!' But if I hadn't met Chester, he'd of got me sure."

"Yes, but listen," said Myrtle Wilson, nodding her head up and down, "at least you didn't marry him."

"I know I didn't."

"Well, I married him," said Myrtle, ambiguously. "And that's the difference between your case and mine."

"Why did you, Myrtle?" demanded Catherine. "Nobody forced you to." Myrtle considered.

"I married him because I thought he was a gentleman," she said finally. "I thought he knew something about breeding, but he wasn't fit to lick my shoe."

"You were crazy about him for a while," said Catherine.

"Crazy about him!" cried Myrtle incredulously. "Who said I was crazy about him? I never was any more crazy about him than I was about that man there."

She pointed suddenly at me, and every one looked at me accusingly. I tried to show by my expression that I had played no part in her past.

"The only *crazy* I was was when I married him. I knew right away I made a mistake. He borrowed somebody's best suit to get married in, and never even told me about it, and the man came after it one day when he was out." She looked around to see who was listening. " 'Oh, is that your suit?' I said. 'This is the first I ever heard about it.' But I gave it to him and then I lay down and cried to beat the band all afternoon."

"She really ought to get away from him," resumed Catherine to me. "They've been living over that garage for eleven years. And Tom's the first sweetie she ever had."

The bottle of whiskey—a second one—was now in constant demand by all present, excepting Catherine, who "felt just as good on nothing at all." Tom rang for the janitor and sent him for some celebrated sandwiches, which were a complete supper in themselves. I wanted to get out and walk eastward toward the Park through the soft twilight, but each time I tried to go I became entangled in some wild, strident argument which pulled me back, as if with ropes, into my chair. Yet high over the city our line of yellow windows must have contributed their share of human secrecy to the casual watcher in the darkening streets, and I was him too, looking up and wondering. I was within and without, simultaneously enchanted and repelled by the inexhaustible variety of life.

Myrtle pulled her chair close to mine, and suddenly her warm breath poured over me the story of her first meeting with Tom.

"It was on the two little seats facing each other that are always the last ones left on the train. I was going up to New York to see my sister and spend the night. He had on a dress suit and patent leather shoes, and I couldn't keep my eyes off him, but every time he looked at me I had to pretend to be looking at the advertisement over his head. When we came into the station he was next to me, and his white shirt-front pressed against my arm, and so I told him I'd have to call a policeman, but he knew I lied. I was so excited that when I got into a taxi with him I didn't hardly know I wasn't getting into a subway train. All I kept thinking about, over and over, was 'You can't live forever; you can't live forever.' "

She turned to Mrs. McKee and the room rang full of her artificial laughter.

"My dear," she cried, "I'm going to give you this dress as soon as I'm through with it. I've got to get another one tomorrow. I'm going to make a list of all the things I've got to get. A massage and a wave, and a collar for the dog, and one of those cute little ash-trays where you touch a spring, and a wreath with a black silk bow for mother's grave that'll last all summer. I got to write down a list so I won't forget all the things I got to do."

It was nine o'clock—almost immediately afterward I looked at my watch and found it was ten. Mr. McKee was asleep on a chair with his fists clenched in his lap, like a photograph of a man of action. Taking out my handkerchief I wiped from his cheek the remains of the spot of dried lather that had worried me all the afternoon.

The little dog was sitting on the table looking with blind eyes through the smoke, and from time to time groaning faintly. People disappeared, reappeared, made plans to go somewhere, and then lost each other, searched for each other, found each other a few feet away. Some time toward midnight Tom Buchanan and Mrs. Wilson stood face to face, discussing in impassioned voices whether Mrs. Wilson had any right to mention Daisy's name.

"Daisy! Daisy! Daisy!" shouted Mrs. Wilson. "I'll say it whenever I want to! Daisy! Dai——"

Making a short deft movement, Tom Buchanan broke her nose with his open hand.

Then there were bloody towels upon the bathroom floor, and women's voices scolding, and high over the confusion a long broken wail of pain. Mr. McKee awoke from his doze and started in a daze toward the door. When he had gone halfway he turned around and stared at the scene—his wife and Catherine scolding and consoling as they stumbled here and there among the crowded furniture with articles of aid, and the despairing figure on the couch, bleeding fluently, and trying to spread a copy of *Town Tattle* over the tapestry scenes of Versailles. Then Mr. McKee turned and continued on out the door. Taking my hat from the chandelier, I followed.

"Come to lunch some day," he suggested, as we groaned down in the elevator.

"Where?"

"Anywhere."

"Keep your hands off the lever," snapped the elevator boy.

"I beg your pardon," said Mr. McKee with dignity, "I didn't know I was touching it."

"All right," I agreed, "I'll be glad to."

. . . I was standing beside his bed and he was sitting up between the sheets, clad in his underwear, with a great portfolio in his hands.

"Beauty and the Beast . . . Loneliness . . . Old Grocery Horse . . . Brook'n Bridge. . . ."

Then I was lying half asleep in the cold lower level of the Pennsylvania Station, staring at the morning *Tribune*, and waiting for the four o'clock train.

William Faulkner (1897-   )

William Faulkner is the American writer in whose work more obvious elements of humor appear than in the work of any of his "serious" contemporaries except Nathanael West. It would almost seem as if Faulkner had set out deliberately to rectify the condition of American literature as he lamented it in 1926: "We have one priceless trait, we Americans. The trait is our humor. What a pity it is that it is not more prevalent in our art." Perhaps the most prevalent American strain of humor in Faulkner's work is the one earlier brought to a high peak by such Southerners as George Washington Harris and Mark Twain, whose Sut Lovingood and Huck Finn are among Faulkner's favorite fictional characters. The tall tale, folk dialect, rustic character, and grotesque situation and misadventure of Southwestern humor appear in a number of his stories and novels such as *Mosquitoes* (1927), *As I Lay Dying* (1930), "Barn Burning" (1939), and *The Hamlet* (1940), the last a brilliantly original contribution to American folk humor. Faulkner has also carried on the more macabre, ironic, and sophisticated humorous tradition of Poe and Hawthorne in such stories as in "A Rose for Emily" (1930). The Rabelaisian elements of Franklin and the verbal wit of the Puritans are additional features of Faulkner's fiction. Faulkner also has roots in such rich resources of the European humorous tradition as Dickens. Often, in fact, European and American humor are fused. In *The Hamlet*, for example, Faulkner parodies the Faust myth in typical American and European folk tradition; Flem Snopes, speaking in Southern dialect, tells how he reversed the traditional mythic pattern and outwitted the Devil in a farcical battle of wits. "Uncle Bud and the Three Madams," a hilarious chapter of *Sanctuary* (1931), is a prime illustration of Faulkner's complex humor and its serious overtones. The garrulous ladies and the perverse little boy might have stepped from the pages of a comic novel by Dickens; the three ladies also recall the women of Chaucer and of Elizabethan popular drama and anticipate the ladies inhabiting Hemingway's "The Light of the World." The light, ironic humor of the beer party in "Uncle Bud and the Three Madams" is comic relief for the funeral party which has preceded it, but the amusing insouciance of the beer party is overcast by the preceding events. With the grim, relentless humor common in medieval English folk plays, Faulkner reveals his moral outrage at the calloused state of the American spirit in the 1920's. Far from being sensational, the surrealistic incongruities of "Uncle Bud and the Three Madams" accurately mirror the ribaldry and grotesquerie which LeRoy Bowman has reported on in *The American Funeral: A Study in Guilt, Extravagance, and Sublimity* (1959).

TEXT: *Sanctuary*, New York, 1931. COMMENTARY: Harry Modean Campbell and Ruel E. Foster, *William Faulkner: A Critical Appraisal*, Norman, Okla., 1951; William Van O'Connor, *The Tangled Fire of William Faulkner*, Minneapolis, Minn., 1954.

UNCLE BUD AND THE THREE MADAMS

The tables had been moved to one end of the dance floor. On each one was a black table-cloth. The curtains were still drawn; a thick, salmon-colored light fell through them. Just beneath the orchestra platform the coffin sat. It was an expensive one: black, with silver fittings, the trestles hidden by a mass of flowers. In wreaths and crosses and other shapes of ceremonial mortality, the mass appeared to break in a symbolical wave over the bier and on upon the platform and the piano, the scent of them thickly oppressive.

The proprietor of the place moved about among the tables, speaking to the arrivals as they entered and found seats. The negro waiters, in black shirts beneath their starched jackets, were already moving in and out with glasses and bottles of ginger ale. They moved with swaggering and decorous repression; already the scene was vivid, with a hushed, macabre air a little febrile.

The archway to the dice-room was draped in black. A black pall lay upon the crap-table, upon which the overflow of floral shapes was beginning to accumulate. People entered steadily, the men in dark suits of decorous restraint, others in the light, bright shades of spring, increasing the atmosphere of macabre paradox. The women—the younger ones— wore bright colors also, in hats and scarves; the older ones in sober gray and black and navy blue, and glittering with diamonds: matronly figures resembling housewives on a Sunday afternoon excursion.

The room began to hum with shrill, hushed talk. The waiters moved here and there with high, precarious trays, their white jackets and black shirts resembling photograph negatives. The proprietor went from table to table with his bald head, a huge diamond in his black cravat, followed by the bouncer, a thick, muscle-bound, bullet-headed man who appeared to be on the point of bursting out of his dinner-jacket through the rear, like a cocoon.

In a private dining-room, on a table draped in black, sat a huge bowl of punch floating with ice and sliced fruit. Beside it leaned a fat man in a shapeless greenish suit, from the sleeves of which dirty cuffs fell upon hands rimmed with black nails. The soiled collar was wilted about his neck in limp folds, knotted by a greasy black tie with an imitation ruby stud. His face gleamed with moisture and he adjured the throng about the bowl in a harsh voice:

"Come on, folks. It's on Gene. It dont cost you nothing. Step up and drink. There wasn't never a better boy walked than him." They drank and fell back, replaced by others with extended cups. From time to time a waiter entered with ice and fruit and dumped them into the bowl; from a suit case under the table Gene drew fresh bottles and decanted them into the bowl; then, proprietorial, adjurant, sweating, he resumed his harsh monologue, mopping his face on his sleeve. "Come on, folks. It's all on Gene. I aint nothing but a bootlegger, but he never had a better friend than me. Step up and drink, folks. There's more where that come from."

From the dance hall came a strain of music. The people entered and found seats. On the platform was the orchestra from a downtown hotel, in dinner coats. The proprietor and a second man were conferring with the leader.

"Let them play jazz," the second man said. "Never nobody liked dancing no better than Red."

"No, no," the proprietor said. "Time Gene gets them all ginned up on free whisky, they'll start dancing. It'll look bad."

"How about the Blue Danube?" the leader said.

"No, no; don't play no blues, I tell you," the proprietor said. "There's a dead man in that bier."

"That's not blues," the leader said.

"What is it?" the second man said.

"A waltz. Strauss."

"A wop?" the second man said. "Like hell. Red was an American. You may not be, but he was. Dont you know anything American? Play I Cant Give You Anything But Love. He always liked that."

"And get them all to dancing?" the proprietor said. He glanced back at the tables, where the women were beginning to talk a little shrilly. "You better start off with Nearer, My God, To Thee," he said, "and sober them up some. I told Gene it was risky about that punch, starting it so soon. My suggestion was to wait until we started back to town. But I might have knowed somebody'd have to turn it into a carnival. Better start off solemn and keep it up until I give you the sign."

"Red wouldn't like it solemn," the second man said. "And you know it."

"Let him go somewheres else, then," the proprietor said. "I just done this as an accommodation. I aint running no funeral parlor."

The orchestra played Nearer, My God, To Thee. The audience grew quiet. A woman in a red dress came in the door unsteadily. "Whoopee," she said, "so long, Red. He'll be in hell before I could even reach Little Rock."

"Shhhhhhhh!" voices said. She fell into a seat. Gene came to the door and stood there until the music stopped.

"Come on, folks," he shouted, jerking his arms in a fat, sweeping gesture, "come and get it. It's on Gene. I don't want a dry throat or eye in this place in ten minutes." Those at the rear moved toward the door.

The proprietor sprang to his feet and jerked his hand at the orchestra. The cornetist rose and played In That Haven of Rest in solo, but the crowd at the back of the room continued to dwindle through the door where Gene stood waving his arm. Two middle-aged women were weeping quietly beneath flowered hats.

They surged and clamored about the diminishing bowl. From the dance hall came the rich blare of the cornet. Two soiled young men worked their way toward the table, shouting "Gangway. Gangway" monotonously, carrying suit cases. They opened them and set bottles on the table, while Gene, frankly weeping now, opened them and decanted them into the bowl. "Come up, folks. I couldn't a loved him no better if he'd a been my own son," he shouted hoarsely, dragging his sleeve across his face.

A waiter edged up to the table with a bowl of ice and fruit and went to put them into the punch bowl. "What the hell are you doing?" Gene said, "putting that slop in there? Get to hell away from here."

"Ra-a-a-a-y-y-y-y!" they shouted, clashing their cups, drowning all save the pantomime as Gene knocked the bowl of fruit from the waiter's hand and fell again to dumping raw liquor into the bowl, sploshing it into and upon the extended hands and cups. The two youths opened bottles furiously.

As though swept there upon a brassy blare of music the proprietor appeared in the door, his face harried, waving his arms. "Come on, folks," he shouted, "let's finish the musical program. It's costing us money."

"Hell with it," they shouted.

"Costing who money?"

"Who cares?"

"Costing who money?"

"Who begrudges it? I'll pay it. By God, I'll buy him two funerals."

"Folks! Folks!" the proprietor shouted. "Don't you realise there's a bier in that room?"

"Costing who money?"

"Beer?" Gene said. "Beer?" he said in a broken voice. "Is anybody here trying to insult me by—"

"He begrudges Red the money."

"Who does?"

"Joe does, the cheap son of a bitch."

"Is somebody here trying to insult me—"

"Let's move the funeral, then. This is not the only place in town."

"Let's move Joe."

"Put the son of a bitch in a coffin. Let's have two funerals."

"Beer? Beer? Is somebody—"

"Put the son of a bitch in a coffin. See how he likes it."

"Put the son of a bitch in a coffin," the woman in red shrieked. They rushed toward the door, where the proprietor stood waving his hands above his head, his voice shrieking out of the uproar before he turned and fled.

In the main room a male quartet engaged from a vaudeville house was singing. They were singing mother songs in close harmony; they sang Sonny Boy. The weeping was general among the older women. Waiters were now carrying cups of punch in to them and they sat holding the cups in their fat, ringed hands, crying.

The orchestra played again. The woman in red staggered into the room. "Come on, Joe," she shouted, "open the game. Get that damn stiff out of here and open the game." A man tried to hold her; she turned upon him with a burst of filthy language and went on to the shrouded crap table and hurled a wreath to the floor. The proprietor rushed toward her, followed by the bouncer. The proprietor grasped the woman as she lifted another floral piece. The man who had tried to hold her intervened, the woman cursing shrilly and striking at both of them impartially with the wreath. The bouncer caught the man's arm; he whirled and struck at the bouncer, who knocked him halfway across the room. Three more men entered. The fourth rose from the floor and all four of them rushed at the bouncer.

He felled the first and whirled and sprang with unbelievable celerity, into the main room. The orchestra was playing. It was immediately drowned in a sudden pandemonium of chairs and screams. The bouncer whirled again and met the rush of the four men. They mingled; a second man flew out and skittered along the floor on his back; the bouncer sprang free. Then he whirled and rushed them and in a whirling plunge they bore down upon the bier and crashed into it. The orchestra had ceased and were now climbing onto their chairs, with their instruments. The floral offerings flew; the coffin teetered. "Catch it!" a voice shouted. They sprang forward, but the coffin crashed heavily to the floor, coming open. The corpse tumbled slowly and sedately out and came to rest with its face in the center of a wreath.

"Play something!" the proprietor bawled, waving his arms; "play! Play!"

When they raised the corpse the wreath came too, attached to him by a hidden end of a wire driven into his cheek. He had worn a cap which, tumbling off, exposed a small blue hole in the center of his forehead. It had been neatly plugged with wax and was painted, but the wax had been jarred out and lost. They couldn't find it, but by unfastening the snap in the peak, they could draw the cap down to his eyes.

As the cortège neared the downtown section more cars joined it. The hearse was followed by six Packard touring cars with the tops back, driven by liveried chauffeurs and filled with flowers. They looked exactly alike and were of the type rented by the hour by the better class agencies. Next came a nondescript line of taxis, roadsters, sedans, which increased as the procession moved slowly through the restricted district where faces peered from beneath lowered shades, toward the main artery that led back out of town, toward the cemetery.

On the avenue the hearse increased its speed, the procession stretching out at swift intervals. Presently the private cars and the cabs began to drop out. At each intersection they would turn this way or that, until at last only the hearse and the six Packards were left, each carrying no occupant save the liveried driver. The street was broad and now infrequent, with a white line down the center that diminished on ahead into the smooth asphalt emptiness. Soon the hearse was making forty miles an hour and then forty-five and then fifty.

One of the cabs drew up at Miss Reba's door. She got out, followed by a thin woman in sober, severe clothes and gold nose-glasses, and a short plump woman in a plumed hat, her face hidden by a handkerchief, and a small bullet-headed boy of five or six. The woman with the handkerchief continued to sob in snuffy gasps as they went up the walk and entered the lattice. Beyond the house door the dogs set up a falsetto uproar. When Minnie opened the door they surged about Miss Reba's feet. She kicked them aside. Again they assailed her with snapping eagerness; again she flung them back against the wall in muted thuds.

"Come in, come in," she said, her hand to her breast. Once inside the house the woman with the handkerchief began to weep aloud.

"Didn't he look sweet?" she wailed. "Didn't he look sweet!"

"Now, now," Miss Reba said, leading the way to her room, "come in and have some beer. You'll feel better. Minnie!" They entered the room with the decorated dresser, the safe, the screen, the draped portrait. "Sit down, sit down," she panted, shoving the chairs forward. She lowered herself into one and stooped terrifically toward her feet.

"Uncle Bud, honey," the weeping woman said, dabbing at her eyes, "come and unlace Miss Reba's shoes."

The boy knelt and removed Miss Reba's shoes. "And if you'll just reach me them house slippers under the bed there, honey," Miss Reba said. The boy fetched the slippers. Minnie entered, followed by the dogs. They rushed at Miss Reba and began to worry the shoes she had just removed.

"Scat!" the boy said, striking at one of them with his hand. The dog's head snapped around, its teeth clicking, its half-hidden eyes bright and malevolent. The boy recoiled. "You bite me, you thon bitch," he said.

"Uncle Bud!" the fat woman said, her round face, rigid in fatty folds and streaked with tears, turned upon the boy in shocked surprise, the plumes nodding precariously above it. Uncle Bud's head was quite round, his nose bridged with freckles like splotches of huge summer rain on a sidewalk. The other woman sat primly erect, in gold nose-glasses on a gold chain and neat iron-gray hair. She looked like a school-teacher. "The very idea!" the fat woman said. "How in the world he can learn such words on an Arkansaw farm, I dont know."

"They'll learn meanness anywhere," Miss Reba said. Minnie leaned down a tray bearing three frosted tankards. Uncle Bud watched with round cornflower eyes as they took one each. The fat woman began to cry again.

"He looked so sweet!" she wailed.

"We all got to suffer it," Miss Reba said. "Well, may it be a long day," lifting her tankard. They drank, bowing formally to one another. The fat woman dried her eyes; the two guests wiped their lips with prim decorum. The thin one coughed delicately aside, behind her hand.

"Such good beer," she said.

"Aint it?" the fat one said. "I always say it's the greatest pleasure I have to call on Miss Reba."

They began to talk politely, in decorous half-completed sentences, with little gasps of agreement. The boy had moved aimlessly to the window, peering beneath the lifted shade.

"How long's he going to be with you, Miss Myrtle?" Miss Reba said.

"Just till Sat'dy," the fat woman said. "Then he'll go back home. It makes a right nice little change for him, with me for a week or two. And I enjoy having him."

"Children are such a comfort to a body," the thin one said.

"Yes," Miss Myrtle said. "Is them two nice young fellows still with you, Miss Reba?"

"Yes," Miss Reba said. "I think I got to get shut of them, though. I aint specially tenderhearted, but after all it aint no use in helping young folks to learn this world's meanness until they have to. I already had to stop the girls running around the house without no clothes on, and they dont like it."

They drank again, decorously, handling the tankards delicately, save Miss Reba who grasped hers as though it were a weapon, her other hand lost in her breast. She set her tankard down empty. "I get so dry, seems like," she said. "Wont you ladies have another?" They murmured, ceremoniously. "Minnie!" Miss Reba shouted.

Minnie came and filled the tankards again. "Reely, I'm right ashamed," Miss Myrtle said. "But Miss Reba has such good beer. And then we've all had a kind of upsetting afternoon."

"I'm just surprised it wasn't upset no more," Miss Reba said. "Giving away all that free liquor like Gene done."

"It must have cost a good piece of jack," the thin woman said.

"I believe you," Miss Reba said. "And who got anything out of it? Tell me that. Except the privilege of having his place hell-full of folks not spending a cent." She had set her tankard on the table beside her chair. Suddenly she turned her head sharply and looked at it. Uncle Bud was now behind her chair, leaning against the table. "You aint been into my beer, have you, boy?" she said.

"You, Uncle Bud," Miss Myrtle said. "Aint you ashamed? I declare, it's getting so I dont dare take him nowhere. I never see such a boy for snitching beer in my life. You come out here and play, now. Come on."

"Yessum," Uncle Bud said. He moved, in no particular direction. Miss Reba drank and set the tankard back on the table and rose.

"Since we all been kind of tore up," she said, "maybe I can prevail on you ladies to have a little sup of gin?"

"No; reely," Miss Myrtle said.

"Miss Reba's the perfect hostess," the thin one said. "How many times you heard me say that, Miss Myrtle?"

"I wouldn't undertake to say, dearie," Miss Myrtle said.

Miss Reba vanished behind the screen.

"Did you ever see it so warm for June, Miss Lorraine?" Miss Myrtle said.

"I never did," the thin woman said. Miss Myrtle's face began to crinkle again. Setting her tankard down she began to fumble for her handkerchief.

"It just comes over me like this," she said, "and them singing that Sonny Boy and all. He looked so sweet," she wailed.

"Now, now," Miss Lorraine said. "Drink a little beer. You'll feel better. Miss Myrtle's took again," she said, raising her voice.

"I got too tender a heart," Miss Myrtle said. She snuffled behind the handkerchief, groping for her tankard. She groped for a moment, then it touched her hand. She looked quickly up. "You, Uncle Bud!" she said. "Didn't I tell you to come out from behind there and play? Would you believe it? The other afternoon when we left here I was so mortified I didn't know what to do. I was ashamed to be seen on the street with a drunk boy like you."

Miss Reba emerged from behind the screen with three glasses of gin. "This'll put some heart into us," she said. "We're setting here like three old sick cats." They bowed formally and drank, patting their lips. Then they began to talk. They were all talking at once, again in half-completed sentences, but without pauses for agreement or affirmation.

"It's us girls," Miss Myrtle said. "Men just cant seem to take us and leave us for what we are. They make us what we are, then they expect us to be different. Expect us not to never look at another man, while they come and go as they please."

"A woman that wants to fool with more than one man at a time is a fool," Miss Reba said. "They're all trouble, and why do you want to double your trouble? And the woman that cant stay true to a good man when she gets him, a free-hearted spender that never give her a hour's uneasiness or a hard word . . ." looking at them, her eyes began to fill with a sad, unutterable expression, of baffled and patient despair.

"Now, now," Miss Myrtle said. She leaned forward and patted Miss Reba's huge hand. Miss Lorraine made a faint clucking sound with her tongue. "You'll get yourself started."

"He was such a good man," Miss Reba said. "We was like two doves. For eleven years we was like two doves."

"Now, dearie; now, dearie," Miss Myrtle said.

"It's when it comes over me like this," Miss Reba said. "Seeing that boy laying there under them flowers."

"He never had no more than Mr Binford had," Miss Myrtle said. "Now, now. Drink a little beer."

Miss Reba brushed her sleeve across her eyes. She drank some beer.

"He ought to known better than to take a chance with Popeye's girl," Miss Lorraine said.

"Men dont never learn better than that, dearie," Miss Myrtle said. "Where you reckon they went, Miss Reba?"

"I dont know and I dont care," Miss Reba said. "And how soon they catch him and burn him for killing that boy, I dont care neither. I dont care none."

"He goes all the way to Pensacola every summer to see his mother," Miss Myrtle said. "A man that'll do that cant be all bad."

"I dont know how bad you like them, then," Miss Reba said. "Me trying to run a respectable house, that's been running a shooting-gallery for twenty years, and him trying to turn it into a peep-show."

"It's us poor girls," Miss Myrtle said, "causes all the trouble and gets all the suffering."

"I heard two years ago he wasn't no good that way," Miss Lorraine said.

"I knew it all the time," Miss Reba said. "A young man spending his money like water on girls and not never going to bed with one. It's against nature. All the girls thought it was because he had a little woman out in town somewhere, but I says mark my words, there's something funny about him. There's a funny business somewhere."

"He was a free spender, all right," Miss Lorraine said.

"The clothes and jewelry that girl bought, it was a shame," Miss Reba said. "There was a Chinee robe she paid a hundred dollars for—imported, it was—and perfume at ten dollars an ounce; next morning when I went up there, they was all waddled in the corner and the perfume and rouge busted all over them like a cyclone. That's what she'd do when she got mad at him, when he'd beat her. After he shut her up and wouldn't let her leave the house. Having the front of my house watched like it was a . . ." She raised the tankard from the table to her lips. Then she halted it, blinking. "Where's my—"

"Uncle Bud!" Miss Myrtle said. She grasped the boy by the arm and snatched him out from behind Miss Reba's chair and shook him, his round head bobbing on his shoulders with an expression of equable idiocy. "Aint you ashamed? Aint you *ashamed?* Why cant you stay out of these ladies' beer? I'm a good mind to take that dollar back and make you buy Miss Reba a can of beer, I am for a fact. Now, you go over there by that window and stay there, you hear?"

"Nonsense," Miss Reba said. "There wasn't much left. You ladies are about ready too, aint you? Minnie!"

Miss Lorraine touched her mouth with her handkerchief. Behind her glasses her eyes rolled aside in a veiled, secret look. She laid the other hand to her flat spinster's breast.

"We forgot about your heart, honey," Miss Myrtle said. "Dont you reckon you better take gin this time?"

"Reely, I—" Miss Lorraine said.

"Yes; do," Miss Reba said. She rose heavily and fetched three more glasses of gin from behind the screen. Minnie entered and refilled the tankards. They drank, patting their lips.

"That's what was going on, was it?" Miss Lorraine said.

"First I knowed was when Minnie told me there was something funny going on," Miss Reba said. "How he wasn't here hardly at all, gone about every other night, and that when he was here, there wasn't no signs at all the next morning when she cleaned up. She'd hear them quarrelling, and she said it was her wanting to get out and he wouldn't let her. With all them clothes he was buying her, mind, he didn't want her to leave the house, and she'd get mad and lock the door and wouldn't even let him in."

"Maybe he went off and got fixed up with one of these glands, these monkey glands, and it quit on him," Miss Myrtle said.

"Then one morning he come in with Red and took him up there. They stayed about an hour and left, and Popeye didn't show up again until next morning. Then him and Red come back and stayed up there about an hour. When they left, Minnie come and told me what was going on, so next day I waited for them. I called him in here and I says 'Look here, you son of a buh—'" She ceased. For an instant the three of them sat motionless, a little forward. Then slowly their heads turned and they looked at the boy leaning against the table.

"Uncle Bud, honey," Miss Myrtle said, "dont you want to go and play in the yard with Reba and Mr Binford?"

"Yessum," the boy said. He went toward the door. They watched him until the door closed upon him. Miss Lorraine drew her chair up; they leaned together.

"And that's what they was doing?" Miss Myrtle said.

"I says 'I been running a house for twenty years, but this is the first time I ever had anything like this going on in it. If you want to turn a stud in to your girl' I says 'go somewhere else to do it. I aint going to have my house turned into no French joint.' "

"The son of a bitch," Miss Lorraine said.

"He'd ought to've had sense enough to got a old ugly man," Miss Myrtle said. "Tempting us poor girls like that."

"Men always expects us to resist temptation," Miss Lorraine said. She was sitting upright like a school-teacher. "The lousy son of a bitch."

"Except what they offers themselves," Miss Reba said. "Then watch them. . . . Every morning for four days that was going on, then they didn't come back. For a week Popeye didn't show up at all, and that girl wild as a young mare. I thought he was out of town on business maybe, until Minnie told me he wasn't and that he give her five dollars a day not to let that girl out of the house nor use the telephone. And me trying to get word to him to come and take her out of my house because I didn't want nuttin like that going on in it. Yes, sir, Minnie said the two of them would be nekkid as two snakes, and Popeye hanging over the foot of the bed without even his hat took off, making a kind of whinnying sound."

"Maybe he was cheering for them," Miss Lorraine said. "The lousy son of a bitch."

Feet came up the hall; they could hear Minnie's voice lifted in adjuration. The door opened. She entered, holding Uncle Bud erect by one hand. Limp-kneed he dangled, his face fixed in an expression of glassy idiocy. "Miss Reba," Minnie said, "this boy done broke in the icebox and drunk a whole bottle of beer. You, boy!" she said, shaking him, "stan up!" Limply he dangled, his face rigid in a slobbering grin. Then upon it came an expression of concern, consternation; Minnie swung him sharply away from her as he began to vomit.

Ernest Hemingway (1898–1961)

In 1938 Ernest Hemingway named "The Light of the World" as one of his stories which he "liked the best" even though "nobody else ever liked" it. This choice is a clue to the important role of humor in his writing. Hemingway's famous ironic style was in part an inheritance from nineteenth-century American humorists who had related the absurd and the terrible, the fantastic and the mundane, with deadpan gravity and understatement. The style came to him directly from Mark Twain, whose *Huckleberry Finn* Hemingway dubbed the fountainhead of modern American literature, though there is no doubt that his irony was also shaped by such favorites as James, Stephen Crane, Fitzgerald, Turgenev, and Maupassant. As an apprentice writer in the 1910's, Hemingway emulated Ring Lardner; his poems and newspaper writings of the 1920's reveal a steady experimentation with burlesque, satire, wit, caricature, parody, epigram, and bawdry. *The Torrents of Spring* (1926), his first published novel, was a hilarious satire of contemporary European and American culture written in a style parodying Sherwood Anderson. The irony of Hemingway's mature style tended to restrain his expression of the more obvious humor visible in his early writings. However, in *The Sun Also Rises* (1926), in many stories such as "Homage to Switzerland," "Mr. and Mrs. Elliott," "The Gambler, the Nun, and the Radio," and "The Light of the World," and in such nonfiction as *Green Hills of Africa* (1935), the humor is unmistakably clear even though it has been fused with the serious. *The Old Man and the Sea* (1953), appearing a year before Hemingway was awarded the Nobel Prize, brilliantly linked the ludicrous cultural mythology and simple-minded virtue of the folk hero with universally heroic strength and dignity in the laconic style Hemingway has made his own. Hemingway once alleged a kinship between "The Light of the World" and Maupassant's "La Maison Tellier." However, Hemingway's story does not reproduce the smirking irony with which Maupassant portrayed the naïveté of a French village whose priest and gentry foolishly believe a group of visiting harlots to be pious middle-class ladies. But Maupassant's irony was also good-humored, a spirit which does re-appear in "The Light of the World." Hemingway takes a great delight in observing innocence as it finds sparks of virtue in dubious places. The boasting match is a common feature of nineteenth-century American humor (see Mark Twain's "Frescoes from the Past," pp. 350–60) which Hemingway adapted with amusing success. His favorite comic writers Fielding and Smollett probably provided precedents for the story's masculine jesting.

TEXT: *Winner Take Nothing*, New York, 1933. COMMENTARY: Carlos

Baker, *Hemingway: The Writer as Artist*, Princeton, N.J., 1952; Charles A. Fenton, *The Apprenticeship of Ernest Hemingway*, New York, 1954; Philip Young, *Ernest Hemingway*, New York, 1952.

THE LIGHT OF THE WORLD

When he saw us come in the door the bartender looked up and then reached over and put the glass covers on the two free-lunch bowls.

"Give me a beer," I said. He drew it, cut the top off with the spatula and then held the glass in his hand. I put the nickel on the wood and he slid the beer toward me.

"What's yours?" he said to Tom.

"Beer."

He drew that beer and cut it off and when he saw the money he pushed the beer across to Tom.

"What's the matter?" Tom asked.

The bartender didn't answer him. He just looked over our heads and said, "What's yours?" to a man who'd come in.

"Rye," the man said. The bartender put out the bottle and glass and a glass of water.

Tom reached over and took the glass off the free-lunch bowl. It was a bowl of pickled pig's feet and there was a wooden thing that worked like a scissors, with two wooden forks at the end to pick them up with.

"No," said the bartender and put the glass cover back on the bowl. Tom held the wooden scissors fork in his hand. "Put it back," said the bartender.

"You know where," said Tom.

The bartender reached a hand forward under the bar, watching us both. I put fifty cents on the wood and he straightened up.

"What was yours?" he said.

"Beer," I said, and before he drew the beer he uncovered both the bowls.

"Your goddam pig's feet stink," Tom said, and spit what he had in his mouth on the floor. The bartender didn't say anything. The man who had drunk the rye paid and went out without looking back.

"You stink yourself," the bartender said. "All you punks stink."

"He says we're punks," Tommy said to me.

"Listen," I said. "Let's get out."

"You punks clear the hell out of here," the bartender said.

"I said we were going out," I said. "It wasn't your idea."

"We'll be back," Tommy said.

"No you won't," the bartender told him.

"Tell him how wrong he is," Tom turned to me.

"Come on," I said.

Outside it was good and dark.

"What the hell kind of place is this?" Tommy said.

"I don't know," I said. "Let's go down to the station."

We'd come in that town at one end and we were going out the other. It smelled of hides and tan bark and the big piles of sawdust. It was getting dark as we came in, and now that it was dark it was cold and the puddles of water in the road were freezing at the edges.

Down at the station there were five whores waiting for the train to come in, and six white men and four Indians. It was crowded and hot from the stove and full of stale smoke. As we came in nobody was talking and the ticket window was down.

"Shut the door, can't you?" somebody said.

I looked to see who said it. It was one of the white men. He wore stagged trousers and lumbermen's rubbers and a mackinaw shirt like the others, but he had no cap and his face was white and his hands were white and thin.

"Aren't you going to shut it?"

"Sure," I said, and shut it.

"Thank you," he said. One of the other men snickered.

"Ever interfere with a cook?" he said to me.

"No."

"You can interfere with this one," he looked at the cook. "He likes it." The cook looked away from him holding his lips tight together.

"He puts lemon juice on his hands," the man said. "He wouldn't get them in dishwater for anything. Look how white they are."

One of the whores laughed out loud. She was the biggest whore I ever saw in my life and the biggest woman. And she had on one of those silk dresses that change colors. There were two other whores that were nearly as big but the big one must have weighed three hundred and fifty pounds. You couldn't believe she was real when you looked at her. All three had those changeable silk dresses. They sat side by side on the bench. They were huge. The other two were just ordinary looking whores, peroxide blondes.

"Look at his hands," the man said and nodded his head at the cook. The whore laughed again and shook all over.

The cook turned and said to her quickly, "You big disgusting mountain of flesh."

She just kept on laughing and shaking.

"Oh, my Christ," she said. She had a nice voice. "Oh, my sweet Christ."

The two other whores, the big ones, acted very quiet and placid as though they didn't have much sense, but they were big, nearly as big as the biggest one. They'd have both gone well over two hundred and fifty pounds. The other two were dignified.

Of the men, besides the cook and the one who talked, there were two other lumberjacks, one that listened, interested but bashful, and the other that seemed getting ready to say something, and two Swedes. Two Indians were sitting down at the end of the bench and one standing up against the wall.

The man who was getting ready to say something spoke to me very low, "Must be like getting on top of a hay mow."

I laughed and said it to Tommy.

"I swear to Christ I've never been anywhere like this," he said. "Look at the three of them." Then the cook spoke up.

"How old are you boys?"

"I'm ninety-six and he's sixty-nine," Tommy said.

"Ho! Ho! Ho!" the big whore shook with laughing. She had a really pretty voice. The other whores didn't smile.

"Oh, can't you be decent?" the cook said. "I asked just to be friendly."

"We're seventeen and nineteen," I said.

"What's the matter with you?" Tommy turned to me.

"That's all right."

"You can call me Alice," the big whore said and then she began to shake again.

"Is that your name?" Tommy asked.

"Sure," she said. "Alice. Isn't it?" she turned to the man who sat by the cook.

"Alice. That's right."

"That's the sort of name you'd have," the cook said.

"It's my real name," Alice said.

"What's the other girls' names?" Tom asked.

"Hazel and Ethel," Alice said. Hazel and Ethel smiled. They weren't very bright.

"What's your name?" I said to one of the blondes.

"Frances," she said.

"Frances what?"

"Frances Wilson. What's it to you?"

"What's yours?" I asked the other one.

"Oh, don't be fresh," she said.

"He just wants us all to be friends," the man who talked said. "Don't you want to be friends?"

"No," the peroxide one said. "Not with you."

"She's just a spitfire," the man said. "A regular little spitfire."

The one blonde looked at the other and shook her head.

"Goddamned mossbacks," she said.

Alice commenced to laugh again and to shake all over.

"There's nothing funny," the cook said. "You all laugh but there's nothing funny. You two young lads; where are you bound for?"

"Where are you going yourself?" Tom asked him.

"I want to go to Cadillac," the cook said. "Have you ever been there? My sister lives there."

"He's a sister himself," the man in the stagged trousers said.

"Can't you stop that sort of thing?" the cook asked. "Can't we speak decently?"

"Cadillac is where Steve Ketchel came from and where Ad Wolgast is from," the shy man said.

"Steve Ketchel," one of the blondes said in a high voice as though the name had pulled a trigger in her. "His own father shot and killed him. Yes, by Christ, his own father. There aren't any more men like Steve Ketchel."

"Wasn't his name Stanley Ketchel?" asked the cook.

"Oh, shut up," said the blonde. "What do you know about Steve? Stanley. He was no Stanley. Steve Ketchel was the finest and most beautiful man that ever lived. I never saw a man as clean and as white and as beautiful as Steve Ketchel. There never was a man like that. He moved just like a tiger and he was the finest, free-est, spender that ever lived."

"Did you know him?" one of the men asked.

"Did I know him? Did I know him? Did I love him? You ask me that? I knew him like you know nobody in the world and I loved him like you love God. He was the greatest, finest, whitest, most beautiful man that ever lived, Steve Ketchel, and his own father shot him down like a dog."

"Were you out on the coast with him?"

"No. I knew him before that. He was the only man I ever loved."

Every one was very respectful to the peroxide blonde, who said all this in a high stagey way, but Alice was beginning to shake again. I felt it sitting by her.

"You should have married him," the cook said.

"I wouldn't hurt his career," the peroxide blonde said. "I wouldn't be a drawback to him. A wife wasn't what he needed. Oh, my God, what a man he was."

"That was a fine way to look at it," the cook said. "Didn't Jack Johnson knock him out though?"

"It was a trick," Peroxide said. "That big dinge took him by surprise. He'd just knocked Jack Johnson down, the big black bastard. That nigger beat him by a fluke."

The ticket window went up and the three Indians went over to it.

"Steve knocked him down," Peroxide said. "He turned to smile at me."

"I thought you said you weren't on the coast," some one said.

"I went out just for that fight. Steve turned to smile at me and that black son of a bitch from hell jumped up and hit him by surprise. Steve could lick a hundred like that black bastard."

"He was a great fighter," the lumberjack said.

"I hope to God he was," Peroxide said. "I hope to God they don't have fighters like that now. He was like a god, he was. So white and clean and beautiful and smooth and fast and like a tiger or like lightning."

"I saw him in the moving pictures of the fight," Tom said. We were all very moved. Alice was shaking all over and I looked and saw she was crying. The Indians had gone outside on the platform.

"He was more than any husband could ever be," Peroxide said. "We were married in the eyes of God and I belong to him right now and always will and all of me is his. I don't care about my body. They can take my body. My soul belongs to Steve Ketchel. By God, he was a man."

Everybody felt terribly. It was sad and embarrassing. Then Alice, who was still shaking, spoke. "You're a dirty liar," she said in that low voice. "You never layed Steve Ketchel in your life and you know it."

"How can you say that?" Peroxide said proudly.

"I say it because it's true," Alice said. "I'm the only one here that ever knew Steve Ketchel and I come from Mancelona and I knew him there and it's true and you know it's true and God can strike me dead if it isn't true."

"He can strike me too," Peroxide said.

"This is true, true, true, and you know it. Not just made up and I know exactly what he said to me."

"What did he say?" Peroxide asked, complacently.

Alice was crying so she could hardly speak from shaking so.

"He said 'You're a lovely piece, Alice.' That's exactly what he said."

"It's a lie," Peroxide said.

"It's true," Alice said. "That's truly what he said."

"It's a lie," Peroxide said proudly.

"No, it's true, true, true, to Jesus and Mary true."

"Steve couldn't have said that. It wasn't the way he talked," Peroxide said happily.

"It's true," said Alice in her nice voice. "And it doesn't make any difference to me whether you believe it or not." She wasn't crying any more and she was calm.

"It would be impossible for Steve to have said that," Peroxide declared.

"He said it," Alice said and smiled. "And I remember when he said it and I *was* a lovely piece then exactly as he said, and right now I'm a better piece than you, you dried up old hot-water bottle."

"You can't insult me," said Peroxide. "You big mountain of pus. I have my memories."

"No," Alice said in that sweet lovely voice, "you haven't got any real memories except having your tubes out and when you started C. and M.

Everything else you just read in the papers. I'm clean and you know it and men like me, even though I'm big, and you know it, and I never lie and you know it."

"Leave me with my memories," Peroxide said. "With my true, wonderful memories."

Alice looked at her and then at us and her face lost that hurt look and she smiled and she had about the prettiest face I ever saw. She had a pretty face and a nice smooth skin and a lovely voice and she was nice all right and really friendly. But my God she was big. She was as big as three women. Tom saw me looking at her and he said, "Come on. Let's go."

"Good-bye," said Alice. She certainly had a nice voice.

"Good-bye," I said.

"Which way are you boys going?" asked the cook.

"The other way from you," Tom told him.

E. B. White (1899–   )

The humane urbanity of E. B. White has not only given the *New Yorker* magazine its admirable catholicity of spirit but has also generated direct pleasure for countless readers of his poems, essays, and stories for children and adults. The parody below provides an excellent example of White's witty style. Perhaps it should properly be called a double parody. White is obviously ridiculing Ernest Hemingway's *Across the River and into the Trees* (1950), but he is also implying that Hemingway was parodying himself.

TEXT: *The Second Tree from the Corner*, New York, 1954.

ACROSS THE STREET AND INTO THE GRILL

(With my respects to Ernest Hemingway)

This is my last and best and true and only meal, thought Mr. Perley as he descended at noon and swung east on the beat-up sidewalk of Forty-fifth Street. Just ahead of him was the girl from the reception desk. I am a little fleshed up around the crook of the elbow, thought Perley, but I commute good.

He quickened his step to overtake her and felt the pain again. What a stinking trade it is, he thought. But after what I've done to other assistant treasurers, I can't hate anybody. Sixteen deads, and I don't know how many possibles.

The girl was near enough now so he could smell her fresh receptiveness, and the lint in her hair. Her skin was light blue, like the sides of horses.

"I love you," he said, "and we are going to lunch together for the first and only time, and I love you very much."

"Hello, Mr. Perley," she said, overtaken. "Let's not think of anything."

A pair of fantails flew over from the sad old Guaranty Trust Company, their wings set for a landing. A lovely double, thought Perley, as he pulled. "Shall we go to the Hotel Biltmore, on Vanderbilt Avenue, which is merely a feeder lane for the great streets, or shall we go to Schrafft's, where my old friend Botticelli is captain of girls and where they have the mayonnaise in fiascos?"

"Let's go to Schrafft's," said the girl, low. "But first I must phone Mummy." She stepped into a public booth and dialled true and well, using her finger. Then she telephoned.

As they walked on, she smelled good. She smells good, thought Perley.

But that's all right, I add good. And when we get to Schrafft's, I'll order from the menu, which I like very much indeed.

They entered the restaurant. The wind was still west, ruffling the edges of the cookies. In the elevator, Perley took the controls. "I'll run it," he said to the operator. "I checked out long ago." He stopped true at the third floor, and they stepped off into the men's grill.

"Good morning, my Assistant Treasurer," said Botticelli, coming forward with a fiasco in each hand. He nodded at the girl, who he knew was from the West Seventies and whom he desired.

"Can you drink the water here?" asked Perley. He had the fur trapper's eye and took in the room at a glance, noting that there was one empty table and three pretty waitresses.

Botticelli led the way to the table in the corner, where Perley's flanks would be covered.

"Alexanders," said Perley. "Eighty-six to one. The way Chris mixes them. Is this table all right, Daughter?"

Botticelli disappeared and returned soon, carrying the old Indian blanket.

"That's the same blanket, isn't it?" asked Perley.

"Yes. To keep the wind off," said the Captain, smiling from the backs of his eyes. "It's still west. It should bring the ducks in tomorrow, the chef thinks."

Mr. Perley and the girl from the reception desk crawled down under the table and pulled the Indian blanket over them so it was solid and good and covered them right. The girl put her hand on his wallet. It was cracked and old and held his commutation book. "We are having fun, aren't we?" she asked.

"Yes, Sister," he said.

"I have here the soft-shelled crabs, my Assistant Treasurer," said Botticelli. "And another fiasco of the 1926. This one is cold."

"Dee the soft-shelled crabs," said Perley from under the blanket. He put his arm around the receptionist good.

"Do you think we should have a green pokeweed salad?" she asked. "Or shall we not think of anything for a while?"

"We shall not think of anything for a while, and Botticelli would bring the pokeweed if there was any," said Perley. "It isn't the season." Then he spoke to the Captain. "Botticelli, do you remember when we took all the mailing envelopes from the stockroom, spit on the flaps, and then drank rubber cement till the foot soldiers arrived?"

"I remember, my Assistant Treasurer," said the Captain. It was a little joke they had.

"He used to mimeograph pretty good," said Perley to the girl. "But that was another war. Do I bore you, Mother?"

"Please keep telling me about your business experiences, but not the rough parts." She touched his hand where the knuckles were scarred and stained by so many old mimeographings. "Are both your flanks covered, my dearest?" she asked, plucking at the blanket. They felt the Alexanders in their eyeballs. Eighty-six to one.

"Schrafft's is a good place and we're having fun and I love you," Perley said. He took another swallow of the 1926, and it was a good and careful swallow. "The stockroom men were very brave," he said, "but it is a position where it is extremely difficult to stay alive. Just outside that room there is a little bare-assed highboy and it is in the way of the stuff that is being brought up. The hell with it. When you make a breakthrough, Daughter, first you clean out the baskets and the half-wits, and all the time they have the fire escapes taped. They also shell you with old production orders, many of them approved by the general manager in charge of sales. I am boring you and I will not at this time discuss the general manager in charge of sales as we are unquestionably being listened to by that waitress over there who is setting out the decoys."

"I am going to give you my piano," the girl said, "so that when you look at it you can think of me. It will be something between us."

"Call up and have them bring the piano to the restaurant," said Perley. "Another fiasco, Botticelli!"

They drank the sauce. When the piano came, it wouldn't play. The keys were stuck good. "Never mind, we'll leave it here, Cousin," said Perley.

They came out from under the blanket and Perley tipped their waitress exactly fifteen per cent minus withholding. They left the piano in the restaurant, and when they went down the elevator and out and turned in to the old, hard, beat-up pavement of Fifth Avenue and headed south toward Forty-fifth Street, where the pigeons were, the air was as clean as your grandfather's howitzer. The wind was still west.

I commute good, thought Perley, looking at his watch. And he felt the old pain of going back to Scarsdale again.

Hart Crane (1899–1932)

The sensational career of Hart Crane has obscured the extent to which humor was an intrinsic part of his life and poetry. "The everlasting eyes of Pierrot/And, of Gargantua, the laughter" were lines he used to describe a dead friend in an elegy, "Praise for an Urn." They serve equally well as a self-description of Crane. His laughter rings out robustly in "Eternity," a description of his adventures in a hurricane; his laughter is muted with compassion in "The River" (*The Bridge*), tinged with self-irony in "My Grandmother's Love Letters," lyrically light in "Virginia" (*The Bridge*), edged with satiric bite in "Bacardi Spreads the Eagle's Wings" and "Imperator Victus," ecstatic in the Dionysian raptures of "Lachrymae Christi." Such variety came naturally to a disciple of Shakespeare and the Elizabethans, of Poe, Melville, Emily Dickinson, and T. S. Eliot. "Chaplinesque" (1921), a tribute to the famous film comedian, is also an ironic vision of the modern artist as a pathetic clown, the Pierrot whom Crane had discovered in the poetry of French symbolist Jules Laforgue.

TEXT: *The Collected Poems of Hart Crane*, ed. Waldo Frank, New York, 1933. COMMENTARY: Philip Horton, *Hart Crane*, New York, 1937; Brom Weber, *Hart Crane*, New York, 1948.

CHAPLINESQUE

We make our meek adjustments,
Contented with such random consolations
As the wind deposits
In slithered and too ample pockets.

For we can still love the world, who find
A famished kitten on the step, and know
Recesses for it from the fury of the street,
Or warm torn elbow coverts.

We will sidestep, and to the final smirk
Dally the doom of that inevitable thumb
That slowly chafes its puckered index toward us,
Facing the dull squint with what innocence
And what surprise!

And yet these fine collapses are not lies
More than the pirouettes of any pliant cane;

Our obsequies are, in a way, no enterprise.
We can evade you, and all else but the heart:
What blame to us if the heart live on.

The game enforces smirks; but we have seen
The moon in lonely alleys make
A grail of laughter of an empty trash can,
And through all sound of gaiety and quest
Have heard a kitten in the wilderness.

Ogden Nash (1902–   )

Ogden Nash is probably the most hilarious light versifier in contemporary American literature. For over thirty years he has devoted himself to the task of learning more about the art of poetry than is known by any one of his "serious" contemporaries, and then has proceeded to use his hard-earned knowledge for high comic effect. No other poet can so dazzlingly mix faulty rhymes, wild clichés, flaws of logic, butchered rhythms, misquotations, grammatical barbarisms, frenzied puns, advertising slogans, and nonsense syllables with utter abandon and disciplined purpose. A poem by Nash is an artistic compilation of the free-association responses which the jangled American mind might give to a psychiatrist's queries. Topical in his choice of subjects, frolicsome rather than bitter, Nash provokes much cheerful laughter and often some thoughtful reflection.

TEXT: *Verses from 1929 On*, Boston, Mass., 1959.

OAFISHNESS SELLS GOOD, LIKE AN ADVERTISEMENT SHOULD

I guess it is farewell to grammatical compunction,
I guess a preposition is the same as a conjunction,
I guess an adjective is the same as an adverb,
And "to parse" is a bad verb.
Blow, blow, thou winter wind,
Thou are not that unkind
Like man's ingratitude to his ancestors who left him the English language
     for an inheritance;
This is a chromium world in which even the Copley Plazas and the Blackstones and the Book Cadillacs are simplified into Sheratons.
I guess our ancient speech has gone so flat that we have to spike it;
Like the hart panteth for the water brooks I pant for a revival of Shakespeare's *Like You Like It.*
I can see the tense draftees relax and purr
When the sergeant barks, "Like you were."
—And don't try to tell me that our well has been defiled by immigration;
Like goes Madison Avenue, like so goes the nation.

Nathanael West (1902–1940)

Nathanael West is the first important modern American novelist whose work was consistently humorous. His comic-satiric novels symbolize the ever-increasing tendency of the modern writer to unite the serious with the humorous in the tradition of Poe, Hawthorne, Melville, Mark Twain, and James. In *The Dream Life of Balso Snell* (1931) West sent his hero on a scatological, Bunyanesque dream-journey through the digestive system of the Trojan Horse. Though weak in structure, the novel offered a stimulating preview of West's extraordinary poetic prose. It also revealed that he could skillfully handle plain style, mock-epic rhetoric, grotesque characterization, parody, satire, irony, and farcical situation. *Balso Snell* was laden with a humor both savage and compassionate, not surprising in view of West's affinity with Poe, Dostoyevsky, Rimbaud, and French surrealists. *Miss Lonelyhearts* (1933) manifested more disciplined artistry and an increased concern for psychological and social inquiry; it possessed all the virtues of *Balso Snell* magnified in quality. The grimly humorous story of a religious spirit driven to self-sacrifice had mythic connotations of death and rebirth such as are found in the work of Faulkner. Furthermore, the conflict between Miss Lonelyhearts and his managing editor, Shrike (bird of prey), was on a scale with the conflict between Faust and Mephistopheles. The buffoonery and extravagant comic rhetoric of Shrike cannot veil the death which is his essence: "He practiced a trick used much by moving-picture comedians—the dead pan. No matter how fantastic or excited his speech, he never changed his expression. Under the shining white globe of his brow, his features huddled together in a dead, gray triangle." The bargain with Shrike which Miss Lonelyhearts had undertaken too lightheartedly becomes a practical joke threatening his humanity; he reverses the joke by discovering that love and sacrifice enable him to triumph over Shrike's values.

TEXT: *Miss Lonelyhearts*, New York, 1933. COMMENTARY: James F. Light, *Nathanael West: An Interpretive Study*, Evanston, Ill., 1961.

MISS LONELYHEARTS IN THE DISMAL SWAMP

Soon after Mrs. Doyle left, Miss Lonelyhearts became physically sick and was unable to leave his room. The first two days of his illness were blotted out by sleep, but on the third day, his imagination began again to work.

He found himself in the window of a pawnshop full of fur coats, diamond rings, watches, shotguns, fishing tackle, mandolins. All these things were the paraphernalia of suffering. A tortured high light twisted on the blade of a gift knife, a battered horn grunted with pain.

He sat in the window thinking. Man has a tropism for order. Keys in one pocket, change in another. Mandolins are tuned G D A E. The physical world has a tropism for disorder, entropy. Man against Nature . . . the battle of the centuries. Keys yearn to mix with change. Mandolins strive to get out of tune. Every order has within it the germ of destruction. All order is doomed, yet the battle is worth while.

A trumpet, marked to sell for $2.49, gave the call to battle and Miss Lonelyhearts plunged into the fray. First he formed a phallus of old watches and rubber boots, then a heart of umbrellas and trout flies, then a diamond of musical instruments and derby hats, after these a circle, triangle, square, swastika. But nothing proved definitive and he began to make a gigantic cross. When the cross became too large for the pawnshop, he moved it to the shore of the ocean. There every wave added to his stock faster than he could lengthen its arms. His labors were enormous. He staggered from the last wave line to his work, loaded down with marine refuse—bottles, shells, chunks of cork, fish heads, pieces of net.

Drunk with exhaustion, he finally fell asleep. When he awoke, he felt very weak, yet calm.

There was a timid knock on the door. It was open and Betty tiptoed into the room with her arms full of bundles. He made believe that he was asleep.

"Hello," he said suddenly.

Startled, she turned to explain. "I heard you were sick, so I brought some hot soup and other stuff."

He was too tired to be annoyed by her wide-eyed little mother act and let her feed him with a spoon. When he had finished eating, she opened the window and freshened the bed. As soon as the room was in order, she started to leave, but he called her back.

"Don't go, Betty."

She pulled a chair to the side of his bed and sat there without speaking.

"I'm sorry about what happened the other day," he said. "I guess I was sick."

She showed that she accepted his apology by helping him to excuse himself. "It's the Miss Lonelyhearts job. Why don't you give it up?"

"And do what?"

"Work in an advertising agency, or something."

"You don't understand, Betty, I can't quit. And even if I were to quit, it wouldn't make any difference. I wouldn't be able to forget the letters, no matter what I did."

"Maybe I don't understand," she said, "but I think you're making a fool of yourself."

"Perhaps I can make you understand. Let's start from the beginning. A man is hired to give advice to the readers of a newspaper. The job is a circulation stunt and the whole staff considers it a joke. He welcomes the job, for it might lead to a gossip column, and anyway he's tired of being a leg man. He too considers the job a joke, but after several months at it, the joke begins to escape him. He sees that the majority of the letters are profoundly humble pleas for moral and spiritual advice, that they are inarticulate expressions of genuine suffering. He also discovers that his correspondents take him seriously. For the first time in his life, he is forced to examine the values by which he lives. This examination shows him that he is the victim of the joke and not its perpetrator."

Although he had spoken soberly, he saw that Betty still thought him a fool. He closed his eyes.

"You're tired," she said. "I'll go."

"No, I'm not tired. I'm just tired of talking, you talk a while."

She told him about her childhood on a farm and of her love for animals, about country sounds and country smells and of how fresh and clean everything in the country is. She said that he ought to live there and that if he did, he would find that all his troubles were city troubles.

While she was talking, Shrike burst into the room. He was drunk and immediately set up a great shout, as though he believed that Miss Lonelyhearts was too near death to hear distinctly. Betty left without saying good-by.

Shrike had evidently caught some of her farm talk, for he said: "My friend, I agree with Betty, you're an escapist. But I do not agree that the soil is the proper method for you to use."

Miss Lonelyhearts turned his face to the wall and pulled up the covers. But Shrike was unescapable. He raised his voice and talked through the blankets into the back of Miss Lonelyhearts' head.

"There are other methods, and for your edification I shall describe them. But first let us do the escape to the soil, as recommended by Betty:

"You are fed up with the city and its teeming millions. The ways and means of men, as getting and lending and spending, you lay waste your inner world, are too much with you. The bus takes too long, while the subway is always crowded. So what do you do? So you buy a farm and walk behind your horses's moist behind, no collar or tie, plowing your broad swift acres. As you turn up the rich black soil, the wind carries the smell of pine and dung across the fields and the rhythm of an old, old work enters your soul. To this rhythm, you sow and weep and chivy your kine, not kin or kind, between the pregnant rows of corn and taters. Your step becomes the heavy sexual step of a dance-drunk Indian and you tread the seed down into the female earth. You plant, not dragon's teeth, but beans and greens. . . .

"Well, what do you say, my friend, shall it be the soil?"

Miss Lonelyhearts did not answer. He was thinking of how Shrike had accelerated his sickness by teaching him to handle his one escape, Christ, with a thick glove of words.

"I take your silence to mean that you have decided against the soil. I agree with you. Such a life is too dull and laborious. Let us now consider the South Seas:

"You live in a thatch hut with the daughter of the king, a slim young maiden in whose eyes is an ancient wisdom. Her breasts are golden speckled pears, her belly a melon, and her odor is like nothing so much as a jungle fern. In the evening, on the blue lagoon, under the silvery moon, to your love you croon in the soft sylabelew and vocabelew of her langorour tongorour. Your body is golden brown like hers, and tourists have need of the indignant finger of the missionary to point you out. They envy you your breech clout and carefree laugh and little brown bride and fingers instead of forks. But you don't return their envy, and when a beautiful society girl comes to your hut in the night, seeking to learn the secret of your happiness, you send her back to her yacht that hangs on the horizon like a nervous racehorse. And so you dream away the days, fishing, hunting, dancing, swimming, kissing, and picking flowers to twine in your hair. . . .

"Well, my friend, what do you think of the South Seas?"

Miss Lonelyhearts tried to stop him by making believe that he was asleep. But Shrike was not fooled.

"Again silence," he said, "and again you are right. The South Seas are played out and there's little use in imitating Gauguin. But don't be discouraged, we have only scratched the surface of our subject. Let us now examine Hedonism, or take the cash and let the credit go. . . .

"You dedicate your life to the pursuit of pleasure. No over-indulgence, mind you, but knowing that your body is a pleasure machine, you treat it carefully in order to get the most out of it. Golf as well as booze, Philadelphia Jack O'Brien and his chestweights as well as Spanish dancers. Nor do you neglect the pleasures of the mind. You fornicate under pictures by Matisse and Picasso, you drink from Renaissance glassware, and often you spend an evening beside the fireplace with Proust and an apple. Alas, after much good fun, the day comes when you realize that soon you must die. You keep a stiff upper lip and decide to give a last party. You invite all your old mistresses, trainers, artists and boon companions. The guests are dressed in black, the waiters are coons, the table is a coffin carved for you by Eric Gill. You serve caviar and blackberries and licorice candy and coffee without cream. After the dancing girls have finished, you get to your feet and call for silence in order to explain your philosophy of life. 'Life,' you say, 'is a club where they won't stand for squawks, where they deal you only one hand and you must sit in. So even if the cards are cold and marked by the hand of fate, play up, play up like a gentleman and a sport. Get tanked, grab what's on the buffet, use the girls upstairs, but remember, when you throw box cars, take the curtain like a dead game sport, don't squawk.' . . .

"I won't even ask you what you think of such an escape. You haven't the money, nor are you stupid enough to manage it. But we come now to one that should suit you much better. . . .

"Art! Be an artist or a writer. When you are cold, warm yourself before the flaming tints of Titian, when you are hungry, nourish yourself with great spiritual foods by listening to the noble periods of Bach, the harmonies of Brahms and the thunder of Beethoven. Do you think there is anything in the fact that their names all begin with B? But don't take a chance, smoke a 3 B pipe, and remember these immortal lines: *When to the suddenness of melody the echo parting falls the failing day.* What a rhythm! Tell them to keep their society whores and pressed duck with oranges. For you *l'art vivant*, the living art, as you call it. Tell them that you know that your shoes are broken and that there are pimples on your face, yes, and that you have buck teeth and a club foot, but that you don't care, for to-morrow they are playing Beethoven's last quartets in Carnegie Hall and at home you have Shakespeare's plays in one volume."

After art, Shrike described suicide and drugs. When he had finished with them, he came to what he said was the goal of his lecture.

"My friend, I know of course that neither the soil, nor the South Seas, nor Hedonism, nor art, nor suicide, nor drugs, can mean anything to us. We are not men who swallow camels only to strain at stools. God alone is our escape. The church is our only hope, the First Church of Christ Dentist, where He is worshiped as Preventer of Decay. The church whose symbol is the trinity new-style: Father, Son and Wirehaired Fox Terrier. . . . And so, my good friend, let me dictate a letter to Christ for you:

Dear Miss Lonelyhearts of Miss Lonelyhearts—
I am twenty-six years old and in the newspaper game. Life for me is a desert empty of comfort. I cannot find pleasure in food, drink, or women— nor do the arts give me joy any longer. The Leopard of Discontent walks the streets of my city; the Lion of Discouragement crouches outside the walls of my citadel. All is desolation and a vexation of the spirit. I feel like hell. How can I believe, how can I have faith in this day and age? Is it true that the greatest scientists believe again in you?
I read your column and like it very much. There you once wrote: 'When the salt has lost its savour, who shall savour it again?' Is the answer: 'None but the Saviour?'
Thanking you very much for a quick reply, I remain yours truly,
A Regular Subscriber."

S. J. Perelman (1904–   )

The world of S. J. Perelman is infinitely more bizarre and varied than that of any other contemporary American writer of humor. Dashing through it at breakneck speed and impressing its peculiar details on his extraordinarily retentive memory, Perelman produces an absurdly extravagant record of modern man's comic nightmares and daydreams. It is no surprise that some of the Marx Brothers' zaniest film fantasy was written by him. There is little of the benign observer in Perelman. With a verbal exuberance like Melville's, a sardonic temper like Hawthorne's, and a compulsive jocularity like Poe's, Perelman scathingly mimics the thoughts, language, and desires of his characters. Nothing is safe from his chameleon-like wit as he moves through high life and low life, through Times Square, Bucks County, Broadway, Southern California, or the Far East. Perelman is happiest, and so are his readers, when, as in "Genuflection on the Sun," he punctures a ridiculous myth, in this instance one of creativity unsupported by self-consciousness and meaningful standards. "Cuckooland" (Hollywood) and "Cloudland" (the popular novel) are points on the American map which he loves to revisit; he has added his anthropological notes on them to those compiled by Thurber in "Soapland."

TEXT: *The Most of S. J. Perelman*, New York, 1958.

GENUFLECTION IN THE SUN

I am not a teetotaler and enjoy a good snort as well as the next one, but for sheer delight and ecstasy in the region of the tonsils none of them can even begin to compare with that strange combination of syrup, ice cream and carbonated water skillfully proportioned and compounded by some Master Dispenser at my favorite Liggett fountain.

I can see him now, this delicate and brilliant chemist, his head tilted forward slightly as his ear reaches for my order— "All black, please."

"All black!" Already his hand has whisked a large-sized tumbler whose narrowed round bottom was scientifically designed to aid the magical blending of all the weird component parts of the soda. Under the chocolate syrup faucet it goes. See how the rich, dark brown goo covers a third of the bottom of the glass, clinging lovingly to the side.

Now a splash of cream and the first of a series of wonderful amalgams has taken place. The dark chocolate is lighter in tone, more fluid, better prepared for the life infusion that follows—the fizzer.

Here is surely the secret of this nectar for the Gods of America, the genius touch of this unknown benefactor of mankind. The Master Dispenser is all concentration now, for this is a solemn moment, the aerating of the milk and chocolate mixture with the wire-thin stream of vital and living fizz. It hisses into the glass as he turns it carefully to all points of the compass. Under the impulse of this injection, the liquid suddenly begins to bubble and boil and heave, seething with a new and inner life of its own. Whereas a moment ago it was somber and viscous, now it is light, merry, purposeful, and gay.

Plop! Into its joyously heaving bosom is dropped a rounded gobbet of smooth, rich ice cream.

Now the Master Dispenser approaches the climax. Infected by his own artistry, he swings the glass and turns on the soda faucet, his eye keen to the task of producing perfection. As the charged water joins the composition, great, luscious brown bubbles begin to rise in the glass. Higher and higher under the watchful gaze of the Super Dispenser. Not yet . . . not yet . . . NOW! A corona of pure aerated chocolate flavor stands an inch high above the glass, a crown of sweet nothing, too superb in texture and flavor for words. A spoon, two straws, and there it is vibrant, pulsating—ready. . . .

Ah, Ye Gods of Gluttony! That first taste, the mouthful of froth, the sweet of the chocolate, the brisk tang of the soda, the ecstasy of the now-you-have-it, now-you-haven't, which sends you on for fulfillment into the first bite of ice cream irrigated with the lovely fluid of the soda.

Rich though these rewards be, they are nothing to the grand finale, the climax of enjoyment, when with froth gone, ice cream gone, you discard the straws, lift the glass, tilt back your head and subject your tonsils to the first superb shock of the pure Ichor of the soda, syrup, bubble water, water, melted ice cream, all blended into one Ambrosia of flavor, action and chill.

What is there to match it? Where is it to be found? Who, oh, who, is the great, great man who thought it all up for the likes of you and me?—*From a Liggett menu.*

Two miles south of Corona del Mar, I saw looming up ahead the Piggy-Wig Drive-In they had told me in Balboa to watch for. Narrowly missing a Hupmobile driven by an old harpy in curlers, who interpreted my left-hand signal as an invitation to sleep with her, I swerved off the Coast Highway and pulled up alongside it. A heavy miasma of frying lard and barbecued ribs drifted across the wheel of asphalt radiating from the structure; somewhere inside, the sepulchral voice of Patti Page sniveled a plaint about a doggie in a window. Three lymphatic carhops, manifestly chosen for their resemblance to porkers, were seated under a bong tree made of papier-mâché, and as one languidly rose and undulated toward me, I noticed a curled pink celluloid tail protruding from her scientifically designed narrowed round bottom, which bobbled as she moved.

"Villa Jacaranda?" she repeated, swallowing a yawn. "What is it— a motel?" I explained I was looking for the residence of Willard Inchcape, the writer. "I wouldn't know, I'm sure," she returned with disdain. "There's some bohemians up that dirt road there. They all sculp or weave or something."

I thanked her and, resisting an impulse to order a slice of quince to see whether it came with a runcible spoon, a form of cutlery that has always pricked my curiosity, drove on. The road straggled into the foothills past a cluster of aggressive ranch-style homes—each equipped with an incinerator adapted for those murders in which Southern California seems to excel—and terminated at a high wall of whitewashed brick. Over the massive gate was a chemically aged plastic shingle bearing the legend "Villa Jacaranda" in Carborundum Old Style. I pushed the gate open and stepped down into a garden choked with poinsettias. Their foliage was so lush that it veiled the outlines of the house beyond, but in a patch of greensward at the far end there was visible a woman laboring at a sculptor's table. As I approached, she turned and I beheld a portly matron of fifty-odd in a green smock, with an uncompromising henna bob and Hashimura Togo spectacles.

"Mrs. Inchcape?" I asked. "I phoned from Los Angeles."

"Oh, yes," she said energetically. "You're the man who wanted to talk to Willard. Come in." She laid her graving tool on the stand, a gesture that automatically drew my eye to the object she was modeling. It was the head of a Scotch collie, carved from a block of castile soap with such fidelity to nature that I had no difficulty repressing a start.

"Aha," I commented with a portentous frown, aware that she was watching me closely. "Er—is that an actual portrait or more of an idealized conception, as it were?"

"Half and half," said Mrs. Inchcape. "I based it on our Timmy. He passed on several years ago."

"You don't say," I murmured, attempting to mingle respect for her bereavement with a note of philosophic fatalism.

"Yes, he's buried right where you're standing." I jerked sidewise, remorseful at having desecrated a tomb. "Do you like it?"

I cocked my head and nodded emphatically. "You certainly got him down cold," I said. Then, conscious of the ambiguity of my critique, I added hurriedly, "What I mean is you sure got him dead to rights." I felt the perspiration start on my forehead. "Of course, I never knew Timmy—"

"You bet you didn't," said Mrs. Inchcape. "If he were alive, you'd never be in this garden. He'd have torn you limb from limb."

"Well, well," I said, feigning admiration for her pet's loyalty. "I guess his death was a real loss."

"I can't imagine to whom," she returned. "He bit everybody, right up to the man who chloroformed him. But I suppose you're one of those people who get sentimental about animals."

It impressed me as singular that she should be immortalizing a beast she abhorred, but I decided not to pry. "Is Mr. Inchcape home?" I asked, looking around. "I wouldn't like to disturb him if he's working."

"Don't get fidgety, he'll be along in a minute," she said, motioning toward a bench. "Sit down while I clean up this mess. Did you ever hear of Daniel Chester French?"

"The sculptor?"

"Well, I certainly don't mean Daniel Chester French the upholsterer," she said with asperity. "The one who did the statue of 'Memory' at the Metropolitan. I studied with him for two years, and let me tell you, young man, there wasn't a mean bone in his body." I tried to recall anything discreditable I had ever heard about French, and failed. "Your ears remind me of his. The way they're articulated to the head."

"Gee," I said, feeling it was incumbent on me to exhibit some sign of elation. "I've never been told that before. You—ah— It must have been a great privilege to know Mr. French."

"That depends on how you look at it," said Mrs. Inchcape acidly. She lapsed into a tight-lipped silence, dusting chips of soap from the stand and casting me an occasional suspicious glance.

Suddenly a man's voice, tremulous with excitement, resounded through the shrubbery. "Rowena!" it called. "Where are you—in the patio?" Her hail of response, easily audible in Mazatlán, flushed up my quarry, a leathery old gentleman with an Armagnac nose, a black velvet tam, and a smoking jacket. In one hand he clenched a Tyrolean porcelain pipe fluttering a pair of green tassels and in the other a typewritten sheet that bristled with interlineations. "Just listen to this, honey bun!" he crowed. "It's the copy for Mother Stentorian's Fish Kebabs, and if I do say so, it's a sockdolager. I couldn't get the exact poetic throb at first—"

"This geezer here's waiting for you," said his wife laconically.

"Well, he's got a stomach—let him hear it, too!" said Inchcape jovially. He rotated toward me. "You the party called me about my ice-cream-soda tribute?"

"I am, sir," I said, extending my hand, "and I've come to tell you it's the finest thing since Baudelaire's *Flowers of Evil*. I just wanted to pay my respects to a great poet."

"Thank you, son, thank you," he replied, his face suffused with pleasure. "But if you think *that* was good, get ready for a real treat." He adjusted a pince-nez secured to his lapel by a silver chain, cleared his throat, and began declaiming in a rich, fruity baritone: " 'Up from the silent, sunless depths of the seven seas into Mother Stentorian's spotless antiseptic kitchens come the hake, the scrod, the plaice, the fluke, the cream of the finny tribe, briny-fresh and jam-packed with succulent vitamins, to tickle the gourmet palate. Man alive, watch these yum-dingers, these dorsal dainties, tumble from the nets in silver iridescence, splendid largess from Nature's treasure-trove, yearning to sputter in butter and ravish the jaded esophagus! Here in this hygienic temple of the culinary art, under the watchful yet kindly eye of Mother Stentorian, they are portioned into appetizing mouth-size chunks, sprinkled with mace, dill, rape, capsicum, and rose leaves, and pre-cooked on skewers over aromatic fires of specially processed driftwood imported from faraway Armenia.' "

"Jiminetty," I ejaculated as he paused for breath. "That's inspired, Mr. Inchcape! You can almost taste the crisp, savory—"

"Wait, you haven't heard anything yet," he broke in. "I'm just warming up. 'Then each individual kebab, its delectable goodness sealed in, is wrapped in gleaming chlorophane—cellophane from which all harmful chlorophyll has been extracted—by deft-fingered, full-bosomed girls pledged to change their uniforms every hour. Now comes the most vital phase in the preparation of Mother Stentorian's Matchless Fish Kebabs. Science has discovered that these fishy shasliks—or, more properly, fishliks—acquire a mysterious added tank when impregnated with the folk songs of Asia Minor. Consequently, before your personalized package of kebabs is handi-packed, it is locked into a special tone chamber—a musical autoclave, so to speak—where it is saturated with rollicking airs like "The Well-Tufted Ottoman," "Sohrab and Rustum Were Lovers," and "Sister, Shake That Amphigouri." Why deny yourself any longer the color and enchantment of the Near East you've always secretly hungered for? Simply perfume your house with the odor of cold mutton fat, heat up a box of Mother Stentorian's Genuine Fish Kebabs, and become part of the world's most ancient culture. As you squat on your hams greedily engorging these zestful tidbits, you, too, will be at one with Shadrach, Meshach, and Abednego, with Nineveh and Tyre.' "

Mrs. Inchcape was the first to break the silence when her husband had concluded. "Will he be staying for lunch?" she demanded, nodding in my direction.

"Why, I can't really say," hesitated Inchcape, obviously derailed. "We haven't had a chance—"

"No, no, thank you," I said hastily. "I'm bound for La Jolla. I'll be leaving very soon."

"Then I'll just make a soybean *pizza* for two," Mrs. Inchcape announced, departing. "Come when I call you, now. It's no good cold."

The bard looked so stricken that first aid was indicated at once. "Mr. Inchcape," I said, "this may sound insincere, but when you were reading that, you brought a lump to my throat. It's tremendous. Absolutely symphonic."

"You think it jells, do you?" he asked eagerly.

"Good heavens, man, it sings!" I said. "They'll be quoting you in advertising circles for years to come. The lyricism—the imagery! It's a downright classic, I promise you."

"Oh, shucks, it's only a pastiche," said Inchcape, buffing his nails on his sleeve. "I mean with a theme as limited as kebabs you don't have the scope, naturally. Now, the ice-cream soda—there I had material to work with. I employed a kind of a cosmic approach, if you noticed."

"It struck me right away," I confessed. "First the syrup, then the cream, then the fizz. Like architecture."

"Each symbolizing a step in the universal creative process," he pointed out. "Fire, earth, and water, all uniting to produce bliss everlasting, or, in the wider sense, the Promethean spark."

"And the whole compounded by a Master Dispenser," I recalled. "Yes, the mystical analogy was perfect. Did you ever get any figures from Liggett's? Were there many conversions?"

"You mean abstainers who took up ice-cream soda as a result?" queried Inchcape. "Frankly, it *was* rather impressive; in fact, for a while they considered having prayers with the sandwiches, but the customers balked." He shrugged. "Ah, well, between you and me, I was shooting at the aesthetic angle more than the religious."

"You hit the bull's-eye, in any case," I declared. "Tell me, how did you happen to get into inspirational writing?"

He pondered for a moment before replying. "Well, it was sort of a call," he said reflectively. "I had my own business up in Hollywood, a few doors from Grauman's Egyptian, on the Boulevard. We eternalized baby shoes —you know, dipped them in bronze for ash trays and souvenirs. The work was creative, but somehow I felt I wasn't realizing my potentialities. Then one day I came across a copy of Elbert Hubbard's magazine, *The Philistine*, and his style reacted on me like a long, cold drink of sauerkraut juice. Right there, I made up my mind to follow in the footsteps of the Sage of East Aurora, and I never deviated one hair from my resolve. Which I'm thankful to say that Rowena—that's Mrs. Inchcape—has always been my shield and my buckler, urging me on and giving unselfishly of her artistic judgment. She's a very gifted woman, as you can see for yourself."

"And a very gracious one," I agreed. "Well, I must be moving on, Mr. Inchcape. Much obliged for the preview of Mother Stentorian's Fish Kebabs. I'll be on the lookout for them."

"Yes, I hear they're quite tasty," he said. "Sure you won't stay and take potluck with us? Rowena can fix you a mock omelet or some toasted dates or something."

"No, thanks a million," I said, backing through the poinsettias. "Well, goodbye, sir, and long may you flourish." I got into my rented convertible, switched on a commercial for atomic laxatives, and drove down to the coast road. As I passed the Piggy-Wig Drive-In, I saw two persons costumed as an owl and a pussycat dancing hand in hand on the edge of the asphalt. At least, I thought I saw them, but it may have been only a mirage. That Southern California sunlight can be pretty tricky at times.

Bernard Malamud (1914–   )

The humor which flourished in central and eastern Europe before World War II added its flavor to American literary humor during the 1940's and 1950's. In "Angel Levine" by Bernard Malamud the dialects and customs of Negroes and Jews are as amusing as they have ever been in popular stage and literary comedy. Just as Finley Peter Dunne, however, transformed the stereotype of the comic Irishman into a profoundly humorous human being, so has Malamud made more of the Jew than any American humorist before him. Manischevitz is unique because Malamud, like Dunne, has plumbed the psychological and religious depths of the culture his immigrant character brought to the United States. Manischevitz's incongruous adventures with the fallen Angel result in the triumph of simple faith in a disoriented world. The ironic finale in which Manischevitz permits the fallen Angel to succor his wife, and thereby saves the Angel for Heaven, is pervaded with the kind of humor found in the paintings of Marc Chagall and the writings of Franz Kafka and Sholem Aleichem. Malamud, who in *The Natural* (1952) wrote one of the best contemporary novels dealing with baseball in a colloquial American idiom, has handled fantasy, the supernatural, and uncertainty in a manner which, though its substance is European, is nevertheless as American in tone as Hawthorne's.

TEXT: *The Magic Barrel*, New York, 1958.

ANGEL LEVINE

Manischevitz, a tailor, in his fifty-first year suffered many reverses and indignities. Previously a man of comfortable means, he overnight lost all he had, when his establishment caught fire and, after a metal container of cleaning fluid exploded, burned to the ground. Although Manischevitz was insured against fire, damage suits by two customers who had been hurt in the flames deprived him of every penny he had collected. At almost the same time, his son, of much promise, was killed in the war, and his daughter, without so much as a word of warning, married a lout and disappeared with him as off the face of the earth. Thereafter Manischevitz was victimized by excruciating backaches and found himself unable to work even as a presser—the only kind of work available to him—for more than an hour or two daily, because beyond that the pain from standing became maddening. His Fanny, a good wife and mother, who had taken in washing and sewing, began before his eyes to waste away. Suffering shortness of breath, she at last became seriously ill and took her to bed. The doctor, a former customer of Manischevitz, who out of pity treated them, at first had difficulty diagnosing her ailment but later put it down as hardening of the arteries at an advanced stage. He took Manischevitz aside, prescribed complete rest for her, and in whispers gave him to know there was little hope.

Throughout his trials Manischevitz had remained somewhat stoic, almost unbelieving that all this had descended upon his head, as if it were happening, let us say, to an acquaintance or some distant relative; it was in sheer quantity of woe incomprehensible. It was also ridiculous, unjust, and because he had always been a religious man, it was in a way an affront to God. Manischevitz believed this in all his suffering. When his burden had grown too crushingly heavy to be borne he prayed in his chair with shut hollow eyes: "My dear God, sweetheart, did I deserve that this should happen to me?" Then recognizing the worthlessness of it, he put aside the complaint and prayed humbly for assistance: "Give Fanny back her health, and to me for myself that I shouldn't feel pain in every step. Help now or tomorrow is too late. This I don't have to tell you." And Manischevitz wept.

Manischevitz's flat, which he had moved into after the disastrous fire, was a meager one, furnished with a few sticks of chairs, a table, and bed, in one of the poorer sections of the city. There were three rooms: a small, poorly-papered living room; an apology for a kitchen, with a wooden icebox; and the comparatively large bedroom where Fanny lay in a sagging secondhand bed, gasping for breath. The bedroom was the warmest room of the house and it was here, after his outburst to God, that Manischevitz, by the light of two small bulbs overhead, sat reading his Jewish newspaper. He was not truly reading, because his thoughts were everywhere; however the print offered a convenient resting place for his eyes, and a word or two, when he permitted himself to comprehend them, had the momentary effect of helping him forget his troubles. After a short while he discovered, to his surprise, that he was actively scanning the news, searching for an item of great interest to him. Exactly what he thought he would read he couldn't say—until he realized, with some astonishment, that he was expecting to discover something about himself. Manischevitz put his paper down and looked up with the distinct impression that someone had entered the apartment, though he could not remember having heard the sound of the door opening. He looked around: the room was very still, Fanny sleeping, for once, quietly. Half-frightened, he watched her until he was satisfied she wasn't dead; then, still disturbed by the thought of an unannounced visitor, he stumbled into the living room and there had the shock of his life, for at the table sat a Negro reading a newspaper he had folded up to fit into one hand.

"What do you want here?" Manischevitz asked in fright.

The Negro put down the paper and glanced up with a gentle expression. "Good evening." He seemed not to be sure of himself, as if he had got into the wrong house. He was a large man, bonily built, with a heavy head covered by a hard derby, which he made no attempt to remove. His eyes seemed sad, but his lips, above which he wore a slight mustache, sought to smile; he was not otherwise prepossessing. The cuffs of his sleevs, Manischevitz noted, were frayed to the lining and the dark suit was badly fitted. He had very large feet. Recovering from his fright, Manischevitz guessed he had left the door open and was being visited by a case worker from the Welfare Department—some came at night— for he had recently applied for relief. Therefore he lowered himself into a chair opposite the Negro, trying, before the man's uncertain smile, to feel comfortable. The former tailor sat stiffly but patiently at the table, waiting for the investigator to take out his pad and pencil and begin asking questions; but before long he became convinced the man intended to do nothing of the sort.

"Who are you?" Manischevitz at last asked uneasily.

"If I may, insofar as one is able to, identify myself, I bear the name of Alexander Levine."

In spite of all his troubles Manischevitz felt a smile growing on his lips. "You said Levine?" he politely inquired.

The Negro nodded. "That is exactly right."

Carrying the jest farther, Manischevitz asked, "You are maybe Jewish?"

"All my life I was, willingly."

The tailor hesitated. He had heard of black Jews but had never met one. It gave an unusual sensation.

Recognizing in afterthought something odd about the tense of Levine's remark, he said doubtfully, "You ain't Jewish anymore?"

Levine at this point removed his hat, revealing a very white part in his black hair, but quickly replaced it. He replied, "I have recently been disincarnated into an angel. As such, I offer you my humble assistance, if to offer is within my province and ability—in the best sense." He lowered his eyes in apology. "Which calls for added explanation: I am what I am granted to be, and at present the completion is in the future."

"What kind of angel is this?" Manischevitz gravely asked.

"A boña fide angel of God, within prescribed limitations," answered Levine, "not to be confused with the members of any particular sect, order, or organization here on earth operating under a similar name."

Manischevitz was thoroughly disturbed. He had been expecting something but not this. What sort of mockery was it—provided Levine was an angel—of a faithful servant who had from childhood lived in the synagogues, always concerned with the word of God?

To test Levine he asked, "Then where are your wings?"

The Negro blushed as well as he was able. Manischevitz understood this from his changed expression. "Under certain circumstances we lose privileges and prerogatives upon returning to earth, no matter for what purpose, or endeavoring to assist whosoever."

"So tell me," Manischevitz said triumphantly, "how did you get here?"

"I was transmitted."

Still troubled, the tailor said, "If you are a Jew, say the blessing for bread."

Levine recited it in sonorous Hebrew.

Although moved by the familiar words Manischevitz still felt doubt that he was dealing with an angel.

"If you are an angel," he demanded somewhat angrily, "give me the proof."

Levine wet his lips. "Frankly, I cannot perform either miracles or near miracles, due to the fact that I am in a condition of probation. How long that will persist or even consist, I admit, depends on the outcome."

Manischevitz racked his brains for some means of causing Levine positively to reveal his true identity, when the Negro spoke again:

"It was given me to understand that both your wife and you require assistance of a salubrious nature?"

The tailor could not rid himself of the feeling that he was the butt of a jokester. Is this what a Jewish angel looks like? he asked himself. This I am not convinced.

He asked a last question. "So if God sends to me an angel, why a black? Why not a white that there are so many of them?"

"It was my turn to go next," Levine explained.

Manischevitz could not be persuaded. "I think you are a faker."

Levine slowly rose. His eyes showed disappointment and worry. "Mr. Manischevitz," he said tonelessly, "if you should desire me to be of assistance to you any time in the near future, or possibly before, I can be found"—he glanced at his fingernails—"in Harlem."

He was by then gone.

The next day Manischevitz felt some relief from his backache and was able to work four hours at pressing. The day after, he put in six hours; and the third day four again. Fanny sat up a little and asked for some halvah to suck. But on the fourth day the stabbing, breaking ache afflicted his back, and Fanny again lay supine, breathing with blue-lipped difficulty.

Manischevitz was profoundly disappointed at the return of his active pain and suffering. He had hoped for a longer interval of easement, long enough to have some thought other than of himself and his troubles. Day by day, hour by hour, minute after minute, he lived in pain, pain his only memory, questioning the necessity of it, inveighing against it, also, though with affection, against God. Why *so much*, Gottenyu? If He wanted to teach His servant a lesson for some reason, some cause—the nature of His nature—to teach him, say, for reasons of his weakness, his pride, perhaps, during his years of prosperity, his frequent neglect of God —to give him a little lesson, why then any of the tragedies that had happened to him, any *one* would have sufficed to chasten him. But *all to-gether*—the loss of both his children, his means of livelihood, Fanny's health and his—that was too much to ask one frail-boned man to endure. Who, after all, was Manischevitz that he had been given so much to suffer? A tailor. Certainly not a man of talent. Upon him suffering was largely wasted. It went nowhere, into nothing: into more suffering. His pain did not earn him bread, nor fill the cracks in the wall, nor lift, in the middle of the night, the kitchen table; only lay upon him, sleepless, so sharply oppressively that he could many times have cried out yet not heard himself through this thickness of misery.

In this mood he gave no thought to Mr. Alexander Levine, but at moments when the pain waivered, slightly diminishing, he sometimes wondered if he had been mistaken to dismiss him. A black Jew and angel to boot—very hard to believe, but suppose he *had* been sent to succor him, and he, Manischevitz, was in his blindness too blind to comprehend? It was this thought that put him on the knife-point of agony.

Therefore the tailor, after much self-questioning and continuing doubt, decided he would seek the self-styled angel in Harlem. Of course he had great difficulty, because he had not asked for specific directions, and movement was tedious to him. The subway took him to 116th Street, and from there he wandered in the dark world. It was vast and its lights lit nothing. Everywhere were shadows, often moving. Manischevitz hobbled along with the aid of a cane, and not knowing where to seek in the blackened tenement buildings, looked fruitlessly through store windows. In the stores he saw people and *everybody* was black. It was an amazing thing to observe. When he was too tired, too unhappy to go farther, Manischevitz stopped in front of a tailor's store. Out of familiarity with the appearance of it, with some sadness he entered. The tailor, an old skinny Negro with a mop of woolly gray hair, was sitting cross-legged on his work-bench, sewing a pair of full-dress pants that had a razor slit all the way down the seat.

"You'll excuse me, please, gentleman," said Manischevitz, admiring the tailor's deft, thimbled fingerwork, "but you know maybe somebody by the name Alexander Levine?"

The tailor, who Manischevitz thought, seemed a little antagonistic to him, scratched his scalp.

"Cain't say I ever heared dat name."

"Alex-ander Lev-ine," Manischevitz repeated it.

The man shook his head. "Cain't say I heared."

About to depart, Manischevitz remembered to say: "He is an angel, maybe."

"Oh *him*," said the tailor clucking. "He hang out in dat honky tonk down here a ways." He pointed with his skinny finger and returned to the pants.

Manischevitz crossed the street against a red light and was almost run down by a taxi. On the block after the next, the sixth store from the corner was a cabaret, and the name in sparkling lights was Bella's. Ashamed to go in, Manischevitz gazed through the neon-lit window, and when the dancing couples had parted and drifted away, he discovered at a table on the side, towards the rear, Levine.

He was sitting alone, a cigarette butt hanging from the corner of his mouth, playing solitaire with a dirty pack of cards, and Manischevitz felt a touch of pity for him, for Levine had deteriorated in appearance. His derby was dented and had a gray smudge on the side. His ill-fitting suit was shabbier, as if he had been sleeping in it. His shoes and trouser cuffs were muddy, and his face was covered with an impenetrable stubble the color of licorice. Manischevitz, though deeply disappointed, was about to enter, when a big-breasted Negress in a purple evening gown appeared before Levine's table, and with much laughter through many white teeth, broke into a vigorous shimmy. Levine looked straight at Manischevitz with a haunted expression, but the tailor was too paralyzed to move or acknowledge it. As Bella's gyrations continued, Levine rose, his eyes lit in excitement. She embraced him with vigor, both his hands clasped around her big restless buttocks and they tangoed together across the floor, loudly applauded by the noisy customers. She seemed to have lifted Levine off his feet and his large shoes hung limp as they danced. They slid past the windows where Manischevitz, white-faced, stood staring in. Levine winked slyly and the tailor left for home.

Fanny lay at death's door. Through shrunken lips she muttered concerning her childhood, the sorrows of the marriage bed, the loss of her children, yet wept to live. Manischevitz tried not to listen, but even without ears he would have heard. It was not a gift. The doctor panted up the stairs, a broad but bland, unshaven man (it was Sunday) and soon shook his head. A day at most, or two. He left at once, not without pity, to spare himself Manischevitz's multiplied sorrow; the man who never stopped hurting. He would someday get him into a public home.

Manischevitz visited a synagogue and there spoke to God, but God had absented himself. The tailor searched his heart and found no hope. When she died he would live dead. He considered taking his life although he knew he wouldn't. Yet it was something to consider. Considering, you existed. He railed against God— Can you love a rock, a broom, an emptiness? Baring his chest, he smote the naked bones, cursing himself for having believed.

Asleep in a chair that afternoon, he dreamed of Levine. He was standing before a faded mirror, preening small decaying opalescent wings. "This means," mumbled Manischevitz, as he broke out of sleep, "that it is possible he could be an angel." Begging a neighbor lady to look in on Fanny and occasionally wet her lips with a few drops of water, he drew on his thin coat, gripped his walking stick, exchanged some pennies for a subway token, and rode to Harlem. He knew this act was the last desperate one of his woe: to go without belief, seeking a black magician to restore his wife to invalidism. Yet if there was no choice, he did at least what was chosen.

He hobbled to Bella's but the place had changed hands. It was now, as he breathed, a synagogue in a store. In the front, towards him, were several rows of empty wooden benches. In the rear stood the Ark, its portals of rough wood covered with rainbows of sequins; under it a long table on which lay the sacred scroll unrolled, illuminated by the dim light from a bulb on a chain overhead. Around the table, as if frozen to it and the scroll, which they all touched wih their fingers, sat four Negroes wearing skullcaps. Now as they read the Holy Word, Manischevitz could, through the plate glass window, hear the singsong chant of their voices. One of them was old, with a gray beard. One was bubble-eyed. One was humpbacked. The fourth was a boy, no older than thirteen. Their heads moved in rhythmic swaying. Touched by this sight from his childhood and youth, Manischevitz entered and stood silent in the rear.

"Neshoma," said bubble eyes, pointing to the word with a stubby finger. "Now what dat mean?"

"That's the word that means soul," said the boy. He wore glasses.

"Let's git on wid de commentary," said the old man.

"Ain't necessary," said the humpback. "Souls is immaterial substance. That's all. The soul is derived in that manner. The immateriality is derived from the substance, and they both, causally an' otherwise, derived from the soul. There can be no higher."

"That's the highest."

"Over de top."

"Wait a minute," said bubble eyes. "I don't see what is dat immaterial substance. How come de one gits hitched up to de odder?" He addressed the humpback.

"Ask me something hard. Because it is substanceless immateriality. It couldn't be closer together, like all the parts of the body under one skin— closer."

"Hear now," said the old man.

"All you done is switched de words."

"It's the primum mobile, the substanceless substance from which comes all things that were incepted in the idea—you, me and everything and body else."

"Now how did all dat happen? Make it sound simple."

"It de speerit," said the old man. "On de face of de water moved de speerit. An' dat was good. It say so in de Book. From de speerit ariz de man."

"But now listen here. How come it become substance if it all de time a spirit?"

"God alone done dat."

"Holy! Holy! Praise His Name."

"But has dis spirit got some kind of a shade or color?" asked bubble eyes, deadpan.

"Man of course not. A spirit is a spirit."

"Then how come we is colored?" he said with a triumphant glare.

"Ain't got nothing to do wid dat."

"I still like to know."

"God put the spirit in all things," answered the boy. "He put it in the green leaves and the yellow flowers. He put it with the gold in the fishes and the blue in the sky. That's how come it came to us."

"Amen."

"Praise Lawd and utter loud His speechless name."

"Blow de bugle till it bust the sky."

They fell silent, intent upon the next word. Manischevitz approached them.

"You'll excuse me," he said. "I am looking for Alexander Levine. You know him maybe?"

"That's the angel," said the boy.

"Oh, *him*," snuffed bubble eyes.

"You'll find him at Bella's. It's the establishment right across the street," the humpback said.

Manischevitz said he was sorry that he could not stay, thanked them, and limped across the street. It was already night. The city was dark and he could barely find his way.

But Bella's was bursting with the blues. Through the window Manischevitz recognized the dancing crowd and among them sought Levine. He was sitting loose-lipped at Bella's side table. They were tippling from an almost empty whiskey fifth. Levine had shed his old clothes, wore a shiny new checkered suit, pearl-gray derby, cigar, and big, two-tone button shoes. To the tailor's dismay, a drunken look had settled upon his formerly dignified face. He leaned toward Bella, tickled her ear lobe with his pinky, while whispering words that sent her into gales of raucous laughter. She fondled his knee.

Manischevitz, girding himself, pushed open the door and was not welcomed.

"This place reserved."

"Beat it, pale puss."

"Exit, Yankel, Semitic trash."

But he moved towards the table where Levine sat, the crowd breaking before him as he hobbled forward.

"Mr. Levine," he spoke in a trembly voice. "Is here Manischevitz."

Levine glared blearily. "Speak yo' piece, son."

Manischevitz shuddered. His back plagued him. Cold tremors tormented his crooked legs. He looked around, everybody was all ears.

"You'll excuse me. I would like to talk to you in a private place."

"Speak, Ah is a private pusson."

Bella laughed piercingly. "Stop it, boy, you killin' me."

Manischevitz, no end disturbed, considered fleeing but Levine addressed him:

"Kindly state the pu'pose of yo' communication with yo's truly."

The tailer wet cracked lips. "You are Jewish. This I am sure."

Levine rose, nostrils flaring. "Anythin' else yo' got to say?"

Manischevitz's tongue lay like stone.

"Speak now or fo'ever hold off."

Tears blinded the tailor's eyes. Was ever man so tired? Should he say he believed a half-drunken Negro to be an angel?

The silence slowly petrified.

Manischevitz was recalling scenes of his youth as a wheel in his mind whirred: believe, do not, yes, no, yes, no. The pointer pointed to yes, to between yes and no, to no, no it was yes. He sighed. It moved but one had still to make a choice.

"I think you are an angel from God." He said it in a broken voice, thinking, If you said it it was said. If you believed it you must say it. If you believed, you believed.

The hush broke. Everybody talked but the music began and they went on dancing. Bella, grown bored, picked up the cards and dealt herself a hand.

Levine burst into tears. "How you have humiliated me."

Manischevitz apologized.

"Wait'll I freshen up." Levine went to the men's room and returned in his old clothes.

No one said goodbye as they left.

They rode to the flat via subway. As they walked up the stairs Manischevitz pointed with his cane at his door.

"That's all been taken care of," Levine said. "You best go in while I take off."

Disappointed that it was so soon over but torn by curiosity, Manischevitz followed the angel up three flights to the roof. When he got there the door was already padlocked.

Luckily he could see through a small broken window. He heard an odd noise, as though of a whirring of wings, and when he strained for a wider view, could have sworn he saw a dark figure borne aloft on a pair of magnificent black wings.

A feather drifted down. Manischevitz gasped as it turned white, but it was only snowing.

He rushed downstairs. In the flat Fanny wielded a dust mop under the bed and then upon the cobwebs on the wall.

"A wonderful thing, Fanny," Manischevitz said. "Believe me, there are Jews everywhere."

Selected Bibliography

Bibliographies of American literary humor and pertinent critical and historical studies can be found in volume III, ed. Thomas H. Johnson, of Robert E. Spiller *et al.*, eds., *Literary History of the United States*, New York, 1948, and *Bibliography Supplement*, ed. Richard M. Ludwig, New York, 1959; William P. Trent *et al.*, eds., *Cambridge History of American Literature*, New York, 1917–1921. The most extensive bibliography available appears in Walter Blair, *Native American Humor* (1800–1900), New York, 1937 (enl. ed., San Francisco, Calif., 1960). Many of the valuable critical and historical studies written during the last four decades are in article and dissertation form; bibliographies are Lewis Leary, ed., *Articles on American Literature, 1900–1950*, Durham, N.C., 1954, and James Woodress, ed., *Dissertations in American Literature, 1891–1955*, Durham, N.C., 1957. These are supplemented by the quarterly bibliographies of articles and dissertations in *American Literature*, the annual bibliographies of American Studies dissertations in *American Quarterly*, and the annual American bibliographies in *PMLA*. The article digests in *Abstracts of English Studies* are helpful.

When using the bibliographies, it is advisable to refer not only to such general categories as "humor," "irony," "almanac," "satire," "wit," and the like, but also to individual author bibliographies. Jacob Blanck, *Bibliography of American Literature*, New Haven, Conn., 1955 (3 vols.–in progress) is invaluable for authors who died prior to 1931; the entries appended to the headnotes in this anthology will also prove useful in this respect.

Special collections of American literary humor are housed in the libraries of the University of Illinois (Meine Collection), Union College (Bailey Collection), and the University of California at Los Angeles. The Illinois collection is largest. Many libraries have special collections of authors of humor; these are listed in the standard guides to special holdings of books and American literary manuscripts.

Critical and historical studies of American literary humor are Walter Blair, *Horse Sense in American Humor: From Benjamin Franklin to Ogden Nash*, Chicago, 1942; Walter Blair, *Native American Humor* (1800–1900), New York, 1937 (enl. ed., San Francisco, Calif., 1960); Will M. Clemens, *Famous Funny Fellows*, New York, 1882; Carl Holliday, *The Wit and Humor of Colonial Days* (1607–1800), Philadelphia, Pa., 1912; Thomas L. Masson, *Our American Humorists*, New York, 1931; Constance Rourke, *American Humor: A Study of the National Character*, New York, 1931; Jennette Tandy, *Crackerbox Philosophers in American Humor and Satire*, New York, 1925.

Critical anthologies include Arthur Palmer Hudson, *Humor of the Old Deep South*, New York, 1936; Stephen Leacock, *The Greatest Pages of American Humor*, New York, 1936; Kenneth S. Lynn, *The Comic Tradition in America*, Garden City, N.Y., 1958; Franklin J. Meine, *Tall Tales of the Southwest*, New York, 1930; Henry Watterson, *Oddities in Southern Life and Character*, Boston, 1882. Blair's *Native American Humor*, cited above, is an anthology as well as a critical study.

The relation between literary humor and folk humor is illuminated by Walter Blair and Franklin J. Meine, eds., *Half Horse Half Alligator*, Chicago, Ill., 1956; Mody C. Boatright, *Folk Laughter on the American Frontier*, New York, 1949; Richard M. Dorson, *American Folklore*, Chicago, Ill., 1959; Richard M. Dorson, *Jonathan Draws the Long Bow*, Cambridge, Mass., 1946; John T. Flanagan and Arthur Palmer Hudson, eds., *Folklore in American Literature*, Evanston, Ill., 1958; Daniel G. Hoffman, *Form and Fable in American Fiction*, New York, 1961; James N. Tidwell, ed., *A Treasury of American Folk Humor*, New York, 1956.

There are a number of studies of American literary figures, periods, and forms which pay more than perfunctory attention to humor. These include, among others, Richard Chase, *Walt Whitman Reconsidered*, New York, 1955; Alexander Cowie, *The Rise of the American Novel*, New York, 1948; Charles H. Foster, *The Rungless Ladder: Harriet Beecher Stowe and New England Puritanism*, Durham, N.C., 1954; Bruce I. Granger, *Political Satire in the American Revolution, 1763–1783*, Ithaca, N.Y., 1960; Ernest Jackson Hall, *The Satirical Element in the American Novel*, Philadelphia, Pa., 1922; Leon Howard, *The Connecticut Wits*, Chicago, Ill., 1943; Harold S. Jantz, *The First Century of New England Verse*, Worcester, Mass., 1944; Kendall B. Taft, ed., *Minor Knickerbockers*, New York, 1947; Moses Coit Tyler, *A History of American Literature During the Colonial Period, 1607–1765*, rev. ed., New York, 1897; Moses Coit Tyler, *The Literary History of the American Revolution, 1763–1783*, New York, 1897. Chapters and occasional paragraphs on humor will often be found in literary histories. The humor of such writers as Benjamin Franklin, Washington Irving, Mark Twain, and Ring Lardner is usually considered in works dealing with them. One of these—Van Wyck Brooks, *The Ordeal of Mark Twain*, New York, 1920 (rev. ed., 1933)—initiated serious modern criticism of American literary humor. *Makers and Finders: A History of the Writer in America, 1800–1915*, 5 vols., New York, 1936–1952, contains Brooks' later studies of humor.

Fruitful directions for the study of American literary humor are suggested by the works of critics and scholars who have either created or responded to seminal changes in the theory and practice of literary criticism and historical study during the past few decades. The following list is representative: Cleanth Brooks, *Modern Poetry and the Tradition*, Chapel Hill, N.C., 1939; Northrop Frye, *Anatomy of Criticism*, Princeton, N.J., 1957; John A. Kouwenhoven, *Made in America: The Arts in Modern Civilization*, Garden City, N.Y., 1948; R. W. B. Lewis, *The American Adam: Innocence, Tragedy, and Tradition in the Nineteenth Century*, Chicago, Ill., 1955; Shields McIlwaine, *The Southern Poor-White: From Lubberland to Tobacco Road*, Norman, Okla., 1939; F. O. Matthiessen, *American Renaissance: Art and Expression in the Age of Emerson and Whitman*, New York, 1941; Samuel Eliot Morison, *The Intellectual Life of Colonial New England*, Ithaca, N.Y., 1956; Henry Nash Smith, *Virgin Land: The American West as Symbol and Myth*, Cambridge, Mass., 1950; Wylie Sypher, *Comedy*, Garden City, N.Y., 1956.

The difficulty of reaching agreement upon the nature and form of humor is illustrated by the disagreements from Plato to the present revealed in the following representative books by a psychologist, philosopher, and anthropologist respectively: Martin Grotjahn, *Beyond Laughter*, New York, 1957; D. H. Monro, *Argument of Laughter*, Melbourne, Austl., 1951; Ralph Piddington, *The Psychology of Laughter: A Study in Social Adaptation*, London, Eng., 1933.

Index

72
74
75
76
77
79
83
85
89